EDUCATIONAL OPPORTUNITIES IN ABOARD

P. V. Gopalakrishnan

PUBLICATIONS

KALPAZ PUBLICATION

Delhi - 110052

Educational Opportunities in Aboard
(*References*)

ISBN : 81-7835-002-5

Published in 2009 in India by
Kalpaz Publications
C-30 Satyawati Nagar,
Phase- III Ashok Vihar
Delhi - 110052

Lasertype Setting :- Apex Computer
Vishal Kaushik Printers Delhi

Contents

Preface

Students who get foreign education often get good jobs and prosperity in India. This is because of the high standard of foreign universities and institutions. Realizing this fact, many have gone abroad in the pursuit of higher education and won name and fame by acquiring high positions in Government and private sectors on their return. Unfortunately studying abroad costs a lot. Hence only rich people could dream of it hitherto.

But today this picture is much changed. Many universities offer scholarships for bright students. Besides this, one can save a lot of money, if he has a thorough knowledge on the living cost and course fee of different towns and universities in the world. A book which deals in all such matters is not available in Indian markets for a reasonable price. I hope that this book would fill such a gap. I have included in this book every possible data that a student who aspires to goin for foreign education wants to know. Details of Universities, scholarships, immigration rules, visa procedure, admission requirements, etc., are given in brief in addition to addresses of Universities this enabling one to contact directly with the university in which he desires to study.

Though the data is correct to this date there are possibilities for changes in some data such as addresses, phone numbers, websites etc., of universities as well as some other important data as and when the authorities desire to bring changes. Hence, it is to contact advisable the Indian addresses of the concerned country university for getting updated information.

Do not forget to contact the diplomatic mission of the concerned country in India before taking a decision to study in a particular University. It would help to get an overall view of the present position of matters.

Wishing you all the best.

P.V. Gopalakrishnan

1, July, 2001

Acknowledgements

I would like to express my sincere thanks to the following persons who are responsible for the information and details included in this book. Sources of information is arranged hereunder are in the order of chapters.

1. Nicolas E. Ledesma, Minister, Embassy of the Argentine Republic, New Delhi.
2. Sheel C. Nuna, Senior Manager (Education and Training), Australian Education International, New Delhi.
3. Elisabeth Kogler, Austrian Embassy, New Delhi.
4. Antonio Alves Junior, First Secretary, Embassy of Brazil, New Delhi.
5. Rakesh Patry, Director, Canadian Education Centre, India, New Delhi.
6. Educational Office, Chinese Embassy in India, New Delhi.
7. Doris Kumarova, Dept. for Culture, Science, Education and Public Relations, Embassy of the Czech Republic in New Delhi.
8. Ravi Kumar, Administrative Officer, Royal Danish Embassy, New Delhi.
9. David Aymonin, Director, Centre for Documentation on Universities, Science and Technology, Embassy of France.
10. Hannelore Bossmann, Director, German Academic Exchange Service, New Delhi.
11. Olga Karachissali, Attache, Embassy of Greece, New Delhi.
12. Johanna Balchandani, Senior Cultural Adviser, Hungarian Information and Cultural Centre, Embassy of the Republic of Hungary, New Delhi.
13. Aingeal O'Donoghue, First Secretary, Embassy of Ireland, New Delhi.
14. Eyal Rak, Head-Academic & Scientific Affairs, Embassy of Israel, New Delhi.
15. Prof. Carlo Buldrini, Director, Italian Embassy Cultural Centre, New Delhi.
16. Radhika, Coordinator, MOSAI Cell, Japan Cultural and Information Centre, New Delhi.
17. Mohammad Al-Khawaldeh, Cultural Counsellor, Embassy of the Hashemite Kingdom of Jordan, New Delhi.
18. Robert Aarsse, First Secretary, Press, Culture and Education, Royal Netherlands Embassy, New Delhi.
19. New Zealand High Commission, New Delhi.
20. T. K. Prabhakaran, Chancellor, Royal Norwegian Embassy, New Delhi.
21. Embassy of the Philippines, New Delhi.
22. Emilio Vilanova Martinez-Frias, Counsellor, Embassy of Spain, New Delhi.
23. Mary Thomas, British Council Division, Chennai.
24. The United States Education Foundation in India, Chennai.

Important Note

Every care has been taken by us to avoid mistakes and omissions. However alteration may happen in data such as addresses, i.e phone numbers, website/E-mail addresses etc. by the passage of time.

This book is being sold on the condition that the author/editor, printer and publisher will not be responsible for any loss or damage caused to anybody because of the information in this edition. Readers are advised to contact with contactable Indian address concerned for latest information.

Argentina

Argentina is organized as a federal republic and is currently divided into 23 provinces and a federal territory containing the capital, Buenos Aires, founded in 1580.

There are in Argentina a large number of regions with different characteristics: they can be grouped as follows :

(i) the mountainous region, which includes the northwestern zone, the Central Andes, the hills of the Pampas and the Andes range in Patagonia and Tierra del Fuego;

(ii) the Plains (Pampas, Chaco, Mesopotamia);

(iii) the tablelands of Patagonia and,

(iv) finally, the Ocean Islands and the Argentine Antarctic.

Buenos Aires, the capital city, is one of the world's largest and most sophisticated metropolis. It is a city that never sleeps, and has something for everyone: lagoons, tennis courts, stadiums, restaurants, horse racing, riding, cycling, nightclubs, theatres including the world famous Colon Theatre, in other words, you name it and it is there ! Just as a small example of its possibilities, it may be mentioned that the city has more than 140 movie houses, around 120 nightclubs, more than 50 theatres, and all of them work daily throughout the year practically at full capacity !

Besides Buenos Aires and an endless number of other places of interest, there are six traditional tourist zones in the country which offer to the visitor a most enjoyable holiday whatever his personal taste may be.

Higher Educational Institutions

Buenos Aires is an excellent study abroad alternative. *The city is a booming metropolis and the governmental, financial, industrial and cultural heart of Argentina.* The modern, cosmopolitan atmosphere lives with a constant buzz of energy, fed by an abundant variety of art galleries, museums, theaters and cinemas to choose from. Culture lovers can enjoy brilliant tango shows, superb ballet performances, classical music and opera concerts or fine exhibits at the museums and art galleries.

Buenos Aires is much more than high culture. The night life is endless: there are cafes, restaurants, descotheques and clubs with every kind of music you can imagine. And if you are enthusiatic about sports, you can attend world class soccer games at nearby stadiums or the fastest polo matches in the world. And you can enjoy them very safely, walking down almost any street at whatever time you choose. *Buenos Aires can boast one of the lowest crime rates in the world.*

Getting from one place to another is really easy: *public transportation is excellent and almost every Argentine can give instructions of how to get from one place to another.* Their warmth allows visitors to become completely immersed into the culture, therefore discovering the city and people on a personal level.

The buildings, parks and streets can be heard whispering the history of Buenos Aires. The greatness of the ornate European architecture throughout the city will never cease to amaze you. The buildings of La Boca, the Civic Center, the National Congress, the Government House, the Municipal Cultural Center and the Teatro Colon, are a few examples of an extraordinary architecture, rich in anarchy and style.

Finally, to make the immersion process complete there are a few "must do's". On any given day, you can go shopping at the quaint markets, elegant boutiques and charming antique shops, dining at a variety of exquisite restaurants and strolling through the peaceful parks of Palermo.

The possibilities in Buenos Aires are boundless.

Universidad de San Andres is the most prestigious private University in Argentina. The modern campus covers fifteen acres in the quiet town of Victoria on the shores of the Rio de la Plata. The faculty consists of 60 professors, 70 per cent of them holding doctorate degrees. Classes are nromally in Spanish. However, Universidad de San Andres professors, staff and students have an excellent command over English.

The University has a wide spectrum of facilities available to its students, including a computer lab connected to the Internet, a computerized library with 13,000 volumes, an art studio, and a sports center with intramural and intercollegiate sports.

The Foreign Study Program at Universidad de San Andres is designed to introduce you to Argentina; its people, literature, arts, politics, and culture and to include you in the academic and social life of this University.

If you are concerned about lodging, relax: the Foreign Student Office of Universidad de San Andres maintains a full time coordinator who arranges housing with an Argentine family, organizes trips and programs around Argentina, and assists in resolving any problems or emergencies.

Each student has an academic advisor to help with course selection.

To maintain the individual attention given to students of Universidad de San Andres, enrollment in this program is limited to 25 students a semester. While our Foreign Study Program is open to students of any discipline, those majoring in Economics, Business Administration, Political Science, International Relations, and Latin American Studies will find the courses we offer most useful. Our program offers a truly unique opportunity for students to meet other promising young students in the same areas of study.

University Calendar

Fall Semester: Beginning of March to first week of July.

Spring Semester: Beginning of August to first week of December.

(Foreign students arrive two weeks early for orientation to the University and Argentina.)

Courses

Students will be enrolled in four courses per semester. There is one required course, "Argentine Society and Culture" designed for students studying abroad. The classes are taken by members of the faculty and speakers include prominent figures in Argentina's political, cultural, and artistic circles.

The other three courses are electives. The courses involve two lectures and two smaller tutorials per week. We offer a range of courses in Arts and Literature, Political Sciences, Business and Economics, including classes with an emphasis on Argentine and Latin American studies. The Art and Literature workshops are run by working Argentine painters and writers. Seminar courses are also offered. Universidad de San Andres will send official transcripts of your grades and their US equivalents directly to the registrar at your home University.

Housing

Foreign students will live with an Argentine family. When possible, students will live with the family of a fellow University student. Breakfast and dinner will be provided by the family and lunch will be provided by the University.

Universidad de San Andres is a premier choice for studying abroad in Latin America. This small, private, highly selective University offers a Study Abroad Program which caters to serious, yet adventurous students with a good command of Spanish.

The Program includes majors in Economics, Business Administration, International Relations, Political Science and Accounting, as well as courses in the Humanities.

Argentina, Buenos Aires, and Universidad de San Andres combine to make an unbeatable intellectual, cultural, and social, study abroad experience.

Argentina proposes a unique mixture of people, cultures and geography that welcome visitors with arms open wide. The rare, comforting warmth of the Argentines is something that makes you feel at home even if you are not.

In addition to their gentle personalties, Argentines possess an intriguingly vivid, diverse culture. This nation is a melting pot of European and South American traditions and influences. Spanish, Italian, Jewish, Criollo, Welsh, English and Gaucho customs intermingle throughout the country giving it its colorful charm and nature.

Another distinctive attraction to Argentina is its impressive geographical variety. Every outdoor activity is possible, including hiking, fishing, skiing and rafting. The region's natural features offer lush tropical rain forests, the illustrious Falls of Iguazu, the High Planes of the Northwest, the mountains and lakes of the Andes, the rich farmlands of the Litoral, the austere beauties of Mendoza, Patagonia, Tierra del Fuego and the Pampas.

Courses

List of Courses on Argentine or Latin American Topics:

- (i) Economic History II (Argentine Economic History)
- (ii) Constitutional Law (Argentine)
- (iii) Foundations of Political Science I and II
- (iv) Comparative Political Systems
- (v) Latin American Political Systems
- (vi) Contemporary Latin American Foreign Policies
- (vii) Political History of Argentina and Latin America
- (viii) International Law and International Organizations
- (ix) Taxes (Theory and Argentine system)
- (x) Firm, Society, and the State
- (xi) Industrial Organization
- (xii) Economic Development

For further information please contact:
Foreign Students Office, Universidad de San Andres, Vito Dumas 284
(1644) - Victoria, Buenos Aires, Argentina.
Phone: (54-1) 746-2608 Fax: (54-1) 746-5090, E-mail: FSO @ udesa.edu.ar

Argentine Universities (Medicine)

1. Facultad de Medicina, Universidad Nacional de Buenos Aires, Paraguay 2155, (1120) Buenos Aires, *Argentina*
2. Facultad de Ciencias Medicas, Universidad Nacional de Cordoba Estafeta 32 Ciudad Universitaria, (5000) Cordoba, *Argentina*
3. Facultad de Ciencias Medicas, Universidad Nacional de Cuyo Centro Universitario Parque Gral. San Martin (5500) Mendoza, *Argentina*
4. Facultad de Ciencias Medicas, Universidad Nacional de La Plata Calle 60 y 120, (1900 La Plata—Buenes Aires), *Argentina*
5. Facultad de Medicina, Universidad Nacional del Nordeste Moreno 1240, (3400) Corrientes, *Argentina*
6. Facultad de Ciencias Medicas, Universidad Nacional de Rosario Santa Fe 3100, (2000) Rosario—Santa Fe, *Argentina*

Argentine Universities

1. Facultad de Ingenieria, Universidad de Buenos Aires
Paseo Colon 850, (1063) Buenos Aires, *Argentina*
2. Facultad de Ingenieria, Centro Universitario Parque Gral. San Martin
(5500) Mendoza, *Argentina*
3. Facultad de Ingenieria, Universidad Nacional de Jujuy
Gorriti 237, (4600) San Salvador de Jujuy, *Argentina*

Argentine Universities (*Business Administration*)

1. Universidad Nacional de Entre Rios, Facultad de Ciencias de la Administration, Alvear 1424 y Rea. del Paraguay, (3200) Concordia—Entre Rios, *Argentina*
2. Universidad del Norte "Santo Tomas de Aquino"
Facultad de Ciencias Administration, 9 de Julio 165 C.C. No. 32
(4000) San Miguel de Tucuman, *Argentina*

Argentine Universities (*Veterinary Sciences*)

1. Universidad Nacional de La Pampa, Facultad de Ciencias Veterinarias
Calle 13 No 974, (6360) Gral. Pico-La Pampa, *Argentina*
2. Universidad Nacional de La Plata, Facultad de Ciencias Veterinarias
Calle 60 y118, (1900) La Plata—Buenos Aires, *Argentina*
3. Universidad Nacional del Litoral, Facultad de Agronomia y Veterinaries
Av. P. Kreder 2805, (3080) Esperanz, Santa Fe, *Argentina*
4. Universidad Nacional del Nordeste, Facultad de Ciencias Veterinarias
Sargento Cabral 2139, (3400) Corrientes, *Argentina*
5. Universidad Nacional de la Rio Cuarto, Facultad Agronomiay Veterinarias
Campo Universitario, Ruta 8 y 36, (5800) Rio Curto, *Argentina*

Argentine Universities (*Economics*)

1. Facultad de Ciencias Economicas y de Administraction
Universidad Nacion de Catamarca, Pabellon No. 2 "General Jose Rafael Herrea"— P. Alta, Maestro Quiroga, Primera Cuadra
(4700) San Fernando del Valle de Catamarca, *Argentina*
2. Facultad de Ciencias Economicas, Avda. Roca 1900
(4000) San Miguel de Tucuman, *Argentina*
3. Universidad de Moron, Cabildo 134, (1708) Moron, Buenos Aires, *Argentina*

Argentine Universities (*Agriculture*)

1. Universidad Nacional de Buenos Aires, Rectorado-Viamonte 430
(1053) Buenos Aires, *Argentina*
2. Universidad Nocional de Cordoba, Obispo Trejo y Sanabria 242
(5000) Cordoba, *Argentina*
3. Universidad Nacional de Catamarca, Republica 350
(4700) San Fernando del Valle de Catamarca, *Argentina*
4. Universidad Nacional de Comahue, Buenos Aires 1400, (8300) Neuquen, *Argentina*
5. Universidad Nacional de Cuyo, Centro Universitario Parque Gral San Martin, (5500) Mendoza, *Argentina*
6. Universidad Nacional de Entre Rios, Galarza 617
(3260) Concepcion del Uruguay—Entre Rios, *Argentina*
7. Universidad Nacional de Jujuy, Avenida Bolivia 2335

(4600) San Salvador de Jujuy, *Argentina*

Argentine Universities

1. Universidad Nacional de Jujuy, Facultad de Ciencias Agrarias
Alberdi 47, (4600) San Salvador de Jujuy, *Argentina*
2. Universidad Nacional de Lomas de Zamora, Facultad de Ingenieria y Ciencias Agrarias, Camino de Cintura, (1836) Lavallol—Buenos Aires
Argentina
3. Universidad Nacional del Nordeste, Facultad de Ciencias Agrarias
Sargento Cabral 2139, Ayacucho y Ruta 12
(3400) Corrientes, *Argentina*
4. Universidad Nacional de Rosario, Facultad de Ciencias Agrarias
Santa Fe 2051, (2000) Rosario—Santa Fe, *Argentina*
5. Universidad de Buenos Aires, Facultad de Agronomia
Avda. San Martin 4453, (1417) Buenos Aires, *Argentina*
6. Universidad Nacional del Litoral, Facultad de Agronomia y Veterinaria
Av. P. Kreder 2805, (3080) Esperanza, Santa Fe, *Argentina*

Argentine Dental Universities

1. Universidad Nacional de Buenos Aires, Facultad de Odontologia
Marcelo T. de Alvear 2142, (1122) Buenos Aires, *Argentina*
2. Universidad Nacional de Cordoba, Facultad de Odontologia
Estafeta 32, (5000) Cordoba, *Argentina*. 3. Universidad Nacional de La Plata, Facultad de Odontologia, Calle 44 No. 674/78
(1900) La Plata—Buenos Aires, *Argentina*
4. Universidad Nacional de Cuyo, Facultad de Odontologia
Centro Universitario Parque Gral San Martin, (5500) Mendoza
Argentina
5. Universidad Nacional de Nordeste, Facultad de Odontologia
Cordoba 794, (3400) Corrientes, *Argentina*
6. Universidad Nacional de Rosario, Facultad de Odontologia
Santa Fe 3160, (2000) Rosario-Santa Fe, *Argentina*
7. Universidad Nacional de Tucuman, Facultad de Odontologia
Avenida Benjamin Araoz 800, (4000) San Miguel de Tucuman
Argentina

Law College in Argentina

1. Universidad de Buenos Aires, Facultad De Derechoy Ciencias SocialesAvda. Pte.

Figuerao, Alcorta 2263, (1425) Capital Federal, *Argentina*

For more details, please contact consular section of the Embassy of the Argentine Republic, B-8/9, Vasant Vihar, New Delhi-110057, Ph: 6141345.

Australia

Australia is the only nation to govern an entire continent and its outlying islands. The mainland, with an area of 7.6 million square kilometres, is the largest island and the smallest continent on the earth. It is also the lowest, with an average elevation of 330 m. Australia is some 3700 km from its most northern to its most southern point, and about 4000 km from east to west.

In land area, Australia is the fifth largest nation after Canada, China, the United States of America and Brazil. Its population, however, is relatively small at 18.3 million

The Australian landscape is highly distinctive, ranging from vast stony and sandy deserts and tablelands in the West and the Centre, to sweeping plateaus and plains flanking narrow coastal slopes to the East. The coastal areas feature broad sandy beaches and lush vegetation backed by a great variety of landforms, ranging from the steep cliffs of the Blue Mountains, West of Sydney and tall graceful eroded volcanic plugs in the Glasshouse Mountains north of Brisbane, to flat plains on the Southern coast, west of Adelaide.

While the natural beauty of the country remains largely intact, in the brief 200 years of European settlement, Australia has developed into one of the most highly urbanized countries in the world. Sophisticated cities accommodate world-class shopping, restaurants, art galleries, museums and cultural festivals.

There are many reasons why international students choose to study in Australia: Standards of education are high in Australia and graduates with Australian qualifications are sought after by employers around the world. Post-secondary education in Australia offers an attractive and stimulating academic environment. The institutions are diverse in size and location and offer a wide range of quality courses and research opportunities. Entry procedures are straghtforward.

Australia has a long history of involvement in international education development, staff and student exchange programs and scholarships. Australia is safe and Australians welcome fees international students. Living costs and tuition costs compare well with other countries and international students are permitted to work part-time in Australia.

The Australian Education System

Australia's education system is divided into five sectors. They are :

(i) the universities ;

(ii) a vocational training system through its Technical and Further Education (TAFE) institutes ;

(iii) the ELICOS institutions which offer English Language Intensive Courses for Overseas Students;

(iv) a number of private colleges and schools giving courses in subjects such as business studies, hotel management and mass communication;

(v) primary and secondary schools.

Higher Education

The higher education system in Australia is a relatively large one for a country of almost 18 million people. There are 37 universities with a total student population of more than 600,000 made up of full-time, part-time and external students. More than half are full-time students, of which most live off campus and travel each day to campus. There were 62,000 international students undertaking higher education courses in Australia in 1997.

Australian universities offer both undergraduate and postgraduate programs. The most popular courses of study for international students have been in the fields of Business, Administration and Economics. Almost half of all international students enrol for courses in these fields. The second most popular field is Science, then the Arts, Humanities and the Social Sciences, followed closely by Engineering and Surveying.

Universities are set up under State or Federal Acts of Parliament. They are governed by a council or senate, comprising representatives from the university and general community. The Federal Government has financial responsibility for university funding. The only private university is Bond University in Queensland.

Universities provide courses and conduct research in a wide range of professional and academic disciplines. They offer bachelors, masters and doctoral degrees as well as postgraduate diplomas.

Universities vary enormously in size, in their location, and in their research and teaching interests. There is also a diversity in the structure of courses and research programs. Students life at all Australian universities, is very similar with a heavy workload involving lectures, tutorials and seminars, plus individual work in laboratories and libraries. Students can also choose from a wide range of.

Technical and Further Education

Australia's Technical and Further Education (TAFE) sector is a nationally recognized government system of vocational education and training. It is the largest provider of tertiary education courses in Australia. Over one million students are enrolled in about 250 TAFE institutes nationwide. TAFE institutes account for about 75 per cent of vocational education enrolments.

TAFE courses provide initial and further education at professional, trade and operative levels. They are developed in collaboration with industry and the community to ensure that the most up-to-date training is provided.

Certificates and diplomas awarded by TAFE institues are respected throughout Australia. Some TAFE courses allow graduates to be admitted with advanced standing into certain undergraduate courses offered by universities.

TAFE courses run from short courses of several hours to three-year, full time courses. Classes are quite small with an average of 15 students and a maximum of about 30 students. Teaching in TAFE is mainly through supervised practical work and classroom teaching. However, a number of classes have adopted the university method of lectures and tutorials. In general, courses are assessed on a continuous basis through written assignments, class discussions, practical work and short tests.

Elicos

English Language Intensive Courses for Overseas Students (ELICOS) attract a large number of students to Australia. In March 1996 there were 9754 international students enrolled in ELICOS: 8442 came from the Asia and Oceania regions; 824 from Europe; 137 from the Americas; 21 from Africa; and 330 from other regions. Some students plan to improve their English for professional and educational purposes, while others are learning English for travel and social purposes.

Many universities and TAFE institutes have ELICOS centres attached to their campuses. About 100 private ELICOS centres are in all the capital cities and in some rural areas.

Unlike the universities and TAFE institutes, the ELICOS centres do not usually have any entrance requirements. Rather, a test of the student's English language proficiency is normally given on arrival at an ELICOS centre.

The standard of facilities and instruction provided by ELICOS institutions are monitored through the National ELICOS Accreditation Scheme (NEAS). Once NEAS has approved an institution it must then register with the Australian Government. In this way, the ELICOS industry and the Australian Government work together to ensure that the training provided by ELICOS institutions is of an international standard.

The Academic Year

The academic year for universities and TAFE institutions runs from late February to late November. For university and TAFE courses, the year is usually divided into two semesters. Bond University is the exception, with its academic year divided into three semesters. Applications generally close in October. There are four terms, each term lasting up to 12 weeks.

The decision to study overseas is possibly one of the most important decisions a student will make. Australia offers excellent education and training services, but, given the relative cost of international education, the prospective student must know very well why he wishes to study in Australia. Such considerations should include a realistic assessment of academic performance to date, financial resources, motive for studying overseas, career goals and personal considerations.

Many overseas students tend to select an institution on grounds of perceived prestige and/or its reputation. These institutions are normally highly selective and competition for entry is fierce. Intending students should critically examine their academic credentials before applying. It should be remembered that Australia's lesser known institutions frequently offer equivalent programs which are as intellectually taxing and just as academically sound. Instead of worrying about the reputation a university may carry, it is preferable that students identify a proposed course of study and determine which institution offers the program best suited to the student's academic needs and career goals.

Australian universities are both research and teaching institutions, although the emphasis placed on one or the other function may vary. Students are advised to carefully consider their proposed course of study before making their choice.

Once the students have selected the institution in which they want to study they may contact the AEC Manager/Education Promotion Officer to find out the institution's representatives in India.

Qualifying for Higher Education in Australia

Entry to Australian universities is competitive: the universities always receive many more applications than the number of seats available. Australian students are usually considered for entry to undergraduate courses on the basis of their final secondary school examination results. International students must achieve at least the same standards as Australian students. When applying for a course in an Australian university, following four main points must be considered in decision to apply for a particular course at a particular university:

Australian Year 12 Qualification and Equivalents

The Australian education system is based upon 13 years of school level education (i.e. primary plus secondary). Each state in Australia has its own secondary school certificate. While these certificates have different names, they all require an equivalent standard of education and can be referred to generally as Australian Year 12 qualifications. All Australian universities recognise the various Year 12 qualifications from different states. The universities also recognize a wide range of secondary school certificates from other countries as being equivalent to the Australian Year 12 qualifications. including the successful completion of class 10+2 from India.

Prerequisite Subjects

Some courses specify 'pre-requisite subjects'. This means that students must have passed this subject as part of their entry qualification; the first year subjects of the course assume that students have a good knowledge of this subject at Australian Year 12 level. Prerequisite subjects vary from course to course. For instance, a Bachelor of Arts degree might have no prerequisite; a Bachelor of Commerce might require General Mathematics and Bachelor of Engineering might require Advanced Mathematics/Calculus, Physics and Chemistry. Students should check the prerequisites for a course carefully. They should not apply for a course if they have not passed the pre-requisite subjects. Some courses, especially in art and design, also require students to submit folios of their work with their applications.

Minimum Standard of Entry

Even if a student has obtained an Australian Year 12 or equivalent, and passed the prerequisite subjects, this does not guarantee entry to a particular course. Because entry is competitive, the universities set minimum standard of entry for students, including international students, for each course. The minimum standard of entry or overall entry score: can vary between courses in the same university, between similar courses in different universities, and from year to year for the same course. Some courses and some universities are in greater demand than others, and demand changes from year to year. Some universities publish their minimum standards of entry; students should study these carefully. If a university does not publish this information, one needs to enquire about its minimum standards of entry before applying. There is no point in applying for courses which have very high requirements if you clearly do not meet them.

English Requirements

Adequate instruction in English language is necessary for entry into an Australian University course.

The following are the most commonly accepted indicators to judge proficiency in English needed to study in Australia:

- English is your first language;
- Satisfactory achievement in Secondary/Tertiary studies to date in an English speaking country;
- English was the language of instruction in your secondary/tertiary studies to date.
- For higher education entry, you may require an overall score of six or better on the International English Language Testing System (IELTS) conducted by the British Council. For TAFE and special studies, entry an overall score of between 5 to 6 is required, depending on the program demands of the courses. For secondary entry an overall IELTS score of between 5 to 6 is recommended depending on the requirements of the school and the availability of English Language support. A score or 550 or better on the American Test of English as a Foreign Language (TOEFL) is also accepted.

Recently the Visa office has been undertaking more stringent checks of the English language ability of student visa applicants. Visa section has decided that in cases where it is not satisfied that an applicant's English skills are sufficient, the applicant is required to provide recent results of an IELTS test.

However, an IELTS certificate is not required in all cases. Need for the IELTS result will not be known until the application is assessed, so in many cases it may be in an applicant's best interest to provide the documents with the application to avoid any delays after lodgement of the application.

ELICOS and Intensive English Training Courses

The vast majority of overseas students entering Australia require additional instruction in English. Intensive English courses are available often on campus at universities and at a large number of TAFE Colleges. Alternatively there are numerous private English Language Colleges throughout Australia. Language Colleges are known as ELICOS (English Language Intensive Courses for Overseas Students) Centres in Australia and all of them offer courses in English. The AEC Manager can provide details.

University Entry through Foundation Studies

The idea behind offering Foundation Studies courses in Australia arose because the universities recognized the need to provide their growing numbers of international students with the knowledge and skills required to succeed in undergraduate studies at Australian universities. There is great variation in secondary schooling from one country to another. Not all final year examinations qualify a student for direct entry to Australian universities. The preparation needed encompasses additional training in English language, especially in academic English, as well as the study of subjects directly related to the undergraduate courses offered. In short, a Foundation Studies course is a great equalizer, providing students from many different educational backgrounds with a standard matriculation qualification and a solid educational base for their further academic studies in Australia. A major advantage of Foundation Studies courses is that students have a place reserved for them at university for the following year and they know at the beginning what grades they need to achieve in order to proceed to this place. They enter their undergraduate courses well prepared both academically and socially and their results, after one year of undergraduate study, are generally very high. Another major advantage of Foundation Studies courses is that the student takes only those subjects which are directly related to their preferred university course. This means that, not only can the students concentrate on subjects relevant to their course, but also that the universities receive students whom they know have the required background for their undergraduate studies and who understand what is required of them in their intended academic study.

Foundation Studies courses are currently being offered throughout the year to fit in with the university intake dates.

Senior Secondary Schooling in Australia

In Australia there is one year of kindergarten/preschool, six years of primary school and six years of secondary education. The last two years, Year 11 and 12 are referred to as the senior secondary years in Australian education.

Many overseas students in Australia take either Years 11 and 12 or just Year 12, depending on their educational background. In studying at the senior secondary level before progressing to university, the student is able to develop his or her language skills, and is able to make the necessary cultural and emotional adjustment, from the life of their home country to Australia.

International students elect to study in Australia at the senior secondary level because it is easier to gain entry to an Australian university having obtained a pre-university qualification in Australia. Entry to all Australian universities is on a competitive basis, for both Australian and international students. Students are ranked according to how well they have performed in their senior secondary education. Each university course sets a certain rank score for entry. This means that students are selected for courses, if their rank score meets the prerequisite rank of the course they are applying for. In addition to this, study at senior secondary level affords the international student an opportunity to obtain the exact pre-requisites for courses like Engineering and Economics.

Senior Secondary Institutions

There are both public and private schools in each of the states and territories. Public schools are administered by State Government authorities. All Australian schools and teachers, however, must be registered with the appropriate authority. Both public and private schools accept international students. In addition, there are a number of fully private international schools in Australia.

In recent years, a few schools have started to offer the International Baccalaureate, a 2 year preuniversity qualification, as an alternative to the State Government programs. The International Baccalaureate was originally designed for the children of the expatriate community who found it difficult to move from one education system to another.

The public and private schools in Australia are too numerous to mention in this publication. If you require more information on school education opportunities, please write to the AEC Manager, Australian Education International, Australian High Commission, New Delhi.

Higher Education University Courses

Higher Education institutions are principal providers of education in professional and educational fields. The Federal Government provides the majority of institutional funding although most institutions operate under State Government legislation. There are 42 higher education institutions in Australia; 36 of these are members of the Unified National System, four are commonwealth funded Government colleges, and two are private universities.

One of the most important characteristics of the system of higher education is the diversity and autonomy of the institutions which allow them to develop their research focus, priorities and strategies. It also allows international students to choose an institution which reflects their priorities and focus of research.

The number of international students in Australian higher education institutions have swelled to 64000 in 1997 indicating that Australia has become a popular destination for international students. This is the result of a major emphasis on research and development. During 1994, expenditure on research and development by all universities totalled AUD 1924 million (at 1996 prices) which is among the highest in the world, in terms of percentage GDP, ranking within the top 8 OECD countries.

Award courses vary considerably with the higher education sector in form, entry requirements, duration and method of assessment. The following awards are offered by Australian universities :

- doctoral degree; masters degree; graduate diploma;
- graduate certificate;
- bachelor degree;
- undergraduate diploma/AQF advanced diploma; and
- associate diploma/AQF diploma.

Undergraduate Studies

Australian universities offer a wide variety of undergraduate courses in a number of disciplines. Information on what courses the various disciplines offer is given as follows :

Humanities—English, Philosophy, History, Ethnic studies, Foreign language studies, Religious studies, Communications, Women's studies.

Education—Education studies, Teaching.

Social Studies—Geography, Library and Archival studies, Behavioral studies, Welfare and Counselling, Sport and Recreation, Political Science, Sociology.

Mathematics and Computing — Mathematics and Statistics, Computer-Based Information Science, Computer Science.

Science — Biological Science, Physics, Earth Sciences, Pharmacology, Veterinary Science, Animal Husbandry, Chemistry.

Visual and Performing Arts--Art, Graphic Arts, Fashion Design, Crafts, Performing Arts, Music.

Engineering—Chemical, Civil, Electrical, Electronic, Structural, Mechanical, Automotive, Aeronautical, Mining, Industrial, General Engineering, Computer Engineering, Telecommunications.

Business, Administration and Law--Economics, Accounting, Commerce, Management, Administration, Secretarial Studies, Sales and Services, Law, Justice, Legal Studies.

Health Sciences—Medical and therapeutic technologies, Nursing, Nutrition, Medical Science, Environmental Health, Optometry, Dentistry, Personal and Family health care.

Agriculture—Agriculture, Forestry, Parks and Wildlife.

Postgraduate Studies

Australia offers a wide variety of choices for postgraduate studies. The individual universities offer different strengths and capabilities, providing a diverse base of research for students. Australian universities pride themselves on a strong research base and devote considerable research facilities and state of the art equipment to their postgraduate schools.

Postgraduate studies are offered in almost all faculties. Postgraduate students undertake specialized research in their chosen discipline, usually through course work and/or a thesis.

Postgraduate degrees either take the form of a Postgraduate diploma, Masters degree, or a Ph. D. Entry criteria for postgraduate studies in Australia varies depending on the chosen Elective or University, but the basic requirement is an Australian undergraduate degree, or its equivalent. Entry to postgraduate programs, it should be noted, is competitive and often complex.

Australian universities often provide special benefits to postgraduate students, in terms of accommodation and resources. For further information, the individual universities/handbooks should be consulted.

Career Building

A major reason applicants pursue postgraduate studies is that such qualifications improve the competitiveness of the student in the job market. Universities take this further by offering postgraduate courses specifically tailored to the world of work. This is particularly evident in such fields as engineering, where training and education runs concurrently with developments in the workforce. The Australian MBA course is one which is specifically tailored to train students for the international business world.

Masters in Business Administration (MBA)

The MBA degree in Australia is intended for those with some practical experience who now wish to widen their managerial knowledge and skills. The common core subjects of an Australian MBA are: Competitive Analysis; Strategic Planning & Policy, Financial Decision Analysis; Marketing; Total Quality Management; Quantitative Methods; Human Resource Management, Organisational Behaviour, Management of Information Systems; followed by a range of elective subjects. As applicants for an MBA are expected to have had two years employment experience following their undergraduate degree, no prior knowledge of management studies is necessary for admision to MBA programs. Australian MBAs are designed with the competitive market in mind, and this is reflected in the "hands on" approach MBA courses adopt in teaching. An interactive teaching approach emphasizes participation, team-work, and case studies, rather than passive lectures. In addition, they provide the opportunity for project work in industry, working on real management and strategic issues. Australian universities offering full-time MBA programs have generally recruited students from overseas. There can be little doubt of the career advantages an MBA student enjoys from being part of an international network of fellow MBA participants. This is particularly evident in the case of Australia's well known universities, because of the high reputation they have overseas.

Entry into Australian MBA's-GMAT Exams

Institutions assess a number of criteria when selecting students for MBA courses, including undergraduate performance, references and work experience. Another criterion for entry into an Australian MBA is the GMAT exam. The GMAT exam was developed in order to provide graduate management and business school around the world with an objective measure of their applicant's general verbal and mathematical skills. Test candidates receive three scores—*Verbal, Quantitative and Total.* The Verbal and Quantitative scores are scaled between 0 and 50. The total is a score between 200 and 800. The higher the score, the better the student has done. A good GMAT score is essential, as most MBA programs have more applicants than seats available and therefore may not take a student with a weak GMAT score.

Doctoral Studies

For doctoral studies, the Ph.D. Committee makes its decision on the basis of the information supplied by the applicant. The applicant must satisfy the Committee that the work already done in his/her graduate course is comparable to that completed by a student at this University who has obtained a Master's degree and also has adequate research preparation. The relevant university should be contacted for details on admission to a Ph.D. school. For university scholarships the student should write to the Universities Scholarship Office requesting for an application form. Competition is extremely keen and applicants must have exceptional academic records to be considered for these scholarships.

Double Degrees

Many Australian universities offer a comprehensive range of double or dual degree programs. Students in these programs study in two faculties and to eventually graduate with two degrees (e.g., BE and BBA or BA and Llb). Double degrees generally take four years to complete and are extremely popular, as they enable students to obtain two qualifications for just one additional year of study.

Vocational Education and Training in Australia

The pride and confidence that Australia has in its VET system is the result of a long tradition in technical education, a decade of continous reform and a national sytem which is truly driven by customers' needs and the quest for quality. Vocational education and training is offered by two types of institutions: Technical and Further Education (TAFE) institutes and private training organizations such as private colleges, industry training centres and individual enterprizes.

These institutions offer a wide variety of training, ranging from preparatory and entry level, through operator and technician to professional levels. A broad spectrum of programs and learning opportunities are delivered with relevant up-to-date industry experience.

The training is competency-based, consistent with national standards and flexibly delivered to meet the needs of industry and individuals. Australian VET providers do more than just deliver courses; they provide a full range of services including:

- analysis of training needs;
- design and development of systems;
- development of curriculum and training materials;
- research and consultancy; and
- establishment of national VET frameworks.

In response to increased trade competition and the need for a high performance workforce, Australian industries and Government have worked together for almost a decade to build a vibrant modern VET system.

Providers of training programs leading to nationally recognized qualifications are registered by Government agencies and monitored to ensure that they are providing quality training, consistent credentials, and best practice in customer service. Serving the needs of industry is the cornerstone of the Australian VET system. Industries work together to set competency standards, which can be registered nationally to form the basis for qualifications. To deliver recognized qualifications, training providers must base their courses on these standards, and deliver in a way that is relevant and convenient to the industry.

1. Technical and Further Education (TAFE)

Australia offers a wide variety of vocational education and training courses. The Australian Technical and Further Education (TAFE) college system is both Government owned and operated. TAFE colleges specialize in training students for the workforce. TAFE graduates are in demand from both business and industry for their wide range of practical and technical skills.

Each year, increasing numbers of international students are choosing the TAFE option, either as a means of training and qualifying for a highly skilled job in business, the arts, or industry, or as an alternative pathway into university degree studies. The advantages for international students choosing to undertake TAFE studies are numerous and include the following facts:

- Security and stability is guaranteed as TAFE is Government owned and operated;
- TAFE qualifications are recognized and transferable internationally;
- Business and industry are directly involved in the design of courses, this provides the skills and knowledge employers want;

- Courses provide hands-on, practical training and students have ready access to sophisticated and specialized equipment;
- TAFE courses can lead on to university courses, some with credit transfer and advanced standing for one and sometimes two years;
- TAFE has a network of overseas student programme officers who are working to forge closer links with educational bodies in India.

TAFE Awards

TAFE courses are offered at different levels, and a different award is given at each level.

(*i*) The *Certificate I* : is a preparatory qualification focussing on a range of basic employment-related skills.

(*ii*) The *Certificate II* : has learning outcomes involving the performing of a prescribed range of functions involving known routines and procedures and some accountability for the quality of outcomes.

(*iii*) The *Certificate III* : has learning outcomes requiring the performance of a defined range of skilled operations, usually within a range of broader related activities involving known routines, methods and procedures, but with some discretion and judgement required. (The usual entry level for Certificate, I, II, III programs is completion of Year 10 or the equivalent).

(*iv*) The *Certificate IV* : has learning outcomes requiring the performance of a broad range of skilled applications, including requirements to evaluate and analyse current practices, develop new criteria and procedures for performing current practices, and with leadership and guidance involved.

(*v*) The *Diploma* : is a para professional qualification. The learning outcomes require the self-directed application of knowledge and skills, with substantial depth of knowledge required in some areas where judgement is required.

(*vi*) The *Advanced Diploma* : is a professional-level qualification with learning outcomes requiring the application of significant range of fundamental principles and complex techniques across a wide and often unpredictable variety of contexts, in relation to either varied or highly specific functions. (Entry to 4, 5 & 6 requires general educational competencies equivalent to Year 12 or to completion of Certificate III in the discipline. Many programs will require a specific level of competence in Mathematics, English, and/ or a Science).

Entry Requirements for TAFE

The entry requirements needed by students for TAFE, are based upon prerequisite secondary education and the successful completion of an English language test.

The secondary education prerequisite needed by students for TAFE depends on the award the student is applying for. A Higher Secondary Certificate or Senior School Certificate is needed for the Diploma and Associate Diploma. The Secondary School Certificate, minimum 5 subjects, is needed for both the Certificate and Advanced Certificate.

The English language requirement is determined by the International English Language Testing Service (IELTS) test. A score of 5.5 is required for entry to most TAFE courses. Students who do not achieve the level of English proficiency required for acceptance into the TAFE course of their choice may enrol in TAFE intensive English language programs before proceeding to a TAFE course.

Support for International TAFE Students

As TAFE institutions recruit a good number of overseas students, they provide various means of support.

In each TAFE college or state office, there is a special unit or person who looks after the needs of international students. These international units or advisers can help students with any difficulties, including finding accommodation, arranging transport to and from the college, sorting out problems with teachers or other students, academic counselling, providing information about recreation and assisting students to get help with medical or financial problems.

Foundation studies and Bridging courses are provided, to help students prepare for study in a specific course or area.

2. Private Colleges

Private colleges offering vocational courses to international students must be registered by the Australian Government. Private college courses are designed to equip students with practical skills for business and the workforce in general, and offer certificates and diplomas. Typical areas of study include: aviation, business management, computer studies, travel and tourism, etc.

Private colleges do not offer the degree of MBA, although an award from them may provide a bridge to some tertiary courses.

PREPARING TO STUDY IN AUSTRALIA

Before applying to an Australian educational institution, a student should be aware of the support services available in India to assist this process.

Established in October, 1994, by the Australian Government, the Australian International Education Foundation (AIEF) is a partnership of the Australian education and training community and the Australian Government. It has four main components: membership, Council, national office, and offshore network.

The AIEF's offshore network operates shopfronts known as Australian Education Centres (AECs). These provide information about Australian education and training and the services available from Foundation members to potential students and their families. The Foundation's offshore offices have active relationships with host country policy-makers, educators and media.

Services offered by AIEF to Indian students are :

AEC-Library Facility

AEC is located within the Australian High Commission in New Delhi and the Australian Consulate-General in Mumbai. The AEC provides generic and detailed information about Australia and its educational institutions. This facility is free of charge. The resources available at the AEC are not limited to Australian education. It has been designed to meet a wider area of growing interest in Australia by Indian students like economic ties, culture, science and technology, history, etc. Prospective students can peruse institution specific brochures, handbooks, CDs, Videos as well as generic information on education and training in Australia.

Group Counselling

Unbiased and impartial generic counselling is provided to prospective students at the Australian High Commission and at the Australian Consulate General in Mumbai.

Enquiry via mail

AIEF also disseminates information through mail to students who write to it for information about studying in Australia. Our contact details are listed below :

Association of Indian Graduates from Australia (AIGA)

If you have completed any course of study or training in Australia then you are eligible to become a member of AIGA. For more details contact AIEF.

Many Australian education and training institutions employ student recruitment agent(s) to represent their interests in India. These representatives can offer a "one stop-shop" facility aimed at providing convenient and personal attention to interested students. Agents in India have formed AAERI. AAERI formally has adopted a "Code of Ethical Practices" and other common modalities obligatory on all member agents. A recommended schedule of fees and services provided by agents is outlined in the charter of AAERI which should be displayed by all agents in their offices.

Prospective students are advised to contact the AIEF for detail on AAERI members. Use of AAERI members is strongly encouraged by the AIEF and the Visa Office.

Visa Formalities

On accepting an offer of admission from an Institution, immediately contact the Visa Office, at the Australian High Commission to know about the visa formalities.

Usually visa processing takes 3-4 weeks. In order to attend the orientation program conducted by the Australian institution, you are advised to apply for a visa upto 6 weeks before the course is to commence. You can apply directly or use a AAERI member.

AIEF wishes you the very best and congratulates you for considering Australia as your study destination

ADCOS-Australian Development Cooperation Scholarship

Financial assistance offered by the Australian Government through the Australian Agency for International Development (AusAID) viz., Australian Development Cooperation Scholarship (ADCOS), is no longer available for the Indian public. A successor scheme is currently being designed in collaboration with the Government of India. If any scholarship for the general public is offered in the future, details will be publicly advertised.

OPRS-Overseas Postgraduate Research Scholarship

Students undertaking postgraduate research may apply for an OPRS. OPRS are managed by universities on a quota system. There are around 300 scholarships offered yearly to students from around the world. Details are available from the Student Officer at the Australian High Commission in New Delhi and the Australian Consulate-General in Mumbai.

Institution Specific Scholarships

Many Australian institutions offer institution specific scholarship/s. For detailed information, you are requested to refer to institution handbooks at the AEC or contact institutions directly.

AIEF-INDIA: CONTACT DETAILS

New Delhi

Australian International Education Foundation
C/O-Australian High Commission, 1/50 G Shanthi Path
Chanakya Puri, New Delhi—110021, TEL #: 00-91-11-6885637, 6888223
FAX #: 00-91-11-6873172, Email: aief. india@dfat.gov.au
Website: http://www.netxpertsindia.com/aief
AIEF homepage: http://www.aief.edu.au

Generic Counselling

Monday through Wednesday and Friday, Timing : 2.30 pm & 3.30 pm. No appointment required.

AEC-Library Facilities

Monday through Friday, Timing : 9.00 am-1.00 pm. Appointment is required.

Mumbai

Australian International Education Foundation,
C/o-Australian Consulate-General, 16th Floor, Marker Tower-E
Cuffe Parade, Colaba, Mumbai-400 005
TEL #: 00-91-22-2181071, 2181072, 2186865, FAX #: 00-91-22-2188228

Generic Counselling

Only on Friday's, Timing : 2.30 pm & 3.30 pm. Appointment is required.

AEC-Library Facilities

Monday through Friday

Timing : 9.00 am - 1.00 pm, Appointment is required.

Information by mail should be addressed to Student Officer, AIEF, New Delhi at the above address.

Postgraduate Research Scholarship Scheme

Scheme Objective

The purpose of the Overseas Postgraduate Research Scholarship (OPRS) Scheme is to attract top quality overseas postgraduate students to areas of research strength in higher education institutions and to support Australia's research effort.

The program offers an opportunity to obtain a postgraduate qualification and to gain experience with leading Australian researchers.

Target Groups

The scholarships will be available for either Ph.D or Masters level overseas students who will undertake quality research (fundamental or applied) in areas of research specialization in individual institutions. These areas are ones in which the institution has particular expertise, has concentrated its research resources and has attracted grants from outside sources.

If successful you will probably become a member of a research team working under the direction of senior researchers.

About 300 scholarships were made available for postgraduate studies in 1998.

Eligibility

You may apply if you are a citizen of any overseas country (except New Zealand), who commenced full-time study in 1998 for a higher degree by research in an Australian higher education institution.

There are no age restrictions.

You are not eligible if you are :

(*i*) an overseas student who has already obtained a Ph.D degree or equivalent;

(*ii*) an overseas student who has already obtained a Masters degree by research and who seeks to undertake another Masters degree by research;

(*iii*) normally, an overseas student who has commenced Ph.D study prior to 1st January of the year for which the scholarship is to be awarded;

(*iv*) normally, an overseas student who wishes to pursue a Masters degree by research under the scholarship and has commenced Masters by Research study prior to 1st January of the year for which the scholarship is to be awarded; or

(*v*) an overseas student who is currently studying or has recently studied on a scholarship sponsored by the Australian Agency for International Development (AusAID). AusAID scholarships require that students and their dependants leave Australia on completion of the course for which the AusAID funding has been provided, and must not return to Australia within 2 years under concessional or family categories. It is not expected that former AusAID students who return on other grounds will receive further Australian Government funding within the 2 year period.

Selection Criteria

Scholarships will be awarded on the basis of academic merit and research capacity.

Scholarship Benefits

The scholarship covers the tuition fees set by the institution and is payable for each year of the course. The duration of the scholarship is normally limited to three years for students enrolled in Ph.D degree programs and two years for students enrolled in Masters degree programs by research. Extensions may be granted in certain circumstances.

Holders of OPRS and their dependants are currently given basic health cover.

The scholarship does not provide financial support for the cost of English language testing, bridging programs of English language programs, nor does it provide a living allowance or allowances covering other expenses.

You cannot receive concurrent assistance from an OPRS and from other Australian Government scholarship programs (for example, the Commonwealth Scholarship and Fellowship Plan, the Australian-European Awards Program, the Development Training Program, the Australian Development Cooperation Scholarships) or under programs to which the Australian Government makes a substantial financial contribution (such as the Fulbright Program). However, you may obtain additional support to cover your living expenses for private sources or from higher education institutions' scholarship programs.

Application Procedure

When seeking enrolment at a higher education institution, you should indicate your interest in applying for an OPRS. The institution will then provide the appropriate application form. You must apply direct to the institution.

The closing date for applications will be set by institutions. Most institutions will set a closing date in September or October, but some may require you to apply earlier.

You will be advised of the outcome of your application by late December.

Further Information

You may obtain general information about study in Australia from Australian Education Centres in certain overseas countries. If your country does not have an Australian Education Centre, you may obtain information from the Australian diplomatic mission.

You may obtain further information about OPRS, and application forms, from higher education institutions.

Students' Entry to Australia From India and Nepal

1. Who needs a Student Visa

Any person who intends to undertake full-time study in a registered course in Australia needs to obtain a Student Visa. A Student Visa permits the holder to travel, to enter and remain in Australia for the duration of the registered course of study. Overseas students cannot undertake part-time study in Australia and must leave Australia on completion of their course of study.

2. Applying for a Student Visa

To be considered for a Student Visa, you must first complete an application form (157W) which is available free of charge either from the Australian High Commission, New Delhi or education agents (see Section 10). The application form must be accompanied by the correct application fee which should be in the form of a bank draft made payable to the Australian High Commission, New Delhi.

The current application fee for a student (temporary) visa is Indian Rs. 7,555. The fee is subject to change without notice. An application will not be accepted unless it is made in the prescribed form and with the correct fee.

The fee is an immigration service charge and is nonrefundable irrespective of the outcome of your visa application.

3. Preliminary Visa Assessment (PVA)

Your application will be assessed on the basis of the following criteria:

(*i*) *Evidence of Enrolment*

One of the important requirements for a student visa application is that you must be accepted for enrolments, to undertake a course, by a Government registered Australian educational institution. This is verified by the advice of acceptance from the Australian institution (commonly known as Letter of Offer), which is issued to a student who has been offered enrolment in a full-time course. You should not pay any part of the course tuition fee prior to the outcome of the PVA.

(*ii*) *Bona Fides*

The bona fides assessment determines whether an applicant is a genuine student who intends to undertake studies in Australia, abide by visa conditions and depart on completion of the course. This involves examining the following :

- academic performance of the applicant;
- applicant's migration history and ties with Australia;
- relevance of the proposed course of the applicant's current academic and employment circumstances;
- whether the applicant's English language skills are adequate for the purposes of the proposed course; and
- applicant's intention to comply with visa conditions and leave Australia at the end of the authorised period of stay

(*iii*) *Adequate Financial Resources*

This involves an assessment of the applicant's or his/her sponsor's ability to finance all expenses pertaining to the applicant's education in Australia. The factors that may be taken into account include:

- capacity to pay for course tuition fee, return air fares to home country and all expenses (including medical insurance) associated with his/her stay in Australia;
- applicant's capacity to repay any loans taken to finance his/her study; and
- if the applicant is married, his/her ability to support any financially-dependent family unit members for the duration of the course.

While an overseas student is permitted to work for 20 hours a week when the course is in session, employment in Australia is not guaranteed. No work restrictions apply during vacations. Students should not expect to fund their studies and living costs in Australia through part-time employment. The approximate cost of living for a single person in Australia is between AUD12,000 and AUD14,000 per annum. This figure will be higher where dependent(s) intend to accompany the student.

4. Further Processing

If you are advised that you meet the PVA requirements, you will be asked to undergo further processing. This includes payment of course tuition fee to the Australian educational institution and a medical examination. It is essential that the student and the accompanying dependent(s) meet the Australian Health requirements before a visa may be granted. This involves a medical check up and an X-ray for applicants over 16 years of age. Applicants will need to present an original valid passport to identify themselves to the Doctor and Radiologist. In some cases medical results will be referred to Australia and as this process takes 3-4 weeks, applicants are advised to allow at least 6 weeks for processing of their visa. Applicants need to take into account postage or courier delays also.

5. Total Processing Time

The Visa Office requires four weeks (from the date of lodgement) to process an application for student visa. This may be longer for applicants living in remote places, due to delays in postal services. In some cases the medical reports are referred to Australia which may extend the processing time further by at least four weeks.

6. Health Insurance

It is compulsory for all international students to have Overseas Student Health Cover (OSHC) for themselves and their dependents, where applicable, for the duration of the visa. The premium for

OSHC is only to be paid once the PVA requirements have been met. The current premiums for OSHC are AUD 274 for a single person and AUD 548 for a whole family.

7. Members of the Family Unit

Dependent(s) of the student may accompany him/her to Australia. A member of the family unit includes spouse (including *defacto* spouse), unmarried dependent, children under the age of 18 and a fiance(e) intending to marry within 3 months of arrival.

A member of the family unit is considered in the same visa class as the student. The name(s) should be included in the same application as that of the student if applying at the same time. Most student dependents are allowed to work 20 hours a week (different conditions apply to spouses of post graduate students).

Members of the family unit cannot enter Australia as dependents if the duration of the proposed course is less than 12 months.

8. Education of School Age Dependents in Australia

Students should be aware that if any of their children (over 5 years of age) intend to join them in Australia, they will be required to provide evidence of the child's enrolment in an Australian school for the duration of the applicant's course. The student is responsible for all expenses associated with their child's education (including tuition fee) in Australia. Students should also check with the Education Authority in the State in which they intend to study for further information including the cost of the schooling.

9. Re-entry into Australia

All Student Visas have a multiple entry facility for the full period of the visa. Students who plan to travel out of, and return to, Australia at any time during their course are advised to check that their visa is valid for return to Australia.

10. Australian Education Representatives (Agents)

Australian education representatives act as agents for Australian education institutions in India. Their services to students include, among others, course counselling and assistance with visa applications. The Australian Education Centre (AEC), located at the Australian High Commission, New Delhi has details of the agents. Please remember that some agents are members of the Association of Australian Education Representatives in India (AAERI). AAERI has, among other things, a Code of Ethical Practices for participating members.

11. Scholarships

No public scholarships are offered to Indian nationals by the Australian Agency for International Development (AusAID).

The public category of the Australian Development Scholarship (ADS) which was earlier known as ADCOS, is not available in India.

Students undertaking postgraduate research however may apply for an Overseas Postgraduate Research Scholarship (OPRS). OPRS is managed by Australian universities on a quota system. There are around 300 scholarships offered each year to international students from around the world. Details are available from the Manager, Australian Education Centre (AEC) or the Education Reference Centre (ERC).

Many Australian institutions offer institution-specific scholarship/s. For detailed information, you are requested to refer to the handbook(s) of the respective institutions(s) available at the AEC and ERC, or you can contact the institutions directly or their in country representatives.

AEC-Library Facility : An AEC is located within the Australian High Commission in New Delhi and an ERC at Australian Consulate-General office in Mumbai. The AEC provides generic and detailed information about Australia and its educational institutions. The facility is free of charge and course related information can be mailed on request. The AEC in New Delhi services Nepal enquiries also.

Group Counselling: Unbiased group counselling is provided at the Australian High Commission New Delhi and Australian Consulate General's office, Mumbai.

For Further Information Contact :

AIEF & AEC (New Delhi,	Fax : 011-6873171
AIEF & ERC (Mumbai)	Fax : 022-2188228
(for counselling and general information on studying in Australia)	
Visa Office	Fax : 011-6887536

(for queries relating to student visa application)
Australian High Commission, 1/50 G. Shantipath, Chanakyapuri,
New Delhi-110021, Tel # : 00-91-11-6885637, 6888223
(AEC and Visa Office in New Delhi)

Applicants from India

How to Communicate with the Visa Office, Australian High Commission, New Delhi

1. Obtaining an Application Form

Application forms for all classes of visa can be obtained directly from the Visa Office, Australian High Commission, New Delhi. Forms for some temporary visa classes only (for example, Students, Visitor, and Temporary Residence) may also be available through agents.

Please / note: / Forms / for / temporary / visa / classes / are / provided Free of Charge. Agents who supply forms on our behalf should do so without obliging the client to accept their services or pay for the form. The Visa Office does not necessarily endorse the services of any particular agent who holds visa application forms.

Information and application forms for *permanent visa classes* are only held at the Visa Office, Australian High Commission, New Delhi. If you wish to receive information about permanent entry to Australia, you may write, fax, or email your request. If you wish to receive a Migration Application Package, please send a bank demand draft for Indian Rs. 265 made payable to the Australian High Commission and indicate the class of visa you wish to apply for.

2. Making an Application

Applications do not have to be made in person. You can mail in your application or send it by courier. For faster turnaround we suggest you use a courier service. The Visa Office has an arrangement with First Flight Couriers Ltd. This company has offices all over India and can collect your individual package from your residence or office and send it via a special service for our Visa Office to New Delhi. They can return your passport and any other papers via the same service directly to your address. Mail can usually be delivered the following day to major centres and one day later for other destinations depending on the locality. You need to add this transportation time to the approximate processing time for the visa class you are applying for to ensure you have allowed plenty of time for them to process your application and return your passport (see checklist for approximate visa processing times).

For further information contact your nearest First Flight office.

3. Cost of the Service

The First Flight charges per packet are set out below for destinations within India:

Delhi and N.C.R#.	: Up to 500 Grams	: Rs 20.00
	: Every Addl 500 Grams	: Rs 10.00
North India*	: Up to 500 Grams	: Rs 30.00

	: Every Addl 500 Grams	: Rs 20.00
Rest of India	: Up to 500 Grams	: Rs 50.00
	: Every Addl 500 Grams	: Rs 30.00

N.C.R : Faridabad; Gurgaon, Ghaziabad, and Noida

* North India : Uttar Pradesh, Punjab, Haryana, Rajasthan, Jammu & Kashmir, Himachal Pradesh and Madhya Pradesh (except Indore)

Note : Service tax @ 5% will be charged.

It is up to each applicant to pay the courier charges for documents sent to the Visa Office. For them to return your documents via the same service, you need to provide them with a bank demand draft, postal or money order for the correct amount, made payable to First Flight Couriers Ltd. If you do not enclose the fee, your passport and other papers will be returned by speed post unless you make your own arrangements in which case you will need to advise us in writing of your requirements.

4. Enquiries

Enquiries may be directed to the Visa Office by mail, telephone, fax or email. As the Visa Office is always very busy you are requested not to make enquiries on the progress of your application unless absolutely necessary, and in any case, not until the usual processing time has elapsed, as responding to enquiries takes away our resources from processing applications.

Their e mail address is: dima.india@dfat.gov.au

Please address all mail to : The Visa Office, Australian High Commission
1/50 G Shantipath, Chanakyapuri, New Delhi 110021

University Contact Details

Australian Catholic University, International Education Office, Mackillop Campus, North Sydney, New South Wales-2059, Phone : 02-9739 2072/2368
Fax : 02-9739 2001/2905, E mail : international@acu.edu.au, Web : www.acu.edu.au

Australian National University,International Education Office, GPO Box 4, Canberra, Australian Capital Territory-0200, Phone : 02-6249 5111, Fax : 02-6249 5550
E mail : International.Enquiries@anu.edu.au, Web : www.anu.edu.au

Bond University Limited, Level 6, The Arch Building University Drive, Robina,
Queensland - 4226, Phone : 07-5595 1111, Fax : 07-5595 1140
E mail : international@bond.edu.au, Web : www.bond.edu.au

Central Queensland University, Bruce Highway, North Rockhampton, Queensland - 4702
Phone : 079-309 746, Fax : 079-309 803, E mail : international-enquiries@cqu.edu.au
Web : www.cqu.edu.au/cquint/home.html

Charles Sturt University,Locked Bag 669, Wagga Wagga, New South Wales-2650,
Phone : 02-6338 4000, Fax : 02-6338 4838, E mail :intoffice@csu.edu.au, Web: www.csu.edu.au

Curtin University of Technology, Kent Street
Bentley, Western Australia - 6102, Phone :08-9266 7331, Fax : 08-9266 2605
E mail :international@cc.curtin.edu.au, Web : www.curtin.edu.au/curtin/dept/io

Deakin University
336 Glenferrie Road, Malvern,Victoria - 3114, Phone : 03-9244 5095, Fax : 03-9244 5094
E mail : du.info@deakin.edu.au, Web : www2.deakin.edu.au/international/

Edith Cowan University, Pearson Street, Churchlands,Western Australia - 6018
Phone : 08-9273 8333, Fax : 08-9273 7095, E mail : iso@cowan.edu.au, Web : www.cowan.edu.au

The Flinders University of South Australia , Sturt Street, Bedford Park, South Australia - 5042
Phone : 08-8201 2768, Fax : 08-8201 3177,E mail : intl.office@flinders.edu.au
Web : adminwww.flinders.adu.au/intloff/home.html

Griffith University, International Centre, Kessels Road, Nathan, Queensland 4111

Phone : 07-38757200 Fax : 07-38755280, Email : guic@ic.gu.edu.au, Web : www.gu.edu.au
James Cook University, Townsville, Queensland - 4811, Phone : 07-4781 4811, Fax : 07-4779 6371
Email : International.Affairs@jcu.edu.au, Web : www.jcu.edu.au
La Trobe University, La Trobe, Victoria - 3083, Phone : 03-9479 2000, Fax : 03-9479 0093
Email : international@latrobe.edu.au, Web : www.latrobe.edu.au
Macquarie University, Herring Balaclava Roads, North Ryde, New South Wales - 2113
Phone : 02-9850 7346, Fax : 02-9850 7733, Email : ISO@ecs/.ocs.mq.edu.au, Web : www.mq.edu.au
Monash University, Wellington Road, Clayton, Victoria - 3168, Phone : 03-9905 4000
Fax : 03-9905 4007, Email : monint@adm.monash.edu.au, Web : www.monash.edu.au
Murdoch University, South Street, Murdoch, Western Australia - 6150 , Phone : 08-9360 6000
Fax : 08-9360 6729, Email : internal@murdoch.edu.au, Web : www.murdoch.edu.au
Northern Territory University, PO Box 40146, Casuarina
Northern Territory - 0810, Phone : 08-8946 7078, Fax : 08-8946 6059
Email : marketing@darwin.ntu.edu.au, Web : www.ntu.edu.au/
Queensland University of Technology, Queensland International, Victoria Park Road, Kelvin Grove, Queensland - 4049, Phone : 07-3864 3142, Fax : 07-3864 3529
Email : qut.international@qut.edu.au, Web : www.qut.edu.au
Royal Melbourne Institute of Technology Melbourne Private Box 2303U, 124 La Trobe Street, Melbourne Victoria - 3000, Phone : 03-9660 5156, Fax :03-9663 6925
Email : isu@rmit.edu.au, Web : www.ip.rmit.edu.au/internat/is/
Southern Cross University, PO Box 157, Military Road, Lismore, New South Wales - 2480
Phone : 02-6620 3000, Fax : 02-6622 1300, Email : intoff@scu.edu.au, Web :www.scu.edu.au
Swinburne University of Technology PO Box 218 Hawthorn 3122 VIC
Phone : 03-9241 8000, Fax : 03-9819 5454, Email : mbrown@swin.edu.au, Web : www.swin.edu.au
University of Adelaide, North Terrace, Adelaide, South Australia - 5005, Phone : 08-8303 4455
Fax : 08-8224 0464, Email : international.programs@registry.adelaide.edu.au
Web : www.adelaide.edu.au
University of Ballarat, PO Box 663, Ballarat, Victoria - 3350, Phone : 03-5327 9000, Fax : 03-5327 9544, Email : international@ballarat.edu.au, Fax :www.ballarat.edu.au
University of Canberra, Kirinari Street, Bruce, Australian Capital Territory - 2616
Phone : 02-6201 5111, Fax : 02-6201 5999, Email : iso@adminserver.canberra.edu.au,
Web : www.canberra.edu.au/new/contents.html
University of Melbourne, Parkville, Victoria- 3052, Phone : 03-9344-4505, Fax : 03-9349 3204
Email : course information@register/unimelb.edu.au, Web : www.unimelb.edu.au.
University of New England, Post Office, Armidale
New South Wales -2351, Phone : 02-6773 3192
Fax : 02-6773 3325, Email : ipo@metz.une.edu.au, Web : www.une.edu.au/
University of New South Wales (The)
International Office, Kensington, New South Wales -2033
Phone : 02-9385 1000, Fax : 02-9385 2000
Email : international office@ unsw.edu.au, Web : www.unsw.edu.au
University of Newcastle (The)
University Drive, Callaghan, New South Wales - 2308
Phone : 02-4921 5495, Fax : 02-4960 1766
Email : vcsd @cc.newcastle.edu.au, Web: www.newcastle.edu.au.
University of Nortre Dame Australia (The), PO Box 1225
Fremantle, Western Australia- 6160, Phone: 08-9239 5524

Fax : 08-9239 5544, Email : pwillix@nd.edu.au
Web : www.nd.edu.au
University of Queensland (The), 'Sir Fred Schonell Drive, St. Lucia
Queensland -4067, Phone: 07-3365 1111, Fax : 07-3365 1199
Email : IEOenquiries@mailbox.uq.edu.au, Web : www.uq.edu.au/
University of South Australia, North Terrace Adelaide
South Australia - 5001, Phone : 08-8302 0114, Fax : 08-8302 0233, Email :
International.Office@unisa.edu.au, Web : www.unisa.edu.au
University of Southern Queensland, West Street/PO Darling Heights Toowoomba
Queensland -4350, Phone : 07-4631-1200, Fax : 07-4636 1762
Email : lack@usq.edu.au, Web : www.usq.edu.au/
University of Sydney, Level-2, Margret Telfer Building
71-79 Arundel Street, Sydney, New South Wales - 2006
Phone : 02-9351-4079, Fax : 02-9351-4013
Email : info@io.usyd.edu.au, Web: www.usyd.edu.au/
University of Tasmania GPO Box 252, Hobart
Tasmania - 70001, Phone : 03-6226 7492, Fax : 03-6226 7826
Email : International.Office@utas.edu.au
Web : www. international.utas.edu.au
University of Technology - Sydney, PO Box 123 Broadway
New South Wales - 2007, Phone : 02-9514 2000, Fax : 02-9514 1551
Email : intlprograms@ uts.edu.au, Web : www.uts.edu.au
University of Western Australia The Perth, Nedlands Western Australia - 6009
Phone : 08-9380 1853, Fax : 08-9380 1129
Email : icweb@acs.uwa.edu.au
Web : www.acs.uwa.edu.au/icwww/home.html
University of Western Sydney-Hawkesbury, Locked Bag 1, Richmond
New South Wales -2753, Phone: 02-4570 1611, Fax : 02-4588 5258
Email : hawkinter@uws.edu.au, Web : www.hawkesbury.uws.edu.au
University of Western Sydney-Macarthur PO Box 555, Campbelltown
New South Wales- 2560, Phone : 02-4620 3028, Fax : 02-4626 06677
Email : i.elliston@uws.edu.au, Web : www.macarthur.uws.edu.au
University of Western Sydney-Nepean PO Box 10 Kingswood
New South Wales- 2747, Phone : 02-9685 9297, Fax : 02-9685 9298
Email : international@uws.edu.au, Web : www.nepean.uws.edu.au
University of Wollongong, Northfield Avenue, Wollongong
New South Wales - 2522, Phone : 02-4221 3555, Fax : 02-4221 3477
Email : uniadvice@uow.edu.au, Web : www.uow.edu.au
Victoria University of Technology, Ballarat Road, Footscray, Victoria- 3000
Phone : 03-9248 1164, Fax : 03-9248 1009
Email : International@VUT.edu.au, Web : www.vut.edu.au

TAFE - Contact Details

ACT Department of Education PO Box 1584 Tuggeranong
Australian Capital Territory- 2901, Phone : 06-6205 9176, Fax : 06-6205 9239
Email : SandraWoolacott@dpa.act.gov.au, Web : www.act.gov.au
Northern Territory Department of Education

Ludmilla School Campus, Bagot Road, Ludmilla, Darwin
Northern Territory -0801, Phone: 08-8999 3244, Fax :08-8999 3245
Email : Kerry.moir@nt.gov.au, Web : www.ntde.nt.gov.au
NSW TAFE Commission Level 15, 1 Oxford Street Darlinghurst
New South Wales - 2010, Phone: 02-9244 5240, Fax : 02-9244 5266
Email : tafeic@tafensw.edu.au, Web : www.tafensw.edu.au/intestud/
TAFE International Western Australia, Level 7,190 St Georges Terrace Perth
Western Australia- 6000, Phone: 08-93203777, Fax : 08-93203700
Email : tiwa@millst.training.wa.gov.au, Web : www.tiwa.com.au
TAFE Queensland International, Level 14, 145 Eagle Street, Brisbane
Queensland - 4001, Phone : 07-3237 1011, Fax : 07-3235 4416
Email : tafe-qld-intl@dtir.qld.gov.au, Web: www.tafe.qld.edu.au/tqi
TAFE South Australia 12th Floor 31, Flinders Street Adelaide
South Australia -5000, Phone : 08-8226 7939, Fax :08-8226 3655
Email : racher@tafe.sa.edu.au
TAFE Tasmania 2/F-99, Bathurst Street, Hobart, Tasmania -7001
Phone : 03-6233 7019, Fax : 03-6233 5655, Email :inter-ed@tafe.tas.edu.au
Web : www.tafe.tas.edu.au, TAFE Victoria,
Rialto Tower S, 525 Collins Street, Melbourne, Victoria - 3000
Phone : 03-9637 2000, Fax : 03-9637 3010
Email : carolyn. fitzgerald@dse.vic.gov.au, Web :www.dse.vic.gov.au/isp
Updated information on Australian higher education can be had from the following address.
Australian Education, International, 1/50G, Shantipath, Chanakyapuri, New Delhi - 110021
Tel : 0091-11-688-8223 or 688-5556, Fax : 0091-11-6873172.

Austria

Students from abroad are required to apply for admission to Austrian institutions of higher education before coming to Austria. Applications for admission must be addressed to specific institutions and indicate in which degree programme the applicant wishes to enrol.

Each university has an office which is responsible for handling applications and admissions (*Studienabteilung*). Students should contact this office and request an application for admission (*Ansuchung um Zulassung Zum Stuciam*). Applications for admission must be made by September for the winter semester and by Ist February for the spring semester.

Students should wait until they are officially notified in writing by university authorities about the status of their applications. Students are advised to apply well in advance.

What are the Admission Requirements for International Students At Austrian Institutions of Higher Education?

- A vacancy at the desired institution and in the desired degree programme
- A secondary school leaving certificate recognized by Austrian academic authorities as proof of adequate preparation for University studies.
- Evidence of special aptitude (for certain degree programmes, e.g. music performance, fine and applied arts, etc.)
- A certificate of good standing (for students already enrolled in an institution of higher education).

Admission of International Students

The admission of international students to Austrian universities and universities of the arts as regular degree programme students (*ordentlicher Hörer*) is subject to a number of legal regulations.

Admission(matriculation) to individual universities and degree programmes is contingent upon vacancies available. If there are a limited number of vacancies, applicants with records of superior academic achievement (as documented by their secondary school leaving certificates or course work at other institutions of higher education) are given priority. International students may be admitted (matriculated) as regular degree students, provided they submit a secondary school leaving certificate recognized as adequate preparation for university level studies in the country in which it was issued, as well as, according to Austrian regulations, or if they have an equivalent level of education and corresponding certificate.

If the secondary school leaving certificate is not equivalent to the Austrian secondary school leaving certificate required for the elected field of study, academic authorities may require the applicant to complete supplementary course work before beginning the regular degree programme. Applicants may attend University Preparation Courses (*Vorstudienlehrgänge*), if there are sufficient vacancies. If applicants upon the basis of their secondary school leaving certificates are not eligible for admission to a university or university programme in the country in which the secondary school leaving certificate was issued or have been excluded from continuing their studies at a university abroad, they will not be admitted to university study programmes in Austria.

As a member of the Council of Europe, Austria has signed the European Convention on the Equivalence of Diplomas leading to admission to Universities. The following countries have acceded to this convention:

Austria
Belgium
Bosnia-Herzegovina
Croatia
Cyprus
Czech Republic
Denmark
France
Finland
Germany
Great Britain-Northern Ireland
Greece
Iceland
Ireland
Israel
Italy
Liechtenstein
Luxembourg
Macedonia
Malta
Netherlands
New Zealand
Norway
Poland
Portugal
Sweden
Slovakia
Slovenia
Spain
Sweden
Switzerland
Turkey
[Yugoslavia]

Futhermore, Austria has concluded bilateral agreements on the equivalence of secondary school leaving certificates with the following countries :

Bosnia-Herzegovina
Bulgaria
Croatia
Finland
Hungary
Italy
Liechtenstein
Luxembourg
Poland
Romania
Slovenia
[Yugoslavia]

Secondary school leaving certificates issued in the above mentioned states entitle their recipients to begin studies at a specific Austrian university of university or the arts-provided vacancies are available - if the recipients of these certificates are entitled to enrol in a corresponding institution of higher education in the country of issue. Applicants must fulfil all of the necessary preconditions for being directly admitted to a specific university degree programme in the state in which their secondary school leaving certificates were issued as well as in Australia.

German is the language of instruction at Austrian institutions of higher education. If there are doubts whether or not applicants have a sufficient command of German, they may be required to pass a German Proficiency Examination (*Hochschulsprachprufung in Deutsch)* before registering for courses as a regular degree programme student.

International students who have been previously enrolled in an institution of higher education must submit a certificate of good standing issued by that institution and official academic records that document the number of semesters enrolled, course work completed, and corresponding grades. These records are particularly important if applicants wish to have academic work completed abroad applied towards Austrian degree programme requirements.

If the desired course of study demands knowledge or skills that are not documented by secondary school leaving certificates or artistic ability, then applicants are required to take corresponding entrance examinations (aptitude tests) dictated by study regulations. Entrance examinations or auditions are required by universities of the arts. In most cases, secondary school leaving certificates are not required for the programmes offered by universities of the arts.

Applying for Admission

Applicants should address a letter to the office for admissions (*Studienabteilung*) at the institution they wish to attend that expresses their interest in being admitted. In turn, they will receive an "Application for Admission" (*Ansuchung um Zulassung zum Studium*) which should be submitted with the following materials :

1. a certified copy of the secondary-school leaving certificate that lists subjects and courses and the grades obtained;
2. documentation of German language proficiency (e.g. transcripts, language school diplomas, or course certificates), if available;
3. documentation indicating that the applicant would be entitled to directly enrol in a comparable degree programme at a university in the country in which the secondary school leaving certificate was issued;
4. The "Application for admission" form completed using a typewriter (or legibly by hand in capital letters).

All documents must be certified by appropriate authorities in the country in which they were issued and by Austrian diplomatic representatives (Austrian embassies or consulates). Applicants are advised to initially submit only certified copies of documents which must be accompanied by certified German translations. The nature and form of the documentation required change on a country-by-country basis. The admission offices (*Studienabteilungen*) at the respective universities provide information regarding which materials are necessary, upon request.

Upon the basis of the material submitted, the Rector or appropriate university authorities decide whether the applicant will be admitted as a regular degree programme student immediately; be required to take supplementary examinations; or not be admitted. The applicant will be informed of this decision in writing. Therefore, it is especially important for applicants to legibly enter their exact home or mailing address on the "Application for Admission."

Note : The deadlines for submitting applications for admision are 1st September for the winter semester and Ist February for the summer semester. Applications submitted after these deadlines will be treated as applications for the semester following the next respective deadline.

Applicants from States of the European Union/EEA

EU/EEA citizens are subject to the same deadlines for admission and course registration that apply to Austrian citizens (generally laters October or late March). However, they are encouraged to apply for admission before Ist September or Ist February, respectively and they are required to submit the same documentation as other international students.

Access to degree programmes at Austrian universities is not limited for applicants from EU/EEA member states if they can document that they are entitled to directly enrol in a comparable degree programme in their home country or in a country in which they have previously studied.

Information International Students Need Austria

General information on Austria is available abroad from Austrian diplomatic missions (embassies, consulates), Austrian Cultural Institutes, branch offices of the Austrian Tourist Office, and Austrian trade delegations. The following publications may be requested free of charge from the Federal Chancellery - Federal Press Service, Ballhausplatz 1, A 1014 Vienna; *Austria in Austrian Press and Information Secrvice at: the Heart of Europe and Austria : Facts and Figures.* Internet users may consult the WWW site of the Austrian press and Information service at : http://www/ austria. org.

Studying in Austria

The essential information on studying in Austria is found in the publications of the Austrian Academic Exchange Service (OAD), which is published in German and English. These information brochures are available at the official Austrian missions mentioned above or can be obtained directly from the Austrian Academic Exchange Service upon request. Further important sources of information are brochures published by the Austrian National Union of Students. (*sterreichische Hochschulerinnenschaft),* the "Study Guides" *Studienfuhrer*) and course catalogues (*Vorlesungsver-*

zeichnis) of the respective institutions, and information sheets (*Merkblatter*) published by individual university institutes and the Federal Ministry of Science and Transport. These materials may be requested from the individual universities and universities of the arts. Relevant postal and WWW addresses, e-mail addresses, and telephone and fax numbers are listed in the appendix of this brochure.

Internet users should consult the WWW site of the Federal Ministry of Science and Transport (http://www.bmw.gv.at.) or the Austrian Academic Exchange Service (http://www.oed.ac.at.). Under "Universities in Austria" there are brief portraits of Austria's eighteen universities and universities of the arts with links to the WWW sites of each institution. These individual WWW sites provide extensive information on university offices, faculty, institutes, degree programmes, curricula, and semester courses offered.

Legal Regulations Entry Visas and Residency Permits

The following regulations apply to all students with the exception of citizens from EU and EFTA member states : All students coming to Austria for the purpose of study or research are required to have a valid visa (*Visum, gultiger Sichtvermerk*) or a residency permit (*Aufenthaltsbewillingung*). Students should not enter Austria as tourists or with a tourist visa.

Who Should Get a Visa ?

Students who plan on studying for a maximum period of 6 months.

Who Needs a Residency Permit ?

Students and academics who want to study or do research for a period longer than 6 months. Students must apply for visas and/or residency permits at the appropriate Austrian diplomatic missions in their countries of origin/residence (at Austrian embassies or consulates, not honorary consulates or Austrian Cultural institutes). Applications for residency permits are processed in Austria : therefore, they should be submitted as early as possible.

Applicants may also submit applications for residency permits directly to universities or universities of the arts which, in turn, forward them to the appropriate authorities in Austria.

Note : It is not possible to submit an initial application for a residency permit in Austria. Therefore, students must have received their visa or residency permits before they begin their studies in Austria. Visa and residency laws are subject to change. Internet users have access to currently valid regulations and visa/residency permit requirements at the WWW site of the Austrian Press and Information Service: http:/www.austria.org/.

University Press

Students who are not Austrian citizens or do not have a legal status comparable to that of Austrian citizens are required to pay a tuition fee of ATS 4,000 upon enrolling for courses at the beginning of each semester. This requirement is waived for students who are citizens of EU/EEA member states as well as in the following cases:

(*a*) Students, who have had their permanent residence in Austria for at least five years and been subject to Austrian income taxes without exception before beginning their studies or whose parents/legal custodians/spouses fulfil these conditions:

(*b*) Recipients of scholarships from public institutions, agences, or NGOs ; in Austria that fulfil Austrian regulations pertaining to minimum levels of student support schemes;

(*c*) Students from countries or universities that have bilateral agreements with Austria or Austrian universities regarding the mutual waiver of tuition fees;

(*d*) Students from developing countries;

(*e*) Students who are stateless and have had a residence in Austria for at least five years; and

(*f*) Geneva Convention refugees.

Applications for tuition waivers must be submitted to the Rector of the respective institution before course registration (*Meldung zur Fortsetzung des Studiums*). There are forms for this purpose.

Cost of living

The following table indicates the estimated monthly cost of living for students who are establishing a new residence in Austria. The figures below are averages and subject to considerable variations on a case-to-case basis. They are exclusively intended to serve as points of orientation and may not be interpreted as binding.

Housing (including host and utilities)	ATS 2,500
Food (without tobacco, alcohol, etc.,)	2,500
Personal expenses, books, culture, entertainment	3,500
	ATS 8,500

Housing costs above are based on the average costs of a dormitory; private accommodations are considerably more expensive.

Are International Students Eligible for Scholarships From Public, Religious, or Private Institutions in Austria ?

Students are strongly advised not to start their studies in Austria unless they have secured financial support necessary for the entire length of their anticipated period of study. International students are eligible for scholarships, which are limited in number, only if they fulfil certain preconditions. Applications for the scholarship programmes of the Austrian Federal Ministry of Science and Transport and the Austrian Federal Ministry for Foreign Affairs are to be submitted to the appropriate Austrian diplomatic missions in the applicant's country of origin/residence.

Degree Programmes at Austrian Universities

- Degree programmes (*Diplomstudien*) are designed to educate students for specific professions. The successful completion of a course of study is the prerequisite for the acquisition of the first academic degree awarded in Austria (the *Diplom* that is generally recognized as equivalent to a master's degree) and requires a thesis (*Diplomarbeit*). As a rule, degree programmes last four to six years at universities and four to eight years at universities of the arts.
- Doctoral programmes (*Doktoratsstudien*) that require a first degree, promote the ability to pursue independent research, require a doctoral thesis, and conclude with a doctoral degree.

The minimum length of doctoral programmes is one year. However, the actual length of doctoral programmes is highly variable. In engineering, for example, students usually need a number of years. The study of medicine represents an exceptional case in so far as no first degree is awarded and the degree programme concludes with a doctorate.

The new University Studies Act also has established criteria that allow universities to establish university graduate course programmes (*Lehrgäange*) whose admission requirements include a *Diplom* or its equivalent and conclude with a Master of Advanced Studies (MAS), Master of Business Administration (MBA) or the title "Academic Accredited ...." followed by a description of the contents of the course absolved.

Thesis and dissertations

As a rule, the language for theses (*Diplomarbeiten*) and doctoral dissertations (*Dissertationen*) is German. However, students have the right to submit a thesis or dissertation in another language if the faculty members responsible for the evaluation thereof (*Begutachter*) agree to review it in a foreign language.

Academic Degrees

Academic degrees are awarded to degree programme students by the competent bodies of the universities in recognition of their academic achievements as documented by examinations.

Academic Equivalencies and the Recognition of Foreign Degrees

Note: Details on the recognition of academic work and/or degrees from abroad are available from the Dean's Office (*Dekanat*) of the respective faculties (law, natural science, humanities, etc.) and the chairpersons of the curricular commissions (*Studienkommissionen*) responsible for specific degree programmes.

(a) First-semester students

First-semester students must have been admitted to a regular degree programme (*Diplomstudium*). Student advising services of the Austrian National Union of Students and at Austrian universities provide valuable advice. Students also are advised to follow recommendations made in course catalogues (*Vorlesungsver—zeichnisse*).

(b) Students who Intend to Complete only Part of their Studies in Austria

and to finish their degree programmes at home, enrol as regular degree programme students. They are advised to inform themselves in advance about the regulations of their home institutions and countries regarding the recognition of academic work performed in Austria and its applicability to degree requirements at home.

(c) Students who have completed part of their studies abroad and intend to complete their first degree in Austria

Register as regular degree programme students. They must submit an application to the chairperson of the curricular commission of the degree programme in which they are enrolled in order to have previously completed academic work evaluated for application towards Austrian degree programme requirements..

(d) Students who have Completed first degrees

Students who have completed their first degrees in Austria and intend to pursue doctoral studies abroad must fulfil the requirements of the foreign institution in which they intend to enrol.

Students who have completed their first degrees abroad and intend to enrol in doctoral programmes in Austria must document that their degrees correspond to Austrian first degrees in terms of the course work, examinations, and written work (thesis) required. If not, they must enrol in a number of semesters as regular degree programme students.

Decisions regarding the application of academic work performed abroad toward the fulfilment of Austrian degree programme requirements are made by the chairpersons of the respective curricular commissions after students have made the appropriate request for review (*Ansuchen um Anerkennung von Studien und Prufungen*). They also are responsible for evaluating if or to what extent written work (thesis and dissertations) fulfil the criteria of Austrian thesis (*Diplomarbeiten*) or dissertations and whether or not they will be recognized as such.

The holders of foreign degrees may apply to Austrian universities or universities of the arts to have their degrees recognized as equivalent to academic degrees awarded in Austria. (This procedure is called *Nostrifizierung.*) The Dean of Studies (*Studiendekan*) is responsible for this evaluation procedure. Detailed information is available from the respective Dean's Office (Dekanaft) or University Administration (*Universitats-direktion*).

(e) Postgraduate and Continuing Education Courses

Austrian universities offer a wide range of postgraduate courses in a variety of disciplines.

Enrolment requirements vary depending upon the nature and degree of spec alization. For further information. consult *Weiterbildung an Universitaten und Hochschulen 1998/99.* published by the Austrian Ministry of Science and Transport (May, 1998).

Higher Studies in Austria : General Guidelines

Foreign nationals are admitted to an Austrian university subject to the availability of places and provided that they are in possession of university entrance qualifications which are recognized as equivalent to the Austrian higher school-leaving certificate, the "Matura". Foreigners cannot be admitted to Austrian universities if they would have been debarred from entering or continuing with university education in their homeland.

Due to the overcrowding of various faculties by Austrian students and the large number of foreign students already studying in Austria, new admissions of foreign students to a number of disciplines such as: medicine, veterinary medicine, psychology, zoology, botany, pharmacy, geography, physical education, architecture, economics and social science are restricted.

Applications by foreigners must be received by 1st September and 1st February respectively for the following semesters (half-yearly terms). Acceptance by the "Rektor" of the university concerned is determined by the number of places available which are allocated in order of previous performance as certified by the documents submitted with the application.

Although higher education is free for Austrian citizens, foreigners are at present required to pay a fee of 4,000, —Schillings on enrolment at the beginning of each semester. This fee is waived for:

- Foreigners who themselves or whose parents or guardians have been fully liable to income tax in Austria for at least six years prior to beginning the course;
- Foreigners who are holders of an Austrian Government scholarship of a certain minimum amount;
- Foreigners whose home country waives study fees for Austrians studying there and
- Students from developing countries

Documents to Accompany the Application

Applications for admission have to be sent to the "**universitatsdirektion**" or the "Rektorat" of the university at which the applicant intends to study. The application must be accompanied by the following documents:

1. A curriculum vitae, stating date of birth, nationality, educational background, the chosen study programme and subject of studies; in German language.

2. An original or authenticated copy of the secondary school-leaving certificate. This certificate must contain the grades in the various subjects of courses attended.

3. In case of transfer from another institution of higher learning, certified translations of all documents relating to previous studies; as well as a statement of honourable dismissal would have to be submitted.

4. Evidence of *proficiency in German* :

Applicants have to submit the originals or officially authenticated copies of the documents; in case these are not in English they must be accompanied by German translations.

The "Rektor" or the academic authorities will, on the basis of the documents submitted, decide whether the applicant may be admitted as a regular degree student immediately or after he has passed supplementary examinations or whether he is not admitted. The applicant will be informed of this decision in writing. It is therefore important to indicate legibly the exact home address in the application for admission.

An applicant is strongly advised to come to Austria only when notification from the respective university has been received that admission is granted.

List of Institutions of Higher Education Universities :

University of Vienna Universität Wien Dr. Karl-Lueger-Ring 1
A-1010 Vienna. Tel. : 43-1/4277 - 2692, Fax: 43-1/4277 777
E-mail : martin.heidl@univie.ac.at; ingrid.riedel-taschneraunivie.ac.at
Karl Franzens University Graz. Karl-Franzens-Universitat Graz
Universitatsplatz 3, A-8010 Graz, Tel. : 43-316/380-2192
Fax : 43-316/338506, E-mail : andreas.szeberenyi@kfunigraz.ac.at
University of Innsbruck, Leopold-Franzens-Universitat Innsbruck
Innrain 52, A-6020 Innsbruck, Tel. : 43-512/507, Fax : 43-512/5072800
E-mail : barbara.fitz@adv-mail.uibk.ac.at
Leoben University of Mining and Metallurgy Montanuniversität Leoben
Franz-Josef-Straße 18, A-8700 Leoben, Tel : 43-3842/402 Fax : 43-3842/4032-308
University of Agriculture, Forestry and Renewable Natural Resources
Universität Fur Bodenkul Tur Wien Gregor-Mendel-Straße 33
A-1180 Vienna, Tel : 43-1/47654, Fax : 43-1/3691659, E-mail: studabtl@ mail.boku.ac.at
University of Veterinary Medicine Veternärmedizinische Universität Wien
Linke Bahngasse 11, A-1030 Vienna
Tel : 43-1/25077, Fax : 3-1/7136895, E-mail : michael.schmeidl@vu-wien.ac.at
University of Salzburg Universität Salzburg Kapitelgasse 4-6
A-5020 Salzburg, Tel : 43-662/8044, Fax : 43-662/8044-214
E-mail :sticksel@edvz.sbg.ac.at
Vienna University of Technology Technische Universität Wien
Karlsplatz 13/A-1040 Vienna, Tel. : 43-1/58801-0, Fax : 43-1/5878905
E-mail: studabt@ud.tuwien.ac.at
Technical University Graz Technische Universität Graz, Rechbauerstraße 12
A-8010 Graz, Tel : 43-316/873-6128, Fax: 43-316/873-6125
E-mail: studienabt@udion.tu-graz.ac.at
Vienna University of Economics and Business Administration
Wirtschaftsuniversität Wien / Augasse 2-6 / A- 1090 Vienna
Tel.: 43-1/31336, Fax : 43-1/31336-740, E-mail : urpayr@mailbox.wu-wien.ac.at
Johannes-Kepler-University Johannes-Kepler-Universität Linz
Schloß Auhof, A-4040 Linz,-Tel : 43-732/2468 Fax : 43-732/246810
E-mail : studabt@ udion.uni-linz.ac.at
University of Klagenfurt Universität Klagenfurt Universitätsstraße 65-67
A-9020 Klagenfurt, Tel : 43-463/2700, Fax : 43-463/2700-101
E-mail : gabriele.fluch@uni-klu.ac.at

Academic Programmes in Austria

The following table is based on *Universitäten und Hochschulen, Studium and Beruf* (Ministry of Science and Transport; Ministry of Education and Cultural Affairs, and Federal Office of the Labor Market Service: Vienna, 1997), pp. 61-77 Key :

- Degree programme with various areas of concentration;
- Degree programme or area of concentration;

EP Experimental Study Programme;
PG Postgraduate Course;
SC Non-Degree Study Course;
SSTA Secondary School Teacher Accreditation

COURSES OF STUDY

COURSES OF STUDIES OFFERED IN UNIVERSITIES/COLLEGES OF AUSTRIA

Degree Programmes/Areas of Concentration	Univ. of Wien	K-F Univ. Graz	Univ. of Innsbruck	Univ. of Salzburg	Vienna UT	TU Graz	Univ. of Leoben	Ag. & Forestry Vienna	Vet. Medicine Vienna	Vienna U. Econ. & Bus. Ad.	JK University Linz	Univ. of Klagenfurt	Fine Arts Vienna	Applied Arts Vienna	Music & Drama Vienna	"Mozarteum" Salzburg	Music & Drama Graz	Art & Indust. Design Linz
Acturial Mathematics (SC)					0													
African Studies	0																	
Agriculture								↓										
c: Agricultural Economics								0										
c: Agronomy								0										
c: Horticulture								0										
c: Livestock Sciences								0										
Ancient History	0	0	0	0														
Applied Geosciences (EP)							↓											
c: Applied Geographics							0											
c: Environmental & Hydrogeology							0											
c: Geology Economics							0											
c: Oil and Gas Exploration							0											
Arabic Studies	0																	

Degree Programmes/Areas of Concentration	Architecture	Art Education	Art History	Assembly Automation (EP)	Astronomy	Bass Tuba	Biology	c: Botany	c: Ecology	c: Genetics	c: Human Biology	c: Microbiology	c: Paleontology	c: Zoology	Biology and Commodity Analysis (SSTA)	Biology and Geosciences (SSTA)	Block Flute
Art & Indust. Design Linz	0	0															
Music & Drama Graz						0											0
"Mozarteum" Salzburg		0				0											0
Music & Drama Vienna						0											0
Applied Arts Vienna	0	0															
Fine Arts Vienna	0	0															
Univ. of Klagenfurt																	
JK University Linz																	
Vienna U. Econ. & Bus. Ad.															0		
Vet. Medicine Vienna																	
Ag. & Forestry Vienna																	
Univ. of Leoben																	
TU Graz	0			0													
Vienna UT	0																
Univ. of Salzburg			0				→	0	0					0	0	0	
Univ. of Innsbruck	0		0		0		→	0	0			0		0	0	0	
K-F Univ. Graz			0		0		→	0				0		0	0	0	
Univ. of Wien			0		0		→	0	0	0	0	0	0	0	0	0	

Degree Programmes/Areas of Concentration	Bulgarian	Business Admin., Law & Economics (PG)	Business Administration	c: Business Administration	c: Applied Business Administration	Byzantine and Modern Greek Studies	Ceramics	Chemical Engineering	c: Machine, Plant and Process Engineering	c: Paper and Pulp Engineering	c: Plant Engineering	Chemistry	c: Biochemistry	c: Chemistry	c: Chemistry (SSTA)	c: Chemistry (Foods)	Church Music/Protestant
Art & Indust. Design Linz							0										→
Music & Drama Graz																	→
"Mozarteum" Salzburg																	→
Music & Drama Vienna																	
Applied Arts Vienna																	
Fine Arts Vienna																	
Univ. of Klagenfurt			→	0	0												
JK University Linz			→	0								→			0		
Vienna U. Econ. & Bus. Ad.			→	0													
Vet. Medicine Vienna																	
Ag. & Forestry Vienna																	
Univ. of Leoben																	
TU Graz		0						→		0	0						
Vienna UT		0						→	0			→			0		
Univ. of Salzburg	0																
Univ. of Innsbruck			→	0								→		0	0		
K-F Univ. Graz			→	0								→		0	0		
Univ. of Wien			→	0		0						→	0	0	0	0	

Degree Programmes/Areas of Concentration	c: Choir Direction	c: Organ	Church Music/Protestant (SC)	Church Music/Roman Catholic	c: Choir Direction	c: Organ	Church Music/Roman Catholic (SC)	Civil Engineering	c: Construction Management and Economics	c: Geodesy and Hydraulic Engineering	c: Infrastructure and Environmental Engineering	c: Structural Engineering	c: Transportation and Structural Planning	c: Water and Environmental Engineering	Clarinet	Classical Archeology	Classical Philology/Greek
Art & Indust. Design Linz																	
Music & Drama Graz	0	0	0	→	0	0	0								0		
"Mozarteum" Salzburg	0	0	0	→	0	0	0								0		
Music & Drama Vienna	0	0	0	→	0	0	0								0		
Applied Arts Vienna																	
Fine Arts Vienna																	
Univ. of Klagenfurt																	
JK University Linz																	
Vienna U. Econ. & Bus. Ad.																	
Vet. Medicine Vienna																	
Ag. & Forestry Vienna																	
Univ. of Leoben																	
TU Graz								→		0	0	0					
Vienna UT								→	0			0	0	0			
Univ. of Salzburg																0	0
Univ. of Innsbruck								→	0			0	0	0		0	0
K-F Univ. Graz																0	0
Univ. of Wien																0	0

Degree Programmes/Areas of Concentration	Classical Philology/Greeks (SSTA)	Classical Philology/Latin	Classical Philology/Latin (SSTA)	Commerce	Comunications and Journalism	Comparative Literature	Composition (Music)	Computer Science (Business and Economics)	Computer Science (EP)	Conducting	c: Choir	c: Correpitition/Coaching	c: Orchestra	Contrabass	Cultural Management (PG)	Czech	Czech (SSTA)
Art & Indust. Design Linz																	
Music & Drama Graz							0			→	0		0	0			
"Mozarteum" Salzburg							0			→	0		0	0			
Music & Drama Vienna							0			→	0	0	0	0	0		
Applied Arts Vienna																	
Fine Arts Vienna																	
Univ. of Klagenfurt																	
JK University Linz				0				0									
Vienna U. Econ. & Bus. Ad.				0													
Vet. Medicine Vienna																	
Ag. & Forestry Vienna																	
Univ. of Leoben																	
TU Graz																	
Vienna UT								0									
Univ. of Salzburg	0	0	0		0				0								
Univ. of Innsbruck	0	0	0			0											
K-F Univ. Graz	0	0	0														
Univ. of Wien	0	0	0		0	0		0								0	0

Degree Programmes/Areas of Concentration

	Descriptive Geometry (SSTA)	Dietary Science (EP)	Direction and Production (Drama and Film)	Drama/Acting	Drama/Directing	Dramaturgy	Dutch Studies (EP)	Economics	Economics Education	Editing and Cutting (Film)	Education	Egyptology	Electrical Engineering	c: Automation and Control	c: Communications and Information Technology	c: Computer Technology	c: Electrical and Sound Engineering's
Art & Indust. Design Linz																	
Music & Drama Graz				0													
"Mozarteum" Salzburg				0	0												
Music & Drama Vienna			0	0	0	0				0							
Applied Arts Vienna																	
Fine Arts Vienna									0		0						
Univ. of Klagenfurt								0									
JK University Linz								0	0								
Vienna U. Econ. & Bus. Ad.																	
Vet. Medicine Vienna																	
Ag. & Forestry Vienna																	
Univ. of Leoben																	
TU Graz	0												→				0
Vienna UT	0												→	0	0	0	
Univ. of Salzburg											0						
Univ. of Innsbruck								0	0		0						
K-F Univ. Graz								0	0		0						
Univ. of Wien		0					0	0			0	0					

Degree Programmes/Areas of Concentration

	c: Electrical Energy Technology	c: Electro-and Biomedical Ingineering	c: Electro-and Communication Technology	c: Power Engineering and Electrical Drives	c: Process Technology	English and American Studies	English and Americal Studies (SSTA)	Ethnology	Ethnology (Ethnologia Europea)	Experimental Visual Design	Fagot	Fashinn Design	Film	Finno-Urgic Studies	Flute	Food Science and Biotechnology	Forestry
Art & Indust. Design Linz										0							
Music & Drama Graz											0				0		
"Mozarteum" Salzburg											0				0		
Music & Drama Vienna											0		0		0		
Applied Arts Vienna												0					
Fine Arts Vienna																	
Univ. of Klagenfurt						0	0										
JK University Linz																	
Vienna U. Econ. & Bus. Ad.																	
Vet. Medicine Vienna																	
Ag. & Forestry Vienna																0	→
Univ. of Leoben																	
TU Graz	0	0	0		0												
Vienna UT				0													
Univ. of Salzburg						0	0										
Univ. of Innsbruck						0	0		0								
K-F Univ. Graz						0	0		0								
Univ. of Wien						0	0	0	0					0			

Degree Programmes/Areas of Concentration	c: Forest Products	c: Watershed Regulation	French	French (SSTA)	Geography	c: Cartography	c: Geography	c: Geography and Economics (SSTA)	c: Urban and Regional Planning	Geographics	Geosciences	c: Geology	c: Mineralogy	c: Mining Geology	c: Paleontolgy	c: Petrology	c: Technical Geology
Art & Indust. Design Linz																	
Music & Drama Graz																	
"Mozarteum" Salzburg																	
Music & Drama Vienna																	
Applied Arts Vienna																	
Fine Arts Vienna																	
Univ. of Klagenfurt			0	0			0	0									
JK University Linz																	
Vienna U. Econ. & Bus. Ad.																	
Vet. Medicine Vienna																	
Ag. & Forestry Vienna	0	0															0
Univ. of Leoben											→			0			
TU Graz											→						0
Vienna UT																	0
Univ. of Salzburg			0	0			0	0			→	0				0	
Univ. of Innsbruck			0	0			0	0			→	0			0	0	
K-F Univ. Graz			0	0			0	0		0	→	0	0	0	0	0	0
Univ. of Wien			0	0		0	0	0	0	0	→	0	0	0	0	0	0

Degree Programmes/Areas of Concentration	German (SSTA)	German Language and Literature	Graphics	Guitar	Handicraft Education (SSTA)	Harp	Harspichord	History	History and Social Studies (SSTA)	Home Economics (SSTA)	Horn	Hungarian (SSTA)	Indology	Industrial Chemical Engineering	Indistrial Design	Industrial Engineering and Consturction	Industrial Engineering and Economics
Art & Indust. Design Linz			0		0										0		
Music & Drama Graz				0		0	0				0						
"Mozarteum" Salzburg				0	0	0	0				0						
Music & Drama Vienna				0		0	0				0						
Applied Arts Vienna			0		0										0		
Fine Arts Vienna			0		0												
Univ. of Klagenfurt	0	0							0					0			
JK University Linz																0	
Vienna U. Econ. & Bus. Ad.																	
Vet. Medicine Vienna																	
Ag. & Forestry Vienna																	
Univ. of Leoben																	
TU Graz																	
Vienna UT																	0
Univ. of Salzburg	0	0						→	0								
Univ. of Innsbruck	0	0						→	0								
K-F Univ. Graz	0	0						→	0								
Univ. of Wien	0	0						→	0	0		0	0				

Degree Programmes/Areas of Concentration	c: Chemical Engineering	c: Energy Technology	c: Microprocessors and EDP	c: Production Engineering	c: Transportation Engineering	Industrial Environmental Engineering (EP)	c: Waste Disposal and Management	c: Recycling and Environmental Protection	Informatics	c: Applied informatics	Int'l Business Administration (EP)	Italian	Italian (SSTA)	Japanese Studies	Jazz (Theory)	Jazz (Instruments and Voice)	Journalism and Communications	Judaic Studies	Landscape Architecture and Planning
Art & Indust. Design Linz																			
Music & Drama Graz															0	0			
"Mozarteum" Salzburg																			
Music & Drama Vienna																			
Applied Arts Vienna																			
Fine Arts Vienna																			
Univ. of Klagenfurt										0		0	0						
JK University Linz									0										
Vienna U. Econ. & Bus. Ad.																			
Vet. Medicine Vienna																			
Ag. & Forestry Vienna																			0
Univ. of Leoben						→	0	0											
TU Graz	0	0	0	0	0														
Vienna UT									0										
Univ. of Salzburg										0		0	0				0		
Univ. of Innsbruck												0	0						
K-F Univ. Graz												0	0						
Univ. of Wien									0		0	0	0	0			0	0	

Degree Programmes/Areas of Concentration	Law	Lied and Oratorio (SC)	Linguistics	c: Applied Linguistics	c: General Linguistics	c: Indo-Germanic Languages	Logistics	Materials Science	Mathematics	Mathematics (SSTA)	MBA (PG)	Mechanical Engineering	c: Chemical and Processing Engineering	c: Energy Technology	c: Industrial Engineering	c: Mechanical Design	c: 'Mechanical Engineering
Art & Indust. Design Linz																	
Music & Drama Graz		0															
"Mozarteum" Salzburg		0															
Music & Drama Vienna		0															
Applied Arts Vienna																	
Fine Arts Vienna																	
Univ. of Klagenfurt										0							
JK University Linz	0									0							
Vienna U. Econ. & Bus. Ad.											0						
Vet. Medicine Vienna																	
Ag. & Forestry Vienna																	
Univ. of Leoben								0									
TU Graz													0	0	0	0	0
Vienna UT										0			0		0		0
Univ. of Salzburg	0		→	0	0	0			0	0							
Univ. of Innsbruck	0		→	0	0	0			0	0							
K-F Univ. Graz	0		→	0	0	0			0	0							
Univ. of Wien	0		→	0	0	0	0		0	0							

Degree Programmes/Areas of Concentration	c: Transportation Engineering	Mechatronics (EP)	Medallions and Small Sculpture	Medicine	Metal (Design)	Metallurgy	c: Ferrous Metallurgy	c: Founding	c: Material Science	c: Metal Forming	c: Non-Ferrous Metallurgy	c: Production and Power Management	Meteorology	Mine Surveying	Mineral Processing	Mining & Heavy Machinery Engineering	Mining Engineering
Art & Indust. Design Linz					0												
Music & Drama Graz																	
"Mozarteum" Salzburg																	
Music & Drama Vienna																	
Applied Arts Vienna			0														
Fine Arts Vienna																	
Univ. of Klagenfurt																	
JK University Linz		0															
Vienna U. Econ. & Bus. Ad.																	
Vet. Medicine Vienna																	
Ag. & Forestry Vienna																	
Univ. of Leoben							0	0	0	0	0	0		0		0	0
TU Graz	0																
Vienna UT																	
Univ. of Salzburg																	
Univ. of Innsbruck				0									0				
K-F Univ. Graz				0													
Univ. of Wien				0									0				

Degree Programmes/Areas of Concentration	Music Education (Instruments) (SSTA)	Music Education (SSTA)	Music Education (Voice & Instruments)	Music : Rythm and Movement	Music : Rythm and Movement (SC)	Musical Theatre Direction and Production	Music Theory	Music Therapy (SC)	Musicology	Oboe	Old Semetic Philology/Oriental Archeology	Opera Performance (SC)	Organ	Painting	Percussion Instruments	Petroleum Engineering	Petroleum Engineering (Int'l Programme)
Art & Indust. Design Linz														0			
Music & Drama Graz	0	0	0			0				0		0	0		0		
"Mozarteum" Salzburg	0	0	0	0	0	0				0		0	0		0		
Music & Drama Vienna	0	0	0	0		0	0	0		0		0	0		0		
Applied Arts Vienna														0			
Fine Arts Vienna														0			
Univ. of Klagenfurt																	
JK University Linz																	
Vienna U. Econ. & Bus. Ad.																	
Vet. Medicine Vienna																	
Ag. & Forestry Vienna																	
Univ. of Leoben																0	0
TU Graz																	
Vienna UT																	
Univ. of Salzburg									0								
Univ. of Innsbruck									0								
K-F Univ. Graz									0								
Univ. of Wien									0		0						

Degree Programmes/Areas of Concentration	Pharmacology	Philosophy	Philosophy (Catholic Theological)	Philosophy, Psych. and Pedagogics (SSTA)	Photography and Camerawork	Physical Education and Sports Science	Physical Education (SSTA)	Physics	Physics (SSTA)	Piano	Piano (Chamber Music)	Piano (Chamber Music) (SC)	Piano (Vocal Accompaniment)	Piano (Vocal Accompaniment) (SC)	Polish	Political Science	Polymer Engineering and Science
Art & Indust. Design Linz																	
Music & Drama Graz										0	0	0	0	0			
"Mozarteum" Salzburg										0	0		0				
Music & Drama Vienna					0					0	0	0	0	0			
Applied Arts Vienna																	
Fine Arts Vienna																	
Univ. of Klagenfurt		0															
JK University Linz									0								
Vienna U. Econ. & Bus. Ad.																	
Vet. Medicine Vienna																	
Ag. & Forestry Vienna																	
Univ. of Leoben																	0
TU Graz									0								
Vienna UT									0								
Univ. of Salzburg		0	0	0		→	0								0	0	
Univ. of Innsbruck	0	0	0	0		→	0	0	0							0	
K-F Univ. Graz	0	0		0		→	0	0	0								
Univ. of Wien	0	0		0		→	0	0	0						0	0	

Degree Programmes/Areas of Concentration	Art & Indust. Design Linz	Music & Drama Graz	"Mozarteum" Salzburg	Music & Drama Vienna	Applied Arts Vienna	Fine Arts Vienna	Univ. of Klagenfurt	JK University Linz	Vienna U. Econ. & Bus. Ad.	Vet. Medicine Vienna	Ag. & Forestry Vienna	Univ. of Leoben	TU Graz	Vienna UT	Univ. of Salzburg	Univ. of Innsbruck	K-F Univ. Graz	Univ .of Wien
Portuguese															0	0		
Prehistory and Early History																0		0
Product Design				0														
Production (Music and Drama)				0														
Psychology																0	0	0
Regional Planning														0				
Religious Education (Protestant)																		0
Religious Education (Roman Catholic)															0	0	0	0
Restoration and Conservation (Art)					0	0												
Romanian															0			0
Russian															0	0	0	0
Russian (SSTA)															0	0	0	0
Saxaphone		0		0														
Scandinavian Studies																		0
Sculpture	0				0	0												
Serbo-Croatian																	0	0
Serbo-Croatian (SSTA)																	0	0

Degree Programmes/Areas of Concentration	Sinology	Siovene	Siovene (SSTA)	Social Economics	Sociology (Faculty of Huminities)	Sociology (Faculty of Social Sciences)	Spanish	Spanish (SSTA)	Sporta Science	Stage Design	Statistics	Surveying	c: Geodesy and Geophysics	c: Geoinformation	Tapestry (EP)	Technical Chemistry	c: Biochemistry
Art & Indust. Design Linz																	
Music & Drama Graz										0							
"Mozarteum" Salzburg										0							
Music & Drama Vienna																	
Applied Arts Vienna										0							
Fine Arts Vienna										0							
Univ. of Klagenfurt		0															
JK University Linz				0							0						
Vienna U. Econ. & Bus. Ad.																	
Vet. Medicine Vienna																	
Ag. & Forestry Vienna																	
Univ. of Leoben																	
TU Graz																→	0
Vienna UT												→	0	0		→	0
Univ. of Salzburg					0		0	0	0								
Univ. of Innsbruck			0		0		0	0	0								
K-F Univ. Graz		0	0		0		0	0	0								
Univ. of Wien	0	0	0		0	0	0	0	0		0						

Degree Programmes/Areas of Concentration	Univ. of Wien	K-F Univ. Graz	Univ. of Innsbruck	Univ. of Salzburg	Vienna UT	TU Graz	Univ. of Leoben	Ag. & Forestry Vienna	Vet. Medicine Vienna	Vienna U. Econ. & Bus. Ad.	JK University Linz	Univ. of Klagenfurt	Fine Arts Vienna	Applied Arts Vienna	Music & Drama Vienna	"Mozarteum" Salzburg	Music & Drama Graz	Art & Indust. Design Linz
c: Chemical Engineering					0	0												
c: Inorganic Chemistry					0													
c: Organic Chemistry					0													
Technical Mathematics					→	→												
c: Actuarial Mathematics					0													
c: Applied Business Mathematics												0						
c: Data Processing Mathematics						0												
c: Economic Mathematics					0							0						
c: Economic Mathematics, Operations R and S						0												
c: Industrial Mathematics											0							
c: Mathematical Computer Science					0						0							
c: Mathematics in the Natural Sciences					0						0							
c: Technomathematics						0												
Technical Physics					0	0					→							
c: Technical Physics											0							
c: Biophysics											0							
Telematics						0												

Degree Programmes/Areas of Concentration

	Textile and Handicraft Education	Textiles (Design)	Theatre	Theology : Protestant	Theology : Roman Catholic	Tibetan & Buddhist Studies	Translation	Translation (Simultaneous)	Trombone	Trumpet	Turkish Studies
Art & Indust. Design Linz	0	0									
Music & Drama Graz									0	0	
"Mozarteum" Salzburg	0								0	0	
Music & Drama Vienna									0	0	
Applied Arts Vienna	0										
Fine Arts Vienna	0										
Univ. of Klagenfurt											
JK University Linz											
Vienna U. Econ. & Bus. Ad.											
Vet. Medicine Vienna											
Ag. & Forestry Vienna											
Univ. of Leoben											
TU Graz											
Vienna UT											
Univ. of Salzburg					0						
Univ. of Innsbruck					0		0	0			
K-F Univ. Graz					0		0	0			
Univ. of Wien			0	0	0	0	0	0			0

Doctoral Programmes*	Univ.of Wien	K-F Univ. Graz	Univ. of Innsbruck	Univ. of Salzburg	Vienna UT	TU Graz	Univ. of Leoben	Ag. & Forestry Vienna	Vet. Medicine Vienna	Vienna U. Econ. & Bus. Ad.	JK University Linz	Univ.of Klagenfurt	Fine Arts Vienna	Applied Arts Vienna	Music & Drama Vienna	"Mozarteum" Salzburg	Music & Drama Graz	Art & Indust. Design Linz
Agriculture, Forestry & Renewable Natural Resources								0										
Mining and Metallurgy							0											
Philosophy (at a Faculty of Catholic Theology)			0	0														
Philosophy or Natural Sciences	0	0	0	0	0	0					0	0			0	0	0	
Law	0	0	0	0							0							
Social Sciences and Economics	0	0	0							0	0	0						
Engineering Sciences			0		0	0					0							
Theology (Catholic)	0	0	0	0							0							
Theology (Protestant)	0																	
Vertarinary Medicine									0									

*Doctoral programmes as defined by the General Higher Education Act (*AHStG*) § 13, which require the completion of a previous degree programme (*Diplomstudium*) or its equivalent.

For more details contact:

AUSTRIAN EMBASSY

EP 13, Chandragupta Marg, Chanakyapuri, New Delhi-110021

Brazil

The history of education in Brazil begins in 1549, with the arrival of the first Jesuitical priests, inaugurating an era that was to leave deep traces in the country's culture and civilization. Moved by intense religious feelings of spreading of the Christian faith, for over 200 years Jesuits were practically the only educators in Brazil. Though they founded several schools for teaching, reading, counting and writing, the Jesuits' priority always was secondary school, level of learning at which they organized a series of schools of recognized quality, some of which reached even the capability of offering modalities of study corresponding to university level.

In 1759 Jesuits were expelled from Portugal and its colonies, opening a wide chasm that would not be filled in the following decades. The measures taken by King Jose I's Minister --the Marquis of Pombal--mainly the creation of the Literary Subsidy, a tax imposed in order to finance elementary schooling, had no effects. It was only at the beginning of the next century, in 1808, with the move of the see of the Kingdom of Portugal, and the transfer of the Royal Family to colonial Brazil, that education and culture would regain momentum, with the creation of cultural and scientific institutions, of technical teaching and of the first university courses (such as those of medicine of the provinces of Rio de Janeiro and Bahia).

The educational work of King João, VI, however, although praiseworthy in many aspects, was axed to the immediate needs of the Portuguese Court in Brazil. The courses and other means of teaching then launched in several fields aimed at meeting the demand for professional training. This specific trait would come to have an enormous influence on the evolution of Brazilian higher learning. It must be added, moreover, that King João VI's educational policy, to the extent that it sought, as a rule, to concentrate on the court's demands, let elementary schooling remain neglected as before.

With the country's Independence, in 1822, some changes in the social and political background seemed to start taking shape, including educational policy. In fact, during the work of the Constituent Assembly of 1823, for the first time universal suffrage were linked to popular education one as the basis for the other. That constituent body also discussed the creation of universities in Brazil, with many proposals tabled. As a result of that movement of ideas,emerged the pledge of the Empire, in the Constitution of 1824, to assure "free elementary schooling to all citizens", soon confirmed by the law of October 15th, 1827, which determined the creation of first grade schools in all cities, towns and villages, involving the three instances of public power. It would have been the "Golden Law" (The law that abolished slavery in Brazil - "Lei Aurea"- of 1888) of education, had it been implemented.

In a similar manner, the idea of creating universities didn't ripen, instead, the foundation of Law graduation courses of São Paulo and Olinda, in 1827, strengthened the utilitarian and professional spirit of the policy first designed by King João VI. A few years later, the promulgation of the Additional Act of 1834, which delegated to the provinces the prerogative of legislating on elementary education, further jeopardized the future of basic education, since it allowed the central government to cast off the responsibility to grant elementary schooling for all. Thus, the absence of a centre of unity and action, which was indispensable, given the characteristics of cultural and political formation of the country, ended up jeopardizing the Imperial educational policy.

The decentralization of basic education, instituted in 1834, was maintained by the Republic, thus preventing the Central Government from taking up the strategic position of formulation and coordination of the policy of Universalizing fundamental teaching, which was then done in European countries, the United States and Japan. As a result of this, the gap between the elites and the popular social strata widened even more.

In the decade of 1920, as consequence of the economic, cultural and political panorama brought about by World War I, Brazil started meditating about itself. At several social levels changes were discussed and announced, and the educational sector participates in the movement for renewal, as many reforms of the elementary school system were carried on at state level. The first generation of great educators came forth with the likes of—Anisio Teixera, Fernando de Azevedo, Lourenco Filho, Almeida Junior, among others-which lead the movement and tried to bring to practice in Brazil the ideals of the New School, releasing the Manifest of Pioneers, in 1932, a milestone document that summarizes the focal points of that movement of ideas, redefining the role of the State in educational matters.

The first Brazilian universities were created in : Rio de Janeiro (1920), Minas Gerais (1927), Porto Alegrea (1934), and the University of São Paulo (1934). The last one, that represents the first consistent university project in Brazil, launched an unprecedented cultural and scientific trajectory.

The Constitution promulgated after the 1930 Revolution, in 1934, registered significant advances in the educational area, incorporating much of what had been discussed in preceding years. In 1937, however, the "Estado Novo" ("New State") regime took power, granting an authoritarian constitution, which was a big step backwards. After the fall of "Estado Novo", in 1945, many ideals were recovered and substantiated with the Draft of the Law of Directives and Basis of National Education, sent to the National Congress in 1948, which was finally approved in 1961 (Law n° 4024).

During the period from the fall of "Estado Novo" to the Revolution of 1994, when a new authoritarian phase was begun, the Brazilian educational system underwent significant changes, especially with the advent, in 1951, of CAPES (Coordination of Improvement of Higher Learning Personnel); the creation of the Federal Counsel of Education, in 1961; campaigns and movements for suppressing adult illiteracy, as well as the expansion of elementary and university level schooling. In the period preceding the approval of Law n° 4024, there was a remarkable movement in favour of free, public, universal school.

The events of 1994 interrupted that tendency. In 1969 and 1971, Laws 5540/68 and 569271 were approved, introducing significant changes in the structure of higher learning and of elementary and secondary schools, texts that were basically in force in those days.

The Constitution of 1988, promulgated after a wide movement in favour of re-democratization of the Country, tried to introduce innovations and pledges, with a stress on universality of fundamental schooling and the eradication of illiteracy.

The Educational System in Brazil

Taking into account that Brazil is a Federal Republic made up of 26 States and the Federal District, the educational system is organized on the basis of a collaboration of the Union, the States, the Federal District and the Municipalities. The Federal Government, represented by the Ministry of Education and sport, organizes and finances the federal educational system and grants technical and financial assistance to the States. The Federal system is basically made up of the Universities, a network of agricultural and technical schools of high school level. Besides, the direct responsibility for the network of higher learning, the Federal Government is also responsible for the national programme of support for postgraduation.

The Brazilian educational system is organized as shown in Table 1.

TABLE 1

ORGANIZATION OF THE BRAZILIAN EDUCATION SYSTEM

	Degree of Learning	*Duration*	*Hours/class*	*Requirements for Entry*
Infantile Education (not compulsory)	Day nursery	Variable	Variable	Aging 0 to 3
	Kindergarten	3 years	Variable	Aging 4 to 6
	Elementary School	8 years	720 per year	Aging 7 or more
	Secondary School	3 years**	2.220	Having finished Elementary School
University	Undergraduation	Variable (2 to 6 years)	Variable	Having finished Secondary School and Passed the entrance exams
	Graduation	variable (2 to 6 years)	variable	Having finished the undergraduate course

* Infantile education is seen as a preliminary step towards schooling, it only started being organized and regulated after the advent of the Federal Constitution of 1988.

** When it includes professional proficiency it may last 4 or 5 years

The educational system administerted by the states is made up of day nurseries, kindergarten schools, 1st degree schools, 2nd degree schools, and, in some states, Universities. There is a trend that the 2nd degree remains ever more the responsibility of States and that day nurseries and kindergarten schools remain within the capacity of municipalities.

Municipalities act, on a priority basis, at infantile education and elementary school levels. These municipal educational systems include day nurseries, kindergarten schools, elementary schools (mainly those located in rural areas), and, in a few Municipalities, 2nd degree schools.

From the administrative point of view, each educational system is regulated by a normative organism and managed by a central executive organism. Thus, on the Federal sphere, the working rules are established by the National Council for Education, and the political, planning and administrative decisions belong to the minister for education, assisted by the several secretariats, organisms and services that make up the Ministry for education. In each State and in the Federal District, the normative functions belong to the respective State Education Councils (CEE), and the administrative functions and the control of private Education of 1st and 1st degree are exerted by the relevant State Secretariats for Education (SEE). At municipality level, the Municipal Councils of Education (and, in the absence of such, the relevant CEE), and the cities' Secretariats or Departments for Education exert, respectively, the normative and administrative functions.

It remains, therefore, clear that each system is autonomous for the purposes of hiring teachers, professors and clerks, as well as for the management of their resources.

There are in Brazil 42.2 million students in the educational system, including infantile schools, read and write classes, elementary schools, high school, university graduating and postgraduation, the distribution of which, as well as the amount of establishments and teachers, are shown below.

TABLE 2
DISTRIBUTION OF STUDENTS AND OTHER VARIABLES IN THE EDUCATION SYSTEM OF BRAZIL

Levels of Teaching	*Variables*	*1991*	*1993*
	Institutions	57.842	84.366
Infantile schooling	Teaching Functions	166.917	197.206
	Registration	3.628.285	4.196.419
	Institutions	51.944	50.646
Reading & Writing classes	Teaching Functions	89.291	75.413
	Registration	1.65.609	1.584.147
	Institutions	193.700	195.840
Elementary School	Teaching functions	1.295.965	1.344.045
	Registration	29.203.724	30.548.879
	Institutions	11.811	12.556
High School	Teaching Functions	259.380	273.539
	Registration	3.770.230	4.183.847
	Institutions	893	873
University Degree	Teaching Functions	133.135	137.156
Undergraduate	Registration	1.565.056	1.594.668
	Institutions	83	91
University Degree Graduate	Teaching Functions	29.351	*31.346
	Registration	54.174	55.229

Sources : MEC/SPE/SEEC amd MEC/CAPES

* Postgraduation professors act simultaneously in graduation, being, therefore, included in the teaching function count of that level of learning.

Levels and Modalities of Teaching

Infantile Education

Infantile education, conceived as a preliminary step to schooling, aims at providing conditions for the physical, psychological and intellectual development of the child between the ages of 0 and 6 years, as a complement to the family's action. It is made up of the services rendered at day nurseries, for children from 0 to 3 years of age; and kindergarten schools, for children in the age span of 4 to 6.

Although the public sector has been developing and maintaining programmes for children under the age of 7 years , its responsibility in this area is quite recent. It was only since the Constitution of 1988, that infantile education entered formally the sphere of action of States, belonging to the Municipalities to foster its development.

The non-governmental sector acts strongly in this area, informal programmes involving families and the communities being found all over the country. The Ministry for Education itself has stimulated experimentation of unconventional forms and methods involving greater participation of communities and collaboration with the public powers.

The infantile education network in the country is still quite restricted. According to the data presented in Table 3, only 17.5 per cent of the population within the age span of 0 to 6 years being given any sort of programme at this level.

TABLE 3
NUMBER AND TOTAL OF ASSISTANCE GIVEN TO CHILDREN IN THE AGE GROUP OF 4 TO 6 YEARS

Children aging	*Assisted Children*		*Total of*
0 to 6 Years	*0 to 4 Years*	*4 to 6 Years*	*Assistance*
23.116.078 (100%)	667.736 (2,9%)	3.375.834 (14,6%)	4.043.570 (17,5%)

Sources : IBGE (Brazilian Institute for Geography and Statistics)

Elementary Education

Elementary education, also called 1st degree schooling, is constitutionally mandatory, it aims at the formation of children and pre-teenagers from the age of 7 to 14 years, and has the following pedagogic goals: /a) progressive command of reading, writing and calculating, as instruments for the understanding and solution of human problems and for systematic access to knowledge;(b) the understanding of the laws that rule nature and social relations in contemporary society; and (c) the development of their capability of thinking and creating, as a means of finding a conscious participation in the social milieu.

The full curriculum of 1st degree is made up of a common nucleon and diversified section. The common nucleon, mandatory at national level, comprehends the following areas: (a) communication and expression (Portuguese language); (b) social studies (Geography, History and Social and Political Organization of Brazil), with emphasis on the knowledge of Brazil within the present perspective of its development; and (c) sciences (mathematics, physical and biological sciences). The diversified part depends on each educational system, and, if such is the case, on each school, according to regional and local characteristics of society, on culture, on the economy and the clientele.

In order to render elementary schooling fully universal, as it is determined, States and Municipalities organize yearly, and sometimes jointly, an assessment of the population in school age and proceed to call them in for school inscription.

Recent data of the Statifstics Service of the Ministry for Education show that 91 per cent of the population from age 7 to 14 years has access to schooling.

Even though the country has succeeded in reaching significant levels of assistance to the eclientele, the quality of teaching is quite low.

Recent data indicate high rates of failures in elementary school, which tend to go beyond 50 per cent for first graders.

The problem of early school dropout is relatively lesser, for first graders reaching only 2.3 per cent, but attaining higher levels as educational failures accumulate reaching 32 per cent at the end of the 4th grade.

Repetition of grades and school dropout, represent, thus, great challenges for the national educational system.

High School

The 2nd degree schooling aims at; (a) the deepening and consolidation of knowledge acquired in elementary school; (b) preparation of the student to go on learning; (c) the understanding of scientific technological fundamentals of productive processes, relating theory to practice; and (d) preparation of the student for the exerting of technical professions.

The curriculum of 2nd degree schooling generally comprehends both a part of general education and a part of education for work: As it happens in the 1st degree, here again there is a common nucleon, made up of communication and Expression (Portuguese language and foreign language); Social Studies (History, Geography and Social and Political Organization of Brazil); Sciences (Mathematics, Physical Sciences and Biological Sciences). The diversified part is established by each school, that is able, therefore, to define its plan of activities, respected the general norms and principles that rule the educational system to which the school is linked.

Technical and professional formation at this level may be obtained in technical schools that issue diplomas for occupations regulated for industry, trade, agriculture and service. At this level it is worth mentioning the Normal School, responsible for the formation of teachers for elementary school (1st to 4th grades).

High school functions as a filter between elementary school and the university. Only 16 per cent of youngsters within the age group of 15 to 19 years is at second degree school. It is necessary to take into account, however, that a fair amount of such youngsters is still attending 1st degree schools, which means that 19 per cent of said age span is at school.

Higher Learning

Higher learning in Brazil aims at the perfecting of the cultural formation of youth, rendering them capable for practising a profession, for the exercise of critical reasoning and the participation in the production and systematising of knowledge. The university system in Brazil is made up of public and private institutions.

Parallel to its teaching tasks, higher learning promotes scientific research and develops programmes of extensions, in the shape of courses, and services rendered directly to the community. Research activities are concentrated in public institutions.

The country counts today on 894 institutions of higher learning (IES), 222 of which are public. The remaining ones belong to religious entities, private groups and non-governmental institutions of different natures.

There is today a diversification in the type of institutions. Universities are the most easily identifiable for they have traits of their own, *vis-a-vis* other institutions, such as being more comprehensive in fundamental areas, having an organic character in their organizational structure and also for their degree of autonomy as far as supervising and control organisms are concerned. There are today in the country, 127 universities, 68 of which are public.

Besides completing the 2nd degree, the student that wishes to be admitted to a university must pass an exam called entry contest, *vestibular*. The chances for a student to pass the entry contest for the most prestigious courses of public universities depend, however, not only on the successful completion of the 2nd degree, but also on the quality of the school he attended. As the best quality 2nd degree schools tend to be private and expensive, it is generally the youths of the socially and economically privileged class of society who have access to the best universities.

In terms of capability of assistance, the Brazilian higher learning system is quite restricted : only 10 per cent of the youths in the relevant age span are able to enter an IES.

Present Targets and Future Perspectives of Education in Brazil

The chief goals and objectives of the Government for the bettering of educational services in the country are expressed in the Ten-Year Plan for All (1993-2003) and more recently redefined in the Political Strategic Plan of the Ministry for Education and Sports 1995/1998.

The goals established by the Plan are the following :

1. Rendering elementary schooling universal. The plan intends to increase to at least 94 per cent the assistance to the population in school age;
2. Reduction of the rates of drop out and failure, so that at least 80 per cent of school generations may finish elementary school with good results and following a regular school trajectory;
3. Valuing the teaching profession and perfecting the initial and continued formation of teachers for elementary school;
4. Re-studying the professorship graduation courses and Normal School in order to assure to the training institutions a high level of quality;
5. Re-structuring of medium education (high school) and reform of curricula;
6. Promoting autonomy and better institutional performance in Public Higher Learning;
7. Progressive increase of the percentile participation of the State in education, in order to reach 5.5 per cent of GNP.

As a development of the Ten-year Plan, the present Government put into practice several initiatives, among which the prominent ones are as follows:

A. Plan for Development of Elementary Schooling and Valuing the Teaching Profession;
B. Creation of a fund to implement the above Plan;
C. Decentralisation in the application of federal resources, with direct transfer of their majority to schools;
D. Programme School by Television;
E. Reform of the curriculum for the whole elementary schooling.

With the implantation of these plans and programmes, the Ministry for Education resumes its role of inductor and co-ordinator of changes in public schooling on a national basis.

As regards admission to universities in Brazil, the interested party should get himself enrolled in any Brazilian educational institution and then apply for visa.

You may write directly to the address given below for the necessary enrolment:

CAPES
Coordenacão do Aperfeicoamento do, Pessoal do Nivel Superior
Setor de Autarquias Sul, Quadra 6, Lote 4, Bloco "L" 70.000-Brasilia, DF Brasi.

Kindly also write directly to the universities in Brazil

Embassy of Brazil can also help you. Address is given below :

Embassy of Brazil, 8, Aurangzeb Road, New Delhi - 110 011, Tel : 11-3017301,
Fax : 11-3793684, E-mail : brasindi@giasdlol.vsnl.net.in

Brazilian Universities

Universidade Federal de Bahia - UFBA, Rua Augusto Viana s/n
Canela - Salvador - Bahia - 40.140

Universidade Federal de Brasilia - UNB, Campus Universitãrio - Reitoria
Asa Norte - Brasilia - DF - 70.910

Universidade Federal do Cearã - UFC, Avenida da Universidade 2853
Benfica - Fortaleza - CE - 60.000

Universidade Federal de Minas Gerais - UFMG, Av. Antonio Carlos 6627
Campus - Pampulha - BH - 31.270

Universidade Federal da Paraiba - UFPB, Campus Universitãrio I s/n
Reitoria - 3q andar, Cidade Universitãria - João Pessoa - PB - 58.000

Universidade Federal de Pernambuco - UFPE
Av. Professor Moraes Rego 1235 - 1q andar
Engenho do Meio - Recife - PE - 50.739

Universidade Federal do Rio de Janeiro - UFRJ,

Av. Brigadeiro Trompowsky s/n
Campus Universitário - Ilha do Governador, Rio de Janeiro - 21.941
Universidade de São Paulo - USP, Rua da Reitoria 109 - Cidade Universitária
Butantã - São Paulo - 05508
Universidade de Campinas - UNICAMP, Cidade Universitária Zeferino Vaz
Barão Geraldo - Campinas - SP - 13.100

Canada

The Canadian education system encompasses both publicly funded and private schools, from kindergarten through to pre-university. Education is a provincial responsibility under the Canadian constitution, which means there are significant differences between the education systems of the different provinces. However, standards across the country are uniformly high.

In general, Canadian children attend kindergarten for one or two years at the age of four or five on a voluntary basis. All children begin Grade One at about six years of age. The school year normally runs from September through to the following June but in some instances, January intake dates are possible (please refer to the charts section for more information on intake dates). Secondary schools go up to Grades 11, 12 or 13, depending on the province. From here, students may attend university, college or Cégep studies. Cégep is a French acronym for College of General and Vocational Education, and is two years of general or three years of technical education between high school and university.

CANADIAN EDUCATION SYSTEM

Grade	P or K	1 2 3 4 5 6 7 8 9 10 11 12 13			Post Secondary
Quebec	2 years	2 years	Secondary	Cegep	College*
Ontario	2 years	2 years			Secondary College*
Atlantic Canada	0 or 1 years	0 or 1 years	Junior High	Senior High	College*
Manitoba	2years	2years			Secondary College*
Alberta & Northwest Territories		1year	1year	High	Junior Senior College
British Columbia & Yukon Territory	1 year	1 year	Junior High	Senior High	College*

*College or University

Preschool (P) & Kindergarten (K) are not compulsory in Canada.

Grade 1 begins when children reach the age of 6 or 7 depending on the province.

A student must have completed high school beore they can enter a post-secondary institution.

Table 1 below provides an overview of the secondary education system. Please note that Ontario requires students to complete Grade 13, or Ontario Academic Credit (OAC) as it is now called, before proceeding on to university and that Quebec has the Cégep system.

STUDENT AUTHORIZATIONS

Getting Approval to Study in Canada

Studying in Canada requires a student authorization. This authorization allows you to remain in Canada to take an academic, professional or vocational training course at an approved university, community college, university college, career college, public or secondary school or private ESL/FSL school.

Student authorization is not required if the course you are taking is an English or French language course that lasts a maximum of three months and is not academic, professional or vocational in nature.

If you are interested in studying in the province of Quebec, you are required to obtain a Certificate of Acceptence (CAQ) from the Quebec government and a student authorization from the Government of Canada. Applications for a CAQ are available at educational institutions in Quebec. A processing fee will be incurred when applying for the CAQ. Students must apply for a CAQ before applying for a student authorization. Students wishing to study in other provinces or territories do not need CAQs.

A Step-By-Step Guide to Obtaining a Student Authorization

1. *Pick up student authorization forms*

You may obtain student authorization forms in your country of origin at the Canadian Embassy, High Commission or Canadian Education Centre. Applications and documentation must then be submitted to the nearest visa office. A person may apply for a student authorization at a Canadian port of entry only if that person is a national of the United States; a permanent resident of the United States; a resident of St. Pierre/Miquelon; or a dependent of a person who is here on an employment or student authorization.

2. *Gather the necessary documents*

It is crucial that you submit all documentation requested with your application. Missing documentation will delay the authorization process.

The following documentation must be included in student authorization application.

***Proof of identity*:** This includes a valid passport or travel document or identity document that guarantees re-entry to the country that issued it; and four recent passport-size photos (2"*2.25") for each family member, with the full name and date of birth recorded on the back of each photo.

***Proof of financial support*:** This should show that you will have enough money during your stay in Canada to cover tuition fees, return transportation and $10,000 per annum for living expenses. Documentation for this requirement could be proof of a Canadian bank account or a bank draft in convertible currency, bank statements for the past four to six months, or proof of payments of tuition and residence fees. (As a guideline, C$10,000 in addition to tuition fees, per academic year, is generally viewed as sufficient).

***A medical examination*:** To be done in your country of origin. Medical exams are required if your stay is longer than six months. Please note that medical processing will add several weeks to the time necessary to obtain a student authorization. In some cases, you may need a medical examination even though your course is less than six months in duration. In these instances, a visa officer will determine whether you will require a medical examination and will send you the appropriate medical forms and instructions.

***Proof of acceptance by an approved educational institution*:** The following information must be included in letters of acceptance: name, date of birth, mailing address of student; the course for which the student has been accepted; the estimated duration or date of completion of the course; the date on which the course begins; the last date on which the course begins; the last date on which the student must register for the course; the academic year which the student will be entering; whether the course is full or part time; the tuition fee; any conditions related to acceptance; clear identification of the educational institution; and licensing information for private institutions. This letter must be signed by an authorized representative of the institution.

If you are minor-aged (typically less than 18 years but this can vary from province to province), proof of custodianship in Canada is required: You must provide a notarized declaration signed by your parent or legal guardian in your country of origin and a notarized declaration signed by the custodian in Canada, stating that adequate arrangements have been made for the custodian in Canada to act in place of a parent in times of emergency, such as when medical attention or intervention is required. For younger children, a broader declaration may be required. Broad declarations must state that the custodian is not only responsible in times of emergency but also for day-to-day care and supervision.

3. *Visit the visa office*

Once you have completed the application forms and have gathered the necessary documentation, proceed to the visa office nearest to you and submit the forms and required information along with a student authorization fee. When reviewing your student authorization application, a visa officer must be satisfied that you meet the requirements of the Canadian Immigration Act and Regulations and that you will only be in Canada temporarily. Once the visa officer is satisfied that you are a "bonafide" student and all statutory requirements are met, you will be given a document to show to immigration officials when you arrive in Canada who will then issue your student authorization. As your student authorization will normally be valid for the duration of your course, please ensure that your travel document (passport) is also valid for that same period of time.

1. ***Visa and Student Authorization***: This is a prerequisite for admission to Canada. Canadian immigration regulations stipulate that such a visa and authorization must be sought and obtained prior to arrival at a Canadian port of entry.

2. ***A Valid Passport***: A valid passport is required for entry to Canada.

3. ***Immigration Medical Clearance***: Student will be required to undergo an immigration medical examination to determine whether they meet Canadian immigration medical requirements. Students will be advised of the required immigration medical procedures in the course of their applications.

4. ***An Original Letter of Acceptance***: Students must present an original letter of unconditional acceptance from the institution to which they have been accepted for study. The letter must bear the institution's letterhead. Photostat copies are not accepted.

5. ***Documentary evidence of possession and availability of funds*** : Students must present satisfactory documentary evidence that they will have sufficient funds available to them in Canada to pay their tuition fees and to finance their maintenance and return transportation, as well as the maintenance and return transportation of any accompanying dependents.

In case the student will be receiving financial assistance from the institution at which he or she will study or will be financed by a sponsoring organizaton, a letter from the sponsoring institution or organization should be presented clearly outlining the nature and the amount of the support that will be provided.

In addition, the student will be required to provide evidence of return transportation or ability to finance this.

Financial Aid

At the undergraduate level there are no scholarships available.

At the graduate level some scholarships are available with the individual universities, based on the students academic record.

For the Commonwealth Scholarship and Fellowship plan please apply to
The External Scholarship Division, Dept. of Education,
Ministry of Human Resources Development,
Government of India, Shastri Bhavan, New Delhi-110001

REQUIREMENTS FOR SPECIFIC PROGRAMS

Please note that requirements vary from one institution to another. The following information is general and may not be applicable to all universities and colleges.

Undergraduate

1. TOEFL score (550-600), 2. Completion of grade 12
3. 70-75% marks

*the range of acceptable marks varies from 60-85%

Graduate (postgraduate)

1. TOEFL score (550-650) 2. Completion of Honours Bachelors Degree
3. 70-75% marks 4. Qualifying test such as GRE

MBA

1. TOEFL score (550-650) 2. GMAT score (550-650)
3. 2-3 years work experience 4. Completion of Honours Bachelors Degree (4 year degree) with B average

Medicine

1. TOEFL score 2. Completion of Bachelors Degree with B average
3. MCAT score

Dentistry

(1. TOEFL score(600) 2. DAT score)
(3.) 2 years of a Bachelors Science Degree with B average

Law

1. TOEFL score 2. LSAT score
3. 2 years of a Bachelors Degree with B average

Courses

Science

• Agriculture • Anatomy • Astronomy • Biology • Biomedical Engineering • Botany • Chemistry • Engineering • Engineering Technology • Environmental Sciences • Geology • Marine Biology • Meteorology • Physics • Veterinary Science • Zoology.

Arts and Socia Sciences

• Anthropology • Archaeology • Drama • English • Geography • History • Linguistics • Labour Studies • Music • Peace and Conflict Studies • Philosophy • Political Science • Psychology • Social Work and Counselling • Sociology • Women's Studies.

Business and Management Studies

• Accounting • Apparel Production Management • Banking • Business Administration • Convention and Meeting Management • Economics • Event Management • Facility Management • Fashion Marketing • Finance • Flight and Aviation Management • Human Resource Management • International Trade • Labour Relations Management • Marketing • Materials Management • Organizational Theory and Behaviour • Property Management • Public Administration • Realty Appraisal • Retail Management • Transportation and Logistics.

Education

• Early Childhood Education • Elementary Education • Secondary Education • Second Language Education • Special Education • Vocational Education

Media and Communications

• Advertising • Broadcast Journalism • Electronic Desktop Composition • Desktop Publishing • Electronic Prepress and Image Assembly • Films • Journalism • Mass Communications• Media Resources • Printing Apprenticeships Television • Telecommunications Technician • Video Editing.

Information Technology and Computer Studies

• Applied Information Technology • Computer Aided Drafting and Design Computer Animation • Data Communications Systems • Graphics • Internet Management Microcomputer Software • Networking Programming • Robotics • Systems Technician • Website Development.

Health

• Ambulance/Emergency Care • Anaesthesia • Chiropody • Dental Hygiene • Dentistry • Diagnostic • Dialysis Techniques • Electro Neurophysiology • Environmental Health • Gerontology • Laboratory Technology • Medical Sonography • Music Therapy • Medical Office Assistant • Medicine • Nuclear Medicine • Nursing • Occupational Therapy • Pharmacy • Physiotherapy • Prosthetics & Orthotics • Radiologist • Therapeutic Recreation.

Technologies

• Aircraft Maintenance • Animal Health • Aquaculture Technology • Cosmetics Forest Resources Technology • Golf Course Technician • Historical Conservation • Industrial Instrumentation • Library and Information • Office Systems • Photography • Piano Technology • Survey and Mapping • Tree Care.

Hospitality and Tourism

• Adventure Tourism • Baker • Bartending • Cook • Culinary Management • Food Preparation • Food and Beverage Service • Hotel and Resort Administration • Leisure Studies • Outdoor Recreation Management • Restaurant Management • Retail Meat Cutting • Tourism Management • Travel Counselling.

Design and Construction

• Architecture • Brick and Stone Construction • Cabinet Making • Carpentry • Collision Repair • Construction Management • Display and Design • Fine Furniture • Gemmology • Industrial Design • Interior Design • Jewellery Repair • Landscape • Horticulture • Package Design • Product Design • Plumbing • Screen Printing • Toolmaking • Visual Production Design • Welding.

Law

• Court Reporter • Court and Tribunal Agent • Criminal Justice • LLB • Law and Security Administration • Law Enforcement • Legal Administration

UNIVERSITY

Acadia University

Registrar's Office, Wolfville, NS BOP IX0, Tel : 902 585 1690
Fax : 902 585 1084, E-mail : Kim.meade@acadiau.ca
Website : http://www.acadiau.ca

Augustana University College

Admissions, 4901 - 46 Avenue, Camrose, AB T4V 2R3, Tel : 403 679 1132
Fax : 403 679 1129, E-mail : admissions@augustana.ab.ca

Brandon University
Office of International Activities, 270 - 18th Street, Brandon, MB R7A 6A9
Tel: 204 727 7477, Fax : 204 729 9016
E-mail : admissions@mail.brandonu.ca, Web : http://www.brandonu.ca

Brock University
International Liaison Office, St. Catharine's, ON L2S 3AI
Tel: 905 688 5550, Fax : 905 684 2277, Web : http://www.brocku.ca/

Carleton University
SLALS, 1125 Colonel By Drive, Room 215, Paterson Hall
Ottawa, ON KÍS 5B6, Tel : 613 520 6612, Fax : 613 520 6641
E-mail : esl@carleton.ca, Website : http://www. carleton.ca

Concordia University
AD-207, 7141 Sherbrooke St. West, Montrèal, PQ H4B IR6
Tel : 514 848 4989, Fax : 514 848 2888, E-mail : Sahni@vax2.concordia.ca
Website : http://www.concordia.ca

Dalhousie University
Registrar's Office, Halifax, NS B3H 4H6, Tel : 902 494 2543
Fax : 902 494 1630, E-mail : Admissions@dal.ca, Website : http://www.dal.ca

Ècole des Hautes Ètudes Commerciales
3000 Chemin de la Cote-Sainte Cathèrine, Montrèal, PQ H3T 2A7
Tel : 514 340 6633, Fax : 514 340 6888, Website : http://www.hec.ca.

Ècole Polytechnique de Montrèal
International Office, C.P. 6079 Succ Centre-Ville, Montrèal, PQ H3C 3A7
Tel : 514 340 4711, Fax : 514 340 4222, E-mail : jmartin@mailsru.polymtl.ca

Lakehead University
Office of the Registrar, 955 Oliver Road, Thunder Bay, ON P7B 5E1
Tel : 807 343 8132, Fax : 807 343 8075, Website : http://www.lakeheadu.ca

McGill University
The Admissions and Registrar's Office, 847 Sherbrooke Street West
Montrèal, PQ H3A 3N6, Tel : 514 398 6424, Fax : 514 398 8939
E-mail : admission@aro.lan.mcgill.ca, Website : http://www.mcgill.ca

McMaster University
Office of International Affairs, 1280 Main Street West, Hamilton, ON L8S 4L8
Tel : 905 525 9140, Fax : 905 546 5212, E-mail : oia@mcmail.mcmaster.ca
Website. : http://www.mcmaster.ca

Memorial University of Newfoundland
Office of Student Recruitment and Promotion, St. John's, NF AIC 5S7
Tel : 709 737 8896, Fax : 709 737 8611
E-mail : sturecru@morgan.ucs.mun.ca, Website. : http://www. mun. ca

Mount Saint Vincent
Admissions, 166 Bedford Hwy, Suite1, Halifax, NS B3M 2J6
Tel : 902 457 6117, Fax : 902 457 6498, Website. : http://www. msvu.ca

Nova Scotia College of Art and Design
Student and Academic Services, 5163 Duke Street, Halifax, NS B3J 3J6
Tel : 902 494 8188, Fax : 902 425 2987, E-mail : tbailey@nscad.ns.ca
Website : http://www.cideo.com/bblhtml/nscad.htm

Queen University
Student Recruitment , 110 Alfred St., Kingston, ON K7 13N6, Tel : 613 545 2217

Fax: 613 545 6810, E-mail: liaison@postqueensu.cu
Website : http://www.queensu.ca

Redeemer College

Registrar's Office, 777 Highway 53E., Ancaster, ON L9K 1J4, Tel : 905 648 2131
Fax : 905 648 2134, E-mail : rwikker@redeemer.on.ca
Website : http://www.redeemer.on.ca

Royal Roads University

Registrar's Office, 2005 Sooke Rd., Victoria, BC V9B 5Y2, Tel : 250 391 2505
Fax : 250 391 2522, E-mail : rruregistrar@ royalroads.ca
Website : http://www.royalroads.ca

Ryerson Polytechnic University

Admissions Liaison/Curriculium Advising, 350 Victoria Street,
Toronto, ON M5B 2K3, Tel : 416 979 5036, Fax : 416 979 5221
E-mail : inquire@acs.ryerson.ca, Website. : http://www.ryerson.ca

Saint Mary's University

Admissions, Halifax, NS B3H 3C3, Tel : 902 420 5415
Fax : 902 496 8160, E-mail : admit.international@stmarys.ca
Website : http://www.stmarys.ca

Simon Fraser University

International and Exchange Student Services, Burnaby, BC V5A 1S6
Tel : 604 291 4232, Fax : 604 291 5880, E-mail : sfu-international@sfu.ca
Web. : http://www.sfu.ca

Trent University

Trent International Program, Peterborough, ON K9J 7B8, Tel : 705 748 1314
Fax : 705 748 1626, E-mail : TIP@trentu.ca, Website. : http://www.trentu.ca

Trinity Western University ESLI

7600 Glovel Road, Langley, BC V2Y 1Y1, Tel : 604 513 2082
fax : 604 513 2071, Website : http://www.esli-intl.com

University of Alberta

Office of the Registrar, 201 Administration Building, Edmonton, AB T6G 2M7
Tel : 403 492 3113, Fax : 403 492 7172, E-mail : registrar@ ualberta.ca
Website : http://www.ualberta.ca

University of British Columbia

International Student Reception, Vancouver, BC V6T 1Z1
Tel : 604 822 1418, Fax : 604 822 9888, E-mail : International. reception@ ubc.ca
Website: http://www.student-services.ubc.ca/intrecep

University of Calgary

International Student Centre, MacEwan Centre, Room 260, Calgary, AB T2N 1N4,
Tel : 403 220 4062, Fax : 403 220 1342, E-mail : rshapiro@acs.ucalgary.ca
Website : http://www.ucalgary.ca

University College of Cape Breton

International Studies, P.O Box 5300, Sydney. NS B1P 6L2, Tel : 902 563 1286
Fax : 902 562 0119, E-mail : Tennyson@ uccb.ns.ca Website. : http //www.uccb.ns.ca

University College of the Cariboo

International Education, P.O.Box 3010, Kamloops, BC, V2C 5N3
Tel : 250 371 5765, Fax : 250 828 5140, E-mail : criggs@ cariboo.bc.ca
Website : http://www.cariboo.bc.ca

University of Guelph

Admission Services, Guelph, ON N1G 2W1, Tel : 519 821 2130
Fax : 519 766 9481, E-mail : moishi@regisrar.uoguelph.ca
Website : http://www.uoguelph.ca.ca

Universitè de Laval
Bureau du registraire, Ste-Foy. PQ G1K 7P4, Tel : 418 656 3080
Fax : 418 656 5216, E-mail : Reg@regulaval.ca, Website. : http://www.ulaval.ca

University of Lethbridge
Recruitment, 4401 University Drive, Lethbridge, AB T1K 3M4
Tel : 403 329 2762, Fax : 403 329 5159, E-mail : Inquiries@ uleth.ca
Website : http://.home.uleth.ca

University of Manitoba
Admissions, 424 University Centre, Winnipeg. MB R3T 2N2, Tel : 204 474 8808
Fax : 204 275 6534, E-mail : hryniuk@cc.umanitoba.ca
Website : http://www.umanitoba.ca

Universitè de Montrèal
Bureau des Admissions, C.P.6128, Succ. Centre-ville, Montrèal, PQ H3C 3J7
Tel : 514 343 7076, Fax : 514 343 5788, E-mail : admissions@ ere. umontreal.ca
Websites. : http://www.umontreal.ca

University of New Brunswick
Research and International Cooperation, P.O. Box 4400, Frederlcton, NB E3B 5A3, Tel : 506 453 5189, Fax : 506 453 3522, Website : http://www.unb.ca

University of Northern British Columbia
International Programs, 3333 University Way, Prince George, BC V2N 4Z9
Tel : 250 960 5702, Fax : 250 960 5546, E-mail : Sheena@unbc.ca
Website : http://www.unbc.ca

University of Ottawa
Admissions, P.O. Box 450 Station A, 550 Cumberland St., Ottawa, ON K1N 6N5
Tel : 613 562 5783, Fax : 613 562 5104, E-mail : liaison@uottawa.ca
Website : http://www.uottawa.ca

University of Prince Edward Island
Education, 550 University Avenue, Charlettetown PEI CIA 4P3, Tel : 902 566 0370, Fax : 902 566 0416, E-mail : registrar@upei.ca, Website : http://www.upei.ca

University of Regina
International Liaison Office, Regina, SK S4S 0A2, Tel : 306 585 4161
Fax : 306 585 4893, E-mail : grad.studies@uregina.ca or esl@uregina.ca
Website : http://www.uregina.ca

University of Saskatchewan
International Admissions., Office of the Registrar, 105 Administration Place
Saskatoon, SK S7N 5A2, Tel : 306 966 6450, Fax : 306 966 6730
E-mail : admissions@usask.ca, Website : http://www.usask.ca

University of Toronto
Admissions & Awards, 315 Bloor Street West, Toronto, ON M5S 1A3
Tel : 416 978 2190, Fax : 416 978 6089, E-mail : ask@adm.utoronto.ca
Website : http://www.utoronto.ca

University of Victoria
Admission Services, P.O. Box 3025 STN CSC, Victoria, BC V8W 3P2
Tel : 250 721 8119, Fax : 250 721 6225, Website. : http://www.uvic.ca

University of Waterloo

Registrar, 200 University Avenue West, Waterloo, ON N2L 3G1
Tel : 519 888 4567, Fax : 519 746 3051, E-mail : jnugent@uwaterloo.ca
Website: http:/www.uwaterloo.ca

University of Western Ontario

Office of the Registrar - Admissions, Department, Room 160, Stevenson-Lawson Building, London, ON N6A 5B8, Tel : 519 661 2100, Fax : 519 661 3710
E-mail : reguwo@ uwo-admin.uwo.ca, Website : http://www.uwo.ca

University of Windsor

Office of International Affairs, 401 Sunset Avenue, Room 418, Chrysler Hall
Windsor, ON N9B 3P4, Tel : 519 253 4232, Fax : 519 973 7032
E-mail : intaff@uwindsor.ca, Website : http://www.unwindsor.ca

University of Winnipeg

Admissions, 515 Portage Ave, Winnipeg, MB R3B 2E9, Tel : 204 786 9057
Fax : 204 779 3343, E-mail : adm@uwinnipeg.ca
Website. : http://www.uwinnipeg.ca

Wilfrid Laurier University

75 University Avenue West, Waterloo, ON N2L 3C5, Tel : 519 884 1970
Fax : 519 746 2472, E-mail : rsmith@ mach 2. Wlu.ca, Website : http://www.wlu.ca

York University

Office of International Admissions, 4700 Keele Street, North York, ON M3J 1P3
Tel : 416 736 5825, Fax : 419 736 5741, E-mail : intleng@ yorku.ca
Website : http://www.yorku.ca

University Colleges

Kwantlen University College

Educational Services, 12666 72nd Avenue, Surrey, BC V3W 2M8
Tel : 604 599 2065, Fax : 604 599 2235, E-mail : derek@kwantlen.bc ca
Website : http://www.kwantlen.bc.ca

Malaspina University College

International Education, 900 Fifth Street, Nanaimo, BC V9R 5S5
Tel : 250 741 2783, Fax : 250 755 8723, E-mail : Zurbrigg@mala.bc.ca
Website : http://www.mala.bc.ca

Okanagan University College

International Education, 1000 K.L.O. Road, Kelowna, BC V1Y 4X8
Tel : 250 862 5443, Fax : 250 862 5470, E-mail : inted@okanagan.bc.ca
Website : http://www.okanagan.bc.ca

University College of the Fraser Valley

International Education Department, 33844 King Road, Abbotsford, BC V2S 7M9
Tel : 604 854 4544, Fax : 604 855 7153, E-mail :info@ucfv.bc.ca
Website. : http://www.ucfv.bc.ca

Community Colleges and Technical Institutes

Algonquin College of Applied Arts and Technology

International Education Centre, 1385 Woodroffe Avenue, Nepean, ON K2G 1V8
Tel : 613 727 4723, Fax : 613 727 7665, E-mail : hodgins@algonquinc.on.ca
Website : http://www.algonquinc.on.ca

British Columbia Institute of Technology

BCIT International, 3700 Willingdon Avenue, Burnaby, BC V5G 3H2
Tel : 604 432 8842, Fax : 604 430 9042, E-mail : HokD8774@bcit.bc.ca
Website : http://142.232.189.3/

Camosun College
International Education, 3100 Foul Bay Road, Victoria, BC V8P 5J2
Tel : 250 370 3174, Fax : 250 370 3689, E-mail : sutherland@ camosun.bc.ca
Website : http://www.camosun.bc.ca

Capilano College
International Student Centre, 2055 Purcell Way, North Vancouver, BC V7J 3H5
Tel : 604 983 7544, Fax : 604 984 1798, E-mail : ghenklem@capcollege.bc.ca
Website : http://www.capcollege.bc.ca

Centennial College
International Education, P.O. Box 631, Station A, Scarborough, ON M1K 5E9
Tel : 416 289 5312, Fax : 416 289 5352, E-mail :internl@cencol.on.ca
Website : http://www.cencol.on.ca

Collège Jean-De-Brèbeuf
3200 Côte Ste-Catherine, Montrèal, PQ W3T 1C1, Tel : 514 342 1320
Fax : 514 342 0130

Collège LaSalle
Admissions Office, 2000 Sainte Catherine Street West, Montrèal, PQ H3H 2T2
Tel : 514 939 2006, Fax : 514 939 2015
E-mail : sheila.zoghaib@admin.clasalle.qc.ca, Website : http://www.clasalle.qc.ca

College of the North Atlantic
International Office, P.O. Box 179, Burin Bay Arm, NF A0E 1G0
Tel : 709 891 1988, Fax : 709 891 1860, E-mail:rkavanag@nf.sympatico.ca
Website : http://www.northatlantic.nf.ca

College of the Rockies
International Education Dept., P.O.Box 8500, Cranbrook, BC V1C 5L7
Tel : 250 489 8248, Fax : 250 489 8254, E-mail : info@cotr.bc.ca
Website : http://www.cotr.bc.ca

Columbia College
500-555 Seymour St., Vancouver, BC V6B 6J9, Tel : 604 683 8360
Fax : 604 682 7191, E-mail : admin@columbiacollege.bc.ca
Website : http://www.columbiacollege.bc.ca

Conestoga College of Applied Arts and Technology
International Education Office, 299 Doon Valley Drive, Kitchener, ON N2G 4M4
Tel : 519 748 3556, Fax : 519 748 3505, E-mail : wwed@conestogac.on.ca
Website : http://www.conestogac.on.ca

Confederation College of Applied Arts and Technology
International, Business & Ventures, 1450 Nakina Drive, P.O. Box 398
Thunder Bay, ON P7C 4W1, Tel : 807 475 6626, Fax : 807 623 4675
E-mail : page@confederationc.on.ca, Website : http://www.confederationc.on.ca

Douglas College
Centre for International Education, 700 Royal Avenue, New Westminster, BC V3L 5B2
Tel : 604 527 5413, Fax : 604 527 5516, E-mail : hosoit@douglas.bc.ca
Website : http://www.douglas.bc.ca

Durham College
International Education, P.O. Box 385, 2000 Simcoe Street North, Oshawa, ON L1H 7L7
Tel : 905 721 2000, Fax : 905 721 3113, E-mail : stedman@durham.durhamc.on.ca
Website : http://www.durham.durhamc.on.ca

Fanshawe College of Applied Arts and Technology
International Partnerships, 1460 Oxford Street East, London, ON N5V 1W2
Tel : 519 452 4467, Fax : 519 659 9393, E-mail : Wilson BL@fanshawec.on.ca
Website : http://www.fanshawec.on.ca

George Brown College of Applied Arts and Technology
International Centre, P.O. Box 1015, Station B, Toronto, ON M5T 2T9
Tel : 416 415 2118, Fax : 416 415 2120, E-mail : inticen@gbrownc.on.ca
Website : http://www.gbrownc.on.ca

Georgian College
International Centre, 1 Georgian Drive Barrie, ON L4M 3X9
Tel : 705 728 1968, Fax : 705 722 5158, Website : http://www.georcoll.on.ca

Grande Prairie Regional College
International Education, 10726 - 106 Avenue, Grande Prairie, AB T8V 3A1
Tel : 403 539 2945, Fax : 403 539 2801, E-mail : Anstey@gprc.ab.ca
Website : http://www.gprc.ab.ca

Humber College of Applied Arts and Technology
Office of the Registrar, 205 Humber College Boulevard
Etobicoke, ON M9W 5L7, Tel : 416 675 8515, Fax : 416 675 2451
E-mail : ico@admin.humberc.on.ca, Website : http://www.humberc.on.ca

John Abbot College
International Language Program, C.P. 2000, Ste-Anne Bellevue, PQ H9X 3L9
Tel : 514 457 3063, Fax : 514 457 6878, E-mail : barryreynolds@johnabbot. qc.ca
Web. : http://www.johnabbot.qc.ca

Langara College
International Education Department, 100 West 49th Avenue, Vancouver, BC V5Y 2Z6,
Tel : 604 323 5661, Fax : 604 323 9210, E-mail : gmcneil@langara.bc.ca

Medicine Hat College
International Education, 299 College Drive S.E., Medicine Hat, AB T1A 3Y6
Tel : 403 529 3847, Fax : 403 504 3512, E-mail : info@mhc.ab.ca
Website : http://www.mhc.ab.ca

Michner Institute for Applied Health Sciences
Business Development Unit, 222 St. Patrick Street, Toronto, ON M5T 1V4
Tel : 416 596 3134, Fax : 416 596 3168, E-mail : ccowling@staff. michener.on.ca
Web. : http://www.michener.on.ca

Mohawk College
International Department, 135 Fennell Ave. West P.O. Box 2034
Hamilton, ON L8N 3T2, Tel : 905 575 2136, Fax : 905 575 2362
E-mail : barsonl@operatns. mohawkc.on.ca, Website : http://www.mohawkc.on.ca

Mount Royal College
Languages Institute, 4825 Richard Road S.W., Calgary, AB T3E 6K6
Tel : 403 240 5513, Fax : 403 240 5506, E-mail : langinst@mtroyal.ab.ca
Website : http://www.mtroyal.ab.ca

Niagara College of Applied Arts and Technology
International Education, P.O. Box. 1005, 300 Woodlawn Road
Welland, ON L3B 5S2, Tel : 905 735 2211, Fax : 905 735 2413
E-mail : International@niagara.on.ca, Website : http://www.niagara.on.ca

Northern College
International Office, Timmins, ON P4N 8R6, Tel : 705 235 3211

Fax : 705 235 7279, E-mail : lamba OP@Kirk.northernc.on.ca
Website : http://www.northernc.on.ca

Northern Lights College

9820 - 120 Ave. P.O.Box. 1000, Fort St. John, BC V1J 6K1
Tel : 250 785 6981, Fax : 250 785 1294, E-mail : Snickel@nlc.bc.ca
Website : http://www.nlc.bc.ca

Red River Community College

International Education, Room D214 2055 Notre Dame Avenue
Winnipeg, Manitoba R3H 0J9, Tel : 204 632 2143, Fax : 204 632 5269
E-mail : intled@rrcc.mb.ca, Website : http://www.rrcc.mb.ca

Saskatchewan Institute of Applied Science & Technology

International Services, 2505 - 23rd Ave., Regina, SK S4P 3A3
Tel : 306 7871374, Fax : 306 787 4840, Website : http://www.siast.sk.ca

Selkirk College

301 Frank Beinder Way, Castlegar, BC V1N 3J1, Tel : 250 365 1293
Fax : 250 365 5410, E-mail : explore@selkirk.bc.ca
Website : http://www.selkirk.bc.ca

Seneca College of Applied Arts and Technology

International Admissions, 1750 Finch Avenue East, North York, ON M2J 2X5
Tel : 416 491 5050, Fax : 416 492 9243, E-mail : angelaw@exec.senecac.on.ca
Website : http://www.senecac.on.ca

Sheridan College of Applied Arts and Technology

International Services, 1430 Trafalgar Road, Oakville, ON L6H 2L1
Tel : 905 815 4007, Fax : 905 815 4004, E-mail : infosheridan@sheridanc.on.ca
Website : http://www.sheridanc.on.ca

St. Clair College of Applied Arts and Technology

International Development Office, 2000 Talbot Road West,
Windsor, ON N9A 6S4, Tel : 519 972 2753, Fax : 519 972 2707
E-mail vmacchiavell@sccc.on.ca, Website : http://www.stclairc.on.ca

Southern Alberta Institute of Technology

Business Development & International Training, 1301 - 16 Avenue N.W. M233
Calgary, AB T2M 0L4, Tel : 403 284 8628, Fax : 403 284 7163
E-mail : jennifer.bennett@sait.ab.ca, Website : http://www.sat.ab.ca

uver Community College

International Education, 1155 East Broadway, Box 24620, Station F
Vancouver, BC V5N 5T9, Tel : 604 871 7490, Fax : 604 682 2857
E-mail : hkpwong@ vcc.bc.ca, Website : http://www.cmysys.com/vcc/

CAERER COLLEGES

Academy of Learning

Foreign Student Department, 100 York Building, Suite 400, Richmond Hill, ON L4B 1J8,
Tel . 905 886 8973, Fax : 905 886 8591, E-mail : admin@academyol.com
Website : http://www.academyol.com

Atlantic Tourism and Hospitality Institute

4 Sydney Street, Charlottetown, PEI CIE IE6. Tel : 902 566 9600
Fax : 902 629 4239, E-mail : jfraser@athi.peca
Website : http://www.hollandc.pe.ca/ATHI

Canada Christian College

Admissions, 50 Gervais Drive, Toronto, ON M3C 1Z3, Tel : 416 391 5000

Fax : 416 391 3969

Century College

Student Office, 200- 1788 West Broadway, Vancouver, BC V6J 1Y1
Tel : 604 731 8869, Fax : 604 731 8830, E-mail : judyl @centurycollege.com
Website : http://www.centurycollege.com

Constellation College of Hospitality

Admissions, 900 Dixon Rd., Etobicoke, ON M9W 1J7, Tel : 416 675 2175
Fax : 416 675 6477, E-mail : college@regalconstellation.com

International Institute of Travel

205 - 10362 King George Highway, Surrey, BC V3T 2W5, Tel : 604 588 7795
Fax : 604 588 3477, E-mail iit@intergate.bc.ca

Glenn Gould Professional School of the Royal Conservatory of Music

RCM Schools, 273 Bloor Street West, Toronto, ON M5A 1W2
Tel : 416 408 2824, Fax : 416 408 3096, Website : http://www.rcmusic.ca

O'Sullivan College

Admission Services, 1191 rue de la Montagne, Montrèal, PQ H3G 1Z2
Tel : 514 866 4622, Fax : 514 866 6663, E-mail : admission@osullivan.edu

Pitman Business College

Admissions, 688 West Hastings St., Vancouver, BC V6B 1P1
Tel : 604 685 7696, Fax : 604 685 9879, E-mail : pitman@pitmancollege.com

Royal Oak College

Student Services,.4551 Wayburne Drive, Burnaby, BC V5G 3L1
Tel : 604 433 5626, Fax : 604 433 5296, E-mail : roc@helix.net
Website : http://www.fleethouse. com/roc

Shaw College

ESL, 365 Bloor Street East, 9th Floor, Toronto, ON M4W 3L4, Tel : 416 920 4380
Fax : 416 920 5838, E-mail : info@shaw-college.com
Website : http://www.shaw-college.com

Soft Train Institute

500 - 4576 Yonge Street, North York, ON M2N 6N4, Tel : 416 730 1774
Fax : 416 730 8543

Tourism Training Institute

1754 West Broadway, Vancouver, BC V6J 1Y1, Tel : 604 736 7008
Fax : 604 736 7723, E-mail : tourism@ tourismti.bc.ca
Website : http://www.axionet.com/tourism

Vancouver Career College

Admissions, 300 - 4680 Kingsway, Burnaby, BC V5H 4R1, Tel : 604 438 688
Fax : 604 438 6801, E-mail : info@ vancouvercareercollege.com
Website : http://www.vancouvercareercollege.com

School Boards/Secondary Schools

Abbotsford School District #34

2790 Tms Street, Abbotsford, BC V2T 4M7, Tel : 604 859 4891
Fax : 604 852 8587, Website : http://www.sd 34.abbotsford.bc.ca

Carleton Board of Education

CENET, The Carleton Education, Network, Inc., 133 Greenbank Road
Nepean, ON K2H 6L3, Tel : 613 721 1820, Fax : 613 596 8729
E-mail : carleton BE@ ocebe. edu.on.ca, Website : http://www.ocebe.edu.on.ca

Edmonton Public Schools
Int'l Monitoring & Planning, One Kingsway, Edmonton, AB T5H 4G9
Tel : 403 429 8358, Fax : 403 425 6405, E-mail : acalverl@ epsb.edmonton.ab.ca
Website : http://www.epsb.edmonton.ab.ca

Evan Hardy Collegiate
International Students, 605 Acadia Drive, Saskatoon, SK S7H 3V8
Tel : 306 683 8353, Fax : 306 683 7707
E-mail : vellowlees.dale@sbevax.sbe.sk.ca

Fort Garry School Division
International Student Program, 181 Henlow Bay, Winnipeg, MB R3Y 1M7
Tel : 204 453 8023, Fax : 204 284 0448, E-mail : gmacleod@mbnet.mb.ca
Website : http://www.fgsd.winnipeg.mb.ca

Frontenac-Lennox and Addington Country
P.O.Box 1058 84 Stephen St., Kingston, ON K76 2C4, Tel : 613 544 4927
Fax : 613 544 9616, E-mail : clifford@mail.flarc.edu.on.ca
Web : http://www.flarc.edu.on.ca

Grand Forks Secondary School
International Student Program, Box 339, Grand Forks, BC V0H 1H0
Tel : 250 442 5338, Fax ; 250 442 2085, E-mail : ykonar@sunshinecable.com

Greater Victoria International Student Program
International Student Program, 2101 Cadboro Bay Road, Victoria, BC V8R 5G4
Tel : 604 592 6871, Fax : 604 592 6327, E-mail : isp@islandnet.com

Howe Sound School District
International Students, Squamish, BC V0N 3G0, Tel : 604 892 5228
Fax : 604 892 1038

Langley School District
International Students Program, 4875 - 222nd Street, Langley, BC V3A 3Z7
Tel : 604 534 7891, Fax : 604 532 1450, E-mail. cspence@sd 35.bc.ca
Website : http://www.sd35.bc.ca

Maple Ridge/Pitt Meadows School District
International Education
22225 Brown Avenue, Maple Ridge, BC V2X 8N6, Tel : 604 463 4200
Fax : 604 463 4546, E-mail : Michael Polan@mail.schdist 42.bc.ca
Web : http://www.schdist 42.bc.ca

New Westminster School District #40
International Education Program, 835 - 8th Street, New Westminster, BC V3M 3S9
Tel : 604 517 6280, Fax : 604 517 6170, E-mail : fching@mail.nwss.sd 40bc.ca
Website : http://www.sd40.bc.ca

North York Board of Education
Visa Student Services, 5050 Yonge Street,North York, ON M2N 5N8, Tel : 416 395 8115,
Fax : 416 395 8476,Web. : http://www.nybe.interlog.com

Powell River School District
International Education, 4351 Ontario Avenue, Powell River, BC V8A 1V3
Tel : 604 485 6271, Fax : 604 485 6435, E-mail : rgrifone@sd 47.bc.ca
Website : http://www.sd47.bc.ca

Red Coat Trail School Division
Box 1330, Assiniboia, SK S0H 0B0, Tel : 306 642 3341
Fax : 306 642 3455, E-mail : ABW@sk.sympatico.ca

Sasktoom Catholic Board of Education
International Student Program, 420 - 22nd Street East, Saskatoon, SK S7K 1X3
Tel : 306 668 7000, Fax : 306 668 7179,
E-mail : rpoisson@stpaulrcssd.saskatoon.sk.ca

School of Continuing and Community Education
164 Van Order Drive, Kingston, ON K7M 1C1, Tel : 613 542 7369
Fax : 613 546 9545, E-mail : Wilsonja@fcbe.edu.on.ca

Frontenac Country Board of Education
220 Portsmouth Ave., Kingston, ON K7L 4X4
E-mail : general@admin.fcbe.edu.on.ca, Website : http://www.fcbe.edu.on.ca

Sheldon - Williams Collegiate
2601 Coronation Street, Regina, SK S4S 0L4, Tel : 306 791 8335
Fax : 306 585 3153, E-mail : sheldon@ rbe.sk.ca, Website : http://www/24.72.1.59

Southwest Regional School Board
International Students Program, 1485 King Street, Bridgewater, NS
Tel : 902 543 7811, Fax : 902 543 1408, E-mail : brokcook@fox.nstn.ca

Vancouver School Board
Continuing Education Services, 1678 West Broadway, Vancouver, BC V6J 1X6
Tel : 604 713 4500, Fax : 604 713 4536, E-mail : kharvey@vsb.bc.ca
Website : http://www.vsb.bc.ca

Viscount Bennet Centre - Adult Education
(Calgary Board of Education), Student Services, 2519 Richmond Road S.W. Room 164, Calgary, AB T3E 4M2, Tel : 403 777 8951, Fax : 403 777 7889
E-mail : aapinfo@cbe.ab.ca

West Vancouver School District
International Education, 1750 Mathers Avenue, West Vancouver, BC V7V 2G7
Tel : 604 981 1158, Fax : 604 981 1101, E-mail : ejackson@sd45.bc.ca
Website : http://www.sd.45.bc.ca

Independent Secondary Schools (CAIS Members)

Athol Murray College of Notre Dame
Box 100, Wilcox, SK S0G 5E0, Tel : 306 732 2080, Fax : 306 732 2117

Balmoral Hall School
Admissions 630 Westminster Avenue, Winnipeg, MB R3C 3S1,
Tel : 204 784 1600, Fax : 204 774 5534, E-mail : balmoral@minet.gov.mb.ca
Website:http://www.BalmoralHall.winnipeg.mb.ca

Bethany Hills School
P.O. Box 10, 727 Bethany Hills Road, Bethany, ON L0A 1A0, Tel 705 277 2866
Fax : 705 277 1279, E-mail : info@bethanyhills.on.ca
Website : http://www.bethanyhills.on.ca

Branksome Hall
10 Elm Avenue, Toronto, ON M4W 1N4, Tel : 416 920 9741, Fax : 416 920 5390
E-mail : admit@branksome.on.ca, Website : http://www.branksome.on.ca

Elmwood School Inc.
261 Buena Vista Road, Ottawa, ON K1M 0V9, Tel : 613 744 7783
Fax : 613 744 7359, E-mail : rand@elmwood.on.ca
Website : http://www.elmwood.on.ca

St. John's Kilmarnock School
Box 179, Breslau, ON N0B 1M0, Tel : 519 648 2183, Fax : 519 648 2186
E-mail : yoskovit@in.on.ca

St. Margaret's School
Admissions Department, 1080 Lucas Avenue, Victoria, BC V8X 3P7
Tel: 604 479 7171, Fax : 604 479 8976, E-mail : stmarg@islandnet.com
Website : http://www.islandnet.com/~stmarg/

PRIVATE SECONDARY SCHOOLS

Academic Ste. Cecile International School
955 Cousineau Rd, Windsor, ON N9G 1V8, Tel : 519 969 1291 Fax : 519 969 7953

Alberta College
10050 MacDonald Drive, Edmonton, AB T5J 2B7, Tel : 403 428 1851
Fax : 403 424 6371, E-mail : registrar@abcollege.ab.ca
Website : http://www.abcollege.ab.ca

Bodwell College
Registrar, 2026 West 12th Avenue, Vancouver, BC V6J 2G2, Tel : 604 737 8221
Fax : 604 737 8213, E-mail : office@ bodwell.edu, Web : http://www.bodwell.edu

Bond International College
Admissions Office, 111Bond Street, Toronto, ON M5B 1Y2, Tel : 416 979 0301
Fax : 416 979 0302

Bronte College of Canada
Admissions, 2186 Hurontario Street, Mississauga, ON L5B 1M9,
Tel : 905 270 7788, Fax : 905 270 7828, E-mail : bronte@titan.tcn.net
Website : http://www.avalonweb.com/bronte/index.html

Calgary International College
1100 - 833 4th Avenue SW, Calgary, AB T2P 3T5, Tel : 403 233 2982
Fax : 403 269 7568, E-mail : cici@cybersurf.net

Canadian International College
2420 Dollarton Highway, North Vancouver, BC V7H 2Y1, Tel : 604 929 1544
Fax : 604 929 2074

Collège Bourget
Administration, 65, St. Pierre, Rigaud, PQ J0P 1P0, Tel : 514 451 0815
Fax : 514 451 4171, E-mail : webmest@collegebourget.qc.ca

Collège Saint-Charles-Garnier
Ateliers de langues, 1150, boul. Renè-Lèvesque Ouest
Quèbec, PQ G1S 1V7, Tel : 418 681 0107, Fax : 418 681 9631
E-mail : Ateliers@ College Garnier.qc.ca, Website : http://www.collegegarnier.qc.ca

Columbia International College
Admissions Office, 1033 Main Street West, Hamilton, ON L8S 1B7
Tel : 905 572 7883, Fax : 905 572 9332, E-mail : columbia@wchat.com

Coquitlam College
516 Brookmere Avenue, Coquitlam, BC V3J 1W9, Tel : 604 939 6633
Fax : 604 939 0336, E-mail : admiss@coq.col.bc.ca
Website : http://www.coq.col.bc.ca

East West Learning English College
188 - 2096 West 41st Avenue, Vancouver, BC V6M 1Y9, Tel : 604 263 9830
Fax : 604 263 2568

Great Lakes College of Toronto
Admissions Office, 323 Keele Street, Toronto, ON M6P 2K6, Tel : 416 763 4121
Fax : 416 763 5225, E-mail : anagy@ica.net
Website : http://users.ica.net/anagy/glctmain.htm

Luther College
1500 Royal St., Regina, SK S4T 5A5, Tel : 306 791 9150
Fax : 306 359 6962, E-mail : lutherhs@dlcwest.com
website:http://www/saskweb.com/luthercollege

McDonald International Academy
Student Affairs, 36 Eglinton Avenue West, Third Floor, Toronto, ON M4R 1A1
Tel : 416 322 1502, Fax : 416 322 5775, E-mail : mia@idirect.com
Web : http://www.mcdonaldacademy.com

Maclachlan College
337Trafagar Road, Oakville, ON L6J 3H3, Tel : 905 844 0372, Fax : 905 844 5928
E-mail : lduranleau@maclachlan.on.ca, Web. : http://www.maclachlan.on.ca

Nancy Campbell Collegiate Institute
45 Waterloo Street South, Stratford, ON N5A 4A8, Tel : 519 273 6435
Fax : 519 273 1973, E-mail : ncci@orc.ca

Niagara Christian Collegiate
Admissions, 2619 Niagara Parkway, Fort Erie, ON L2A 5M4, Tel : 905 871 6980
Fax : 905 871 9260, E-mail : ncc@niagaracc.com

Pensionnat du Saint-Nom-de-Marie
628;chemin de la Côte Ste-Catherine, Outremont, Quèbec H2V 2C5
Tel : 514 735 5261, Fax : 514 735 5266, E-mail : k.caissy@psmn.qc.ca

Queen City Collegiate
Registrar, 1915 Retallack Street, Regina, SK S4T 2K1, Tel : 306 781 7055
Fax : 306 781 7201

Regent Christian Academy
ESL, 15100 66A Ave, Surrey, BC V5J 3E4, Tel : 604 599 8171, Fax : 604 597 9090

Richmond International High School and College
Registrar, 8671 Odlin Crescent, Richmond, BC V6X 1G1, Tel : 604 244 0100
Fax : 604 244 0102, E-mail : study@rihsc.bc.ca

Scarborough Christian College
Admissions, 4600 Steeles Avenue East, Markham, ON L3R 0L2
Tel : 905 477 4433, Fax : 905 477 1574, E-mail : scs@titan.tcn.net

Southern Ontario College
Main Office, 35 Brant Street, Hamilton, ON L8L 4C6, Tel : 905 546 1500
Fax : 905 546 5415

St. John's International School
Admissions, 1088 Homer Street, Vancouver, BC V6B 2W9, Tel : 604 683 4572
Fax : 604 683 4679, E-mail : ljarecki@stjohnsintlsch.vancouver.bc.ca
Website : http://www.stjohnsintlsch.vancouver.bc.ca

St Luke's College
Admissions, 10419 - 159 Street, Edmonton, AB T5P 3A6, Tel : 403 486 7422
Fax : 403 424 3137, E-mail : stlukes@compusmart.ab.ca
Website : http://www.compusmart.ab.ca/st.lukes

Vancouver Formosa Academy
Admissions, 5621 Killarney Street, Vancouver, BC V5R 3W4, Tel : 604 436 2332
Fax : 604 436 2331, E-mail: angelac@ vfa.bc.ca, Website : http://www.vfa.bc.ca

LANGUAGE SCHOOLS

Alberta Centre for English
Admissions, 660 - 840 6th Avenue SW, Calgary, AB T2P 3ES, Tel : 403 237 6647

Fax : 403 237 6648, E-mail : ace@cadvision.com

Apex English College

500 - 555 W. Hastings, Vancouver, BC V0N 1V0, Tel : 604 886 3185
Fax : 604 886 3958, E-mail : apexcan@intergate.bc.ca
Web : http://www.apexcan.com

Applied Linguistics Centre

575 Wall Street, Winnipeg, MB R3G 2T5, Tel : 204 774 4689, Fax : 204 772 3145
E-mail : aicentre@escape.ca, Website : http://www.escape.ca/-alcentre

Aspect International Language School

150 - 1111 Melville Street, Vancouver, BC V6E 3V6, Tel : 604 602 9818
Fax : 604 602 9819, E-mail : learn@aspectworld.com

Bouchereau Lingua International Inc.

2 rue du St. Sacrement, Montrèal, PQ H2Y 1W8, Tel : 514 842 3847
Fax : 514 842 3840, E-mail : montreal@bli.ca, Website : http://www.bli.ca

Burnaby College

ESL Downtown Campus, 101 - 1199 West Pender Street,
Vancouver, BC V6E 2R1, Tel : 604 684 9511, Fax : 604 684 0626
E-mail : Peterkinch@ lynx.bc.ca

Canada House English Language Centre

720 Bathurst St. Suite 304, Toronto, ON M5S 2R4, Tel : 416 538 4442
Fax : 416 538 6363, E-mail : hknoll@total.net
Website : http://www.eslcanadahouse.com

Canadian As A Second Language Institute (CSLI)

Admissions, 88 - 1155 Robson Street, Vancouver, BC V6E 1B5
Tel : 604 683 2754, Fax : 604 683 8667, E-mail : esl@csli.com
Website : http://www.ebei.com

Canadian Business English Institute

Registrar's Office, 400 - 1130 West Pender Street, Vancouver, BC V6E 4A4
Tel : 604 685 0291, Fax : 604 685 0294, E-mail : info@cbei.com
Website : http://www.cebi.com

Cegep de Saint-Jerome

International Language School, 455, rue Fournier, Saint-Jerome, PQ J7Z 4V2
Tel : 514 436 1580, Fax : 514 431 4199, E-mail : sdi@cegep-st-jerome.qc.ca
Website : http://www.cegep-st.jerome.qc.ca

Canadian International Language School

Student Affairs Department, Suite 1350, 815 - 8th Avenue S.W.
Calgary, AB T2P 3P2, Tel : 403 265 6680, Fax : 403 265 6686
E-mail : dyates@comfo.ca

College Bois-de-Boulogne

10555, avenue de Bois-de-Boulogne, Montreal, PQ H4N 1L4, Tel : 514 332 3000
Fax : 514 332 3235, E-mail : dmarcotte@ collegebdeb.qc.ca
Website : http://www.collegebdeb.qc.ca

Centre Linguistique

College de Jonquière, 2505 St-Hubert, Jonquière, PQ G7X 7W2,
Tel : 418 542 0352, Fax : 418 542 3536, E-mail : centling@cjonquiere.qc.ca
Website : http://www.college.cjonquiere.qc.ca/centre-linguistique/

Collège de Rivière-du-Loup

L'Ecole de francais, 80 rue Frontenac, Rivière-du-Loup, PQ G5R 1R1

Tel : 418 867 2130, Fax : 418 867 2137, E-mail : serfoacegep-rdl-qc.ca
Website : http://www.cegep.rdl-qc.ca

Connections Canada Inc.
Student Services, 1000 - 10089 Jasper Avenue, Edmonton, AB T5J 1V1
Tel : 403 428 8145, Fax : 403 425 7101
E-mail : concaned@comcept.ab.ca
Website : http://www.alberta.com/web/connectionscanada

Crowsnest International School
Admissions, P. O. Box 982, Blairmore, AB T0K 0E0, Tel : 403 562 7314
Fax : 403 562 7173, E-mail : cints@canuck.ab.ca, Website: http://www.canuck.com/clc

Discovery Language Centre
14 Queen St., Hamilton, ON L8R 2T8, Tel : 905 526 9700
Fax : 905 526 9700, E-mail : dislang@netaccess.on.ca

Eastern Canada College of Languages
550 University Avenue, Charlottetown PEI CIA 4P3, Tel : 902 566 0585
Fax : 902 566 0586, E-mail : eccl@upei.ca, Website : http:/www.eccl.ca

Ècole Internationale De Francais
Universitè du Quèbec à trois-Rivières, C.P. 500, trois-Rivières, PQ G9A 5H7
Tel : 819 376 5124, Fax : 819 376 5166, E-mail : eif@ uqtr.uquebec.ca
Website : http://www.uqtr.uquebec.ca/eif/

Ècole De Langue Francaise et De Culture Quèbècoise
555, boul. Universitè, Chicoutimi, PQ G7H 2B1, Tel : 418 545 5036,
Fax : 418 545 5012, E-mail : ecolanfr@uqac. uquebec.ca
Website : http://www.venus d4m.com/ecoledelange

Educere Learning Centre
430 - 910 7th Avenue S.W., Calgary, AB T2P 3N8, Tel : 403 266 2366
Fax : 403 263 8766, E-mail : educere@cadvision.com

ELS Language Centres
Admissions, 549 Howe Street, 6th Floor, Vancouver, BC V6C 2C2
Tel : 604 684 9577, Fax : 604 684 9588, E-mail :- info@elscanada.com
Website: http:/www/.elscanada.com

Groupe CCL
112 Saint Paul St. West #503, Montrèal, PQ H2Y 1Z3, Tel : 514 281 6700
Fax : 514 281 1733, E-mail : ccl@cclmontreal.com. Web : http://www.cclmontreal.com

Global Awareness Through English Enterprises
141 Woolwich Street #102, Guelph, ON N1H 8M5, Tel : 519 756 1157
Fax : 519 766 1021, E-mail : bsmith@ gate-enterprises.com
Website : http://www.gate-enterprises.com

Global International College
310 - 625 Howe Street, Vancouver, BC V6C 2T6, Tel : 604 488 1672
Fax : 604 488 1673

Helen's Homestay & English School
Tryon, RR#1, Albany, PEI C0B 1A0, Tel : 902 658 2560, Fax : 902 658 2560
E-mail : hgreen@isnet, Website : http://www.peihomestay.com

Interlangues
ESL, 908 - 130 Albert Street, Ottawa, ON K1P 5G4, Tel : 613 236 3763
Fax : 613 230 2047, E-mail : interlng@cyberus.ca

International Language Academy of Canada

920 Yonge St., 4th Floor, Toronto, ON M4W 3C7, Tel : 416 961 5151
Fax : 416 961 5988, E-mail : info@ilac.on.ca, Website : http://www.ilac.on.ca

International Language Centre of Canada

Registration. 300 - 5233 Dundas Street West, Toronto, ON M9B 1A6
Tel : 416 233 3991, Fax : 416 233 2968, E-mail : intlang@gate.maloca.com
Website : http://www.ilc-canada-com

International Language Institute

The Registrar, 5151 Terminal Road 8th Floor, Halifax, NS B3J 1A1
Tel : 902 429 3636, Fax : 902 429 2900, E-mail : study@ili.halifax.ns.ca
Website : http://www.ili.halifax.ns.ca

International Language Learning Centre

78 - 1687 West Broadway, Vancouver, BC V6J 1X2, Tel : 604 739 9836
Fax : 604 739 9839, E-mail : info@illc.com, Website : http://www.illc.com

International Language School of Canada

Marketing Department, 510 West Hastings Street, 2nd Floor
Vancouver, BC V6B 1L8, Tel : 604 689 9095, Fax : 604 683 0771
E-mail : ilscan@ axionet.com, Website : http://www.ilsc.vancouver.com

Kamloops International College

P.O. Box 538, Kamloops, BC V2C 5L2, Tel : 250 374 9235
Fax : 250 374 8098, E-mail : gmcrae@mail.netshop.net
Website : http://www.kicollege.com

Kester Grant College

Admissions Department, 2412 Laurel Street, Vancouver, BC V5Z 3T2
Tel : 604 877 0355, Fax : 604 877 0375, E-mail : kgc@lynx.bc.ca
website: http://www.lynx.bc.ca/kgc

King George International College

#450 - 188 West Georgia St., Vancouver, BC V6E 4A2, Tel : 604 608 1135
Fax : 604 608 1132, E-mail : kgis@ kgic.bc.ca, Website : http:// www.kgic.bc.ca

Language Connection International

Admissions Department, 500 - 60 Bloor Street West, Toronto, ON M4W 3B8
Tel : 416 323 3085, Fax : 416 323 9814, E-mail : info@lci-toronto.com
Website : http://www.lci-toronto.com/

Languages International (Toronto) Inc.

910 - 330 Bay Street, Toronto, ON M5H 2S8, Tel : 416 361 2411
Fax : 416 361 2403, E-mail : litoront@istar.ca
Website : http://home.istar.ca/~litoront/

Language Studies International

101 - 308 Nelson Street
Vancouver, BC V6Z2H2
Tel. 6046837654 Fax: 6046837554
E-Mail : Van@LSI.edu
Website : http://www.LSI.edu
or

LSI Toronto

160 Bloor St.E.# 1152, Toronto, ON M4W 1B9

London English Language College

35 Jim Ashton Street, London, ON N5V 3H4, Tel : 519 453 4007
Fax : 519 453 3119, E-mail : londoncollege@ londoncollege.on.ca

Website : http://www.londoncollege.on.ca

MLS Centre Linguista

500 blvd., Renè Lèvesque W., 8th Floor, Montrèal, PQ H2Z 1W7
Tel : 514 397 1736, Fax : 514 397 9007, E-mail : miscl @ generation.net
Web : http://www.generation.net/miscl OR 2 Bloor Street West, Suite 902
Toronto, ON M4W 3E2

Omnicom School of Language

Language Training, 2 Sheppard Avenue East, Suite 1002, Toronto, ON M2N 5Y7
Tel : 416 224 0750, Fax : 416 224 0813, E-mail : school@ onmicomtrans.com
Website : http://www.omnicomtrans.com

Pacific Gateway International College

303 -1155 Robson Street, Vancouver, BC V6E 1B5, Tel : 604 687 3595
Fax : 604 687 3586, E-mail : info@pgic.com, Website : http://www.pgic.com

Pacific Language Institute

Registrar, Suite 450-1090 West Georgia St., Vancouver, BC V6E 3V7
Tel : 604 688 7223, Fax : 604 688 7242, E-mail : headoffice@pli.ca
Website : http://www.pli.ca

Pacific Northwest Language Studies

Registrar, 571 Howe Street, Vancouver, BC V6C 2C2, Tel : 604 681 9137
Fax : 604 681 9167, E-mail : pnw@pnwvancouver.com
Website : http://www.pnwvancouver.com

Robson College

International Language Institute, 541 Seymour Street, Vancouver, BC V6B 3H6
Tel : 604 687 3259, Fax : 604 687 3295, E-mail : info@robsoncollege.com
Website : http://www.robsoncollege.com

Royal Language Centre

1457 Drouillard Road, Windsor, ON N8Y 2R8, Tel : 519 974 164
Fax : 519 974 8135, E-mail : philrlc@netcore.ca

Shoore Centre for Learning

201 - 801 Eglinton Avenue West, Toronto, ON M5N 1E3, Tel : 4 6 781 4754
Fax : 416 781 0163

Tamwood Language Institute Ltd.

909 Burrard St., 3rd Floor, Vancouver, BC, Tel : 604 899 4480, Fax : 604 899 4481
E-mail : tamsin@ tamwood.com, Website : http://www.tamwood.com

U-Canadu Learning Centres Inc.

130 Willowdale Ave., Toronto, ON M4N 4Y2, Tel : 416 225 0266
Fax : 416 225 7869, E-mail syntality@ u-candu.com,
Website : http://www.u-candu.com/~syntalit

Union College

Admissions Office, 2651 East Hastings Street, 2nd Floor,
Vancouver, BC V5K 1Z5, Tel : 604 253 4788, Fax : 604 253 1677
E-mail : union-college@bc.sympatico.ca

UTS College of Language Arts

Curriculum Development, 369 Columbia St., New Westminster, BC V3L 5T6
Tel : 604 515 1233, Fax : 604 515 1255, E-mail : uts@smartt.com
Website : http://www.utscollege.com

Vancouver English Centre

200 - 840 Howe Street, Vancouver, BC V6Z 2L2, Tel : 604 687 1600

Fax : 604 687 1660, E-mail : info@vec.bc.ca, Website : http://www.vec.bc.ca

Vancouver Maple Leaf Language College

250 - 815 West Hastings Street, Vancouver, BC V6C 1B4, Tel : 604 688 7942
Fax : 604 688 7985, E-mail : Study@vlc-canada.com
Web : http://www.discovervancouver.com/vlc-maple-leaf/

Van West College

Registrar, 200 - 1215 West Broadway, Vancouver, BC V6H 1G7,
Tel : 604 731 5256, Fax : 604 739 0913, E-mail : marketing@vanwest.com
Web : http://www.vanwest.com

Victoria Language Institute

Admissions Office, 4680 ElK Lake Drive, Victoria, BC V8Z 5M1
Tel : 250 658 5258, Fax : 250 658 2378, E-mail : viclang@islanet.com
Web : http://www.viclang.com

Western Town College

Administration, 303 - 770 Pacific Boulevard Southm Vancouver, BC V6B 5E7
Tel : 604 844 7660, Fax : 604 688 0559, E-mail : info@wtccanada. com
Web : http://www.wtccanada.com

Whistler Language Institute

Registrar, 301 - 4204 Village Square, Whistler, BC V0N 1B4
Tel : 604 938 6693, Fax : 604 938 6679, E-mail : info@ wli.whistler.bc.ca

Winfield College

201 - 788 Beatty Street, Vancouver, BC V6B 2M1, Tel : 604 608 0538
Fax : 604 608 0539, E-mail : study@winfield college.com
Web : http://www.winfieldcollege.com

YMCA English Language Institute

Admissions, 200 - 1166 Alberni Street, Vancouver, BC V6E 3Z3
Tel : 604 899 4161, Fax : 604 899 4162, E-mail : sally-thompson@ymca.ca
Web : http://www.ymca.ca

Y & N Language Company

404, Saint-Pierre, Suite 201, Montrèal, PQ H2Y 2M2, Tel : 514 840 7228
Fax : 514 840 7111, E-mail : yan 99@ aol.com

CAMPS

Bark Lake

International Learning Centre, Irondale, ON K0M 1X0, Tel : 705 447 2447
Fax : 705 447 2475

Canadian Int'l Summer Camp for Young People

Learning English, 490 Ontario Street, Toronto, ON M4X 1M4
Tel : 416 927 8466, Fax : 416 929 1687

Centauri Summer Arts Camp

7 Harshaw Avenue, Toronto, ON M6S 1X9, Tel : 416 766 7124
Fax : 416 766 7655, E-mail : hartley@ interlog.com

Westbound Adventures Teen Travel Camp Inc.

11123 Kennedy Road, Markham, ON L6C 1P2, Tel : 905 887 1400
Fax : 905 887 1887, E-mail : mail@westbound.com
Web : http://www.westbound.com

TRAINING ORGANIZATION

Amulet Consulting Ltd.

390 King St. Suite 207, Fredericton, NB E3B 1E3
Tel : 506 456 9021, Fax : 506 451 9022, E-mail : amulet@ nbnet. nb.ca

Web: http://www.amulet.nb.ca

Canadian Professional Qualifications Council

Admissions, (RO) Ste. 312, 15 Wertheim Court, Richmond Hill, ON L4B 3H7
Tel : 416 226 6476, Fax : 416 226 6472, E-mail : canadacouncil@ibm.net

Centre for Language Training & Assessment

Peel Board of Education, 2 Robert Speck Parkway, Suite 300,
Mississauga, ON L4Z 1H8, Tel : 905 274 1175, Fax : 905 274 1175
E-mail : acocq@clta.on.ca, Web : http://www.clta.on.ca

Creative Career Systems Inc.

RR#5, Owen Sound, ON N1K 5N7, Tel : 519 376 7396, Fax : 519 376 6772
E-mail : info@creative.on.ca, Web : http://www.creative.on.ca

World University Service of Canada

P.O. Box 3000, Station C, 1404 Scott Street, Ottawa, ON K1Y 4M8
Tel : 613 798 7477, Fax : 613 798 0990, E-mail : WUSC@WUSC.CA
Web : http://www.wusc.ca

CORPORATIONS

ICI Communications Canada

212 - 133 Princess Street, Kingston, ON K7L 1A8, Tel : 613 542 3368
Fax : 613 542 2907, E-mail : icican@ limestone.kosone.com

NATIONAL EDUCATION ASSOCIATIONS

Association of Universities and Colleges of Canada

Suite 600, 350 AlbertSt., Ottawa, ON K1R 1B1, Tel : 613 563 1236
Fax : 613 563 9745, Web : http://www.aucc.ca

Association of Canadian Community Colleges

1223 Michael Street North, Suite 200, Ottawa, ON K1J 7T2, Tel : 613 746 2222
Fax : 613 746 6721, Web : http://www.accc.ca

Council of Ministers of Education, Canada

252 Bloor Street West, Suite 5-200, Toronto, ON M5S 1V5
Tel : 416 964 2551, Fax : 416 964 2296, Web : http://www.cmec.cmec.ca

Canadian Association of Independent Schools

Box 1502, St. Catherine's, ON L2R 7J9
Tel : 905 688 4866, Fax : 905 688 5778, E-mail : cais@ ridley.on.ca

Canadian Education Association

Suite 8-200, 252 Bloor Street, Toronto, On M5S 1V5, Tel : 416 924 7721
Fax : 416 924 3188, Web : http://www.acea.ca

Department of Foreign Affairs and International Trade

Ottawa, ON, Tel : 416 994 4000, Web : http://www.dfait-maeci.gc.ca

Department of Citizenship and Immigration

Hull, Quebec, Tel : 604 666 2171 (Vancouver);, 416 973 4444 (Toronto);
514 496 1010 (Montreal), Elsewhere within Canada, Toll Free : 1-800-242-2100
Web : http://www.cicnet.ingenia.com

CEC India was opened in June 1997 by the Government of Canada, under the auspices of the Canadian High Commission, to provide information and counselling services to Indian students interested in studying abroad. There are currently 14 Canadian Education Centres active around the world, providing information to students in Argentina, Australia, Brazil, Chile, China, Hong Kong, Indonesia, Malaysia, Mexico, Singapore, South Korea, Taiwan, Thailand and, of course, India. We provide students in India with detailed information on educational programmes and facilities in Canada, as well as counselling to help focus their search and ensure that they make the best possible choice for their education.

We can provide information on undergraduate, postgraduate, college and technical programmes, pre-requisite testing information, advice on specific institutions, admission procedures, assistance in preparation of application forms, and follow up checks.

Their Resource Centre offers the opportunity to browse through course calendars and videos, or take an interactive CD-ROM tour of the campus of your choice. Expert counsellors are on hand to provide you with educational advice as well as information on life in Canada.

The CEC also conducts seminars in Indian schools and universities, free introductory orientations, and pre-departure briefings for Canada-bound students. The CEC being completely independent of the immigration process, can provide assistance in preparing the application by ensuring that all documentation is in place. Application forms and information on the fees incurred in the immigration process are available through CEC.

The CEC is currently based in New Delhi, but we do conducts regular seminars across the country - contact the CEC to find out the date of the next seminar in your area.

In addition to opportunities for students, the CEC can also assist corporations in facilitating the development and implementation of a wide range of executive training programmes available through Canadian institutions.

Contact for Information

Canadian Education Centre

Dl/56 Vasant Vihar, New Delhi 110 057, India, TEL (91 11) 614-6648
FAX (91 11) 614-6078, E-mail : cec@delhi.icco.net

China

China's Academic Degrees include Bachelor's, Master's, and Doctorate. There are 12 fields of learning : Philosophy, Economics, Law (including Politics, Sociology, study of Ethics). Mathematics, Pedagogics (including Physical training studies), Literature including Language Studies, Art studies, Library science), History, Natural Sciences, Engineering, Administration, Medicines and Military.

Bachelor's Degree

Undergraduates who have completed all the requirements by education planning can graduate after the authorities' examinations. Students are allowed to graduate and granted Bachelor's degree only if courses grades and diplomas (including graduating resolutions and other practical links concerned with graduation) meet the requirements will receive Bachelor's degrees.

Master's Degree

Postgraduates of universities and scientific research institutions or individuals of equivalent educational level who have passed the examination and thesis for Master's are awarded the Master's degree.

Doctorate Degree

Doctoral students of universities and institutions of scientific research, or individuals of equivalent educational level who have passed the examination and thesis for Doctorate are conferred the Doctorate degree.

General Introduction

Foreign students education in New China began in 1950 and has developed a lot during the recent years. According to statistics, more than 41,000 foreign students within the 1995-1996 academic year came from 125 countries and regions to China including trainees focusing on languages, undergraduates, postgraduates, doctoral students, common trainees, advanced trainees, scholars who conduct research and participants of all kinds of short-term training courses.

Universities in China employ distinctive teaching and training methods in line with different conditions of the foreign students.

Language Trainees

Applicant should be minimum high school graduates. Learning Chinese languages of courses last 1 or 2 years. Training certificates are confered available after the course work is finished.

Undergraduates

The course work is completed in 4-5 years in accordance with China's education system and educational planning for Chinese undergraduates. Lectures for international students are given together with native Chinese students. Some selected courses are while other courses are specially included in accordance to distinct conditions of foreign students. Bachelor's degree will be received after necessary examinations are passed and graduation theses are finished.

Postgraduates

The course is completed in 2-3 years in line with China's education system and education planning for Chinese postgraduates. The students will receive a Master's degree after they finish the formulated courses, pass examinations, accomplish postgraduate thesis and successfully hold oral graduation examinations under the direction of tutors in line with the educating plan.

Doctorate Students

The education is conducted 3 years in accordance with China's education system and education planning for Chinese doctoral students. The students will receive a doctorate after they finish formulated courses, pass examinations, accomplish doctoral graduation paper and the thesis with the training plan under the direction of tutors.

Common Trainees

The foreign students taking refresher courses may choose to have classes together with Chinese students or have courses separately according to the subjects. The training term lasts for 1 or 2 years. Refresher certificates will be awarded after examinations or tests are passed.

Advanced Trainees

A tutor will be assigned to direct the research work and university authorities will arrange social surveys and visits concerned with research subject as determined ahead of time in accordance with research subjects. The research term lasts 1 or 2 years. Refresher certificates are awarded after the refresher plan is accomplished.

Research Scholars

In line with a researched subject, a tutor will be assigned by the University authorities even though the research work is mainly done by the scholars independently. Related social surveys and visits will be confirmed and arranged ahead of time. The research term is determined in accordance with the needs of research.

Foreign students are encouraged to work toward postgraduates and doctoral degrees in China's universities, and those who have graduated in China are welcome to return for further education. Courses directly in foreign languages are available for these students in some universities.

Major Bodies and Their Functions for Foreign Students Affairs

The State Education Commission

Is involved in formulating basic principles, policies, regulations and measures and coordinating, directing and administrating in general the work of nationwide foreign students affairs.

The State Education Commission, also conducts the enrolment and administration of foreign students to China who enjoy scholarships by the Chinese Government.It deals with the applications of those who are sent to study in China by foreign academic and educational organizations, and non-governmental friendship teams or organizations.

China Service Center for Scholarly Exchanges

Providing consultation and other kinds of services for foreign students who plan to study in China.

Provincial Education Commissions

These take charge of drawing foreign students principle policy, regulation and methods for each own jurisdiction. Under each provincial education commission is set up a special organization in charge of coordinating foreign students affairs within its own jurisdiction and providing advices and other kinds of services.

Universities and colleges accepting foreign students usually have special Foreign Students Agents, dealing with foreign students' enrolment applications, enrolment registrations, everyday courses, administrations, consultation and daily services.

TYPES AND QUALIFICATIONS OF FOREIGN STUDENTS ACCEPTED

Type	Age	Qualification	Term
Under-graduate	Under full 25	Above the equal of high school graduates in China, having passed examinations or tests by Chinese universities or colleges, and admitted	4-5 years
Post-graduate	Under full 35	College graduate, recommendations of two vice-professors or with titles above, having passed enrollment examinations or tests; or graduating as an undergraduate in China at the same year, excellent in courses, recommended to be admitted without entrance examinations	2-3 years
Doctoral student	Under full 40	Postgraduate, recommended by more than two vice-professors, passed entrance examinations or tests	3 years
Trainee of Chinee languages	Under full 55	Above the equal of high school graduates in china	1-2 years
Common trainees	Under full 35	Above a sophomore's degree	1-2 years
Advanced trainees	Under full 45	With or above Master's degree or studying for doctoral degree	Within 1 year
Researching scholar	Under full 55	Wtth or above vice-professor degree	Within 1 year
Short-term refresher	Under full 60	Equal of or above high school graduates in China	4-20 weeks

Ways to Apply to Study in China

· Exchanges between governments

· Handled in the light of the bilateral exchanges agreements between the governments.

· Inter-college exchanges

Handled in accordance with exchange agreements between the colleges or universities.

· Recommendations by groups

Applying by means of China's relevant organizations or directly to related universities or colleges in China by foreign universities or colleges, educational organizations, friendship groups.

· Individual Applications

Individual students may apply through China's concerned organizations or directly to the proper universities or colleges in China.

Classifications of Scholarships in China

Chinese Governmental Scholarship

This scholarship is offered to relevant countries for all types of students studying in China by means of governmental exchanges, individual applications will not be dealt with. The Governmental scholarship is classified into two categories :

Full Scholarship : tuition, emergency medical fee, course materials fee and lodging fee (These four kinds of fees are allocated to university authorities for overall uses), and some amount of living expense for every month (delivered to individuals by the university authorities).

Part scholarship : one or some items of the full scholarship.

Chinese Governmental Special Scholarships

Consigned to the China Scholarship Council by the State Education Commission of China.

Special scholarships include the Great Wall Scholarship, Scholarship for Excellent Students, Scholarship for HSK Winners, Scholarship of Chinese Culture Research, Scholarship for Chinese-Teaching Composium, and so on.

Besides, local governments and relevant universities in China have their own various scholarships to offer. Please directly consult relevant local education departments or universities.

Learning Chinese--Preparatory Education for Foreign Students

Chinese is the major teaching language for foreign students studying in China's universities. Moreover, reserved books, magazines and other literal materials in university libraries and archive houses are also mainly in Chinese. So foreign students will have to grasp Chinese so as to smoothly finish their schooling tasks. A primary stage C Grade qualification of the Chinese proficiency Test (HSK) is necessary for these to be scientific or technological undergraduates, and medium stage C grade for Chinese literature, Chinese history, philosophy and Chinese medicines.

Undergraduates who have not learned Chinese before they come to China or who fail to conform to the Chinese standard required will have to learn fundamental Chinese for 1-2 years after they arrive in China. Refreshers and postgraduates who use foreign languages as medium of study are also required to learn some Chinese for the convenience both in daily life and study.

Preparation of Application Materials

- Study-in-China application forms are obtained from Chinese consulates Universities.
- Physical Examination Record for Foreigner is required.
- Certificates of the latest degree, courses learned and transcripts are to be atteched.
- As an extra, recommendation letters by two vice-professors (or the equivalent) or persons of higher positions for those who apply for Master's degree or doctoral degree studies.

Apart from the above, consignee identification of matters in China and certificate of economic guarantee need to be provided in the case of those who are at their own expense.

The above materials must be in Chinese or English, or translation in any of these two languages. Relevent forms may be available from Chinese embassies (consulates) or concerned universities in China.

Selection of University/College and Subject

The following materials can be of great help in selection of university/college and subjects for study in China :

(i) Books introducing universities in China and their subjects are recommended they included :

Brief introductions to Universities and Colleges Accepting Foreign Students in China. Compiled with the authority of the Foreign Affair Bureau of the (SEDC) State Education Commission, and including introductions to universities and colleges that accept foreign students in China and subjects.

(ii) Encyclopedia of China's Universities and Colleges

This is a comprehensive book with the ABC of Universities and colleges in China, compiled by the Planning and Constructing Bureau and the Financial Bureau both under the State Education (SEDC).

(iii) Introduction to China's Universities and their subjects accepting of Foreign Students

This has the Listing China's Universities and their subjects. These are approved by the State Education Commission to accept Foreign Students on Governmental Scholarships, compiled and printed in 1997 by the China Scholarship Council.

When and How to Apply

(i) Foreign students of bilateral exchanges projects between governments should apply through relevant departments of their own countries, which are in charge of choosing and sending students to China, from January 1 to April 30.

(ii) Usually for students of inter-college exchanges projects or self-supporting students, those who enroll in spring must obtain their applications during September 15-15 December year, and those in autumn during February 15-15 May of the year. It is possible that these dates or other details may change these therefore the applicant is advised so it is advisable to directly ask relevant universities or colleges for recruitment specifications and enrolment application forms.

Enrolment Examinations and Tests

For freshers and trainees of Chinese languages, the best will be chosen on merit in light of education certificates.

For be undergraduates of arts, enrolment will be on the basis of competition in light of degree certificates, medium stage C grade certificates of HSK, and the examinations and tests held by the universities.

For scientific, medical, agronomical or technological undergraduates, enrolment will be on the basis of competitive selection in light of degree certificates, primary stage C grade of HSK tests, and the enrolment examinations.

The aspirants for postgraduation ought to have Bachelor's degree certificates, certificates for courses already attended and lists of related remarks, recommendations of two vice-professors (or above this level), and will have to pass the entrance examinations arranged by relevant universities. Only by means of attending courses arranged by the universities and passing courses examinations after they arrive in China can these students gain their qualifications to prepare thesis, otherwise they will have to graduate as trainees. The applicants already in China should attend united postgraduate enrolment examinations held by China. The fresh graduates from universities in China and of the same year may be enrolled by universities and colleges in light of the China's recommendation enrolment methods without usual entrance examinations.

Those to be doctoral students must have Master's degree certificates, certificates for course already attended and transcripts, recommendations of two vice-professors (persons of higher positions), and pass the examinations or tests held by the universities and colleges. Applicants already in China should attend united doctoral students enrolment examinations held for native students. Foreign postgraduates in China who reach the standards of graduating and studying for doctorates ahead of schedule can study for doctoral degrees in advance in conformance with the relevant regulations.

The would-be undergraduates, postgraduates and doctoral students of fine arts colleges are required to offer the photos or tape records of their artistic works and tutor's recommendations as well.

Foreign students graduated from China will be favoured if they re-apply to study in China.

Foreign students, of all types, that universities in China decide by themselves to accept will be examined by relevant universities, and enrolment will be on the basis of competitive selection.

How to Apply for Chinese Scholarships

Chinese Governmental Scholarship

Applicants should submit applications through the foreign student assigning departments of their own countries to the China Scholarship Council and Enrollment will be on the basis of competitive selection by China's relevant universities and colleges.

Chinese Governmental Special Scholarships

The Great Wall Scholarship : Provided to the headquarters of UNESCO. Applicants may submit applications to the local ESCO agencies or agencies of the ESCO or directly to the headquarters, the headquarters will make recommendations to the China Scholarship Council.

Scholarship for Excellent Students : Provided to foreign students who have finished a degree education in China and are receiving a higher degree and are both virtuous and good at courses. Applications should be recommended by the Universities they are studying in and submit applications through the university authorities to the China Scholarship Council.

Scholarship for HSK Winners : Offered to the overseas who get outstanding marks in HSK tests. After receiving a Certificate of HSK Winner, Applicants may submit applications to the China Scholarship Council directly or through local Chinese embassies or consulates.

Scholarship of Chinese Culture Research : Offered to overseas experts or scholars who are specialized in the research of Chinese cultural research. Applicants may submit applications to local Chinese embassies and consulates, relevant universities in China or proper professors in these universities, for consequent recommendations to the China Scholarship council.

The applicants may also directly apply to the China Scholarship Council. Please consult the list of Scholarship tutors of Chinese Cultural Research before applying.

Scholarship for Overseas Chinese-Teaching Composium : Provided to overseas teachers who specialize in the Chinese teaching. Applicants should submit applications through local Chinese embassies or consulates to the China Scholarship Council.

The above-mentioned methods for scholarships or proper application forms may be consulted or asked for in local Chinese embassies or consulates.

Study Cost for Self-supported Students

The following is a list of charges in different Chinese universities which may be helpful to self-supporting foreign students. (See the following table) Please consult entrance specifications of concrete universities for precise information.

	Sorts of foreign studends	Fee Standard (per person per year)
Tuition fee for arts	undergraduates Chinese-learning students, common trainees	US$1,700-3,200
	Postgraduates	US$2,00-3700
	doctorial students	US$2,700-4,200
	Short-term students	US$ 350-600 per month
Tuition fee for science, technology, agrinomy, medics, sports, art	Undergraduates, common trainees	US$1,800-6,400
	Postgraduates	US$2,500-7,400
	Doctoral students	US$2,900-8,400
	Short-term students	US$350-1,200
Registration fee		US$50-100
Loadging	US$2-3 per person per bed (two-bed room, public toilet and bath rooms), rooms of other standards will be charged according to the level of the accomodation qualities.	
Course Materials fee	US$30-50 for arts subjects, a little bit higher for subject of sciences, agronomy, medics, sports and art	
Accomodation fee	Some US$40-60 per person per month for foreign students dining hall; US$20-30 per person per month for native students dining hall	

Handling of the Visa to China

Foreign students of governmental scholarships can, have the Admission and the Visa Application Form for Studing visa Application Form for the foreigners wishing to Study in China (JW201 form) in China both delivered by the Chinese universities. Other formalities include Physical Examination Record for Foreigners, submit applications to Chinese embassies and consulates for X visa within due terms.

Students of in-college exchange projects and self-paid students chosen by the Chinese universities can, have the admission and the Visa Application form for Self-Supporting Foreigners Wishing to Study in China (JW202 form) Form both delivered by the Chinese universities other formalities included the Physical Examination Record for Foreigners, submit applications to Chinese embassies and consulates for X visa within due terms.

Those who stay in China for less than half a year may apply for an F visa.

Entrance Procedures

Foreign students should enter China within the due terms of the visas, and undergo the inspections at frontier inspection station, customs and health department.

Frontier Inspection

Generally foreign students should choose a port of entry which is nearest to the University where admitted. A passport inspection at the frontier inspection station is required for entrance into China.

Foreign students with X visas must handle provisional accommodation registrations within 24 hours, and residence permits at local police stations within 30 days after they pass the frontier inspections.

Custom Inspection

Foreign students must accurately complete the Passenger's Application for Articles in their luggage and report to Customs regarding what they carry when entering China. Customs will release items without payment of duty or tax them in line with relevant regulations.

Health Quarantine

Foreign students entering China are required to truthfully fill the Passenger's Health Report formalities and show the Physical Examination Record for Foreigner by hospitals or their protective inoculation certificates. On their arrival of universities, they need fo go to local health quarantine departments for an inspection of their health certificates. If the health records are found out of date, or some items are incomplete or not proper, then re-examinations are necessary. Residence and enrolment procedures are dealt with only after they pass the certificate inspections or health inspections by the health quarantine departments.

Enrolment Registration

All sorts of foreign students enrolled by Chinese universities need to register in person at the receptions according to the dates by the Entrance Notice. Those who fail to do so due to reasonable reasons should ask for permissions from the universities in advance, or otherwise the enrolment may be cancelled.

All the registering foreign students need to participate in the procedures of accommodation, health quarantine, residence and payment of registration fee.

Types of Short-term Training Courses

Chinese Classes: Conducted by universities, colleges of arts, and normal colleges, receiving foreign postgraduates, middle school students, members of friendship groups, staff members and others who love Chinese culture. The short-term classes are classified into primary class, medium class and advanced class in line with the students' level in Chinese.

Chinese Culture Classes : In major subjects including Chinese Politics, Economy and Trade, Foreign Relations and Traditional Culture.There are lectured in Chinese or English or with interpreters. Students will be organized to visit factories, the countryside, residence spots and scenic spots and historical sites which are helpful to or in connection with the class.

Chinese Medicine Class: Conducted for foreign doctors of traditional Chinese medical science, acupuncturists, and postgraduates and graduates at medical colleges who all understand Chinese or English, including acupuncture, moxibustion, massage and Chinese internal medicine. The classes are raised in combining lectures and clinical practices.

Law Class : Giving lectures on China's Constitution, Civil Laws, Economic Laws, as well as laws and regulations concerned with Sino-foreign co-investment. In reference to the course contents, students will be organized to visit and talk to lawyers, as well as audit trials.

Handwriting, Calligraphy and Painting Class : Mainly teaching the theory and skills of

Chinese handwriting and calligraphy and Chinese traditional paintings (including mountains and waters paintings, flowers and birds paintings, and figures paintings).

Ancient Architecture Class : Lecturing on the history of ancient Chinese architecture, and the techniques of ancient buildings in China, visiting ancient buildings and gardens of distinctive styles which are conspicuous in China.

Gastronomy Class : Focusing on the features and cooking methods of major Chinese cooking styles. Every student has an opportunity to cook by himself.

Sports Class : Mainly lecturing on Chinese traditional martial arts, Qigong and modern sports items. Different classes may focus on each subject.

Apart from the above-mentioned classes, the Chinese universities and colleges can also hold short-term courses of other subjects for foreigners. Please consult the subject introductions by each Chinese university and college and directly contact it.

Time

The time taken for the above courses will be from four to twenty weeks.

Ways to Apply for Enrolment and Handle Visa

Foreign faculties and friendship groups which hope to participate in the Composiums in China may ask the foreign students' administrative organizations in Chinese universities and colleges for recruitment specifications and discuss with them the details to conduct the seminars. Individuals can also directly contact the universities and colleges for the intended documents.

Anyone aged between 16-60 years and in good health can apply. Applicants need to carefully complete the Application for Foreigners' Composium printed by the recruiting universities and colleges.

The enrolled can apply for an F visa at the local Chinese embassy or consulate by submitting the admission and the Visa Application Form for Foreigners wishing to study in China Self-supporting (JW202) Forms sent by the universities and colleges, and register within the due time.

Costs of Short-term Training Courses

The charges of short-term classes are subject to the times, subjects, teaching manners, and studying and accommodating conditions. Please refer to the column about self-supporting foreign students in this book and the Admission Brochures by each university and college.

The China Scholarship Council

The China Scholarship Council is a non-profit corporate organization directly under the State Education Commission.

The Council aims to be in line with the central government's laws, regulations and concerned principles and policies and finance China's citizens studying abroad and foreigners to study in China. The Council was established for the purpose of helping developing China's exchanges of education, sciences, technology and culture and cooperation of economy and trade with other countries and regions, furthering the friendship and understanding between the Chinese people and other peoples in the world, and accelerating China's modernization drive and world's peace efforts.

The funds of the Council mainly come from the financial allocation by the state's study-abroad funds. At the same time, the Council accepts support from enterprises, social communities, friendly individuals both at home and abroad, and other organizations.

The major tasks of the Council are (1) to manage affairs concerning Chinese students going abroad and foreign students to China by means of laws and economic methods; (2) administration and utilization of the foundation, determine the supported items and supporting manners; (3) formulate administrative rules; (4) make the most use of the funds and develop them; (5) control bilateral, multilateral or single-party scholarship under a certain consignment; (6) accept consignment from related organizations or individuals both at home and abroad to manage other businesses relevant with educational exchanges and scientific and technological cooperation, finance the items which while benefiting China's education and foreign relationships, require foreign funds, expand fund resource, increase the funds accumulation, establish relations to responding organizations abroad, and conduct exchanges and cooperations with them.

The Council has a committee and a secretariat. The committee is in charge of counsel and examination, and the secretariat as a standing unit, is occupied in carrying out the working principles and plans by the executive committee, organizing the finances for Chinese students going abroad and foreigners to China, formulating regulations and measures, handling the applications, examinations, approvals and fee releases concerned with the supporting item, offering relevant counsel and services, supervising and inspecting the items supported by the Council and how the supported persons are using the money.

Mailing Address :

Chinese National Society of Universities and Colleges for Foreign Student Affairs
160, Fuxingmennei Street, Beijing, 100031, China, Tel : 86-10-66063253
Fax : 86-10 66063255, website://http : www.csc.edu.cn, E-mail : Laihua@csc.edu.cn

Chinese Service Center for Scholarly Exchange

Providing services to international students to Study in China

Chinese Service Centre for Scholarly Exchange (CSCSE) is a legally established non-profit, paid service agency under the State Education Commission of China. CSCSE provides applicants wishing to study in China's higher institutes of learning with the following services:

1. Educational information and consulting services

(a) General introduction of the educational system in China;

(b) Rules on recruiting international students to study in China (including academic programs, requirements and applications procedures for international students);

(c) Replying inquiries coming by mail or e-mail, both in Chinese and English;

2. Recruiting self-financing international students on behalf of the colleges and universities in China

(a) Introduction through the Internet (http://www.cscse.edu.cnn) general conditions of the colleges and universities which have been granted permission by the State Education Commission and has entrusted CSCSE to recruit international students, as well as the academic programs, majors, curriculum, tuition and living conditions such as accommodation;

(b) Providing auxiliary services after the applicants put forward their applications;

(c) Points of Attention before coming to China;

3. Providing paid airport pick-up services, ticket booking and accommodation for international students to China on the way to Beijing ;

4. Organizing travels and entertainment activities during vacations for international students in cooperation with the colleges or universities.

5. Purchasing medical and accident insurance on behalf of international students

Entrust CSCSE to go through the formalities for your self-financing study in China and you will :

* Get the latest and the most accurate information;
* Receive the admission Notice from a Chinese college or university in the shortest time possible;

* Obtain the best services.

Address :

Division for Foreigner Studying in China, Chinese Service Center for Scholarly Exchange (CSCSE), 15 Xueyuan Road, Haidian District Beijing 100083, China, Tel : 86-10-62314632
Fax : 86-10-62314386, E-mail : laihua@stnet.cscse.edu.cn

Addresses of Institutions

1. (Institutions) : Beijing Language and Culture University
(Telephone) : (010) 62314075, (Fax) : (010) 62314073
(P.C) : 100083, (Address) : 15 Xieyuan Road, Haidian District, Beijing, China.
(Division) : Foreign Student Office.
2. (Institutions) : Beijing University, (Telephone) : (010) 62751230, 62751231
(Fax) : (010) 62751233, (P.C) : 100871, (Address) : Haidian District, Beijing, China
(Division) : Foreign Student Office.
3. (Institutions) : Renmin University of China,
(Telephone) : (010) 62511588 62515343, (Fax) : (010) 62515241, (P.C) : 100872
(Address) : 39 Haidian Road, Beijing, China, (Division) : Foreign Student Office.
4. (Institutions) : Beijing Normal University,
(Telephone) : (010) 62207986 (8364,0325), (Fax) : (010) 62200567
(P.C) : 100875, (Address) :19 Xinjiekou Wai Street, Haidian District, Beijing, China, (Division) : Foreign Student Office.
5. (Institutions) : Bejing Foreign Studies University
(Telephone) : (010) 68468167 68422587, (Fax) : (010) 68422587
(P.C) : 100081, (Address) : 2 Xisanhua North Road, Beijing, China.
(Division) : Foreign Student Office.
6. (Institutions) : Tsinghua University, (Telephone) : (010) 62771142, 62784621
(Fax) : (010) 62771134, (P.C) : 100084, (Address) : 1 Tsinghua Yuan, Beijing, China.
(Division) : Foreign Student Office.
7. (Institutions) : Beijing University of Science and Technology,
(Telephone) : (010) 62332942, (Fax) : (010) 62327878, (P.C) : 100083
(Address) :30 Xue Yuan Road, Haidian District, Beijing China.
(Division) : Foreign Student Office.
8. (Institutions) : Northern Jlaotong University, (Telephone) : (010) 63240311 63240351
(Fax) : (010) 62255671, (P.C) : 100044, (Address) : XizhiMenwai, Shangyuancun, Beijing China. (Division) : Foreign Student Office.
9. (Institutions) : Beijing University of Posts and Telecommunication
(Telephone) : (010) 62281949, 62282639, (Fax) : (010) 62028643
(P.C) : 100088, (Address) :42 Xueyuan Road, Haidian District, Beijing, China.
(Division) : Foreign Student Office.
10. (Institutions) : Beijing Medical University, (Telephone) : (010) 62017192, 62091253, (Fax) : (010) 62015681, (P.C) : 100083, (Address) : 38 Xueyuan Road, Haidian District, Beijing, China., (Division) : Foreign Student Office.
11. (Institutions) : Bejing University of Traditional Chinese Medicine
(Telephone) : (010) 64213458, 64286323, (Fax) : (010) 64220858, (P.C) : 100029, (Address): 11 Beisanhuan East Road, Beijing, China.
(Division) : Foreign Student Office.
12. (Institutions) : Central Institute of Fine Arts, (Telephone) : (010) 64380464

(Fax) : (010) 64380466, (P.C) : 100730, (Address) : 5 Xiaowei Hutong, Dong Cheng District, Beijing, China., (Division) : Foreign Student Office.
13. (Institutions) : Central Academy of Arts Design
(Telephone) : (010) 65082233-2608 65067964, (Fax) : (010) 65067964
(P.C) : 100020, (Address) : 34 North Donghuan Road, Beijing, China.
(Division) : Foreign Student Office.
14. (Institutions) : Central Academy of Drama, (Telephone) : (010) 64035626
(Fax) : (010) 64016479, (P.C) : 100710, (Address) : 39 Dong Mianhua Hutong, Beijing, China
(Division) : Foreign Student Office.
15. (Institutions) : Central Conservatory of Music
(Telephone) : (010) 66052585, 66053531-228, (Fax) : (010) 66013138
(P.C) : 100031, (Address) : Baojia Street, Xichen District,
Beijing China (Division) : Foreign Student Office.
16. (Institutions) : Beijing University of Physical Education
(Telephone) : (010) 62989341, 62989391, (Fax) : (010) 62989472
(P.C) : 100084, (Address) : Yuanmingyuan East Road, Beijing China.
(Division) : Foreign Student Office.
17. (Institutions) : Capital Normal University
(Telephone) : (010) 68420845, 68902433, (Fax) : (010) 68416837
(P.C) : 100037, (Address) : Fuwai Huayuancun, Haidian District, Beijing, China.
(Division) : Foreign Student Office.
18. (Institutions) : Capital University of Economy and Trade,
(Telephone) : (010) 65006091 65064328, (Fax) : (010) 65006091, (P.C) : 100026
(Address) : Hongmiao Chaoyang Menwei, Beijing, China.
(Division) : Foreign Student Office.
19. (Institutions) : Beijing Institute of Commerce
(Telephone) : (010) 68429875, 68904774, (Fax) : (010) 68417834, (P.C) : 100037
(Address) : 11Fucheng Road, Beijing, China (Division) : Foreign Student Office.
20. (Institutions) : China University of Agriculture,
(Telephone) : (010) 62632736, (Fax) : (010) 62582332, (P.C) : 100094
(Address) : 2 Yuanmingyuan West Road., Haidian District, Beijing China.
(Division) : Foreign Student Office.
21. (Institutions) : University of International Business and Economics
(Telephone) : (010) 64928099, (Fax) : (010) 64928098, (P.C) : 100029
(Address) : HuiXin East Street, Beijing, China.
(Division) : Foreign Student Office.
22. (Institutions) : China University of Political Science and Law
(Telephone) : (010) 62229012, (Fax) : (010) 62229012, (P.C) : 100088
(Address) : 41 Xueyuan Road, Haidian District, Beijing, China.
(Division) : Foreign Student Office.
23. (Institutions) : Beijing Second Foreign Language Institute
(Telephone) : (010) 65778564 (5), (Fax) : (010) 65762520, (P.C) : 100024
(Address) :1 Din Fu Zhuang, Chao Yang District, Beijing, China.
(Division) : Foreign Student Office.
24. (Institutions) : Beijing Film Academy, (Telephone) : (010) 62013876, 62018899-560, (Fax) : (010) 62012132, (P.C) : 100088
(Address) : 4 Xi Tu Cheng Road, Haidian, District, Beijing, China.
(Division) : Foreign Student Office.

25. (Institutions) : Central University of Nationalitites,
(Telephone) : (010) 68933266, (Fax) : (010) 68933982, (P.C) : 100081
(Address) : 27 27 BaiShiQiao Road, Beijing, China
(Division) : Foreign Student Office.
26. (Institutions) : Beijing University of Technology
(Telephone) : (010) 67391858, (Fax) : (010) 67392319, (P.C) : 100022
(Address) : 100 Pingle Yuan. Chao Yang District, Beijing, China.
(Division) : Foreign Student Office.
27. (Institutions) : Beijing College of Accupuncture & Orthopaedics
(Telephone) : (010) 64361227, (Fax) : (010) 64377082, (P.C) : 100015
(Address) : 6 Zhong Huan sorth Road, Chaoyang District, Beijing China.
(Division) : Foreign Student Office.
28. (Institutions) : Academy of Chinese Traditional Opera
(Telephone) : (010) 63539354, (Fax) : (010) 63539354, (P.C) : 100054
(Address) : 3 Liren street, Xuan Wu District, Beijing China.
(Division) : Foreign Student Office.
29. (Institutions) : Beijing University of Chemical Technology
(Telephone) : (010) 64213610, (Fax) : (010) 64213610, (P.C) : 100029
(Address) : 15 Beisanhuan East Road, Chaoyang District, Beijing, China.
(Division) : Foreign Student Office.
30. (Institutions) : North China University of Technology
(Telephone) : (010) 68875831, (Fax) : (010) 68875846, (P.C) : 10009[illegible]
(Address) : Xiaojiahe Zhenglhuangqi, Shijingshan District, Beijing, China.
(Division) : Foreign Student Office.
31. (Institutions) : Peking Union Medical University
(Telephone) : (010) 65133091 65295964, (Fax) : (010) 65133091, (P.C) : 100730
(Address) : 9 Dongdan santiao Street, Beijing, China.
(Division) : Foreign Student Office.
32. (Institutions) : Beijing University of Aeronautics and Astronautics
(Telephone) : (010) 62015856 62017251-7586, (Fax) : (010) 62015347
(P.C) : 100083, (Address) : 37 Xueyuan Road, Haidian District, Beijing, China.
(Division) : Foreign Student Office.
33. (Institutions) : Central University of Finance and Banking
(Telephone) : (010) 62255676, 62251188 - 337, (Fax) : (010) 62255676
(P.C) : 100081, (Address) :39 Xueyuan South Road, Haidian District,
Beijing, China.
(Division) : Foreign Student Office.
34. (Institutions) : China Conservatory of Music, (Telephone) : (010) 64878917
(Fax) : (010) 64879974, (P.C) : 100101, (Address) : Sizhuyuan Deshenmen wai,
Beijing, China, (Division) : Foreign Student Office.
35. (Institutions) : Beijing Broadcasting Institute
(Telephone) : (010) 65762817 65779359, (Fax) : (010) 65779138, (P C) : 100024
(Address) :1 Dingfuzhuang East Street, Chaoyang District, Beijing, China.
(Division) : Foreign Student Office.
36. (Institutions) : Beijing Dance Academy, (Telephone) : (010) 68411605
(Fax) : (010) 68411605, (P.C) : 100081, (Address) : Min zu xue yuan South Road, Haidian
District, Beijing China., (Division) : Foreign Student Office.
37. (Institutions) : Beijing Forestry University, (Telephone) : (010) 62554411 -2271 62338271,

(Fax) : (010) 62310316, (P.C) : 100083, (Address) : Tsinghua East Road, Beijing, China, (Division) : Foreign Student Office.

38. (Institutions) : Beijing Teachers College of Physical Education
(Telephone) : (010) 62031125, (Fax) : (010) 62012987, (P.C) : 100088
(Address) : 21 Beihuan West Road, Haidian District, Beijing, China.
(Division) : Foreign Student Office.

39. (Institutions) : .Fudan University, (Telephone) : (021) 65117628
(Fax) : (021) 65117298, (P.C) : 200433, (Address) : 280 Zherong Road, Shanghai, China.
(Division) : Foreign Student Office.

40. (Institutions) : East China Normal University, (Telephone) : (021) 62572289 62577577 - 2277, (Fax) : (021) 62570590, (P.C) : 200062
(Address) : 3663 Zhongshan North Road, Shanghai, China.
(Division) : Foreign Student Office.

41. (Institutions) : Tongji University, (Telephone) : (021) 65983636 65983615
(Fax) : (021) 65028933, (P.C) : 200092, (Address) : 1239 Siping Road, Shanghai, China, (Division) : Foreign Student Office.

42. (Institutions) : Shanghai University, (Telephone) : (021) 56626286
(Fax) : (021) 56635364, (P.C) : 200072, (Address) : 149 Yan Chang Road, Shanghai, China, (Division) : Foreign Student Office.

43. (Institutions) : East China University of Science and Technology
(Telephone) : (021) 64252187 64252769, (Fax) : (021) 64250735, (P.C) : 200237
(Address) : 130 Meilong Road, Shanghai, China,
(Division) : Foreign Student Office.

44. (Institutions) : China Textile University (Telephone) : (021) 62708702 62199898-798, (Fax) : (021) 62194722, (P.C) : 200051, (Address) : 1882 Yan an West Road, Shanghai, China, (Division) : Foreign Student Office.

45. (Institutions) : Shanghai University, (Telephone) : (021) 59528926 59534472-287, (Fax): (021) 59529932, (P.C) : 201800, (Address) : 20 Cheng Zhong Road, Jiading District, Shanghai, China, (Division) : Foreign Student Office.

46. (Institutions) : Shanghai Medical University, (Telephone) : (021) 64037310 64041900 - 212, (Fax) : (021) 64037395, (P.C) : 200032, (Address) : 138 Yixueyyan Road, Shangai, China. (Division) : Foreign Student Office.

47. (Institutions) : Shanghai Second Medical University
(Telephone) : (021) 63847078 63846590-512, (Fax) : (021) 63847078
(P.C) : 200025, (Address) : 227 Chong qing South Road, Shanghai China.
(Division) : Foreign Student Office.

48. (Institutions) : Shanghai College of Traditional Medicine
(Telephone) : (021) 64171226, (Fax) : (021) 64178290, (P.C) : 200032
(Address) : 530 Hingling Road, Shanghai, China.
(Division) : Foreign Student Office.

49. (Institutions) : Shanghai Conservatory of Music
(Telephone) : (021) 64330536 64370137-2108, (Fax) : (021) 64330866
(P.C) : 200031, (Address) : 20 Fen Yang Road, Shanghai, China.
(Division) : Foreign Student Office.

50. (Institutions) : Shanghai International Studies University
(Telephone) : (021) 65360599, (Fax) : (021) 65313756, (P.C) : 200083
(Address) : 555 Chifeng Road, Shanghai, China.
(Division) : Foreign Student Office.

51. (Institutions) : Shanghai Normal University
(Telephone) : (021) 64770700-2824, (Fax) : (021) 64700700, (P.C) : 200234
(Address) :100 Guilin Road, Xuhui District, Shanghai, China.
(Division) : Foreign Student Office.
52. (Institutions) :East China Institute of Politics & Law
(Telephone) : (021) 62512190-217 62512497, (Fax) : (021) 62512497
(P.C) : 200042, (Address) :1575 Wanhangdu Road, Shanghai, China.
(Division) : Foreign Student Office.
53. (Institutions) : Shanghai University
(Telephone) : (021) 56626286 56631515-2771, (Fax) : (021) 56635364
(P.C) : 200434, (Address) : 661 Sanmen Road, Shanghai, China.
(Division) : Foreign Student Office.
54. (Institutions) : Shanghai Academy of Drama, (Telephone) : (021) 62482920
(Fax) : (021) 62482624, (P.C) : 200040, (Address) : 630 Huashan Road, Shanghai, China., (Division) : Foreign Student Office.
55. (Institutions) : Shanghai Institute of Physical Education
(Telephone) : (021) 65485546, 65490649, (Fax) : (021) 65490649
(P.C) : 200433, (Address) : 650 Qingyuan Huan Road, Shanghai, China
(Division) : Foreign Student Office.
56. (Institutions) : Shanghai Jlaotong University, (Telephone) : (021) 64383540
(Fax) : (021) 64383540, (P.C) : 200030, (Address) : 1954 Huashan Road, Shanghai, China., (Division) : Foreign Student Office.
57. (Institutions) : Shanghai University of Engineering Science
(Telephone) : (021) 62759779, (Fax) : (021) 62758481, (P.C) : 200335
(Address) : 350 Xian Xia Road, Shanghai, China.
(Division) : Foreign Student Office.
58. (Institutions) : East China University of Technology
(Telephone) : (021) 65432967, (Fax) : (021)65431258, (P.C) : 200093
(Address) : 516 Jungong Road, Shanghai, China.
(Division) : Foreign Student Office.
59. (Institutions) : Shanghai Institute of Foreign Trade
(Telephone) : (021) 62748250, (Fax) : (021)62748814, (P.C) : 200335
(Address) : 620 Gubei Road, Shanghai, China.
(Division) : Foreign Student Office.
60. (Institutions) : Nankai University, (Telephone) : (022) 2350 8825
(Fax) : (022) 23502990, (P.C) : 300071,
(Address) : 94 Weijin Road, Nankai District, Tian Jin, China.
(Division) : Foreign Student Office.
61. (Institutions) : Tianjin University (Telephone) : (022) 23350853
(Fax) : (022) 23350853, (P.C) : 300072, (Address) : 92 Weijin Road, Nankai District, Tian Jin, China, (Division) : Foreign Student Office.
62. (Institutions) : Tianjin Foreign Language Institute
(Telephone) : (022) 23280875, (Fax) : (022) 23282410, (P.C) : 300204
(Address) : Machangda, Hexi District, Tian jin, China
(Division) : Foreign Student Office.
63. (Institutions) : Tianjin College of Traditional Chinese Medicine
(Telephone) : (022) 27370627, (Fax) : (022) 27370636, (P.C) : 300193
(Address) : Xihucun, Nankai District, Tian jin, China.

(Division) : Foreign Student Office.
64. (Institutions) : Tianjing Institute of Light Industry
(Telephone) : (022) 28341803 28342821, (Fax) : (022) 28341536, (P.C) : 300222
(Address) : 1038 Dagu South Road, Hexi District, Tian jin, China.
(Division) : Foreign Student Office.
65. (Institutions) : Tianjin Normal University, (Telephone) : (022) 23351260
(Fax) : (022) 23358494, (P.C) : 300074, (Address) : Balitai Weijin Road, Hexi District, Tian jin, China., (Division) : Foreign Student Office.
66. (Institutions) : Nanjing University, (Telephone) : (025) 3593587, 3593785
(Fax) : (022) 3316747, (P.C) : 210093, (Address) : 22 Hankou Road, Nanjing, Jiangsu, China, (Division) : Foreign Student Office.
67. (Institutions) : Nanjing Normal University, (Telephone) : (025) 3717160
(Fax) : (025) 3717160, (P.C) : 210097, (Address) : 122 Ning hai, Road, Nanjing Jiangsu, China, (Division) : Foreign Student Office.
68. (Institutions) : South East China, (Telephone) : (025) 3615736 7714233
(Fax) : (025) 7712719, (P.C) : 210096, (Address) : 2 Sipailou, Nanjing, Jiangsu, China.
(Division) : Foreign Student Office.
69. (Institutions) : Wuxi University of Light Industry
(Telephone) : (0510) 5806751, (Fax) : (0510) 5807976, (P.C) : 214036
(Address) : 170 Hui he Road, Wu xi, Jiangsu, China.
(Division) : Foreign Student Office.
70. (Institutions) : China Pharmaceutical University, (Telephone) : (025) 3213611
(Fax) : (025) 3213611, (P.C) : 210009, (Address) : 24 Tongjia xong, Nanjing, Jiangsu, China, (Division) : Foreign Student Office.
71. (Institutions) : Nanjing College of Traditional Chinese Medicine
(Telephone) : (025) 6607127 6506645, (Fax) : (025) 6607127, (P.C) : 210029
(Address) : 282 Han zhong Han Nanjing, Jiangsu, China.
(Division) : Foreign Student Office.
72. (Institutions) : Hehai University, (Telephone) : (025) 3708419
(Fax) : (025) 3708419, (P.C) : 210098, (Address) : 1 Xikang Road, Nanjing, Jiangsu, China, (Division) : Foreign Student Office.
73. (Institutions) : Jlangnan Institute, (Telephone) : (0510) 5512506
(Fax) : (0510) 5512506, (P.C) : 214063, (Address) : 100 Liangxi Road, Wuxi, Jiangsu, China, (Division) : Foreign Student Office.
74. (Institutions) : Yangzhou University, (Telephone) : (0514) 7352262
(Fax) : (0514) 7311374, (P.C) : 215002, (Address) : Thin West-lake beside, Yang xhou, Jiangsu, China, (Division) : Foreign Student Office.
75. (Institutions) : Nanjing University of Science and Technology
(Telephone) : (025) 4432727, (Fax) : (025) 4431622, (P.C) : 210014
(Address) : 200 Xiao Ling wei, Nanjing, Jiangsu, China.
(Division) : Foreign Student Office.
76. (Institutions) : China University of Mining and Technology
(Telephone) : (0516) 3885745, (Fax) : (0516) 3888682, (P.C) : 221008
(Address) : South suburbs, Xuxhou, Jiangsu, China.
(Division) : Foreign Student Office.
77. (Institutions) : Jiangsu University of Science and Technology
(Telephone) : (0511) 8780035, (Fax) : (0511)8780036, (P.C) : 212013
(Address) : Zhenjiang City, Jiangsu, China, (Division) : Foreign Student Office.

78. (Institutions) : Xuzhou Teachers University, (Telephone) : (0516) 3845547
(Fax) : (0516) 3845547, (P.C) : 221009, (Address) : 57 Heping Road, Xuxhou, Jiangsu, China, (Division) : Foreign Student Office.
79. (Institutions) : Suzhou University, (Telephone) : (0512) 5221028 223614-874 879, (Fax) : (0512) 5221028, (P.C) : 215006, (Address) : 1 Shizi Street, Suzhou, Jiangsu, China, (Division) : Foreign Student Office.
80. (Institutions) : Zhejiang University, (Telephone) : (0571) 7951386
(Fax) : (0571) 7951755, (P.C) : 310027, (Address) : Yuquan Hangzhou, zhejiang, China, (Division) : Foreign Student Office.
81. (Institutions) : Zhejiang Agricultural University
(Telephone) : (0571) 6971060, (Fax) : (0571) 6041053, (P.C) : 310029
(Address) : 268 Kaixuan Road, Hang zhou, Zhejiang, China.
(Division) : Foreign Student Office.
82. (Institutions) : China Academy of Fine Arts, (Telephone) : (0571) 7079178
(Fax) : (0571) 7070039, (P.C) : 310062, (Address) : 218 Nanshan Road, Hangzhou, Zhejiang, China, (Division) : Foreign Student Office.
83. (Institutions) : Hangzhou University, (Telephone) : (0571) 8071224-2740 2745, (Fax) : (0571) 8070107, (P.C) : 310028, (Address) : 34 Tian mu shan Road, Hangzhou, Zhejiang, China, (Division) : Foreign Student Office.
84. (Institutions) : Zhejiang College of Traditional Chinese Medicine
(Telephone) : (0571) 7046071, (Fax) : (0571) 7046071, (P.C) : 310009
(Address) : Qing Chun Street, Hangzhou Zhejiang, China.
(Division) : Foreign Student Office.
85. (Institutions) : Zhejiang Medical University, (Telephone) : (0571) 7077855
(Fax) : (0571) 7077389, (P.C) : 310031, (Address) : 353 Yanan Road, Hangzhou, Zhejiang, China., (Division) : Foreign Student Office.
86. (Institutions) : Hangzhou Teachers College
(Telephone) : (0571) 8078124-222, (Fax) : (0571) 8081082, (P.C) : 310036
(Address) : 96 Wenyi Road, Hangzhou, Zhejiang, China.
(Division) : Foreign Student Office.
87. (Institutions) : Zheijiang University of Technology
(Telephone) : (0571) 5237595, (Fax) : (0571) 5237605, (P.C) : 310032
(Address) : Zhaohui six District, hangzhou, Zhejiang, China.
(Division) : Foreign Student Office.
88. (Institutions) : Shangdong University
(Telephone) : (0531) 85655623 8564946, (Fax) : (0531) 8564501, (P.C) : 250100
(Address) : 27 Shanda South Road, Jinan, Shandong, China.
(Division) : Foreign Student Office.
89. (Institutions) : Shandong Normal University, (Telephone) : (0531)2966954
(Fax) : (0531) 2966594, (P.C) : 250014, (Address) : 88 Wenhua East Road, Jinan, Shandong, China, (Division) : Foreign Student Office.
90. (Institutions) : Shandong College of Traditional Chinese Medicine
(Telephone) : (0531) 2968823, (Fax) : (0531) 2968823, (P.C) : 250014
(Address) : 53 Jingshi Road, Qingdao, Shandong, China.
(Division) : Foreign Student Office.
91. (Institutions) : Qingdao University, (Telephone) : (0532)5894822
(Fax) : (0532) 5894822, (P.C) : 266071, (Address) : 103 Zhanliu gan Road, Qingdao, Shandong, China, (Division) : Foreign Student Office.

92. (Institutions) : Yantai University, (Telephone) : (0535) 6888358
(Fax) : (0535) 6888358, (P.C) : 266003, (Address) : Qing quanzhai East subuxis, Yantai, Shandong, China, (Division) : Foreign Student Office.
93. (Institutions) : Qingdao University of Oceanography
(Telephone) : (0532) 2032436 2032826, (Fax) : (0532) 2032805
(P.C) : 266003, (Address) : 5 Yuxhan Road, QingDao, Shandong, China.
(Division) : Foreign Student Office.
94. (Institutions) : Shandong Institute of Economics
(Telephone) : (0531) 8934167-287, (Fax) : (0531) 8938821, (P.C) : 250014
(Address) : 4 Yanzishan East Road, JiNan, Shandong, China.
(Division) : Foreign Student Office.
95. (Institutions) : Qufu Normal University
(Telephone) : (0537) 4412551 4411831, (Fax) : (0537) 4412551, (P.C) : 273165
(Address) : JingXuan West Road, QuFu, Shandong, China.
(Division) : Foreign Student Office.
96. (Institutions) : Yantai Teachers College, (Telephone) : (0535) 6246451 675
(Fax) : (0535) 6253005, (P.C) : 264025, (Address) : Hongqizhong Road, Yantai, Shandong, China, (Division) : Foreign Student Office.
97. (Institutions) : Xiamen University, (Telephone) : (0592) 2186211
(Fax) : (0592) 2086402, (P.C) : 361005, (Address) : Siming South Road, Xiamen, Fujian, China., (Division) : Foreign Student Office.
98. (Institutions) : Fuzhou University, (Telephone) : (0591) 3713866
(Fax) : (0591) 3713229, (P.C) : 35002, (Address) : 523 Gongye Road, Fuzhou, Fujian, China., (Division) : Foreign Student Office.
99. (Institutions) : Huaqiao University, (Telephone) : (0595)2680680
(Fax) : (0595) 2686969, (P.C) : 362011, (Address) : Cheng East Suburbs, Quanzhou, Fujian, China, (Division) : Foreign Student Office.
100. (Institutions) : Fujian College of Traditional Chinese Medicine
(Telephone) : (0591) 7842528 7841708-3168, (Fax) : (0591) 7842524
(P.C) : 350003, (Address) : 282 Wuisi Road, Fuzhou, Fujian, China.
(Division) : Foreign Student Office.
101. (Institutions) : Fujian Normal University
(Telephone) : (0591) 3442840 3441616-302, (Fax) : (0591) 3442840
(P.C) : 350007, (Address) : 3 Shangshan Road, Cangshan District, Fuzhou, Fujian, China, (Division) : Foreign Student Office.
102. (Institutions) : Fujian Medical College, (Telephone) : (0591) 3314289
(Fax) : (0591) 3351345, (P.C) : 350004, (Address) : 88 Jiaotong Road, Fuzhou, Fujian, China. (Division) : Foreign Student Office.
103. (Institutions) : Zhonghsan University, (Telephone) : (020) 84185465
(Fax) : (020) 84184860, (P.C) : 510275, (Address) : Xingang West Road, Haizhu District, Guangzhou, Guangdong, China, (Division) : Foreign Student Office.
104. (Institutions) : Sun Yatsen University of Medical Science
(Telephone) : (020)87303601, (Fax) : (020) 87303601, (P.C) : 510089
(Address) : 74 Zhongshan Two Road, Guangzhou, Guangdong, China.
(Division) : Foreign Student Office.
105. (Institutions) : Guangzhou University of Traditional Chinese Medicine
(Telephone) : (020) 86593715 86591233, (Fax) : (020) 86593715
(P.C) : 510407, (Address) : 10 Jichang Road, Sanyuan Li District, Guangzhou, Guangdong,

China, (Division) : Foreign Student Office.
106. (Institutions) : South China Agricultural University
(Telephone) : (020) 87592114, (Fax) : (020) 87592114, (P.C) : 510642
(Address) : Wushan Guangzhou, Guangdong, China.
(Division) : Foreign Student Office.
107. (Institutions) : Wuyi University, (Telephone) : (0750) 3352112 3334312
(Fax) : (0750) 3354323, (P.C) : 529020, (Address) : Jiangmen Guangdong, China,
Division : Foreign Student Office.
108 .(Institutions) : Shenzhen University, (Telephone) : (0755) 6660277-2108 6661940,
(Fax) : (0755) 6660462, (P.C) : 518060, (Address) : Nantou, Shenzhen Guangdong, China,
(Division) : Foreign Student Office.
109. (Institutions) : South China Normal University, (Telephone) : (020) 87501131
(Fax) : (020) 87501131, (P.C) : 510631, (Address) : Tianhe District, Guangzhou, Guangdong,
China, (Division) : Foreign Student Office.
110 .(Institutions) : Guangzhou Academy of Fine Arts
(Telephone) : (020) 84429572, (Fax) : (020) 84429572, (P.C) : 510261
(Address) : 257 Changgang East Road, Guangzhou, Guangdong, China.
(Division) : Foreign Student Office.
111. (Institutions) : Guangdong University of Foreign Language and Trade
(Telephone) : (020) 84185465, (Fax) : (020) 86627367, (P.C) : 510421
(Address) : Huangshi East Road, Baiyun District, Guangzhou, Guangdong, China.
(Division) : Foreign Student Office.
112 .(Institutions) : Shantou University, (Telephone) : (0754) 8510520
(Fax) : (0754) 8510505, (P.C) : 515063, (Address) : Santou, Guangdong, China.
(Division) : Foreign Student Office.
113. (Institutions) : Jinan University, (Telephone) : (020) 87579341
(Fax) : (020) 85516941, (P.C) : 510632, (Address) : Shipai, Tianbhe District, Guangzhou, Guangdong, China.
(Division) : Foreign Student Office.
114. (Institutions) : South China University of Technology
(Telephone) : (020) 87110595 87110592, (Fax) : (020) 85516862, (P.C) : 510641
(Address) : Wushan, Guangzhou, Guangdong, China.
(Division) : Foreign Student Office.
115. (Institutions) : Wuhan University, (Telephone) : (027) 7863154
(Fax) : (027) 7863154, (P.C) : 430072, (Address) : LuoJiashan Wuchang Road, Wuhan, Hubei,
China, (Division) : Foreign Student Office.
116. (Institutions) : Central China University of Science & Technology
(Telephone) : (027) 7542457, (Fax) : (027) 7547063, (P.C) : 430074
(Address) : Yujiashan, Wuchang District, Wuhan, Hubei, China.
(Division) : Foreign Student Office.
117. (Institutions) : Wuhan China University of Transportation & Technology
(Telephone) : (027) 6554406, (Fax) : (027) 6554406, (P.C) : 430063
(Address) : Yujiatou Wuchange District, Wuhan, Hubei, China.
(Division) : Foreign Student Office.
118. (Institutions) : China University of Geosciences
(Telephone) : (027) 7802136-391, (Fax) : (027) 7801763, (P.C) : 430074
(Address) : Yujiashan, Wuchange District, Wuhan, Hubei, China.
(Division) : Foreign Student Office.

119. (Institutions) : Tongji Medical University, (Telephone) : (027) 3622600 5866811-2920 (Fax) : (027) 3647920, (P.C) : 430030
(Address) : 13 Hangkong Road, Wuhan, Hubei, China.
(Division) : Foreign Student Office.
120. (Institutions) : Hubei Medical University, (Telephone) : (027) 7360601
(Fax) : (027) 7816966, (P.C) : 430071, (Address) : 39 Donghu Road, Wuhan, Hubei, China,
(Division) : Foreign Student Office
121. (Institutions) : Central China Normal University
(Telephone) : (027) 7815696 7875696, (Fax) : (027) 7875696, (P.C) : 430070
(Address) : Guizishan, Wuchang District, Wuhan, Hubei, China.
(Division) : Foreign Student Office.
122. (Institutions) : Central China University of Agriculture
(Telephone) : (027) 7815057 7815681-226, (Fax) : (027) 7815057, (P.C) : 430070
(Address) : Shizishan South Lake, Wuchang District,
Wuhan, Hubei, China, (Division) : Foreign Student Office.
123. (Institutions) : Hubei College of Traditional Chinese Medicine
(Telephone) : (027) 8910230, (Fax) : (027) 8852621, (P.C) : 430061
(Address) : Yunjiaqiao, Wuchang District, Wuhan, Hubei, China.
(Division) : Foreign Student Office.
124. (Institutions) : Central South Institute of Nationalities
(Telephone) : (027) 7801740-323, (Fax) : (027) 7801223, (P.C) : 430074
(Address) : 5 Minzu Road, Wuchang District, Wuhan, Hubei, China.
(Division) : Foreign Student Office.
125. (Institutions) : Hubei University, (Telephone) : (027) 6811903-328 6814263 (Fax) : (027) 6814263, (P.C) : 430062, (Address) : Baojian Wuchang District, Wuhan, Hubei, China, (Division) : Foreign Student Office.
126. (Institutions) : JIanghan University, (Telephone) : (027) 2872837-3032 2873132, (Fax) : (027) 2871533, (P.C) : 430010, (Address) : 18 Jiangda Road, Hankou District, Wuhan, Hubei, China, (Division) : Foreign student office.
127. (Institutions) : Wuhan TEchnical University of Surveying & Mapping
(Telephone) : (027) 7865973, (Fax) : (028) 7865973, (P.C) : 430070
(Address) : 39 Luoyu Road, Wuchang, District, Wuhan, Hubei, China.
(Division) : Foreign Student Office.
128. (Institutions) : Sichuan Joint University, (Telephone) : (028) 5417169
(Fax) : (028) 5213555, (P.C) : 610064, (Address) : Juyanqiao, Chengdu, Sichuan, China, (Division) : Foreign Student Office.
129. (Institutions) : Chengdu University of Traditional Chinese Medicine
(Telephone) : (028) 7769241 7784542, (Fax) : (028) 7763471, (P.C) : 610075
(Address) : 37 12 Liao Road, Chentgdu, Sichuan, China.
(Division) : Foreign Student Office.
130. (Institutions) : Southewast Institute for Nationalities
(Telephone) : (028) 5553811-6042, (Fax) : (028) 5589294
(P.C) : 610041, (Address) : 21 Xunianqiao Heng Street, Chengdu, Sichuan .China.
(Division) : Foreign Student Office.
131. (Institutions) : Sichuan Normal University, (Telephone) : (028) 4442612-5250 445100, (Fax) : (028) 4451003, (P.C) : 610068, (Address) : Shizi. Road, East Suburbs, Chengdu, Sichuan China.
132. (Institutions) : Sichuan Institute of Foreign Language

(Telephone) : (023) 65311737-3077, (Fax) : (023) 65315875, (P.C) : 630031
(Address) : Lieshimu Shapingba District, Chongqine, China.
(Division) : Foreign Student Office.

133. (Institutions) : Chongqing University, (Telephone) : (023) 65102449 65112324
(Fax) : (023) 65106656, (P.C) : 630044, (Address) : 174 Shazbeng Street, Shapingba, District, Chongqing China, (Division) : Foreign Student Office.

134. (Institutions) : Southwest Normal University, (Telephone) : (023) 68863901-2225 68863805, (Fax) : (023) 68863805, (P.C) : 630715
(Address) : Beipei District, Chongqing, China,
(Division) : Foreign Student Office.

135. (Institutions) : Guangxi Medical University, (Telephone) : (0771) 5311477-8540, (Fax) : (0771) 5312523, (P.C) : 530027, (Address) : 6 Binghu Road, Nanning, Guangxi, China., (Division) : Foreign Student Office.

136. (Institutions) : Guangxi Normal University, (Telephone) : (0773) 3126960
(Fax) : (0773) 3127591, (P.C) : 541001, (Address) : Wangehen, Gu Guangxi, China, (Division) : Foreign Student Office.

137. (Institutions) : Guangxi University, (Telephone) : (0771) 3823743 3833381-5229, (Fax) : (0771) 3823743, (P.C) : 530004, (Address) : 10 Xitangxiang Road, Nanning, Guangxi, China, (Division) : Foreign Student Office.

138. (Institutions) : Guangxi College of Traditional Chinese Medicine
(Telephone) : (0771) 3835812 3834562, (Fax) : (0771) 3835812
(P.C) : 530001, (Address) : 21 Mingxin East Road, Nanning, Guangxi, China.
(Division) : Foreign Student Office.

139. (Institutions) : Guangxi Institute for Nationalities,
(Telephone) : (0771) 3137401, (Fax) : (0771) 3135812, (P.C) : 530006
(Address) : 74 Xitangxiang Road, Nanning, Guangxi, China.
(Division) : Foreign Student Office.

140. (Institutions) : Liaoning University, (Telephone) : (024) 6843428 6862028
(Fax) : (024) 6852421, (P.C) : 110036, (Address) : 66 Chongshanzhong Road, Shenyang, Liaoning, China, (Division) : Foreign Student Office.

141. (Institutions) : Northeast University,
(Telephone) : (024) 3891829 3893000-2745, (Fax) : (024) 3891829,
(P.C) : 110006, (Address) : Wenhua Road, Heping District, Shenyang, Liaoning, China, (Division) : Foreign Student Office.

142. (Institutions) : Dalian Maritime University,
(Telephone) : (0411) 4671611-9656, (Fax) : (0411) 4671395, (P.C) : 116024
(Address) : Lingshuiquia, Dalian, Liaoning, China., (Division) : Foreign Student Office.

143. (Institutions) : China Medical University, (Telephone) : (024) 3866766-5112 3865197
(Fax) : (024) 3875539, (P.C) : 110001, (Address) : Beierma Road, Hepign District, Shenyang, Liaoning, China., (Division) : Foreign Student Office.

144. (Institutions) : Liaoning Normal University, (Telephone) : (0411) 4211181-8562
(Fax) : (0411) 4200935, (P.C) : 116022, (Address) : 850 Huanghe Road, Dalian, Liaoning, China., (Division) : Foreign Student Office.

145. (Institutions) : Dalian Institute of Foreign, Languages,
(Telephone) : (0411) 2803121-239 2807175, (Fax) : (0411) 2648152, (P.C) : 116001
(Address) : Nanshan Road, Zhongshan District, Dalian, Liaoning, China
(Division) : Foreign Student Office.

146.(Institutions) : Liaoning College of Traditional, Chinese Medicine,

(Telephone) : (024) 6861407, (Fax) : (024) 6861407, (P.C) : 110032, (Address) : Chongshan East Road, Huanggu , District, Liaoning, China., (Division) : Foreign Student Office.

147. (Institutions) : Shenyang Teachers College, (Telephone) : (024) 6847417 (Fax) : (024) 6845844, (P.C) : 110031, (Address) : Huanghe street, Huanggu District, Liaoning, China., (Division) : Foreign Student Office.

148. (Institutions) : Northeast University of Finance and Economics (Telephone) : (0411) 4672708, (Fax) : (0411) 4672708,(P.C) : 116023 (Address) : Jianshan Street, Dabekou District, Dalian, Liaoning, China. (Division) : Foreign Student Office.

149. (Institutions) : Dalian University of Science and Technology (Telephone) : (0411) 4671616, (Fax) : (0411) 4671009, (P.C) : 116023 (Address) : Linggong Road, Ganjingzi District, Dalian, Liaoning, China. (Division) : Foreign Student Office.

150. (Institutions) : Shenyang University of Pharmacy (Telephone) : (024) 3891685, (Fax) : (024) 3891576,(P.C) : 110015 (Address) : Wenhua Road, Shenhe district, Shenyang, Liaoning, China. (Division) : Foreign Student Office.

151. (Institutions) : Shenyang University, (Telephone) : (024) 3894438 (Fax) : (024) 3894560, (P.C) : 110041, (Address) : 55 Wencul Road, Dongll District, Shenyang, Liaoning, China., (Division) : Foreign Student Office.

152. (Institutions) : Luxun Academy of Fine Arts (Telephone) : (024) 3892635 3892467, (Fax) : (024) 3890334, (P.C) : 110003 (Address) : 19 Sanhao Street, Heping District, Shenyang, Liaoning, China. (Division) : Foreign Student Office.

153. (Institutions) : Jilin University, (Telephone) : (0431) 8922331-2680 5623264 (Fax) : (0431) 8923907, (P.C) : 130023, (Address) : 117 Jiefnng Big Road, Changchun Jili, China., (Division) : Foreign Student Office.

154. (Institutions) : Jilin University of Technology, (Telephone) : (0431) 5684468 5682351-2133, (Fax) : (0431) 5684468, (P.C) : 130025, (Address) : Renmin Gig Road, Changchun Jili, China, (Division) : Foreign Student Office.

155. (Institutions) : Changchun University of Science & Technology (Telephone) : (0431) 8963476, (Fax) : (0431) 8928327, (P.C) : 136026 (Address) : 6 Minzhu West Street, Changchun Jili,China. (Division) : Foreign Student Office.

156. (Institutions) : Changchun University, (Telephone) : (0431) 5687435, (Fax) : (0431) 5687435, (P.C) : 130022, (Address) : 1 Weixing Road, Changchun Jili, China. (Division) : Foreign Student Office.

157. (Institutions) : Yanbian University, (Telephone) : (0433) 2756759, (Fax) : (0433) 2756759 (P.C) : 130002, (Address) : 105 Gongyuan Road, Yanji, Jilin, China. (Division) : Foreign Student Office.

158. (Institutions) : Changchun College of Traditional Chinese Medicine (Telephone) : (0431) 5940940, (Fax) : (0431) 5958760, (P.C) : 130021, (Address) : 15 Gongnong Road, Changchun Jili, China., (Division) : Foreign Student Office.

159. (Institutions) : Northeast Normal University (Telephone) : (0431) 5685722, (Fax) : (0431) 5684009, (P.C) : 130024, (Address) : Renmin Street, Changchun Jili, China., (Division) : Foreign Student Office.

160. (Institutions) : Medical College of Yanbian University, (Telephone) : (0433) 2611305

(Fax) : (0433) 2611305, (P.C) : 133000, (Address) : 121 Juzi Street Yanji, Jilin, China. (Division) : Foreign Student Office.

161. (Institutions) : Jilin Institute of Technology, (Telephone) : (0431) 595521-228 (Fax) : (0431) 5952413, (P.C) : 130021, (Address) : Yanan Road, Chanyang District, Changchun, Jilin, China., (Division) : Foreign Student Office.

162. (Institutions) : Xpan University of Highway Transportation (Telephone) : (029) 5264024 5268346-4158, (Fax) : (029) 5261532, (P.C) : 710064 (Address) : 3 Cuihua Road, Xian, Shanxi, China., (Division) : Foreign Student Office.

163. (Institutions) : Xpan Jiaotong University, (Telephone) : (029) 3268230, (Fax) : (029) 3234716, (P.C) : 710049,(Address) : 28 Xian Ning Xi Road, Xian, Shanxi, China. (Division) : Foreign Student Office.

164. (Institutions) : Northwest University, (Telephone) : (029) 7231494, (P.C) : 710069 (Address) :Xiao Nan men Wai, Xian, Shanxi, China. (Division) : Foreign Student Office.

165. (Institutions) : Shanxi Normal University, (Telephone) : (029) 5235942, (Fax) : (029) 5261391 (P.C) : 710062 (Address) : Changchun South Road, Xian, Shanxi, China. (Division) : Foreign Student Office.

166. (Institutions) : Xpan College of Foreign Languages, (Telephone) : (029) 5246154 (Fax) : (029) 5246154, (P.C) : 710061, (Address) : WujiaFen South Suburbs, Xian, Shanxi, China. (Division) : Foreign Student Office.

167. (Institutions) : Xpan Conservatory of Music, (Telephone) : (029) 5255855, (Fax) : (029) 5241605, (P.C) : 710061 (Address) : 18 Changan zhong Road, Xian, Shanxi, China. (Division) : Foreign Student Office.

168. (Institutions) : Hebei Normal University, (Telephone) : (0311) 6049413 6049941-86228 (Fax) : (0311) 6049413, (P.C) : 050016, (Address) : Yuhua Zhong Road, Shijia Ehuang, Hebei, China. (Division) : Foreign Student Office.

169. (Institutions) : Chinese Medicine College of Hebei Medical University (Telephone) : (0311) 3831950 3031950, (Fax) : (0311) 3831950 (P.C) : 050091, (Address) : Xinxishi South Road, Shijia Zhuang, Hebei, China. (Division) : Foreign Student Office.

170. (Institutions) : Heilongjiang University, (Telephone) : (0451) 6662786 (Fax) : (0451) 6665470, (P.C) : 150080, (Address) : XueFu Road, NanGang District, HaErBin, HeilLongJiang, China. (Division) : Foreign Student Office.

171. (Institutions) : Heilongjiang Institute of Commerce, (Telephone) : (0451) 4603227 (Fax) : (0451) 4601086, (P.C) : 150076, (Address) : TongDa street, DaoLi District, HaErBin, HeiLongJiang, China. (Division) : Foreign Student Office.

172. (Institutions) : Heilongjiang College of Traditional Chinese Medicine (Telephone) : (0451) 2112786, (Fax) : (0451) 2112786, (P.C) : 150040 (Address) : HePing Road, Dongli District, HaErBin, HeiLongJiang, China. (Division) : Foreign Student Office.

173. (Institutions) : Haerbin Normal University, (Telephone) : (0451) 6315015 (Fax) : (0451) 6305382, (P.C) : 150080, (Address) : Hexing Road, NanGang District, HaErBin, Hei Long Jiang, China.(Division) : Foreign Student Office.

174. (Institutions) : Haerbin University of Technology, (Telephone) : (0451) 6416601 (Fax) : (0451) 6416602, (P.C) : 150001, (Address) : 92 92 XiDaZhi Street, HaErBin,

HeiLongJiang, China. (Division) : Foreign Student Office.

175. (Institutions) : Haerbin University of Science and Technology (Telephone) : (0451) 6661081-6352 6682604, (Fax) : (0451) 6682604, (P.C) : 150080 (Address) : XueFu Road, NanGang District, HaErBin, HeiLongJiang, China. (Division) : Foreign Student Office.

176. (Institutions) : Anhui Normal University, (Telephone) : (0553) 3869406 (7) (Fax) : (0553) 3834817, (P.C) : 241000, (Address) : 1 Renmin Road, Wuhu, AnHui, China. (Division) : Foreign Student Office.

177. (Institutions) : Anhui University, (Telephone) : (0551) 5112832, (Fax) : (0551) 5112999 (P.C) : 230039, (Address) : 3 Feixi Road, HeFei AnHui, China. (Division) : Foreign Student Office.

178. (Institutions) : University of Science and Technology of China (Telephone) : (0551) 3602847, (Fax) : (0551) 3632579, (P.C) : 230026 (Address) : 96 JinZhai road, HeFei AnHui, China.(Division) : Foreign Student Office.

179. (Institutions) : Anhui College of Traditional Chinese Medicine (Telephone) : (0551)2816548, (Fax) : (0551) 2816548, (P.C) : 230038, (Address) : Meishan Road, HeFei AnHui, China.(Division) : Foreign Student Office.

180. (Institutions) : Hunan University, (Telephone) : (0731) 8824287, (Fax) : (0731) 8824287 (P.C) : 410082, (Address) : Yuelushen, Changsha, HuNan, China. (Division) : Foreign Student Office.

181. (Institutions) : Hunan Ormal University, (Telephone) : (0731) 8883131 (Fax) : (0731) 8851226, (P.C) : 410081, (Address) : ErliBan Hexi, Changsha, HuNan, China. (Division) : Foreign Student Office.

182. (Institutions) : Hunan College of Traditional Chinese Medicine (Telephone) : (0731) 5556660-287, (Fax) : (0731) 5532948, (P.C) : 410007 (Address) : 107 Shaoshan Road, Changsha, HuNan, China. (Division) : Foreign Student Office.

183. (Institutions) : Central South University of Technology (Telephone) : (0731) 8879256, (Fax) : (0731) 8826136 , (P.C) : 410083 (Address) : Lushan South Road, Changsha, HuNan, China. (Division) : Foreign Student Office.

184. (Institutions) : Hunan Medical University, (Telephone) : (0731) 4474411-2824 (Fax) : (0731) 4471339, (P.C) : 410078, (Address) : 22 Beizhan Road, Changsha, HuNan, China. (Division) : Foreign Student Office.

185. (Institutions) : Xiangtan University, (Telephone) : (0732) 8292130, (Fax) : (0731) 8292282, (P.C) : 411105, (Address) : Yang Gu Ku Tang, XiangTan, HuNan, China. (Division) : Foreign Student Office.

186. (Institutions) : Jiangxi College of Traditional Chinese Medicine (Telephone) : (0791) 6824015-223, (Fax) : (0791) 6820664, (P.C) : 330006 (Address) : 20 Yang Min Road, NanChang, JiangXi, China. (Division) : Foreign Student Office.

187. (Institutions) : Yunnan University (Telephone) : (0871) 5148513, (Fax) : (0871) 5153832, (P.C) : 650091 (Address) : 52 Cuihu North Road, KunMing, YunNan, China. (Division) : Foreign Student Office.

188. (Institutions) : Yunnan Institute for Nationalities, (Telephone) : (0871) 5154308 (Fax) : (0871) 5154308, (P.C) : 650031, (Address) : LianHua Chi, Kun Min, YunNan, China. (Division) : Foreign Student Office.

189. (Institutions) : Yunnan Normal University , (Telephone) : (0871) 5322930-6149 (Fax) : (0871) 5323804, (P.C) : 650092, (Address) : 58 Huan Cheng North Road, KunMin, YunNan, China. (Division) : Foreign Student Office.

190. (Institutions) : Shanxi University, (Telephone) : (0351) 7010333, (Fax) : (0351) 7040981
(P.C) : 030006, (Address) : WuCheng Road, TaiYuan, shanXi, China.
(Division) : Foreign Student Office.

191 (Institutions) : Zhengzhou University, (Telephone) : (0371) 7970475, (Fax) : (0371) 7070475
(P.C) : 450052, (Address) : Da Xue Road, Zhen Zhou, HeNan, China.
(Division) : Foreign Student Office.

192. (Institutions) : Heinan College of Traditional Chinese Medicine
(Telephone) : (0371) 5956348-3088 5962930, (Fax) : (0371) 595565C, (P.C) : 450003
(Address) : 1 Jin Shui Road, Zhon Zhou, HeNan, China.
(Division) : Foreign Student Office.

193. (Institutions) : Henan University, (Telephone) : (0378) 5958833 5952311, (Fax) : (0378) 5951029, (P.C) : 475001, (Address) : 85 MingLun Street, KaiFeng, HeNan, China.
(Division) : Foreign Student Office.

194. (Institutions) : Lanzhou University, (Telephone) : (0931) 8822991-3642, (Fax) : (0931) 8618777, (P.C) : 730000, (Address) : 216 Tianshui Road, Lan Zhou, GanSu, China.
(Division) : Foreign Student Office.

195. (Institutions) : Northwest Normal University, (Telephone) : (0931) 7666821-624
(Fax) : (0931) 7668159, (P.C) : 730070, (Address) : 95 AnNing East Road, LanZhou, GanSu, China. (Division) : Foreign Student Office.

196. (Institutions) : Inter Mongolia Normal University
(Telephone) : (0471) 4964444-2415, (Fax) : (0471) 4964887, (P.C) : 010022
(Address) : Xin Cheng Nan MenWai, HuHeHaote. Lnter Mongolia, China.
(Division) : Foreign Student Office.

197. (Institutions) : Inter Mongolia University, (Telephone) : (0471) 4954433-2278
(Fax) : (0471) 4951761, (P.C) : 010021,(Address) : Xin Cheng District, HuHeHaoTe, Inter Mongolia, China. (Division) : Foreign Student Office.

198. (Institutions) : Xinjiang Normal University, (Telephone) : (0991) 4812513, (P.C) : 830053
(Address) : XinQu Road, WuluMuQi, XinJiang, China.
(Division) : Foreign Student Office.

199. (Institutions) : Xinjiang University, (Telephone) : (0991) 2862753-2221, (Fax) : (0991) 286006
(P.C) : 830046, (Address) : Sheng Li Road, WuLuMuQi, XinJiang, China.
(Division) : Foreign Student Office.

For details on Chinese education contact:
Educational Office, Chinese Embassy in India, 50-D, Shantipath
Chanakyapuri New Delhi- 110021

Czech Republic

Faculty of Philosophy ***Filozofická fakulta***
Dean's Office : nám. J. Palacha 2, 116 38 Praha 1,
Phone : 422/24 81 11 26, Fax : 422/24 81 21 66
Dean : Doc. PhDr. Frantisek Vrhel, Cse.
Faculty of Law **Právnická fakulta**
Dean's Office : nám. Curieových 7, 116 40 Praha 1, Phone : 422/24 81 26 79
Fax : 422/24 81 04 72, Dean : Prof. JUDr. Dusan Hendrych, CSc.
Faculty of Education
Pedagogická Fakulta
Dean's Office : M.D. Rettigové 4, 116 39 Praha 1-Nové Mesto,
Phone : 422/24 91 56 17-25,Fax : 422/29 02 25, Dean : Prof. PhDr.Zdenek Helus, DrSc.
Faculty of Social Sciences
Fakulta sociálních ved
Dean's Office : Smetanovo nábr. 6, 110 01 Praha 1, Phone : 422/24 81 08 04,
Fax : 422/24 81 09 87, Dean : Prof. PhDr. Miloslav Petrusek, CSc.
THE FIRST FACULTY OF MEDICINE
1. Lékarská fakulta
Dean's Office : Katerinská 32, 121 08 Praha 2, Phone : 422/24 91 03 05
Fax : 422/24 91 54 13, Dean : Doc. MUDr. Petr Hach, CSc.
The Second Faculty of Medicine
2. Lékarská fakulta
Dean's Office : V úvalu 84, 150 18 Praha 5-Motol, Phone : 422/24 43 11 11,
Fax : 422/24 43 64 20, Dean : Prof. MUDr. Josef Koutecký, DrSc.
The Third Faculty of Medicine
3. Lékarská fakulta
Dean's Office : Ruská 87, 100 00 Praha 10, Phone : 422/67 10 21 11
Fax : 422/67 31 18 12, Dean : Prof. MUDr. Cyril Höschi, DrSc.
Faculty of Medicine in Plzen
Lékarská fakulta Plzen
Dean's Office : Husova 13, 306 05 Plzen Phone : 4219/722 12 00, Fax : 4219/722 14 60
Dean : Prof. MUDr. Jirí Valenta, DrSc.
Faculty of Medicine in Hradec Královè
Lèkarská fakulta Hradec Královè
Dean's Office : Simkova 870, 500 38 Hradec Královè,
Phone : 4249/25 701-8, 25 341-3, Fax : 4249/26 595
Dean : Doc. MUDr. Karel Barták, CSc.
Faculty of Pharmacy in Hradec Králové
Farmaceuticka fakulta
Dean's Office : Heyrovského 1203, 501 65 Hradec Králové.
Phone : 4249/523 50 21, Fax : 4249/521 00 02

Dean : Doc. RNDr. Ludek Jahodár, CSc.

Faculty of Natural Sciences

Prírodovedecká fakulta

Dean's Office : Albertov 6, 128 43 Praha 2, Phone : 422/24 91 54 72, Fax : 422/29 60 84

Dean : Prof. RNDr. Petr Cepek, CSc.

Faculty of Mathematics and Physics

Matematicko-fyzikáiní fakulta

Dean's Office : Ke Karlovu 3, 121 16 Praha 2, Phone : 422/21 91 11 11, Fax : 422/29 92 72, Dean : Prof. RNDr. Bedrich Sedlák, DrSc.

Faculty of Physical Education and Sport

Fakulta telesné výchovy a sportu

Dean's Office : José Martího 31, 162 52 Praha 6-Veleslavin, Phone : 422/36 99 41-9, Fax : 422/36 40 75 Dean : Doc. PhDr. Josef Dovalil, CSc.

Faculty of Catholic Theology

Katolicka teologická fakulta

Dean's Office : Thákurova 3/676, 160 00 Praha 6-Dejvice Phone :422/33 15 111, Fax : 422/331 52 15,Dean : Prof. ThDr. Václav Wolf

Faculty of Protestant Theology

Evangelická teologická fakulta

Dean's Office : Jungmannova 9, 115 55 Praha 1, Phone : 422/24 22 14 25 Fax : 422/24 22 65 66, Dean : Prof. ThDr. Ing. Jakub Trojan

Faculty of Hussite Theology

Husitská teologická fakulta

Dean's Office : Wuchterlova 5, 160 00 Praha 6, Phone : 422/24 31 13 95 Fax : 422/34 27 54, Dean : Prof. ThDr. Zdenek Kucera

MASARYK UNIVERSITY

Masarykova Univerzita

Rector's Office : Zerotínovo nám. 9, 601 77 Brno, Phone: 425/42 128 111 Fax : 425/42 128 300, E-mail : schmidt@muni.cz

Rector : Prof. RNDr. Eduard Schmidt, CSc.

Faculty of Medicine

Lékarská fakulta

Dean's Office : Komenského nám, 2, 662 43 Brno, Phone : 425/42 12 61 11 Fax : 425/42 21 39 96, Dean : Prof. MUDr. Josef Bilder, CSc.

Faculty of Science

Prírodovedecká fakulta

Dean's Office : Kotlárská 2, 611 37 Brno, Phone : 425/41 12 91 11 Fax : 425/41 21 12 14, Dean : Prof. RNDr. Jaroslav Jonas, CSc.

Faculty of Philosophy

Filozofická fakulta

Dean's Office : Arne Nováka 1, 660 88 Brno, Phone : 425/41 32 12 58 Fax : 425/41 21 12 41, Dean : Prof. PhDr. Jaroslav Mezník, CSc.

Faculty of Education

Pedagogická fakulta

Dean's Office : Porící 7, 603 00 Brno, Phone : 425/43 32 12 16, 43 21 00 87-9 Fax : 425/43 21 11 03, Dean : Doc. RNDr. Josef Janás, CSc.

Faculty of Law
Právnická fakulta
Dean's Office : Veverí 70, 611 80 Brno,Phone : 425/41 32 12 97,
Fax : 425/41 21 31 62, Dean : Doc. JUDr. Josef Bejcek, CSc.
Faculty of Economics and Administration
Fakulta ekonomicko správaní
Dean's Office : Zeiný trh 2/3, 657 90 Brno, Phone : 425/42 21 59 18
Fax : 425/42 21 48 69, Dean : Doc.Ing. Ladislav Blazek, CSc.
Faculty of Informatics
Fakulta Informatiky
Dean's Office : Buresova 20, 602 00 Brno, Phone : 425/41 32 12 37
Fax : 425/41 21 27 47, Dean : Doc. RNDr. Jirí Zlatuska, CSc.
PALACKÝ UNIVERSITY
Universita Palackého
Dean's Office : Krizkovského 8, 771 47 Olomouc, Phone : 4268/5508 111,
Fax : 4268/264 76, E-mail : Jarab@risc.Upol.cz, Dean : Prof. PhDr. Josef Jarab, CSc.
Faculty of Medicine
Lékarská fakulta
Dean's Office : tr. Svobody 8, 771 26 Olomouc, Phone : 4268/5223 061-3,
Fax : 4268/52 23 907, Dean : Doc. MUDr. et PhDr. Jana Macáková, CSc.
Faculty of Natural Sciences
Prírodovedecká fakulta
Dean's Office : tr. Svobody 26, 771 46 Olomouc, Phone : 4268/522 24 51-6
Fax : 4268/522 57 37, Dean : Doc. RNDr. Lubomir Dvorák, CSc.
Faculty of Philosophy
Filozofická Fakulta
Dean's Office : Krízkovského 10, 771 80 Olomouc, Phone : 4268/55 08 111
Fax : 4268/522 51 48, Dean : Doc. PhDr. Jindrich Schulz, CSc.
Faculty of Education
Pedagogická Fakulta
Dean's Office : Zizkovo nám, 5, 771 40 Olomouc
Phone : 4268/299 51-5, 189 15-8, Fax : 4268/284 55
Dean : Doe. Phdr. Frantisek Mexijorák, CSc.
Faculty of Law
Prácnická Fakulta
Dean's Office : tr. 17. Listopadu 6,8, 771 47 Olomouc
Phone : 4268/522 41 41-3 295 12, Fax : 4268/522 35 37
Dean : Doc. JUDr. Miroslav Ulberda
Faculty of Physical Education
Fakulta telesné Kultury
Dean's Office : tr. Míru 115, 771 47 Olomouc-Neredín,
Phone : 4268/5412 173 ; Fax : 4268/5412 899
Dean : Prof. PhDr. Bohuslav Hodan, CSc.
Faculty of Theology of St. Cyril And St. Methodius
Cyrilometodejská teologická Fakulta
Dean's Office : Univerzitní 22, 771 00 Olomouc, Phone : 4268/263 51-5
Fax : 4268/52 241 74, Dean : Doc PhDr. Ladisiav Tichý

UNIVERSITY OF SOUTH BOHEMIA
JIHOCESKÁ UNIVERZITA
Rector's office : Branisovská 31, 370 05 Ceské Budejovice,
Phone : 4238/817, Fax : 4238/402 20, E-mail : divisek@jcu.cz
Rector : Doc. PhDr. Jirí Divísek, Csc.

Faculty of Education
Pedagogická Fakulta
Dean's Office : Jeronýmova 10, 371 15 Ceské Budejovice, Phone : 4238/731 21 87
Fax : 4238/731 21 94, Dean : Prof. RNDr. Miroslav Papácek, CSc.

Faculty of Agriculture
Zemedelská Fakulta
Dean's Office : Studentská 13, 370m05 Ceské Budejovice
Phone : 4238/770 39 11, Fax : 4238/403 01
Dean : Prof. Ing. Frantisek Strelecek, CSc.

Faculty of Management
Fakulta Managementu
Dean's Office : Jarosovská 1117/ll, 377 01 Jindrichüv Hradec,
Phone : 42331/240 03, Fax : 42331/249 77,
Dean : Doc. Ing. Zdenek Zemlicka, CSc.

Faculty of Biological Sciences
Biologická Fakulta
Dean's Office : Branisovská 31, 370 05 Ceské Budejovice,
Phone : 4238/817,
Fax : 4238/459 85
Dean : Doc. RNDr. Pavel Blazka, CSc.

Faculty of Health and Social Care
Zdravontne sociální Fakulta
Dean's Office : Knezská 35, 370 01 Ceské Budejovice, Phone : 4238/539 10
Fax : 4238/539 10, Dean : Doc. PhDr. Jana Semberová, CSc.

Faculty of Theology
Theologická Fakulta
Dean's Office : Kanovnická 22, 370 01 Ceské Budejovice,
Phone : 4238/731 16 83, Fax : 4238/731 16 80, Dean : Prof. ThDr. Ing. Frantisek Kopecký

UNIVERSITY OF WEST BOHEMIA IN PILSEN
ZÁPADOCESKÁ UNIVERZITA
Rector's office : Americká 42, 306 14 Plzen, Phone : 4219/72 35 551-5, 72 35 801-5,
Fax : 4219/722 00 19,E-mail : holenda@zeus. zcu.cz
Rector : Doc. RNDr. Jirí Holenda, CSc.

Faculty of Mechanical Engineering
Fakulta stronjní
Dean's Office : Univerzitní ul., 306 14 Plezen, Phone : 4219/21 71 637
Fax : 4219/21 17 47, Dean : Prof. Ing. Jan Skopek, CSc.

Faculty of Electrical Engineering
Fakulta elektrotechnická
Dean's Office : Sady Petatricátníkü 14, 306 14 Plezen, Phone : 4219/723 74 61-5
Fax : 4219/722 56 85, Dean : Doc. Ing. Vlastimil Skocil, CSc.

Faculty of Applied Sciences
Fakulta aplikovaných ved
Dean's Office : Univerzitní 22, 306 14 Plezen, Phone : 4219/2˙ 71 637
Fax : 4219/27 17 47, Dean : Prof. RNDr. Stanislav Míka, CSc.
Faculty of Economics
Fakulta ekonomická
Dean's Office : Hradební 22, 350 11 Cheb, Phone : 42166/234 51-2
Fax : 42166/233 95, Dean : Doc. Ing. Jirí Beck, CSc.
Faculty of Law
Fakulta právnická
Dean's Office : Sady Petricátnikü 27, 306 14 Plzen, Phone : 4219/722 08 79
Fax : 4219/722 76 02, Dean : JUDr. Vladimír Balas
Faculty of Education
FakultaPedagogická
Dean's Office : Veleslavínova 42, 306 19 Plzen
Phone : 4219/72 379 51-5,
Fax : 4219/72 355 22
Dean : Doc. RNDr. Jaroslav Drábek, CSc.
J.E. PURKYNE UNIVERSITY
Universita J.E. Purkyne
Rector's Office : Horení 13, 400 11 Usti nad Labem,
Phone : 4247/452 41-2, 450 41-2, 450 29-30, Fax : 4247/430 10
Rector : Prof. RNDr. Viastimil Novobilský, CSc.
Faculty of Education
Fakulta pedagogická
Dean's Office : Ceské miádeze 8, 400 96 Ústí nad Lebem,
Phone : 4247/452 41-2, 450 29-30, Fax : 4247/430 10
Dean : Prof. PhDr. Doubrava Moidanová, CSc.
Faculty of Social Studies and Economics
Fakulta sociánine ekonomická
Dean's Office : Lipová ul. 8, 400 96 Ústí nad Labem,
Phone : 4247/643 61, Fax : 4247/643 61, Dean : Doc. Ing. Antonin Pesek, CSc.
Faculty of Environmental Studies
Fakulta Zivotního prostredí
Dean's Office : Na Okraji 1001, 400 96 Ústi nad Labem, Phone : 4247/560 14 01,
Fax : 4247/560 15 87, Dean : Ing. Jaroslav Zahálka, CSc.
Institute of Fine Arts Culture
Institut Výtvarné kultury
Dean's Office : Velká hradební 13, 400 01 Ústi nad Labem
Phone : 4247/52 10 350, Fax : 4247/52 12 053
OSTRAVA UNIVERSITY
Ostravská Univerzita
Rector's Office : Dvorákova 7, 701 03 Ostrova, Phone : 4269/622 60 66,
Fax : 4269/622 28 03, E-mail : hubacek@oudec.osu.cz
Rector : Prof. RNDr. Jirí Mockor, DrSc.
Faculty of Education
Fakulta pedagogická
Dean's Office : Dvorákova 7, 701 03 Ostrava,

Phone : 4269/622 60 66, Fax : 4269/622 28 03, Dean : Doc. Rudolf Bernatík

Faculty of Philosophy

Fakulta filozofická

Dean's Office : Dvorákova 7, 701 03 Ostrava, 1
Phone : 4269/622 60 66, Fax : 4269/622 28 03, Dean : Doc. PhDr. Eva Mrhacová, CSc.

Faculty of Natural Sciences

Fakulta prírodovedecká

Dean's Office : Bratova Dvorákova 7, 701 03 Ostrava,
Phone : 4269/622 28 08, Fax : 4269/622 28 03, Dean : Doc. RNDr. Kvetoslav Burian, CSc.

Faculty of Health and Social Care

Fakulta zdravotne sociální

Dean's Office : tr. 17. listopadu 1790, 708 52 Ostrava-Poruba,
Phone : 4269/698 22 61, Fax : 4269/698 30 70, Dean : Doc. MuDr. Jaroslav Simicek, CSc.

SILESIAN UNIVERSITY

Slezská Univerzita

Rector's office : Bezrucovo nám 13, 746 01 Opava, Phone : 42653/454 111
Fax : 42653/21 80 19, E-mail : martin. Tcernohorsky@ descu.fpf.slu.cz
Rector : Prof. RNDr. Martin Cernohorský, CSc.

Faculty of Philosophy And Science

Filozoficko-prírodovedecká Fakulta

Dean's Office : Bezrucovo nám, 13, 746 01 Opava,
Phone : 42653/454 111, Fax : 42653/21 69 48, Dean : Doc. PhDr. Jaroslav Bakala, CSc.

Faculty of Business

Obchodne podnikatelská Fakulta

Dean's Office : Univerzitní nám. 76, 733 40 Karviná, Phone : 426993/639 81 11,
Fax : 426993/631 20 69, Dean : Doc. PhDr. Stanislav Poloucek, CSc.

UNIVERSITY OF VETERINARY AND PHARMACEUTICAL SCIENCES

Veterinární a Farmaceutická Univerzita

Rector's Office : Palaekého 1-3, 612 42 brno, Phone : 425/41 32 11 07,
Fax : 425/41 21 11 51, E-mail : zima@.csbrmu 11.bitnet
Rector : Prof. RNDr. Stanislav Zima, DrSc.

Faculty of Veterinary Medicine

Fakulta veterinárního lékarství

Dean's Office : Palackého 1-3, 612 42 Brno, Phone : 425/41 32 11 07
Fax : 425/41 21 11 51, Dean : Doc. MVDr. RNDr. Petr Horín, CSc.

Faculty of Veterinary Hygiene and Ecology

Fakulta veterinární hygieny a ekologie

Dean's Office : Palackého 1-3, 612 42 Brno, Phone : 425/41 32 11 07
Fax : 425/41 21 11 51, Dean : Doc. MVDr. Vladimír Veeerek, CSc.

Faculty of Pharmacy

Fakulta farmaceutická

Dean's Office : Palackého 1-3, 612 42 Brno, Phone : 425/41 32 11 07
Fax : 425/41 21 11 51, Dean : Prof. RNDr. Václav Suchý, DrSc.

UNIVERSITY OF ECONOMICS

Vysoká Skola Ekonomická

Rector's Office : nám. W. Churchilla 4, 130 67 Praha 3-Zizkov
Phone : 422/24 09 51 11, Fax : 422/24 22 06 57, E-mail : zima@.csbrmu 11.bitnet
Rector : Prof. Ing. Jan Seger, CSc.

Faculty of Economics and Public Administration
Fakulta národohospodárská
Dean's Office : nám. W. Churchilla 4, 130 67 Praha 3, Phone : 422/24 09 51 11
Fax : 422/24 22 06 57, Dean : Doc. Ing. Milan Zák, CSc.
Faculty of Business Administration
Fakulta podnikohospodarska
Dean's Office : nám. W. Churchilla 4, 130 67 Praha 3, Phone : 422/24 09 51 11
Fax : 422/24 22 06 57, Dean : Prof. Radim Vicek, CSc.
Faculty of International Relations
Fakulta mezinárodních vztahü
Dean's Office : nám. W. Churchilla 4, 130 67 Praha 3, Phone : 422/24 09 51 11
Fax : 422/24 22 06 57, Dean : Prof. Jirí Jindra, CSc.
Faculty of Finance and Accounting
Fakulta financí a úcetnictví
Dean's Office : nám. W. Churchilla 4, 130 67 Praha 3, Phone : 422/24 09 51 11
Fax : 422/24 22 06 57, Dean : Doc. Ing. Stępánka Nováková, CSc.
Faculty of Computer Science and Statistics
Fakulta informatiky a statistiky
Dean's Office : nám. W. Churchilla 4, 130 67 Praha 3, Phone : 422/24 09 51 11
Fax : 422/24 22 06 57, Dean : Doc. RNDr. Jan Pelikán, CSc.
HIGHER SCHOOL OF EDUCATION
Vysoká Skola Pedagogická
Rector's Office : Vita Nejediého 573, 500 03 Hradec Králové 3, Phone : 049/420 26
Fax : 425 19, E-mail : Jipa@ earn.cvut.cz, Rector : Doc. PhDr. Oldrich Richterek, CSc.
Faculty of Education
Pedagogická Fakulta
Dean's Office : Nám, Svobody 301, Hradec Králové 2,
Post Address : V. Nejediého 573, 500 03 Hradec Králové 3
Phone : 049/252 26, Fax : 257 85
Dean : Doc. RNDr. PhDr. Zdenek Pülpán, CSc.
Faculty of Management and Information Technology
Fakulta rízení a informacní technologie
Dean's Office : Nám, Svobody 301, Hradec Králové 2,
Post Address : V. Nejediého 573, 500 03 Hradec Králové 3, Phone : 049/252 26
Fax : 257 85, Dean : Doc. RNDr. Jaroslava Mikulecká, CSc.
CZECH TECHNICAL UNIVERSITY
Ceské Vysoké Ucení Technické
Rector's office : Zikova 4, 166 35 Praha 6, Phone : 422/24 35 11 11
Fax: 422/311 73 61, E-mail : hanzl @ vcnet. vc.cvut.cz
Rector : Prof. Ing. Stanislav Hanzl, CSc.
Faculty of Civil Engineering
Fakulta stavební
Dean's Office : Thákurova 7, 166 29 Praha 6, Phone : 422/24 35 11 11
Fax : 422/24 35 48 73
Dean : Prof. Ing. Jirí Witzany, DrSc.
Faculty of Mechanical Engineering
Fakulta Strojní
Dean's Office : Technická 4, 166 07 Praha 6, Phone : 422/24 35 11 11
Fax : 422/243 10 292, Dean : Prof. Ing. Petr Zuna, CSc.

Faculty of Electrical Engineering
Fakulta elektrotechnická
Dean's Office : Technická 2, 166 27 Praha 6, Phone : 422/24 35 11 11
Fax : 422/243 10 784, Dean : Doc. Ing. Jan Uhlír, CSc.
Faculty of Nuclear Sciences and Physical Engineering
Fakulta Jaderná a fyzikálne inzenýrská
Dean's Office : Brehová 7, 115 19 Praha 1-St. Mesto
Phone : 422/23 15 212, 23 15 256, Fax : 422/232 08 61
Dean : Doc. Ing. Ladislav Musílek, CSc.
Faculty of Transport
Fakulta dopravní
Dean's Office : Konviktská 22, 110 00 Praha 1, Phone : 422/24 22 92 01
Fax : 422/24 22 92 01, Dean : Doc. Ing. Petr Moos, CSc.
Faculty of Architecture
Fakulta Architektury
Dean's Office : Thákurova 7, 166 34 Praha 6, Phone : 422/24 35 11 11
Fax : 422/243 10 573, Dean : Prof. Ing. Arch. Vladimír Slapeta, DrSc.
Masaryk Institute of Advanced Study
Masaniküv ústav vyssích studií
Institute Office : Konviktská 20, 110 00 Praha 1
Phone : (422) 24 21 33 69, Fax : 422/24 22 17 22
TECHNICAL UNIVERSITY BRNO
Vysoké Ucení Technické
Rector's Office : Kounicova 67 a, 601 90 Brno, Phone : 425/41125 111
Fax : 41 21 13 09, E-mail : vavrin@ro.vutbr.cz
Rector : Prof. Ing. Alois Vavrom DrSc
Faculty of Civil Engineering
Fakulta stavební
Dean's Office : Veverí 95, 662 37 Brno, Phone : 425/7261 111
Fax : 425/74 51 47, Dean : Doc. Ing. Alois Materna, CSc.
Faculty of Mechanical Engineering
Fakulta strojní
Dean's Office : Technická 2, 616 69 Brno, Phone : 425/4114 1111
Fax : 425/41 21 19 94, Dean : Prof. RNDr. Ing. Jan Vrbka, DrSc.
Faculty of Electrical Engineering and Computer Science
Fakulta elektrotechniky a informatiky
Dean's Office : Údolní 53, 602 00 Brno, Phone : 425/43 167 111
Fax : 425/43 21 12 05, Dean : Doc. Ing. Jirí Kazelle, CSc.
Faculty of Architecture
Fakulta architektury
Dean's Office : Porící 5, 662 83 Brno, Phone : 425/421 42 111
Fax : 4267/42 14 21 25, Dean : Doc. Ing. arch. Alois Nový, CSc.
Faculty of Technology
Fakulta technologická Zlín
Dean's Office : nám. T.G. Masaryka 275, 762 72 Zlín,Phone : 4267/282 41-8
Fax : 4267/269 84, Dean : Doc. Ing. Petr Sáha, CSc.
Faculty of Business and Management
Fakulta podnikatelská
Dean's Office : Technická 2, 616 69 Brno, Phone :425/41 14 11 11

Fax : 425/41 21 14 10, Dean : Doc. Ing. Miloslav Kerkovský, CSc.

Faculty of Chemistry
Fakulta Chemická
Dean's Office : Veslarská 230, 637 00 Brno, Phone : 425/43 32 12 95
Fax : 425/43 21 11 01, Dean : Prof. Ing. Lubomír Lapcik, DrSc.

Faculty of Fine Arts
Fakulta výrvarných umení
Dean's Office : Rybárská 13/15, 603 00 Brno, Phone : 425/41 21 72 82
Fax : 425/41 21 72 82, Dean : Prof. ak. Sochar Vladimír Preclík

UNIVERSITY OF CHEMICAL TECHNOLOGY
Vysoká Skola Chemicko-Technologická
Rector's Office : Technická 5, 166 28 Praha 6, Phone : 422/24 31 09 56
Fax : 422/243 11 082, E-mail : stibor@vshct. cz, Rector : Doc. Ing. Josef Koubek, CSc.

Faculty of Chemical Technology
Fakulta Chemické technologie
Dean's Office : Technická 5, 166 28 Praha 6,
Phone : 422/332 37 68, Fax : 522/ 24 31 04-22, Dean : Prof. Ing. Libor Cervený, DrSc.

Faculty of Food and Biochemical Technology
Fakulta potravinárské a biochemické technologie
Dean's Office : Technická 5, 166 28 Praha 6, Phone : 422/332 38 90
Fax : 422/311 99 90, Dean : Prof. Ing. Pavel Kadlec, DrSc.

Faculty of Environmental Protection Technology
Fakulta technologie ochrany Prostredí
Dean's Office : Technická 5, 166 28 Praha 6, Phone : 422/332 32 76
Fax : 422/311 52 16, Dean : Doc. Ing. Gustav Sebor, CSc.

Faculty of Chemical Engineering
Fakulta chemicko-inzenýrská
Dean's Office : Technická 5, 166 28 Praha 6, Phone : 422/332 38 91
Fax : 422/311 36 29, Dean : Prof. Ing. Oskar Schmidt, CSc.

UNIVERSITY OF PARDUBICE
Univerzita Pardubice
Rector's Office : nám Cs legií 925, 532 10 Pardubice, Phone : 4240/582 111
Fax : 4240/51 41 01, E-mail : cpvjc@ earn. cz
Rector : Prof. Ing. Ladislav Kudlácek, CSc.

Faculty of Chemical Technology
Fakulta chemicko-technologická
Dean's Office : nám, Cs. legií 925, 532 10 Pardubice, Phone : 4240/58 23 23
Fax : 4240/54 41 01, Dean : Prof. Ing. Jaromír Snuparek, DrSc.

Faculty of Economics and Administration
Fakulta ekonomicko-správní
Dean's Office : Studentská ul. 84, 530 09 Pardubice-Polabiny, Phone : 4240/474 60
Fax : 4240/476 47, Dean : Doc. Ing. Radim Roudný, CSc.

Jan Perner Faculty of Transport
Dopravní Fakulta Jana Pernera
Dean's Office : Studentská 84, 530 09 Pardubice-Polabiny, Phone : 4240/424 61-8
Fax : 4240/484 00, Dean : Prof. Ing. Hynek Sertier, DrSc.

Institute of Foreign Languages
Ústav cizích jazykü
Institute Office : Studentská 84, 530 09 Pardubice, Phone : 4240/42 980, 47 461

Fax : 4240/48 400

TECHNICAL UNIVERSITY OF MINING AND METALLURGY

Vysoká Skola Bánská - Technická Univerzita Ostrava

Rector's Office : tr. 17. listopadu 15, 708 33 Ostrava-Poruba, Phone : 4269/699 11 11
Fax : 4269/691 85 07, E-mail : tomas.cermak@ vsb.cz
Rector : Prof. Ing. Tomás Cermák, CSc.

Faculty of Mining and Geology

Hornicko-geologická Fakulta

Dean's Office : tr. 17. listopadu 15, 708 33 Ostrava, Phone : 4269/699 11 11
Fax : 4269/691 85 89, Dean : Prof. Ing. Ctirad Schejbal, CSc.

Faculty of Metallurgy and Materials Engineering

Fakulta metalurgie a materiálového inzenýrství

Dean's Office : tr. 17. listopadu 15, 708 33 Ostrava-Poruba
Phone : 4269/699 11 11, Fax : 4269/691 85 92
Dean : Prof. Ing. Pe. Jelínek, CSc.

Faculty of Mechanical Engineering

Fakulta strojní

Dean's Office : tr. 17. listopadu 15, 708 33 Ostrava-Poruba
Phone : 4269/699 11 11
Fax : 4269/691 64 90
Dean : Doc. Ing. Pavel Noskieve, CSc.

Faculty of Electrical Engineering and Informatic

Fakulta elektrotechniky a informatiky

Dean's Office : tr. 17. listopadu 15, 708 33 Ostrava- Poruba, Phone : 4269/699 11 11
Fax : 4269/691 96 97, Dean : Prof. Ing. Pavel Santarius, CSc.

Faculty of Economics

Fakulta ekonomická

Dean's Office : Sokolská 33, 701 21 Ostrava 1, Phone : 4269/622 57 44
Fax : 4269/622 28 41, Dean : Prof. Ing. Miroslav Nejezchieba, CSc.

TECHNICAL UNIVERSITY LIBEREC

Technická Univerzita Liberec

Rector's office : Hálkova 6, 461 17 Liberec, Phone : 4248/254 41-5
Fax : 4248/233 17, Rector : Prof. Ing. Zdenek Kovár, CSc.

Faculty of Mechanical Engineering

Fakulta strojní

Dean's Office : Hálkova 6, 461 17 Liberec, Phone : 4248/254 41-5
Fax : 4248/23 317, Dean : Prof. Ing. Jaroslav Exner, CSc.

Faculty of Textile Engineering

Fakulta Textilní

Dean's Office : Hálkova 6, 461 17 Liberec, Phone : 4248/254 41
Fax : 4248/273 83, Dean : Prof. Ing. Jirí Militký, CSc.

Faculty of Education

Pedagogická Fakulta

Dean's Office : Voronezská 1329/13, 460 01 Liberec, Phone : 4248/5227 111
Fax : 4248/5227 332, Dean : Doc. RNDr. Vaclav Pecina, CSc.

Faculty of Economics

Hospodárská Fakulta

Dean's Office : Voronezská 1329/13, 460 01 Liberec, Phone : 4248/5227 111

Fax : 4248/5100 865, Dean : Doc. Ing. Jaroslav Jágr

Faculty of Architecture

Fakulta architektury

Dean's Office : Hálkova 6, 461 17 Liberec, Phone : 4248/254 41-5, Fax : 4248/233 17
Dean : Doc. Ing. arch. akad. arch. Jirí Suchomel

Faculty of Mechanotronics and Interdisciplinary Engineer Studies

Fakulta mechatroniky a mezioborových inzenýrských studií

Dean's Office : Hálkova 6, 461 17 Liberec, Phone : 4248/254 41-5, Fax : 4248/233 17
Dean : Prof. Ing. Jirí Zelenka, DrSc.

CZECH UNIVERSITY OF AGRICULTURE

Ceská Zemedelská Univerzita

Rector's Office : Kamýcká ul. 129, 165 21 Praha 6-Suchdol, Phone : 422/338 11 11
Fax : 422/341969, E-mail : hron@ pefl. vsz.cz Rector : Prof. Ing. Jan Hron, DrSc.

Faculty of Agronomy

Agronomická Fakulta

Dean's Office : Kamýcká 957, 165 21 Praha 6- Suchdol
Phone : 422/388 11 11, Fax : 422/34 44 18, Dean : Prof. Ing. Václav Vanek, CSc.

Faculty of Engineering

Technická Fakulta

Dean's Office : Kamýcká 872, 165 21 Praha 6- Suchdol
Phone : 422/388 11 11, Fax : 422/39 33 03, Dean : Doc. Ing. Siavomír Procházka, CSc.

Faculty of Agricultural Economics

Fakulta Provozne Ekonomická

Dean's Office : Kamýcká 959, 165 21 Praha 6-Suchdol, Phone : 422/ 338 11 11
Fax : 422/338 23 29, Dean : Doc. Ing. Miroslav Svatos, CSc.

Facultyof Forestry

Lesnická Fakulta

Dean's Office : Kamýcká 957, 165 21 Praha 6- Suchdol,
Phone : 422/338 11 11
Fax : 422/325 863
Dean : Prof. Ing. Ivan Roeek, CSc.

MENDEL UNIVERSITY OF AGRICULTURE AND FORESTRY

Mendelova Zemedelská a Lesnická Univerzita

Rector's Office : Zemedelská 1, 613 00 Brno, Phone : 425/4513 11 11
Fax : 425/45 21 11 28, Rector : Prof. Ing. MVDr. Pavel Jelínek, DrSc.

Faculty of Agronomy

Agronomická Fakulta

Dean's Office : Zemedelská 1, 613 00 Brno, Phone : 425/45 13 11 11
Fax : 425/45 21 20 44, Dean : Prof. Ing. Jirí Zelenka, CSc.

Faculty of Agricultural Economics

Provozne Ekonomická Fakulta

Dean's Office : Zemedelská 1, 613 00 Brno,Phone : 425/ 45 13 11 11
Fax : 425/45 21 22 87, Dean : Prof. Ing. Jirí Lanca, CSc.

Faculty of Forestry and Wood Industry

Fakulta lesnická a drevarská

Dean's Office : Zemedelská 3, 613 00 Brno, Phone : 425/45 13 11 11
Fax : 425/45 21 14 22, Dean : Doc. Ing. Ladislav Sionek, CSc.

Faculty of Horticulture

Zahradnická Fakulta

Dean's Office : Valtická 533, 691 44 Lednice na Morave
Phone : 42627/98 210-12, Fax : 42627/98 411
Dean : Doc. Ing. Jan Golias, DrSc.

ACADEMY OF PERFORMING ARTS

Academie Múzických Umení

Rector's Office : Trziste 18, 118 00 Praha 1, Phone : 422/53 09 43, 53 24 78
Fax : 422/53 05 01, E-mail : jaroslav.vostry@amu.cz Rector : Prof. Jaroslav Vostrý

Faculty of Music

Hudební Fakulta

Dean's Office : Malostranské nám 12, 118 00 Praha 1
Phone : 422/53 09 43, 422/53 24 78
Dean : Prof. Josef Chuchro

Faculty of Theatre

Duvadelní Fakulta

Dean's Office : Karlova 26, 116 65 Praha 1, Phone : 422/24 21 88 54-6
Fax : 422/24 22 24 42, Dean : Doc. Milos Horanský

Faculty of Film and Television

Fakulta filmová a televizní

Dean's Office : Smetanovo nabr, 2, 116 65 Praha 1 Phone : 422/24 22 94 68
Dean : PhDr. Jan Bernard

JANÁCEK ACADEMY OF MUSIC AND DRAMATIC ARTS JANACKOVA AKADEMIE MÚZICKÝCH UMENÍ

Rector's Office : Komenského nám, 6, 662 15 Brno, Phone : 425/42 32 13 07
Fax : 425/42 21 32 86, Rector : Prof. Alena Stepánková-Veselá

Faculty of Music

Hudební Fakulta

Dean's Office : Komenského nám 6, 662 15 Brno
Phone : 425/42 32 13 07, 42 21 70 04-9, Fax : 425/42 21 32 86
Dean : Prof. Bohumil Smejkal

Faculty of Theatre

Divadeiní Fakulta

Dean's Office : Mozartova 1, 662 15 Brno, Phone : 425/42 21 21 35, 42 21 50 43
Fax : 425/42 21 29 75, Dean : Doc. PhDr. Josef Kovalcuk

Academy of Fine Arts

Akademie Výtvarných Umení

Rector's Office : U Akademie 4, 170 22 Praja. 7 Phone : 422/373 641-6
Fax : 422/375 781
Rector : Prof. Milan Knízák

ACADEMY OF ARTS, ARCHITECTURE AND DESIGN

VYSOKÁ SKOLA UMELECKO-PRÜMYSLOVÁ

Rector's Office : Nám, Jana Palacha 80, 116 93 Praha 1
Phone : 422/24 81 11 72 Fax : 422/23 26 884
Rector : Doc. PhDr. Josef Hiavácek, CSc.

MILITARY AND POLICE HIGHER EDUCATION INSTITUTIONS

Military Adademy

Vojenská Akademie

Rector's Office : Kounicova 65, 612 00 Brno, Phone : 425/41182636
Fax : 525/41182888, Rector : plk. Doc. Ing. Jirí Moc, CSc.

Command and Staff Faculty
Fakulta Velitelská a stabni
Dean's Office : Kounicova 65, 612 00 Brno, Phone : 425/4118 2482,
Fax : 425/4118 2888
Dean : plk. Doc. Ing. Arnost Vraný, CSc.

Faculty of Military Technology
Fakulta vojensko-technická druhú vojsk
Dean's Office : Kounicova 65, 612 00 Brno, Phone : 425/4118 2708
Fax : 425/4118 2888
Dean : plk. Prof. Ing. Vladimir Klaban, CSc.

Air Force and Air Defence Faculty
Fakulta letectva a protivzdusné obrany
Dean's Office : Kounicova 65, 612 00 Brno, Phone : 425/4118 2534
Fax : 425/4118 2888, Dean : plk. Doc. Ing. Lvan Hamtil, CSc.

MILITARY COLLEGE OF GROUND FORCES
VYSOKÁ VOJENSKÁ SKOLA POZEMNÍHO VOJSKA
Rector's Office : Víta Nejediého, 683 02 Vyskov 3
Phone : 42507/22124,
Fax : 42507/22124
Dean : plk. Doc. Ing. Lubomír Odehnal, CSc.

Faculty of Military Systems Control
Fakulta rízení vojenských systémü
Dean's Office : Vita Nejediého, 683 02 Vyskov 3, Phone : 42507/22124
Fax : 42507/22124

Faculty of State Defence Economy
Fakulta ekonomiky obrany
Dean's Office : Vita Nejediého, 683 02 Vyskov 3
Phone : 42507/22124, Fax : 42507/22124

Military Medicine Academy J.E. Purkyne
Vojenská Lékarská Akademie J.E. Purkyné
Rector's Office : PS 35, 502 60 Hradec Králové, Phone : 049/25339
Fax : 049/25339, Rector : plk. Prof. MUDr. Josef Fusek, DrSc.

Police Academy
Policejní Akademie
Rector's Office : sídlo : Lhotecká ul. 100, 140 00 Praha 4, Postal Address : P.O. Box 7063, 170 21 Praha 7, Phone : 422/4772140, 4772141, Fax : 422/4714131
Rector : Doc. JUDr. Jan Musil, CSc.

MINISTRY OF EDUCATION, YOUTH AND SPORT OF THE CZECH REPUBLIC MINISTERSTVO SKOLSTVÍ, MLÁDEZE A TELOVÝCHOVY CESKÉ REPUBLIKY
Address : Karmelitská 7, 118 12 Praha 1, Phone : 422/51 93 111, Fax : 422/51 93 790
Minister of Education, Youth and Sport : Ing.Ivan Pilip
First Deputy Minister : Ing. Jan Koucký
Deputy Minister for Primary and Secondary Education : RNDr. Miroslav Bartosek
Deputy Minister for Science and Higher Education : Prof. Ing; Emanuel Ondrácek, CSc.
Deputy Minister for Youth and Sport : PhDr. Jan Belohlávek
Division of Science and Higher Education

(Skupina pro vedu a vysoké skolství)
Consists of following departments :
Department of Higher Education
(Odbor Vysokoskolského vzdelávání)
Director : Ing. Josef Benes, CSc.
Phone: 422/5193 244
Responsibilities :

- Admission to higher education institutions
- Fields of study in bachelor, magister, engineer and postgraduate study
- Statutes of higher education institutions
- Recognition of foreign higher education diplomas
- Secretariat of the Accredation Commission of the government of the Czech Republic

Organization and Administration Department
(Odbor organizacne správní)
Director : RNDr. Vladimír Roskovec, CSc.
Responsibilities :

- Preparation of legal norms for higher education
- Student dormitories and canteens
- Scholarships

Department of Lifelong Education
(Odbor celozivotního vzdelávání)
Director : PhDr. Zdenek Palán
Responsibilities :

- Distance education
- Adult education
- Requalification
- Accreditation of education institutions

Department of International Relations
(Odbor zahranicních vztahú)
Director : Ing. Jan Kolron
Responsibilities :

- Multilateral international programmes in education
- Bilateral cultural agreements
- Cooperation with international organisations (Organisation of United Nations, UNESCO, Council of Europe, OECD, UNESCO, CEEPUS)

OTHER IMPORTANT INSTITUTIONS CONCERNING HIGHER EDUCATION
Czech Rectors; Conference Ceská konference rektoru
Address of Secretariat : Kancelá Ceské konference rektoru
Masarykova univerzita, Zerotínovo nám. 9, 601, 77 Brno
Phone : 425/42 12 82 70, 42 12 82 72
Fax : 425/42 12 83 00, 42 12 82 62
E-mail : fojtikova@muni.cz
Chairman : Prof. Ing. Stanislav Hanzi, CSc.
Responsibilities of Conference :

- Represents rectors of higher education institutions
- negotiates important problems concerning higher education

Council of Higher Education Institutions
Rada Vysokých skol

Address of Agency of Council : Agenture Rady vysokých skol
Ul. José Martího 31, 162 52 Praha 6-Veleslavin,
Phone: 422/337 21 48-9, 36 99 41-9, Fax : 422/316 27 03
The Council consists of members elected in higher education institutions and in faculties The Council represents higher education institutions in relations to the Ministry of Education, Youth and Sport.

Negotiations take place among the members of the Council on the distribution of the financial means allocated from the state budget, and other important issues concerning the higher education.

Centre for Higher Education Studies

Centrum pro studium Vysokého Skolství

Address : U Luzického semináre 13/90, 118 00 Praha 1
Phone : 422/55 19 46 Fax : 422/55 19 45
Responsibilities of the Centre :

- Research in higher education
- Research and coordination of distance education and monitoring of activities in this field.
- Processing of information on higher education in the Czech Republic and abroad
- Collaboration with international organisations (Council of Europe, OECD, UNESCO, CHER, IGIP, SEFI, ATEE)

The parts of the Centre are :

- Centre for Certificate Equivalence in Higher Education
- National Centre of Distance Education
- Agency for Educational European Union Programmes (TEMPUS, SOCRATES)

Institute for Information in Education

Ustav pro informance ve vzdelání

Address : Senovazne namesti 26, 111 21 Praha 1, Phone : 422/24 22 97 14-16
Responsibilities of the Institute :

- Collecting and processing of statistical data at all levels of the educational system in the Czech Republic.
- Edition of statistical and informative publications about the education in the Czech Republic.

ACADEMIC INFORMATION AGENCY

Akademická informacní agentura

Address : Senovazné námestí 26 111, 21 Praha 1
Phone : 422/24 22 97 14-21, 24 22 96 98
Responsibilities of the Agency :

- Collecting of information on possibilities of studies and study visits for Czech students abroad.
- Facilitating of study visits for Czech students abroad
- Implementation of Austrian - Czech Academic Exchange Programme (AKTION)

New Phone Code Czech Republic : 410
Further details can be had from :
Dept. of Culture, Science, Education and Public Relations, Embassy of the **Czech Republic** in New Delhi
50 - M Niti Marg, Chanakyapuri, New Delhi -110 021
Phone : 0091 - 11 - 6110205, 6110318, 6110382, 6888082
Fax : 0091 - 11 - 6886221, E-mail : newdelhi@embassy.mzc.cz

Denmark

In Denmark more than 130 institutions of higher education offer courses and study programmes with varying lengths and levels. The institutions can be classified into two sectors, the university and college sectors.

The University Sector includes five multifaculty universities; ten universities specializing in such fields as engineering, veterinary science, pharmacy, art, architecture and business studies; and two academies of music. These institutions award research-based degrees both at the undergraduate and postgraduate levels.

The College Sector comprises more than 100 specialized colleges of higher education that normally offer short-and medium-term professionally oriented programmes of higher education in teacher training, social work, physiotherapy, nursing, engineering, design, music and other disciplines. Most of the colleges are small, specialized institutions with 400-600 students and offer one or a few study programmes in a specific field.

The state finances and regulates most institutions of higher education; there are very few private institutions.

Most university programmes consist of a 3 year bachelor's degree programme followed by a 2 year programme leading to a *Candidatus* degree (master's degree). Most degree programmes are self-contained, and students choose their speciality when they begin their studies. Progarmmes for the *Candidatus* degree include 6 months of work on a thesis. A few disciplines (such as medicine, veterinarian medicine and pharmacy) do not award a bachelor's degree : only the *Candidatus* degree after 5 to 6½ years of study. Three years of supervised postgraduate studies after the *Candidatus* degree leads to a Ph.D. degree.

The degree programmes offered by Aalborg University and Roskilde University begin with 1or 2- year basic programmes with a broad and interdisciplinary introduction to the more specialized degree programmes. The study methods at these universities focus on problem-centered and project-oriented group work.

Most college programmes last 3 or 4 years. They are professionally oriented and normally include periods of practical training. The general admission requirements are the same as for the university degreé programmes. Some countries offer comparable courses of study as part of their University programmes, but Denmark has a long tradition of offering them at specialized institutions.

Apart from the regular degree-oriented study programmes, Danish institutions also offer courses through open education.

Denmark's institutions of higher education expect students to be very independent and active. Besides traditional lectures, most teaching is conducted in the form of seminars and small work groups in which all participants are expected to contribute actively. Part of the studies consist of independent project and research work.

The academic year is divided into two terms : the Autumn semester (from August or September until the end of December) and the Spring semester (from January or February to May or June). Examinations are conducted in January and June.

Danish Institutions do not normally charge tuition for regular study programmes. Participation in open education programmes is subject to fees.

Courses Conducted in Languages other than Danish

The usual language of instruction is Danish, but more and more institutions offer some of their regular courses in English or another foreign language or have special arrangements for non-Danish students. Nevertheless, opportunities to take a full degree in a language other than Danish are still limited. Further information about courses in other languages are available from the individual institutions (see list of addresses and Websites).

Denmark's International Study Program (DIS), an institution affiliated with the University of Cophenhagen, offers tuition-based courses in English for students who want to spend one or two semesters in Denmark studying within such fields as the humanities and social sciences, international business, architecture and design, marine biology and ecology, engineering and environmental studies. Applications must be submitted through a university or college in the United States, Canada and Australia with which DIS has an agreement. Further information can be obtained from DIS (see list of Addresses).

Admission

Regular Students

General Admission Requirements

Non-Danish students aiming at a full degree from an institution of higher education in Denmark must apply for admission on the same terms as Danish students. They are eligible for admission if they can prove that they have sufficient command of Danish and hold either a Danish qualifying examination or qualifications recognized or assessed as being comparable to the Danish entrance qualifications. Examples include :

* Upper secondary certificates and diplomas from the Nordic countries, European Union countries and other countries that have signed the European Conventions on the Equivalence of Diplomas leading to Admission to Universities;
* The International and the European Baccalaureate:
* High school diplomas from the United States either followed by up to two years of university or college studies in relevant subjects or supplemented by three advanced placement examinations in relevant subjects with a grade of 3 or higher. This also applies to applicants with a high school diploma from countries with a similar educational system; and
* Bachelor's degrees in relevant subjects from Universities in Bangladesh, India, Pakistan and the Philippines.

Each individual institution decides on admission. Further information about entrance qualifications and supplementary tests can be obtained from the admission offices at the institutions.

Course Requirements

Fulfilling the general admission requirements is often not enough to be admitted to a given programme. Many programmes have specific course requirements, such as a given combination of subjects or a minimum score in certain subjects.

Language requirements

Proof of a good command of both Danish and English is a prerequisite for admission as a regular student. Students from outside the Nordic countries must pass a Danish test. The test normally required is *Danskprove 2* (Danish Test 2) from Studieskolen or an equivalent test. The test comprises both an oral and a written examination. Registration for the tests and the preparatory courses takes place at Studieskolen (see list of Addresses). Students applying for admission for August or September must have passed the required Danish test no later than May or June.

Alborg University

Admission Restrictions

Each institution decides how many places are available for most disciplines. The Ministry of Education regulates admission in such fields as medicine, teacher and educator training. In 1995 about 60,000 students applied for admission, and about 40,000 were admitted. When there are more qualified applicants than places available, the applicants are normally admitted according to the following system.

The available places are divided into two quota systems. Places in the first quota are distributed to applicants with Danish qualifying examinations based on the average mark obtained at their final examination at the upper secondary level.

Places in the second quota are awarded based on individual assessment by the institution. Applicants with an international or foreign qualifying examination are also admitted through this quota.

Some institutions, including the Royal Academy of Fine Arts, the music academies and the Danish School of Journalism, have their own aptitude tests.

Application and deadlines

The application deadlines for all applicants with examinations from outside Denmark, regardless of nationality are :

* Admission in August or September : 15 March
* Admission in January or February : 1 September.

Application forms can be obtained from the Danish institutions of higher education (see list

of addresses) approximately 2 months before the deadlines.

Guest Students

Students who wish to attend advanced courses at a Danish institution of higher education for 3–12 months as part of their current studies in their home countries may apply for admission as guest students either individually (called free movers) or under the terms of an official exchange agreement (such as Socrates/Erasmus or a bilateral agreement). Applicants must be enrolled at an institution of higher education outside Denmark and must have completed studies equivalent to at least 1 year of studies at an institution of higher education in Denmark. Guest students are not required to take any Danish test, but some institutions require a good working knowledge of Danish or recommend that guest students take Danish courses. Many institutions offer intensive language courses before the start of the term.

Potential guest students should normally apply to the international office of the Danish institution or to the student's home institution if the visit falls under a formal exchange programme.

Ph.D. Students

The usual entrance requirement for Ph.D. programmes in Denmark is a Danish master's (*Candidatus*) degree or an equivalent academic level. Although Danish is the basic language at all Denmark's universities, Ph.D. Programmes are increasingly being conducted in English; in principle, English-speaking students can obtain a Ph.D. degree in most subjects at a Danish university without knowing Danish. As each Ph.D. programme is primarily planned by the host university faculty or department, all questions about admission of or visits from non-Danish students should be directed to the relevant faculty or department.

Non-Danish student must enter into an agreement with a university researcher who agrees to supervise the Ph.D. studies before applying for a Ph.D. programme.

Very few state-financed scholarships are available to non-Danish Ph.D.students, and it is difficult to find private grants. Non-Danish students therefore usually need sufficient external money to cover their living expenses. They also have to negotiate individually the financial conditions for being accepted as a Ph.D. student, as each University has different financing and regulations.

Residence permit

Students from the Nordic countries do not need a residence permit to study in Denmark. For students of all other nationalities, a residence permit is required if the stay is expected to be longer than 3 months. No residence permit is required if the stay is expected to be shorter than 3 months, but a visa may be required for the nationals of certain countries.

(A) *Students from Non-Nordic European Union Countries*

Students from European Union countries who have been accepted for enrolment at a recognized educational institution in Denmark are entitled to a residence permit for European Union citizens for the study period. The student must have health insurance if necessary and money to cover his or her living expenses. The institution in Denmark may be able to assist accepted students who need to apply for a permit.

(B) *Students from Other Countries*

The applicant must apply for a residence permit for studying in Denmark through the Danish diplomatic mission in the home country when accepted for admission. The permit must be issued before the student arrives in Denmark. A student cannot expect to obtain a residence permit if the sole purpose of the stay is to learn Danish, and a residence permit cannot be obtained during a temporary stay in Denmark.

To obtain a residence permit, a student must prove that he or she can pay all costs related to the stay.

Work Permit

Students from Nordic and European Union countries may work in Denmark without a permit.

Students from other countries can take paid employment if they obtain a work permit. This permit must be applied for through Denmark's diplomatic mission in the student's home country before departure for Denmark. Work permits are not normally issued to people with residence permits for studying in Denmark.

Health Services

Anyone staying in Denmark is entitled to free emergency hospital treatment.

(A) *Students without a residence permit*

Students from the Nordic countries and the United Kingdom are entitled to the same health services as Danes when acute medical treatment is needed. Students from other European Union countries and Liechtenstein are also entitled to the same health services as residents of Denmark when acute medical treatment is needed if they bring an E-111 form from their home country. Students from other countries are not entitled to any free medical care except the emergency hospital treatment mentioned above and are urged to obtain health insurance.

(B) Students with a residence permit

Students who are registered with the national registry in Denmark are automatically covered by Denmark's health insurance scheme after a period of 6 weeks. Students coming from European Union countries, Croatia, Iceland, Liechtenstein, Morocco, Norway, Pakistan, Quebec, Slovenia, Switzerland and Turkey can avoid the waiting period if they are covered by the public health insurance scheme of their home countries and bring the necessary documentation.

How to Apply

If the student thinks that he or she can comply with the requirements outlined previously, the next step is to contact the educational institution directly to ensure that an existing diploma can qualify for admission.

Nevertheless, four requirements as mentioned earlier must be emphasized:

1. The language requirement
2. Admission restrictions
3. The application deadline
4. Residence permit.

Grants and Scholarships

Danish educational institutions are generally unable to offer financial support or scholarships to non-Danish students.

Students from European Union countries and other countries participating in the Socrates/Er-asmus and Leonardo da Vinci programmes may apply for special exchange and mobility grants to carry out a fully recognized period of study (3-12 months). Students from the Nordic countries, the Baltic States and certain other countries in central and eastern Europe have other possibilities, such as the Nordplus and Tempus programmes. Students should seek further information about these opportunities at the institution at which they are studying in the home country.

A few state scholarships are available to non-Danish students and researchers from countries with which Denmark has a bilateral agreement. The scholarships are granted for 4-9 months to supplement higher education the applicant is taking or has taken elsewhere. The scholarships are not granted for elementary studies of Danish. All applications for Danish state scholarships must be submitted through the authorities of the applicant's home country.

Financial support may be available for doctoral training and scientific cooperation, but only for limited stays. Scientists interested in coming to Denmark for research training are advised to contact Danish colleagues. At the postdoctoral level, funding is available through European Union programmes such as the TMR programme (Training and Mobility for Researchers). Further information on financial support can be obtained from the Danish Research Academy (Forskerakademiet; see list of addresses).

ADDRESS AND WEB SITES

Institutions of Higher Education

All universities are listed but, for space reasons, selected colleges are listed for each field of study. These colleges can supply potential applicants with the addresses of other relevant institutions. The Secretariat of the Danish Rectors' Conference can also provide the addresses of appropriate institutions.

Kobenhavns Universitet (University of Copenhagen), Norregade 10, Postboks 2177, DK-1017 Copenhagen K, Tel. +45 35 32 26 26, Fax +45 35 32 26 28, www.ku.dk

Aarhus Universitet (University of Aarhus), Nordre Ringgade 1, DK-8000 Aarhus C, Tel. +45 89 42 11 66, Fax +45 86 19 70 29, www.aau.dk

Odense Universitet (Odense University), Campusvej 55, DK-5230 Odense M, Tel. +45 66 15 86 00, Fax +45 66 15 84 28, www.ou.dk

Roskilde Universitetscenter (Roskilde University), Postboks 260 DK-4000 Roskilde, Tel. +45 46 75 77 11, Fax +45 46 75 74 01, www.ruc.dk

Aalborg Universitet (Aalborg University), Postboks 159, DK-9100 Aalborg, Tel. +45 98 15 85 22, Fax +45 98 15 15 22, www.auc.dk

Danmarks Tekniske Universitet (Technical University of Denmark), Bygning 101, Anker Engelundsvej 1, DK-2800 Lyngby, Tel. +45 45 25 25 25, Fax +45 45 88 17 99, www.dtu.dk/cwis/welcome

Danmarks Laererhøjskole (Royal Danish School of Educational Studies),

Emdrupvej 101 DK-2400 Copenhagen NV, Tel. +45 39 69 66 33, Fax +45 39 66 00 81, www.dlh.dk

Den Kgl. Veterinaer- og Landbohøjskole (Royal Veterinary and Agricultural University), Bülowsvej 13, DK-1870 Frederiksberg C, Tel. +45 35 28 28 28, Fax +45 35 28 20 79, www.kvl.dk

Handelshøjskolen i København (Copenhagen Business School), Struenseegade 7-9, DK-2200 Copenhagen N, tel. +45 38 15 38 15 38 15, Fax +45 38 15 20 15, www. cbs.dk

Handelshøjskolen i Arhus (Aarhus School of Business), Fuglesangs Allé 4, DK-8210 Aarhus V, Tel. +45 89 48 66 88, Fax +45 86 15 01 88, www.hha.dk

Handelshøjskole Syd (Southern Denmark Business School ; campuses in Esbjerg, Kolding, Sønderborg, Varde and Flensburg, Germany), Grundtvigs Allé 150, DK-6400 Sønderborg, Tel. +45 79 32 11 11, Fax +45 79 32 12 87, www.hhs.dk

Danmarks Farmaceutiske Højskole (RoyalDanish School of Pharmacy), Universitets - parken 2, DK-2100 Copenhagen Ø, Tel. +45 35 37 08 50, Fax : +45 35 37 57 44, www.info.dfh.dk

Kunstakademiets Arkitektskole (Royal Danish Academy of Fine Arts, School of Architecture), Philip de Langes Allé 10, DK-1435 Copenhagen K, Tel. +45 32 68 60 00, Fax +45 32 68 61 11

Det Kgl. Danske Kunstakademi (Royal Danish Academy of Fine Arts, School of Visual Art and School of Conservation), Kongens Nytorv 1, DK-1050 Copenhagen K, Tel. +45 33 12 68 60, Fax +45 33 32 24 35

Arkitektskolen i Aarhus (Aarhus School of Architecture) Nørreport 20, DK-8000 Aarhus C, Tel. +45 89 36 00 00, Fax +45 86 13 06 45

Det Kgl. Danske Musikkonservatorium (Royal Danish Academy of Music), Niels Brocks Gade 1, DK-1574 Copenhagen V, Tel. +45 33 12 42 74, Fax +45 33 14 09 11

Det Jyske Musikkonservatorium (Royal Academy of Music, Aarhus), Fuglesangs Allé 26, DK-8210 Aarhus V, Tel. +45 89 48 33 88, Fax +45 89 48 33 22

Det Fynske Musikkonservatorium (Carl Nielsen Academy of Music, Odense), Islandsgade 2, DK-5000 Odense C, Tel. +45 66 11 06 63, Fax +45 66 17 77 63

Nordjysk Musikkonservatorium (Academy of Music, Aalborg), Ryesgade 52, DK-9000 Aalborg, Tel. +45 98 12 77 44, Fax +45 98 11 37 63

Vestjysk Musikkonservatorium (Acadamy of Music, Esbjerg), Islandsgade 50, DK-6700 Esbjerg, Tel. +45 75 12 61 00, Fax +45 75 18 06 59

Rytmisk Musikkonservatorium (Rhythmic Music Conservatory), Leo Mathisensvej, Holmen, DK-1437 CopenhagenK, Tel. +45 32 68 67 00, Fax +45 32 68 67 66

Danmarks Journalisthøjskole (Danish School of Journalism), Olof Palmes Allé 11, DK-8200 Aarhus N, Tel. +45 86 16 11 22, Fax +45 86 16 89 10, www.djh.dk

Danmarks Biblioteksskole (Royal School of Librarianship), Birketinget 6, DK-2300 Copenhagen S, Tel. +45 31 58 60 66, Fax +45 32 84 02 01, www.db. dk

Danmarks Højskole for Legemsøvelser (Danish State Institute of Physical Education), Nørre Allé 51, DK-2200 Copenhagen N, Tel. + 45 35 30 05 00, Fax +45 35 36 24 14

Den Grafiske Højskole (Graphic Arts Institute of Denmark), Glentevej 67, DK-2400 Copenhagen NV, Tel. +45 38 10 11 77, Fax +45 38 33 06 30, www.dgh.dk

Danmarks Designskole (Denmark's Design School), Strandboulevarden 47, DK-2100 Copenhagen Ø, Tel. +45 35 27 75 00, Fax +45 35 27 76 00

Den Sociale Højskole i København (National Danish School of Social work, Copenhagen), Ø Tel +4503142 4601, fax +45 31 42 07 61.

Den Sociale Højskole i Århus (National Danish School of Social Work, Aarhus), Stenvej 4, DK-8270 Højberg, Tel. +45 86 27 66 22, Fax +45 86 27 74 76

Den Sociale Højskole i Esbjerg (National Danish School of Social Work, Esbjerg), Storegade 182, DK-6705 Esbjerg Ø, Tel. +45 75 13 35 00, Fax +45 75 12 09 04

Den Sociale Højskole i Odense (National Danish School of Social Work, Odense), Campusvej 55, DK-5230 Odense M, Tel. +45 66 15 86 00, Fax +45 65 93 09 34

Colleges of Engineering

Denmark has seven colleges of Engineering located in Aarhus, Copenhagen, Haslev, Herning, Horsens, Odense and Sønderborg. The address of the college in Copenhagen is :

Københavns Teknikum (Engineering College of Copenhagen), Lautrupvang 15, DK-2750 Ballerup, Tel. +45 44 97 80 88, Fax +45 44 97 81 72, www.cph ih.dk.

Colleges of Education

Teacher training is offered at 18 colleges of education throughout Denmark. An example is :

Jelling Statsseminarium (Jelling State College of Education), Vejlevej 2, DK-7300 Jelling, Tel. +45 75 87 16 00, Fax +45 75 87 12 27

Colleges of Educator Training

A total of 32 institutions train students for such occupations as preschool teachers, recreation centre teachers and social educators. One such institution is :

Viborg-seminariet (Viborg College of Educator Training), Reberbanen 13, DK-8800 Viborg, Tel. +45 86 62 42 00, Fax +45 86 61 49 09

Colleges for Art, Crafts, Textile and Fashion Design

Denmark has eight of these colleges located in : Copenhagen (2), Højer, Nørre Sundby, Nykøbing Falster, Odense, Kerteminde and Skals. An example:

Hellerup Håndarbejdsseminarium (Hellerup College for Art, Crafts, Textile and Fashion Design), Frederikkevej 8-10, DK-2900 Hellerup, Tel. +45 39 61 93 93, Fax +45 39 61 97 97

Health Education Institutions

Nurses (22 schools)

Hovedstadens Sygehusfaellesskab, Sygeplejerskeuddanelsen, Tuborgvej 235, DK-2400 Copenhagen NV, Tel. +45 35 31 36 93, Fax +45 35 31 24 67

Medical laboratory technicians (2 schools)

Hospitalslaborantskolen i Århus (School for Medical Laboratory Technicians in Aarhus), Studsgade 29, DK-8000 Aarhus C, Tel. +45 86 12 63 66, Fax +45 86 12 62 08

Midwifery

(2 departments : Copenhagen and Aalborg)

Danmarks Jordemoderskole (Danish Midwifery School – Copenhagen Department), Rigshospitalet, afsnit 7211, Tagensvej 18, DK-2200 Copenhagen N, Tel. +45 35 45 72 16, Fax +45 35 36 18 10

Occupational Therapists (6 schools)

Ergoterapeutskolen i Århus (School of Occupational Therapy in Aarhus), Skejbyvej 15, DK-8240 Risskov, Tel. +45 86 21 16 11, Fax +45 86 21 29 12

Physiotherapists (8 schools)

Fysioterapeutskolen i Århus

(School of Physiotherapy in Aarhus), Skejbyvej 15, DK-8240 Risskov,
Tel. +45 86 21 14 55, Fax +45 86 21 29 12

Danish Language Courses

Year-round courses

Studieskolen i København, Antonigade 6, DK-1106 Copenhagen K, Tel. +45 33 14 40 22, Fax +45 33 14 81 45

Studieskolen i Århus, Immervad 7, DK-8000 Aarhus C, Tel. +45 86 19 05 66, Fax +45 86 19 15 68

Studieskolen i Odense, Munkebjergvaenget 40, DK-5230 Odense M
Tel. +45 66 15 90 60, Fax +45 66 15 90 17

Summer Courses

Det Danske Kulturinstitut (Danish Cultural Institute), Kultorvet 2, DK-1175 Copenhagen K, Tel. +45 33 13 54 48, Fax +45 33 15 10 91

Den Internationale Højskole (International People's College), Montebello Allé, DK-3000 Helsingør, Tel. +45 49 21 33 61, Fax +45 49 21 21 28

Accommodation

The educational Institutions have no residential facilities of their own, and non-Danish students normally have to make their own arrangements. Nevertheless, some of the major cities have student dormitories and other housing facilities coordinated regionally by:

Centralindstillingsudvalget, H C Andersens
Boulevard 13, DK-1553 Copenhagen V, Tel. +45 33 11 64 44, Fax +45 33 11 17 27

Roskilde regionale indstillingsudvalg, Parkvej
5, DK-4000 Roskilde, Tel. +45 42 36 22 02

RIU-Fyn, Hinderupgård, Niles Bohrs Allé 21, DK-5230 Odense M, Tel. +45 66 13 40 08, Fax +45 65 90 61 77

Indstillingsudvalget for Aalborg Kollegier (IFAK), Nyhavnsgade 15, Postboks 1713, K-9000 Aalborg, Tel. +45 98 13 44 30, Fax +45 99 31 27 99

Kollegiekontoret i Århus (AMBA), Vesterport 1, st., DK-8000 Aarhus C, Tel. +45 86 13 21 66, Fax +45 86 13 21 80

International Exchange Programmes

Rektorkollegiets Sekretariat (Secretariat of the
Danish Rectors' Conference), H C Andersens
Boulevard 45, DK-1553 Copenhagen V, Tel. +45 33 92 54 06, Fax +45 33 92 50 75

The Secretariat is responsible for administration in Denmark of the European Union programmes for higher education (Socrates/Erasmus, Leonardo da Vinci, Tempus, and the NARIC centre on academic recognition) and the cultural agreement programmes.

ICU - Informations center for Udveksling
(Information Centre for Exchange), Vandkunsten 3, DK-1467 Copenhagen K,
Tel. +45 33 14 20 60, Fax +45 33 14 36 40

The Centre is Denmark's agency for the following European Union programmes : Socrates/Comenius, Socrates/Chapter III, CEDEFOP, Youth for Europe and Action for Voluntary Service as well as for the Ministry of Education's Visitors' Service.

Other Relevant Addresses

Udenrigsministeriet
(Ministry of Foreign Affairs), Asiatisk Plads 2, DK-1448 Copenhagen K,
Tel. +45 33 92 00 00, Fax +45 31 54 05 33
www.um.dk

Undervisningsministeriet, Det Internationale kontor (Ministry of Education,

International Relations Division), Frederiksholms Kanal 21, DK-1220 Copenhagen K, Tel. +45 33 92 50 00, Fax +45 33 92 55 67, www.uvm.dk/eng.htm

Universitetsafdelingen, Undervisningsministeriet (Department of Higher Education), HC Andersens Boulevard 40, DK- 1553 Copenhagen V, Tel. +45 33 92 53 00,
Fax +45 33 92 53 25

Kulturministeriet (Ministry of Cultural Affairs),
Nybrogade 2, DK-1203 Copenhagen K, Tel. +45 33 92 33 70, Fax +45 33 91 33 88

Forskerakademiet (Danish Research Academy), Observatorievejen 3, DK- 8000 Aarhus C, Tel. +45 86 14 48 98, Fax +45 86 14 48 71, www.dmanphd.dk

Denmark's International Study Program
(DiS), Vestergade 7, DK-1456
Copenhagen K, Tel. +45 33 11 01 44, Fax +45 33 93 26 24, www disp.dk

Danmark-Amerika Fondet/Fulbright
Kommissionen (Denmark-America Foundation/Fulbright Commission),
Fiolstraede 24, 3. Sal, DK-1171 Copenhagen K, Tel. +45 33 12 82 23,
Fax +45 33 32 53 23

Udlaendingestyrelsen
(Danish Immigration Service),
Ryesgade 53, DK-2100 Copenhagen Ø, Tel. +45 35 36 66 00, Fax +45 35 36 50 29

For more details, contact :
Royal Danish Embassy
11, Aurangzeb Road, New Delhi -110011 Tel : (11) 3010900 Fax : (11)3010961
Telex : 31-66160 AMDK IN Telegr . adr. Ambadane

France

Studying in France means choosing the excellence of European education which is 'a must for your future'.

Education in France is one of the top priorities of the state and a lot of emphasis is given to the pursuit of academic excellence. Today, France is the 4th major nation on the world economic scene. It is located in the heart of Europe, which accounts for two thirds of all trading activities. The Paris Stock Exchange is one of the most important in the world with a market capitalization of around US$500 billion. France has the third largest network of banks and insurance companies in the world. The dynamic impetus which has continued to motivate the economy is the quality of management within French companies.

France is also a centre for scientific and technological innovation. The electronic chip on our credit cards (France makes 80 per cent of the chips produced globally), TGV (the high-speed train which connects the different European capitals in record time) and the Ariane rockets are among notable French innovations. The high level of achievement reflects the quality of engineering studies in France and gives you enough reasons to want to benefit from its experience. In the last 7 years, four French scholars have been recipients of the prestigious Nobel Prize.

Coming to study in France also means the opportunity to discover a country full of contrasts, from coastlines to mountains. Its rich cultural heritage makes France the most popular tourist destination in the world with 61 million visitors each year. As a leading global tourist destination it will aim to give managers of tomorrow its real expertise in Tourism and Hotel Management. Moreover, while in France, students may learn and practise the French language spoken by over 160 million people around the world.

The French system of higher education includes different kinds of institutions with varying objectives, structures, and admission requirements. These institutions fall into three main categories which exist side by side:

Universities welcome holders of the French secondary school diploma (*baccalaureat*) or the equivalent, for long and short programs of study. They provide theoretical, practical and vocational aim teaching in all disciplines (the humanities, human sciences, law, economics, management, natural sciences, medicine, pharmacology, technology, the arts, political sciences, etc.) and train students for research.

The grandes éoles provide high-level training for specific professional purposes and goals, such as engineering, or business and management for company executives.

Other advanced schools provide high-level specific education in all fields: art, architecture, agriculture, law, administration.

Admission to all these schools is highly selective and their student enrolments are restricted.

Foreign students may be admitted to these institutions at every level of study provided the latter recognize their diplomas.

Higher Education in France offers 2 main options:

(i) Competitive Universities and (ii) State Universities

Competitive Universities

Entry is very selective at the Competitive Universities. Specialization is available in engineering, commerce, civil services and teaching. Depending on the course, the duration varies from 3-5 years. Many of them offer a 1 year MBA degree/diploma.

State Universities

Any student who has completed the secondary school diploma may qualify in the State Universities. Two categories of courses are offered: general courses and professional courses.

General Courses

These are divided into 3 cycles.

The 1st cycle is of 2 years for undergraduate studies;

The 2nd cycle is of 2 to 3 years of graduate studies;

The 3rd cycle is of 1 to 3 years of postgraduate studies;

Each cycle leads to a national degree.

Professional Courses

These are offered at IUP's (Institut Universitaire Professionnalise). The curriculum consists of 3 year technological courses with 6 months vocational training and practice in an international firm.

Medical studies which include medicine, dental studies and pharmacology are also offered at the universities at the Faculty of Medical Studies. The duration of these courses is 7 years.

Fields like design, architecture, agriculture, public administration, etc. are offered in specialized schools.

Admission Time

November 15 and January 15

It is the best time to seek provisional admission. The form is available at the Cultural, Scientific and Technical Section of the French Embassy in Delhi or directly from the university, as the case may be.

February 1

The form should be duly completed and accompanied by required documents and sent to the office from which it was obtained. Admission applications and results will be sent by March.

With a few exceptions, the academic year runs from September to June.

For admission into the First Cycle of a French University, it is preferable for the candidate to have a Bachelor's Degree. However a candidate with a 10+2 may appear for the entrance examination. The University to which he applies will decide upon the equivalence to be granted. Any other examination which makes a candidate eligible for university studies in his own country may also be accepted for the purpose of enrolment.

This procedure does not apply for Engineering studies. Those interested in enrolling for Engineering studies are requested to write directly to the French University and Engineering Institution of their choice.

No scholarships are offered by the University to foreign students either at the undergraduate or postgraduate level of studies. Candidates have to meet their own expenses: tuition fee, living expenses, travel, etc. (roughly 40,000 French Francs per year, more than Rs 2 lakhs).

Recognition of Qualifications

In France, there is no list of officially accepted foreign equivalents of formal French qualifications. Decisions as to exemption are a matter for the "President" (Vice-Chancellor) or the Principal of the institution to which an application for enrolment is made and are taken on the recommendation of a committee duly appointed to examine the case for exemption.

Registration for postgraduate studies at a university is subject to acceptance of the case submitted by the foreign applicant. Whatever the formal qualifications already possessed by the candidate, admission is by no means automatic but is entirely a matter for an individual decision by the university. This being so, and since different universities' requirements governing enrolment for various courses may not be the same, a candidate could well be accepted by one university and not by another.

Indian nationals seeking admission into French Universities of the undergraduate level (First Cycle), must undertake the formalities of a "pre-inscription" (provisional enrolment). Pre-inscription forms are available every year from 1st December to 15th January of the following year at:

CEDUST

Centre for Documentation on Universities,
Science and Technology, Embassy of France, 2, Aurangzeb Road, New Delhi 110011
Tel : 3014682, Fax : 3016442, Telex : 31-62262
Candidates seeking admission into the First Cycle will have to undergo a French language test in the 2nd week of February. For candidates from Delhi, this test is held at the CEDUST (address given above). For those outside Delhi, it will be held at the Alliance Francaise nearest to their place of residence.

Alliance Francaise

The Alliance Francaise functions as a Cultural Centre. It holds French language courses for different levels and organizes various cultural shows, exhibitions, film shows, etc. There are 15 such Centres in India.

Alliance Francaise, Shahid Vir Kinarivala Marg, Opp. Gujarat College
Ellis Bridge, **Ahmedabad 380006,** Tel (0272) 441551
Alliance Française
Thimmaiah Road Millers Tank Street, Opp. Cant Railway Station
Bangalore 560052, Tel (080) 2268762
Alliance Française, E2/134, Arera Colony, Bhopal 462016
Tel (0755) 566595 Alliance Française, 40, New Marine Lines, Theosophy Hall
Mumbai 400020, Tel (022) 295993/296187/2016202, Fax (022) 2080404
Alliance Française, 24, Park Mansions, Park Street
Calcutta 700016, Tel (033) 298793/298794, Fax (033) 2422863
Alliance Française "*Le Corbusier*", 210 Sector 36 A
Chandigarh 160023, Tel (0172) 535342, Fax (0172) 530531
Alliance Française, D-13 South Extension Part II, New Delhi 110049
Tel (011) 6440128/6417574
Alliance Française, Near College of Commerce, Altinho
Panjim 403001, Tel (0832) 223274, Fax (0832) 44904
Alliance Française, Adarsh Nagar
Hyderabad 500463, Tel (040) 236646, Fax (040) 231684
Alliance Française, Maison de France, 3, Rue Deitha **Karikal 609602,** Alliance Française, 40, College Road, Nungambakkam
Chennai 600006, Tel (044) 8271477/8279803, Fax (044) 8251165
Cercle d'Etudes Francaises,
Mahe 673310, Alliance Francaise, 38, Rue Suffren, P.B. 49
Pondicherry 605001, Tel (0413) 38146, Alliance Francâise, 270 D, Patrakar Nagar Road

Pune 411016

Tel (0212) 337848, Alliance Francaise, Deepom Vellayambalam

Thiruvananathapuram 695010, Tel (0471) 67776, Fax (0471) 66754

Student Visa

In order to obtain a student visa, the candidate should produce the following documents:

* a certificate of admission/pre-enrolment obtained from the French University/Institution (attested copy).
* a sponsorship letter from the person or institution financing the studies, living and travel expenses of the candidate (see Annexures). This should be accompanied by a bank's financial guarantee of the sponsor or a letter from his employer certifying : the availability of the minimum funds required by the candidate for his studies and living expenses in France. According to the regulations, a minimum amount

equivalent to 30,000 Francs per year is required for this purpose in foreign exchange (roughly equivalent to US$ 5000) or a Reserve Bank of India permit certifying the availability of the above sum in foreign exchange.

* a medical certificate by a registered medical practitioner attesting the good health of the candidate (see Annexures).

The passport should be valid for a minimum period of at least 12 months when applying for a visa.

* students who have got pre-enrolment into the 1st cycle or 2nd cycle, should, after showing the above documents, get a recommendation note for obtaining a visa from :

Cultural and Scientific Section,
French Embassy
2, Aurangzeb Road, New Delhi 110011

Visa applications without all the above documents will not be considered. Candidates are also warned that it will not be possible to get a student status once in France if they have not completed the above formalities before their departure.

Candidates will have to apply for their visa to the Consulate under whose jurisdiction their place of issue of passport falls.

* Applicants residing in the States of Andhra Pradesh, Gujarat, Maharashtra, Goa, Madhya Pradesh, Karnataka, should submit their visa applications to the ***Consulate General of France,*** Datta Prasad Building, 2nd Floor, 10-Nowroji Gamadia Cross Road, Off Peddar Road, *Mumbai* 400026 (Tel 4949808).

* Applicants residing in the States of Pondicherry, Karaikal, Mahe, Yanaon, Tamil Nadu, Kerala, should submit their visa applications to the ***Consulate General of France*** 2 Rue de la Marine, ***Pondicherry*** 605001 (Tel 34058) or to the Honorary Consulate of France in *Chennai*-Kumal Engineering Co. Ltd., Ambattur, *Chennai* 600058 (Tel 652922, 652754).

* Applicants residing in the States of Bihar, West Bengal, Orissa, Assam, Manipur, Tripura, Nagaland, Chandernagore, should submit their visa applications to the ***Consulate of France in Calcutta,*** 26 Park Mansions, Park Street, ***Calcutta*** 700016 (Tel 290978)

* Applicants residing in the States of Uttar Pradesh, Punjab, Haryana, Jammu & Kashmir, Rajasthan, Himachal Pradesh, Andaman Nicobar, Delhi, should apply to the:

Consular Section, French Embassy, 2/50 Shanti Path, Chanakyapuri,
New Delhi 110021, Tel 604300

Visa for the spouse or family
Of Scholarship/fellowship holders

Candidates going to France on a long-term visa for studies on a scholarship/fellowship and other schemes under the Indo-French student exchange programme, and who desire to take their spouse/family to France as their dependant(s) for this period, should complete the following formalities:

* fill up the visa application form (No 65/VI) in duplicate, for every accompanying member of the family with a separate passport.

* provide a certificate of financial support issued by the authority or the individual supporting them (boarding, lodging and travel expenses).

* get these documents verified from the Cultural, Scientific and Technical Section of the French Embassy, 2 Aurangzeb Road, New Delhi 110011, and get a covering note of recommendation forwarding these papers.

Of non-scholarship/fellowship holders

Candidates going to France on a long-term visa for studies, at their own expenses, and who desire to take their spouse/family over to France as their dependant(s) for this period, should complete the following formalities:

* Dependants should contact the Consular section of the French Embassy-New Delhi or the Consulates under whose jurisdiction they fall, (refer above), to get the visa form required (No 65/VI).
* 7 copies of this form (No 65/VI) should be filled in and returned to the concerned Consulate of the French Embassy (refer above) accompanied by a letter from the candidate's University stating that he/she is a bonafide student in France.

GRANDES ECOLES

Centre d'Enseignement et de Recherche, Appliquées au Management-CERAM
Sophia Antipolis- B.P. 120, **06561 Valbonne-cedex,** Tel 93954545 Fax 93 65 4524
Centre d'Etudes Supérieures Industrielles-CESI
297, rue de Vaugirard **75015 Paris** Tel 42501151/42502506
Centre d'Etudes Supérieures Industrielles-CESI
Château de Galice **13090 Aix-en-Provence** Tel 42201772
Centre d'Etudes Supérieures Industrielles-CESI
7, rue Diderot B.P. 125 **62000 Arras** Tel 21516718
Centre d'Etudes Supérieures Industrielles-CESI
Château de Pêchaurolle B.P. 22 **31130 Balma** Tel 61836268
Centre d'Etudes Supérieures Industrielles-CESI
60, rue de Mauriau **33290 Blanquefort** Tel 56570960
Centre d'Etudes Supérieures Industrielles-CESI
19, avenue Guy de Collongues **69131 Ecully** Tel 78331873
Centre d'Etudes Supérieures Industrielles-CESI
6, boulevard de l'Europe **91033 Evry cedex** Tel 60781267
Centre d'Etudes Supérieures Industrielles-CESI
21, rue de la Mare du Parc **7100 Rouen** Tel 35625022
Centre d'Etudes Supérieures
des Techniques Industrielles-CESTI
3, rue Fernand Hainaut **93407 Saint-Ouen cedex** Tel 40114385 Fax 40126840
Conservatoire National des Arts
et Métiers-CNAM 292, rue Saint-Martin **75141 Paris cedex 03** Tel 40272000 Fax 42719329
Centre National d'Etudes Agronomiques
des Régions Chaudes-CNEARC Domaine de Lavalette Avenue du Val de Montferrand B.P. 5098 **34033 Montpellier cedex** Tel 67545533
Cours Supérieur d'Armement-COSAR
Ecole Militaire 1, place Joffre **75007 Paris** Tel 45503280
Cours Supérieur des Systèmes d'Armes
Terrestres-COSSAT Ecole Militaire 1, place Joffre **75007 Paris** Tel 45559230
Centre Universitaire des Sciences
et Techniques-CUST Institut des Sciences Rue des Meuniers B.P. 48 **63170 Aubière** Tel : 73264110
Ecole de l'Air-EA
Base Aérienne **13661 Salon de Provence cedex** Tel 90532235 Fax : 90555927
Ecole d'Application des Hauts Polymères-EAHP
4, rue Boussingault **67000 Strasbourg** Tel 88416500
Ecole Européenne des Affaires-EAP
108, boulevard Malesherbes **75017 Paris** Tel 47546500 Fax 42674619

Ecole Catholique des Arts et Métiers-ECAM
40, Montée Saint-Barthélemy **69321 Lyon cedex 05** Tel 78378181 Fax : 72402239
Ecole Centrale-ECL
36, avenue Guy de Collongue **69131 Ecully cedex** Tel 78338127 Fax : 78433962
Ecole Centrale des Arts et Manufactures-ECP
Grande Voie des Vignes **92290 Châtenay-Malabry cedex** Tel 46836464 Fax : 46603610
Ecole des Hautes Etudes Commerciales-HEC
1, rue de la Libération
78350 Jouy-en-Josas Tel 39567000 Fax 39567440
Ecole des Hautes Etudes Commerciales du Nord-EDHEC 58, rue du Port **59046 Lille cedex** Tel 20542534 Fax 20308306
Ecole des Hautes Etudes Industrielles-HEI
13, rue de Toul **59046 Lille cedex** Tel 20308314 Fax 20428146
Ecole Française de Papeterie & des Industries Graphiques-EFP Domaine universitaire Rue de la Papeterie B.P. 65 **38402 Saint-Martin d'Hères cedex** Tel 76826900 Fax 76447138
Ecole Française d'Electronique & d'Informatique-EFREI 10, rue Amyot **75005 Paris** Tel 47070595 Fax 43374296
Ecole Europeenne des Hautes Etudes des Industries Chimiques-EHICS 1, rue Blaise Pascal B.P. 296 **67008 Strasbourg cedex** Tel 88416800 Fax 88617852
Ecole Internationale des Affaires-EIA
Domaine de Luminy Case 921 **13288 Marseille cedex 9** Tel 91269800 Fax 91415596
Ecole d'Ingénieurs-EIT
Rue Marcel Dassault **37004 Tours** Tel 47272020
Ecole des Ingénieurs-EIVP
57, boulevard Saint-Germain **75005 Paris** Tel 46342199 Fax: 46340201
Enseignement Militaire Supérieur de l'Armée de Terre-EMSST Ecole Militaire 1, place Joffre **75997 Paris** Tel 45553663 Fax 45553923
Ecole Navale-EN
Lanvéoc-Poulmic **29240 Brest** Tel 98275220 Fax 98273704
Ecole Nationale d'Administration-ENA
13, rue de l'Université **75007 Paris** Tel 49264545
Ecole Nationale de l'Aviation Civilo-ENAC
7, avenue Edouard Belin B.P. 4005
31055 Toulouse cedex Tel 61557999 Fax 61557927
Ecole Nationale des Chartes-ENC
19, rue de la Sorbonne **75005 Paris** Tel 46334182
Ecole Nationale du Génie Rural des Eaux & des Forêts-ENGREF Centre de Kourou B.P. 316 97379 Kourou cedex
Ecole Nationale du Génie Rural des Eaux & des Forêts-ENGREF Domaine de la Valette Avenue du Val de Montferrand **B.P. 5093, 34033** Montpellier cedex Tel 67544696
Ecole Nationale du Génie Rural des Eaux & des Forêts-ENGREF
14, rue Girarder **54042 Nancy cedex** Tel 83351020
Ecole Nationale du Génie Rural des Eaux & des Forêts-ENGREF 19, avenue du Maine **75732 Paris cedex 15** Tel 45498800 Fax 45498827

Ecole Nationale d'Ingénieurs-ENI 8, boulevard Anatole France B.P. 525 **90016 Belfort cedex** Tel 84213700 Fax 84540062

Ecole Nationale d'Ingénieurs-ENI Avenue Le Gorgeu **29287 Brest cedex** Tel 9803303 Fax 98472825

Ecole Nationale d'Ingénieurs-ENI Ille du Saulcy **57045 Metz cedex 1**Tel 87325305 Fax 87303989

Ecole Nationale d'Ingénieurs-ENI 50-60, rue Jean Parot **42023 Saint-Etienne cedex 2** Tel 77257140 Fax 77375560

Ecole Nationale d'Ingénieurs-ENI Chemin d'Azereix B.P. 311**65013 Tarbes cedex** Tel 62939821Fax 62936331

Ecole Nationale d'Ingénieurs des Travaux Agricoles-ENITA 1, Cours du Général de Gaulle **33170 Gradignan** Tel 56040303 Fax 56809056

Ecole Nationale d'Ingénieurs des Travaux Agricoles-ENITA Marmilhat **63370 Lempdes** Tel 73925236

Ecole Nationale d'Ingénieurs des Travaux Agricoles-ENITA Boulevard Olivier-de-Serres **21802 Quétigny cedex** Tel 80463001 Fax 80709148

Ecole Nationale d'Ingénieurs des Travaux des Eaux & Forêts-ENITEF Domaine des Barres **45290 Nogent-sur-Vernisson** Tel 38976020 Fax 38976144

Ecole Nationale d'Ingénieurs des Travaux de l'Horticulture & du Paysage-ENITHP 2, rue Le Nôtre **49045 Angers cedex** Tel 41483624 Fax 41731557

Ecole Nationale d'Ingénieurs des Techniques des Industries Agricoles & Alimentaires-ENITIAA Domaine de la Géraudière **44072 Nantes cedex 03** Tel 40400300 Fax 40596336

Ecole Nationale d'Ingénieurs des Travaux Ruraux & des Techniques Sanitaires-ENITRTS 1, quai Koch B.P. 1039 **67070 Strasbourg cedex** Tel 88256772 Fax 88370497

Ecole Nationale de la Météorologie-ENM Centre Météorologique du Mirail 42, avenue Gustave Corialis **31057 Toulouse** Tel 61079090 Fax 61079630

Ecole Nationale des Ponts & Chaussées-ENPC La CourtineBoîte 105 **93194 Noisy-le-Grand cedex** Tel 43044098

Ecole Nationale des Ponts & Chaussées-ENPC 28, rue des Saints-Pères **75007 Paris** Tel 42603413 Fax 42604072

Ecole Normale Supérieure-ENS 61, avenue du Président Wilson **94230 Cachan** Tel 46402000 Fax 47402074

Ecole Normale Supérieure-ENS 31, avenue Lombart **92260 Fontenay-aux-Roses** Tel 7026050 Fax 47023432

Ecole Normale Supérieure de Lyon-ENS 44, allée d'Italie **69375 Lyon cedex 7** Tel 72728000 Fax 72728080

Ecole Normale Supérieure-ENS 45, rue d'Ulm **75230 Paris cedex 05** Tel 43291225 Fax 43297369

Ecole Nationale Supérieure Agronomique-ENSA 9, place Pierre Viala **34060 Montpellier cedex** Tel 67612266 Fax 67612580

Ecole Nationale Supérieure Agronomique-ENSA 66, rue de Saint-Brieuc **35042 Rennes cedex** Tel 99285000 Fax 99287510

Ecole Nationale Supérieure Agronomique-ENSA 145, avenue de Muret **31076 Toulouse cedex** Tel 61428398 Fax 61423929

Ecole Nationale Supérieure de l'Aéronautique & de l'Espace-ENSAE 10, avenue Edouard Belin B.P. 4032 **31400 Toulouse** Tel 61334848 Fax 61334949

Ecole Nationale Supérieure de la Statistique & de l'Administration Economique-ENSAE Division des Statisticiens 3, avenue Pierre Larousse **92241 Malakoff cedex**

Tel 45401009 Fax 40921191

Ecole Nationale Supérieure d'Agronomie & des Industries Alimentaires-ENSAIA 2, avenue de la Forêt de Haye B.P. 172 **54500 Vandoeuvre cedex** Tel 83595959 Fax 83595955

Ecole Nationale Supérieure des Arts & Industries-ENSAIS 24, boulevard de la Victoire **67084 Strabsourg cedex** Tel 88355505 Fax 88241490

Ecole Nationale Supérieure des Arts& Industries Textiles-ENSAIT 2, place des Martyrs de la Résistance **59070 Roubaix cedex** Tel 20709482 Fax 20248406

Ecole Nationale Supérieure des Arts & Métiers-ENSAM Centre Régional d'Angers 2, boulevard de Ronceray B.P. 3525 **49035 Angers** Tel 41885425

Ecole Nationale Supérieure des Arts & Métiers-ENSAM 151, boulevard de l'Hôpital **75640 Paris cedex 13** Tel 43364955 Fax 45858704

Ecole Nationale Supérieure des Arts & Métiers-ENSAM Esplanade des Arts & Métiers **33405 Talence cedex** Tel 56807650

Ecole Nationale Supérieure Agronomique-ENSAT 145, avenue de Muret **31076 Toulouse cedex** Tel 61428396

Ecole Nationale Supérieure des Bibliothécaires-ENSB 21, rue d'Assas **75006 Paris** Tel 42223452

Ecole Nationale Supérieure de Biologie Appliquée à la Nutrition & à l'Alimentation-ENSBANA Campus de Montmuzard **21100 Dijon** Tel 80396600 Fax 80396773

Ecole Nationale Supérieure de Chimie-ENSC Ensemble Scientifique Cézeaux 24, avenue des Landais B.P. 71 **63170 Aubière** Tel 73264110

Ecole Nationale Supérieure de Chimie-ENSC B.P. 108, Domaine Universitaire **59652 Villeneuvo-d'Ascq cedex** Tel 20434889 Fax 20470599

Ecole Nationale Supérieure de Chimie-ENSC 8, rue de l'Ecole Normale **34075 Montpellier cedex** Tel 67635273 Fax 67635970

Ecole Nationale Supérieure de Chimie-ENSC 3, rue Alfred Werner **68093 Mulhouse cedex** Tel 89427020 Fax 89599859

Ecole Nationale Supérieure de Chimie-ENSC 11, rue Pierre et Marie Curie **75231 Paris cedex 05** Tel 43362525 Fax 43257975

Ecole Nationale Supérieure de Chimie-ENSC Avenue du Général Leclerc **35700 Rennes** Tel 99362995

Ecole Nationale Supérieure de Chimie-ENSC 118, route de Narbonne 31077Toulouse cedex Tel 61175656 Fax 61175600

Ecole Nationale Supérieure do Céramique Industrielle-ENSCI 47 à 73, avenue Albert Thomas **87065 Limoges cedex** Tel 55793480

Ecole Nationale Supérieure de Chimie & de Physique-ENSCP 351, Cours de la Libération **33405 Talence cedex** Tel 56807893

Ecole Nationale Supérieure de l'Electronique & de ses Applications-ENSEA Les Chênes Pourpres B.P. 105 **95000 Cergy** Tel 30736666 Fax 30736667

ENSEEG Domaine Universitaire B.P. 75 **38042 Saint-Martin d'Hères cedex** Tel 76826500 Fax 76826630

Ecole Nationale Supérieure d'Electrotechnique, d'Electronique, d'Informatique & d'Hydraulique-ENSEEIHT 2, rue Camichel **31071 Toulouse cedex** Tel 61588200 Fax 61620976

Ecole Nationale Supérieure d'Electricité & de Mécanique-ENSEM 2, rue de la Ciladelle, B.P. 850 **54011 Nancy cedex** Tel 83323901

Ecole Nationale Supérieure d'Electronique & de Radio-Electricité-ENSERB 351, Cours de la Libération 33405 Talence cedex Tel 56846500 Fax 56372023

Ecole Nationale Supérieure d'Electronique & de Radio-Eloctricité de Grenoble-ENSERG 23, avenue des Martyrs, B.P. 257 38016 Grenoble cedex Tel 76876976 Fax 76433796

Ecole Nationale Supérieure Féminine d'Agronomie-ENSFA 65, rue de Saint-Brieuc **35042 Rennes cedex** Tel 99285000 Fax 99287510

Ecole Nationale des Sciences Géographiques-ENSG (Institut Géographique National) 2-4, avenue Pasteur **94160 Saint-Mandé** Tel 43741215

Ecole Nationale Supérieure de Géologie-ENSG 94 avenue de Lattre de Tassigny B.P. 452 **54001 Nancy cedex 01** Tel 83328586 Fax 83302137

Ecole Nationale Supérieure d'Horticulture-ENSH 4, rue Hardy **78009 Versailles cedex** Tel 39506087

Ecole Nationale Supérieure d'Hydraulique & de Mécanique de Grenoble-ENSHMG Domaine Universitaire B.P. 95 **38402 Saint-Martin d'Hères cedex** Tel 76825000 Fax 76825001

Ecole Nationale Supérieure des Industries Agricoles & Alimentaires-ENSIAA 105, rue de l'Université **59509 Douai** Tel 27870360

Ecole Nationale Supérieure des Industries Agricoles & Alimentaires-ENSIAA 1, avenue des Olympiades **91305 Massy** Tel 69200523 Fax 69200230

Ecole Nationale Supérieure des Industries Agricoles & Alimentaires-ENSIAA Avenue du Val-de-Montferrand Locaux du CNEARC **34033 Montpellier** Tel 67543524

Ecole Nationale Supérieure des Industries Chimiques-ENSIC 1, rue Grandville, B.P. 451 **54042 Nancy cedex** Tel 83352121 Fax 83350811

Ecole Nationale Supérieure d'Ingénieures de Constructions Aéronautiques-ENSICA 49, avenue Léon Blum **31056 Toulouse cedex** Tel 61587500

Ecole Nationale Supérieure d'Ingénieurs- Electriciens-ENSIEG Domaine Universitaire, B.P. 46 **38402 Saint-Martin d'Hères cedex** Tel 76826200 Fax 76826301

Ecole Nationale Supérieure d'Ingénieurs des Etudesand and Techniques de l'Armement-ENSIETA Rue François Verny Pontanzen **29240 Brest Naval** Tel 98348800 Fax 98228376

Ecole Nationale Supérieure d'Ingénieures du Génie Chimique-ENSIGC Chemin de la Loge **31078 Toulouse cedex** Tel 61529241 Fax 61553861

Ecole Nationale Supérieure d'Informatique & de Mathématiques Appliquées-ENSIMAG BP 53X, Domaine Universitaire **38402 Saint-Martin d'Hères cedex** Tel 76514646 Fax 76513379

Ecole Nationale Supérieure d'Ingénieurs de Mécanique Energétique de Valenciennes-ENSIMEV Le Mont-Houy **59236 Valenciennes cedex** Tel 27424100

Ecole Nationale Supérieure des Industries Textiles-ENSITM 11, rue Alfred Werner **68093 Mulhouse cedex** Tel 89596320 Fax 89596319

Ecole Nationale Supérieure de Mécanique-ENSM 1, rue de la Noë **44072 Nantes cedex 03** Tel 40371600 Fax 40747406

Ecole Nationale Supérieure des Mines-ENSM Parc de Saurupt **54042 Nancy cedex** Tel 83574232 Fax 83579794

Ecole Nationale Supérieure des Mines-ENSM 60, boulevard Saint-Michel **75006 Paris** Tel 42349000 Fax 43259495

Ecole Nationale Supérieure des Mines-ENSM 158, Cours Fauriel **42023 Saint-Etienne cedex** Tel 77420123 Fax 77420000

Ecole Nationale Supérieure de Mécanique & d'Aérotechnique-ENSMA 2, rue Guillaume-le-Troubadour **86034 Poitiers cedex** Tel 49605050 Fax 40655000

Ecole Nationale Supérieure de Mécanique and des Microtechniques-ENSMM La Bouloie Route de Gray **25030 Besançon cedex** Tel 81666615 Fax 81886680

Ecole Nationale de la Santé Publique-ENSP Avenue du Professeur Léon Bernard **35043 Rennes cedex** Tel 99592936 Telex ENSP 741465 F

Ecole Nationale Supérieure de Physique-ENSP Domaine Universitaire B.P. 46 **38402 Saint-Martin d'Hères cedex** Tel 76826200 Fax 76826301

Ecole Nationale Supérieure de Physique-ENSP 13, domaine de Saint-Jérôme13397Marseille cedex 13 Tel 91288089 Fax91288067

Ecole Nationale Supérieure de Physique-ENSP 7, rue de l'Université **67000 Strasbourg** Tel 88355150 Fax 88607550

Ecole Nationale Supérieure du Pétrole and des Moteurs-ENSPM 1 & 4, avenue de Bois-Préau B.P. 311 **92506 Rueil-Malmaison cedex** Tel 47526604 Fax 47490411

Ecole Nationale Supérieure des Sciences Agronomiques Appliquées-ENSSAA 26, boulevard du Docteur Petitjean **21000 Dijon** Tel 80665412 Fax 80674205

Ecole Nationale Supérieure des Sciences Appliquées and des Technologies-ENSSAT
6, rue de Kerampont, B.P. 447
22305 Lannion
Tel 96465030

Ecole Nationale Supérieure, des Télécommunications-ENST
46, rue Barrault
75634 Paris cedex 13
Tel 45817777, Fax 45897906

Ecole Nationale Supérieure des, Télécommunications-ENST
B.P. 832
29285 Brest cedex
Tel 98001111, Fax 98455133

Ecole Nationale Supérieure, des Techniques Avancées-ENSTA
32, boulevard Victor, **75015 Paris ,** Tel 45524408, Fax 45525587

Ecole Nationale Supérieure, des Techniques Industrielles &, des Mines-ENSTIMA
6, avenue de Clavières, **30107 Alès cedex,** Tel 66785000, Fax 66785034

Ecole Nationale Supérieuredes Techniques Industrielles & des Mines-ENSTIMD
941, rue Charles Bourseul, B.P. 838, **59508 Douai cedex,** Tel 27932222, Fax 27883036

Ecole Nationale des Travaux Publics de l'Etat-ENTPE, B.P. 2
Rue Maurice Audin,
69120 Vaulx-en-Velin, Tel 74047104, Fax 72046254

Ecole Nationale Vétérinaire-ENV, 7, avenue du Général de Gaulle
94704 Maisons-Alfort cedex, Tel 43967100, Fax 53967125

Ecole Nationale Vétérinaire-ENV, B.P. 527
44026 Nantes cedex, Tel 40300840, Fax 40251705

Ecole Nationale Vétérinaire-ENV, 23, Chemin des Capelles
57076 Toulouse cedex, Tel 61491140, Fax 61310036

Ecole & Observatoire de Physique, du Globe-EOPGS, 5, rue René Descartes
67084 Strasbourg cedex, Tel 88416300

Ecole Polytechnique-EP, Route de Saclay
91128 Palaiseau cedex, Tel 69418200, Fax 69419442

Ecole Polytechnique Féminine-EPF, 3 bis, rue Lakanal
92330 Sceaux
Tel 46603331, Fax 46603994
Ecole Supérieure d'Agriculture-ESA
24, rue Auguste Fonteneau, B.P. 748
49007 Angers cedex
Tel 41885812, Fax 41882538
Ecole Supérieure d'Application des Corps Gras-ESACG
Rue Monge, Parc Industriel, **33600 Pessac,** Tel 56360044
Ecole Supérieure d'Agriculture de Purpan-ESAP
75, voie de Toec, **31076 Toulouse cedex,** Tel 61492311, Fax 61319148
Ecole Supérieure Du Bois-ESB, 6, avenue de Saint-Mandé, **75012 Paris,** Tel 46280933
Ecole Supérieure de Commerce-ESC, 680, Cours de la Libération, **33405 Talence cedex**
Tel 56807050, Fax 56374880
Ecole Supérieure de Commerce-ESC, 2, avenue de Provence-BP 124, **29272 Brest cedex**
Tel 98032501

Ecole Supérieure de Commerce-ESC, 4, boulevard Trudaine,
63037 Clermont-Ferrand cedex, Tel 73923971, Fax 73902645
Ecole Supérieure de Commerce-ESC, 29, rue Sambin, **21000 Dijon**
Tel 80721240, Fax 80744960
Ecole Supérieure de Commerce-ESC, 7, rue Hoche, **38000 Grenoble**
Tel 76430212, Fax 76569052
Ecole Supérieure de Commerce-ESC, 1, rue Emile Zola, **76087 Le Havre cedex**
Tel 35211218, Fax 35213296
Ecole Supérieure de Commerce-ESC, Avenue Gaston Berger, **59045 Lille cedex**
Tel 20526259

Ecole Supérieure de Commerce-ESC, 23, avenue Guy de Collongue, **69130 Ecully cedex**
Tel 72202525, Fax 78336169
Ecole Supérieure de Commerce-ESC., Domaine de Luminy-Case 911
13288 Marseille cedex 9, Tel 91269800, Fax 91415596
Ecole Supérieure de Commerce-ESC, 2300, avenue des Moulins, B.P. 6069
34030 Montpellier cedex, Tel 67404243, Fax 67451356,
Ecole Supérieure de Commerce-ESC, 8, route de la Jonelière-BP 72, **44003 Nantes cedex**
Tel 40373434, Fax 40373407
Ecole Supérieure de Commerce-ESC, Sophia Antipolis-BP 20, **06561 Valbonne cedex**
Tel 93954545

Ecole Supérieure de Commerce-ESC, 79, avenue de la République, **75011 Paris**
Tel 43553908, Fax 43559963
Ecole Supérieure de Commerce-ESC, 74, allée de Morlaas, **64000 Morlaas**
Tel 59028851

Ecole Supérieure de Commerce-ESC, 11, rue de l'Ancienne Comédie,
86001 Poitiers cedex, Tel 49882575
Ecole Supérieure de Commerce-ESC, 59, rue Pierre Taittinger-BP 302, **51061 Reims cedex**
Tel 26080604, Fax 26046993
Ecole Supérieure de Commerce-ESC, Boulevard André Siegfried, B.P. 188
76130 Mont-Saint-Aignan, Tel 35740300, Fax 35760662
Ecole Supérieure de Commerce-ESC, 20, bd. Lascrosses, **31068 Toulouse**

Tel 61294949, Fax 61294994
Ecole Supérieure de Commerce-ESC, 1, rue Léo Delibes, **37005 Tours cedex**
Tel 47274243., Fax 47275655
Ecole Supérieure de Chimie Industrielle-ESCIL, 43, boulevard du 11 novembre 1918
B.P. 2077
69616 Villeurbanne cedex, Tel 72448496, Fax 78946732
Ecole Supérieure de Chimie-ESCM, Faculté des Sciences, Avenue Normandie-Niémen
13397 Marseille cedex 13, Tel 91983901
Ecole Supérieure de Chimie Organique & Minérale-ESCOM, 12, rue Cassette
75006 Paris, Tel 45488743, Fax 40490249
Ecole Supérieure d'Electricité-ESE, Plateau de Moulon, **91190 Gif-sur-Yvette**
Tel 69418040, Fax 60191059
Ecole Supérieure d'Electronique, de l'Armée de Terre-ESEAT, Quartier Leschi
35998 Rennes, Tel 99833142, Ecole Supérieure de l'Energie
& des Matériaux-ESEM, Allée du Château, B.P. 6749, **45067 Orléans cedex 02**
Tel 38417052
Ecole Supérieure d'Electronique de l'Ouest-ESEO, 4, rue Merlet-de-la-Boullaye
49000 Angers, Tel 41866767, Fax 41879927
Ecole Supérieure de Fonderie-ESF, 44, avenue de la Division Leclerc, **92310 Sèvres**
Tel 4507819

Ecole Supérieure du Génie Militaire-ESGM, 3, rue de l'Indépendance Américaine
B.P. 1321,**78013 Versailles cedex,** Tel 39501654
Ecole Supérieure des Géomètres & Topographes-ESGT, 18, allée Jean Rostand, B.P. 77
91002 Evry cedex, Tel 60779740
Ecole Supérieure des Industries du Cacutchouc-ESICA, 60, rue Aube
944408 Vitry-sur-Seine cedex, Tel 46719122
Ecole Supérieure d' Informatique, d'Electronique & d'Automatique-ESIEA
9, rue Vésale, **75005 Paris** ,Tel 43377843
Ecole Supérieure d'Ingénieursen Electro-Technique & Electronique-ESIEE
Cité Descartes, 2, boulevard Blaise Pascal, B.P. 99
93162 Noisy-le-Grand cedex, Tel 45926500, Fax 45926699
Ecole Supérieure d'Ingénieurs en Génie Electrique-ESIGELEC
58, rue Méridienne, B.P. 1012, **76171 Rouen cedex,** Tel 35728094
Ecole Supérieure d'Ingénieurs-ESIM/ISBA, 28, rue des Electriciens, B.P. 64
13375 Marseille cedex 12, Tel 91499140
Ecole Supérieure d'Ingénierie & de Synthèse Organique Indsutrielle-ESIPSOI
Avenue Normandie-Niémen, **13397 Marseille cedex 13,** Tel 91983389
Ecole Supérieure des Industries Textiles-ESITP 85, rue d'Alsace
88000 Epinal, Tel 29355052
Ecole Supérieure d'Ingénieurs, & de Techniciens pour l'Agriculture-ESITPA
Rue Grande, BP. 201, **27100 Val-de-Reuil,** Tel 32591459, Fax 32598732
Ecole Spéciale Militaire de Saint-Cyr-ESM, Saint-Cyr Coëtquidan, B.P. 30
56381 Guer cedex, Tel 97757575, Fax 97757654
Ecole Supérieure de Métrologie-ESM, 941, rue Charles Bourseul, B.P. 838
59508 Douai cedex, Tel 27932222
Ecole Spéciale de Mécanique & d'Electricité-ESME, 4, rue Blaise Desgoffe
75006 Paris, Tel 45480370, Fax 45448066
Ecole Supérieire d'Optique-ESO, Centre Scientifique, B.P. 43-Bât 503

91406 Orsay cedex, Tel 69416811, Fax 69413192
Ecole Supérieure de Physique & Chimie Industrielle-ESPCI
10, rue Vauquelin, **75231 Paris cedex 05,** Tel 43377700, Fax 43314222
Ecole Supérieure du Soudage & de ses Applications-ESSA, 90, rue des Vanesses
ZI Paris Nord II, **93420 Villepinte,** Tel 49903600, Fax 49903659
Ecole Supérieure des Sciences Commerciales-ESSCA
B.P. 2007, 1, rue Lakanal, **49016 Angers cedex,** Tel 41483055, Fax 41734748
Ecole Supérieure des Sciences Economiques & Commerciales-ESSEC
Avenue de la Grande Ecole, B.P. 105, **95021 Cergy-Pontoise cedex,** Tel 3038300
Fax 34433010

Ecole Supérieure des Sciences & Technologies des Industries du Bois-ESSTIB
Allée des Hêtres, **88000 Epinal,** Tel 29340287
Ecole Supérieure des Sciences & Technologies de l'Ingénieur-ESSTIN
Parc Robert Bentz, **54500 Vandoeuvre,** Tel 83555444
Ecole Supérieure des Techniques Aérospatiales-ESTA, Bât. 502 bis, Compelxe scientifique
91405 Orsay cedex, Tel 69286857
Ecole Supérieure des Techniques Aéronautiques & de Construction, Automobile-ESTACA, 3, rue Pablo Neruda, **92300 Levallois-Perret,** Tel 47318100
Ecole Supérieure des Techniques Industrielles & des Textiles-ESTIT
Allée Lakanal, B.P. 209, **59654 Villeneuve-d'Ascq cedex,** Tel 20913521
Fax 20910318

Ecole Spéciale des Travaux Publics-ESTP 57, boulevard de Saint-Germain
75240 Paris cedex 05, Tel 46342199, Fax 46340201
Ecole Universitaire d'Ingénieurs-EUDIL B.P. 36
Université des Sciences & Techniques
59655 Villeneuve-d'Ascq cedex, Tel 20434343, Fax 20434995
Formation d'Ingénieurs de l'Université-FIUPSO Centre d'Orsay-Bât. 220
91405 Orsay Cedex, Tel 69417822
Ingénieur Manager, 41, rue du Port, **59046 Lille cedex,** Tel 20308314, Fax 20545666
Institut Agricole & Alimentaire-IAAL Université des Sciences, Bâtiment 06
59655 Villeneuve-d'Ascq cedex, Tel 20434343
Institut Catholique des Arts & Mtiers-ICAM, 6, rue Aubert, **59046 Lille cedex**
Tel 20935855, Fax 20931489
Institut de Chimie & de Physique, Industrielle-ICPI, 31, place Bellecour
69288 Lyon cedex 02, Tel 78375286, Fax 78423916
Institut de Management Hôtelier, International-IMHI, Avenue de la Grande Ecole
B.P. 105
95021 Cergy-Pontoise cedex, Tel 30383800, **Institut de Recherche & d'Enseignement Supérieur aux Techniques, de l'Electronique-IRESTE,** La Chantrerie
44300 Nantes, Tel 40633000
Institut des Sciences de l'Ingénieur-ISIM, Place Eugène Bataillon
34060 Montpellier cedex, Tel 67633030, Fax 67543079
Institut des Sciences de l'Ingénieur en Thermique Energétique & Matériaux-ISITEM
2, rue de la Houssiniere, **44072 Nantes cedex 03,** Tel 40373037
Institut des Sciences de la Matière & du Rayonnement-ISMRA, 5, avenue d'Edimbourg
14032 Caen cedex, Tel 31933714, Fax 31933912
Institut des Sciences & Techniques des Aliments-ISTAB, Avenue des Facultés

33405 Talence cedex, Tel 56806800
Institut des Sciences & Techniques-ISTG, Domaine Universitaire, B.P. 68
38402 Saint-Martin d'Hères cedex Tel 76514600, 76514711
Institut d'Etudes Supérieures d'Industrie & d'Economie Laitières-IESIEL
16, rue Claude Bernard, **75231 Paris cedex 05,** Tel 47071645
Institut d'Informatique d'Entreprise-IIE; 18, allée Jean Rostand, B.P. 77
91002 Evry cedex, Tel 60779740
Institut Européen d'Administration des Affaires-INSEAD, Boulevard de Constance
77305 Fontainebleau, Tel 60724000, Fax 60724242
Institut Français du Froid Industriel-IFF, 292, rue Saint-Martin, **75141 Paris cedex 03**
Tel 4271241

Institut "Image & Communication"-IMAC, Place du 8 mai 1945,
93206 Saint-Denis cedex, Tel 42354471
Institut Industriel du Nord-IDN, Cité Scientifique, B.P. 48
59651 Villeneuve-d'Ascq cedex, Tel 20910115, Fax 20671844
Institut International d'Administration Publique-IIAP, 2, avenue de l'Observatoire
75006 Paris, Tel 43264900
Institut National Agronomique, Paris-Grignon-INAPG, 16, rue Claude Bernard
75005 Paris, Tel 43371550, Fax 43318382
Institut National Agronomique Paris-Grignon-INAPG
Centre de Grignon, **78850 Thiverval-Grignon,** Tel 40544510
Institut National Polytechnique-INP, 46, avenue Félix Viallet, **38031 Grenoble cedex**
Tel 76574500, Fax 76468824
Institut National Polytechnique-INP, B.P. 3, 2, avenue de la Forêt de la Haye
54501 Vandoeuvre cedex, Tel 83595959, Fax 83574755
Institut National Polytechnique-INP Place des Hauts-Murats, B.P. 354,
31006 Toulouse cedex, Tel 61522137
Institut National de Promotion, Supérieure Agricole-INPSA, Rue des Champs-Prévois
21100 Dijon, Tel 80667227
Institut National des Sciences Appliquées-INSA, 20, av. Albert Einstein
69621 Villeurbanne cedex, Tel 78948112, Fax 72440800
Institut National des Sciences Appliquées-INSA, 20, avenue des Buttes de Coësmes
35043 Rennes cedex, Tel 99286400, Fax 99636705
Institut National des Sciences Appliquées-INSA, Place Emile Blondel-BP 8
76130 Mont-Saint-Aignan, Tel 35146350, Fax 35146034
Institut National des Sciences Appliquées-INSA, Avenue de Rangueil,
31077 Toulouse cedex, Tel 61559513, Fax 61559500
Institut National des Sciences & Techniques Nucléaires-INSTN, CEN-Saclay
91191 Gif-sur-Yvette cedex, Tel 68082159, 69082419
Institut National des Télécommunications-INT, Ilôt des Epinettes, 9, rue Charles Fourier
91011 Evry cedex, Tel 60764040, Fax 60776529,
Institut "Sciences & Technologies"-IST, 4, place Jussieu, **75252 Paris cedex 5**
Tel 43362525

Institut Supérieur Agricole de Beauvais-ISAB, Rue Pierre Waquet, B.P. 313
60026 Beauvais cedex, Tel 44458263
Institut Supérieur des Affaires-ISA, 1, rue de la Libération, **78350 Jouy-en-Josas**
Tel 39567000

Institut Supérieur d'Agriculture-ISA, 13, rue du Port, **59046 Lille cedex**
Tel 20308314, Fax 20428146
Institut Supérieur d'Agriculture-ISARA, 31, place Bellecour, **69288 Lyon cedex 2**
Tel 78421078, Fax 78423916
Institut Supérieur du Bâtiment & du Génie Civil-ISBA, 28, rue des Electriciens
B.P. 64, **13375 Marseille cedex 12,** Tel 91499140
Institut Supérieur d'Electronique-ISEP, 21, rue d'Assas, **75270 Paris cedex 06**
Tel 45545200, Fax 49545201
Institut Supérieur d'Electronique du Nord-ISEN, 41, boulevard Vauban
59046 Lille cedex, Tel 20306220, Fax 20545666
Institut Supérieur de Gestion-ISG, 8, rue de Lota, **75116 Paris**
Tel 45538746, 45536027, Telex 611631
Institut Supérieur d'Ingénieurs en Packaging-ISIP, Faculté des Sciences
Moulin de la Housse, B.P. 347, **51062 Reims cedex,** Tel 26050901
Institut Supérieur des Matériaux & de la Construction Mécanique-ISMCM
3, rue Fernand Hainaut, **93407 Saint-Ouen cedex,** Tel 46064085
Institut Textile & Chimique-ITECH, 181-203, avenue, Jean Jaurès, B.P. 7C34
69342 Lyon cedex 7, Tel. 78722831, Fax 78610333
Institute Universitaire des Systemes Thermiques Industriels-IUSTI-UP
Centre de Saint-Jerome, Avenue Normandie-Niemen, **13397 Marseille cedex**
Tel 91028956

Institut Universitaire des Sciences Pour l'Ingenieur-IUSPIM-GISAI
Campus Saint-Jerome, Avenue Escadrille, Normandie-Niemen,
13397 Marseille cedex 13, Tel 91282230/91980553
Universite de Technologie de Compiege-UTC, Centre Benjamin Franklin, B.P. 649
60206 Compiegne cedex, Tel 44209977, Fax 44864390

TECHNICAL INSTITUTES

Université d'Aix Marseille II, Avenue Gaston Berger, **13625 Aix-en-Provence cedex 1**
Tel 42265723, Fax 42266873,
Université de Picardie Jules Verne (Amiens), Avenue des Facultés-Le Bailly
80025 Amiens cedex, Tel 22534040, Fax 22896633
Université d'Angers, 4, boulevard Lavoisier, **49016 Angers cedex,** Tel 41735300
Université de Poitiers, 4, avenue de Varsovie, **16021 Angoulême cedex**
Tel 45254861

Université de Savoie (Chambéry), 9, rue de l'Arc en Ciel, B.P. 240
74942 Annecy-le-Vieux cedex, Tel 50232993
Université de Cergy-Pontoise, 95, rue Valère Collas, **95100 Argenteuil,** Tel (1) 39826759
Université de Clermont-Ferrand I, Ensemble universitaire des Cézeaux, B.P. 86
63172 Aubière cedex, Tel 73407575
Université Paul Sabatier (Toulouse III), 24, rue Embaques, **32000 Auch**
Tel 62055544

Université de Clermont-Ferrand I, Rue de l'École Normale, **15013 Aurillac**
Tel 71482988

Université d'Avignon, 2, rue Pierre Auguste Renoir, **84000 Avignon**
Tel 90841400

Université de Pau et des Pays de l'Adour, 3, avenue Darrigrand, **64100 Bayonne**
Tel 59633972

Université de Picardie Jules Verne (Amiens), Rue des Tanneurs, **60000 Beauvais**
Tel 44452121

Université de Franche-Comté (Besançon), 11, rue Engel Gros, B.P. 527
90016 Belfort cedex, Tel 84210100
Université de Franche-Comté, 30, avenue de l'Observatoire, B.P. 1559
25009 Besançon cedex, Tel 81666808
Université d'Artois, Rue du Moulin-à-Tabac
62408 Béthune cedex, Tel 21576080
Université des Sciences et Techniques du Languedoc (Montpellier II)
6, rue Barbeyrac, **34500 Béziers,** Tel 67289899
Université de Nice Sophia Antipolis, Quartier des Templiers, 650, route des Colles
06410 Biot, Tel 93654793
Université de Paris-Nord (Paris XIII), Centre de la Vache-à-l'Aise
Avenue de la Convention, **93000 Bobigny,** Tel (1) 48362419
Université d'Orléans, 63, avenue du Maréchal de Lattre de Tassigny
B.P. 4029, **18020 Bourges,** Tel 48242418
Université de Bretagne Occidentale, Rue de Kergoat, **29287 Brest cedex**
Tel 98316050

Université de Limoges, 3, rue Jules Vallés, **19100 Brive,** Tel 55867300
Université Louis Lumière (Lyon II), 5, avenue Pierre-Mendès-France, **69676 Bron cedex**
Tel 78772301

Université de Paris-Sud (XI), 9, avenue de la Division Leclerc, **94230 Cachan**
Tel 46641032

Université de Caen, Boulevard du Maréchal Juin, **14032 Caen cedex,** Tel 21344880
Universite de Littoral, Rue Louis-David-B.P. 689, **62228 Calais cedex,** Tel 21344880
Université Paul Sabatier (Toulouse III), 1, bd Henri Sizaire, **81100 Castres,** Tel 63590275
Université de Cergy-Pontoise, 1, allée des Chênes-Pourpres,
95014 Cergy-Pontoise cedex, Tel (1) 34254295
Université de Dijon, 1, allée des Granges-Forestières, **71100 Châlon-sur-Saône**
Tel 85489948

Université d'Orléans, Lycée Marceau, 12, rue Saint-Michel, **28000 Chartres**
Tel 37365188

Université d'Orléans, 15, rue de la République, **36000 Châteauroux,** Tel 54273162
Université de Poitiers, Rue Édouard Branly, **86400 Châtellerault,** Tel 49219610
Université de Haute-Alsace (Mulhouse), Place du 2 Février, **68000 Colmar**
Tel 89419141, 89415478, 89234142
Université Pascal Paoli (Corse), 7, avenue Jean Nicoli, BP 52, **20250 Corte**
Tel 95461731

Université de Picardie Jules Verne (Amiens), Lycée Jules Uhry,
7, rue Aristide Briand, BP 112, **60107 Creil cedex,** Tel 44240021
Université de Paris-Val-de-Marne (Paris XII), Avenue du Général de Gaulle
94010 Créteil cedex, Tel (1) 48989144, poste 2202,
Université de Picardie Jules Verne (Amiens), Centre de formation EDF-GDF

02880 Cuffies, Tel 23590002
Université de Caen, Montfoulon, **61250 Damigni,** Tel 33275650
Université de Dijon, Boulevard du Docteur Petijean, BP 510, **21014 Dijon cedex**
Tel 80396401, Fax 80396464
Université du Littoral, Centre universitaire de la Citadelle, B.P. 5526
59379 Dunkerque cedex 01, Tel 28590875
Université de Limoges, Avenue de la Gare, **19300 Égletons,** Tel 55930878
Université Nancy II, 7, rue des Fusillés de la Résistance, B.P. 392, **88010 Épinal**
Tel 29823789

Université de Rouen, 43, rue Saint-Germain , **27000 Évreux,** Tel 32312279, 32311230
Université d'Évry-Val-d'Essonne, 22, allée Jean Rosland, **91011 Évry cedex**
Tel (1) 69477200

Université de Paris-Val-de-Marne (Paris XII), 164, rue Grande, **77300 Fontainebleau**
Tel (1) 64221203

Université d'Aix-Marseille II, Rue Bayard, **05000 Gap,** Tel 92519870
Université des Sciences Sociales (Grenoblo II), Place Doyen Gosse
38041 Grenoble cedex, Tel 76284509, **Université des Antilles-Guyane**
Lotissement Branly, promenade du Lac, Bois-Chaudat, **97387 Kourou cedex (Guyane)**
Tel (594) 321200

Université d'Orléans, Rue Georges Brassens, **36100 Issoudun,** Tel 54031344
Université de Toulon et du Var, Avenue de l'Université, BP 132, **83957 La Garde cedex**
Tel 94142203

Université Rennes I, Rue Édouard Branly, BP 150, **22302 Lannion cedex**
Tel 96484334

Université de La Rochell, Rue de Roux, **17026 La Rochelle cedex,** Tel 46513900
Université de Nantes, 13, rue de la République, **85000 La Roche-sur-Yon,** Tel 51370523
Université du Maine (Le Mans), 25, rue de la Maillarderie, **53000 Laval,** Tel 43671492
Université de Bourgogne (Dijon), 12, rue de la Fonderie, **71200 Le Creusct,** Tel 85803030
Fax 85803615

Université du Havre, Place Robert Schuman, **76610 Le Havre,** Tel 35472847
Université du Maine, Route de Laval, BP 535, **72017 Le Mans cedex,** Tel 43833400
Université Lille II, Rue de l'Université, BP 16, **62037 Lens cedex,** Tel 21426846
Université Paris VIII, Ancien groupe scolaire Jules Ferry,
93290 Le Tremblay-en-France, Tel (1) 49631556
Université Charles de Gaulle (Lille III), 9, rue Auguste Angellier, **59046 Lille cedex**
Tel 20308585

Université de Limoges, Allée André Maurois, **87065 Limoges cedex,** Tel 55015342
Université Nancy I, Route de Romain, **54400 Longwy Haut,** Tel 82245683
Université de Bretagne occidentale (Brest), Rue Jean Zay, **56100 Lorient**
Tel 97373933

Université Aix-Marseille II, 163, avenue de Luminy, case 909,
13288 Marseille cedex 9, Tel 91412558

Université de Droit, d'Économie et des, Sciences (Aix-Marseille III),
Traverse Charles Susini, **13388 Marseille cedex 13,** Tel 91289300

Université de Marne la Vallée, 69, avenue Henri Dunant, **77100 Meaux,** Tel (1) 64332525
Université de Metz, Ile du Saulcy, **57045 Metz cedex 1,** Tel 87301525
Université de Besançon, Rue du Mont Bart, BP 427, **25211 Montbéliard,** Tel 81994600
Université de Pau et des Pays de l'Adour, 335, rue Saint-Pierre, **40000 Mont-de-Marsan** Tel 58063390

Université Clermont-Ferrand II, Avenue Aristide Briand, BP 408, **03107 Montluçon cedex,** Tel 70293655
Université des Sciences et Techniques du, Languedoc (Montpellier II), 99, avenue d'Occitanie, **34096 Montpellier cedex 5,** Tel 67144040
Université Paris VIII, 18-20, rue Anatole France, **93100 Montreuil-sous-Bois** Tel (1) 48708668

Université de Rouen Haute-Normandie, Rue Lavoisier, BP 246, **76137 Mont-Saint-Aignan cedex,** Tel 35146000
Université de Haute Alsace, 61, rue Albert Camus, **68093 Mulhouse cedex,** Tel 89424846
Université Nancy II, 2 bis, boulevard Charlemagne, **54000 Nancy,** Tel 83913131
Université Paris X-Nanterre, 4, allée de l'Université, **92001 Nanterre cedex,** Tel (1) 40977281
Université de Nantes, 3, rue du Maréchal Joffre, **44041 Nantes cedex 01,** Tel 40306090
Université de Nice Sophia Antipolis, 41, boulevard Napoléon III, **06041 Nice cedex** Tel 93217900

Université des Sciences et Techniques du, Languedoc (Montpellier II), 8, rue Jules Raimu **30907 Nimes cedex,** Tel 66628500, Fax 66628501
Université de Poitiers, Centre Du Guesclin, place Chanzy, **79000 Niort,** Tel 49242269 Fax 49285362

Université de Caen, Rue Max-Pol Fouchet, BP H 8, **50130 Octeville,** Tel 33082900 (Département GEII), 33082950 (Département TC)
Université d'Orléans, Rue d'Issoudun, BP 6729, **45067 Orléans cedex 2,** Tel 38417575
Université Paris-Sud (Paris XI), Plateau du Moulon, BP 127, **91403 Orsay cedex 3** Tel (1) 69410040

Université René Descartes (Paris V), 143, avenue de Versailles, **75016 Paris** Tel (1) 45244602

Université de Pau et des Pays de l'Adour, 1, avenue de l'Université, **64000 Pau** Tel 59840080

Université Bordeaux 1, 39, rue Paul Mazy, **24019 Périgueux cedex,** Tel 53532476
Université de Perpignan, Chemin de la Passio-Vella, **66860 Perpignan cedex** Tel 68671213

Université de Poitiers, 6, allée Jean Monnet, **86034 Poitiers cedex,** Tel 49453400
Université de Brotagne occidentale (Brest), 2, rue de l'Université, BP 319 **29191 Quimper cedex,** Tel 98900227
Université de Reims Champagne-Ardenne, Rue des Crayères, BP 257, **51059 Reims cedex,** Tel 26053000
Université Rennes 1, Rue de Clos-Courtel-BP 1144, **35014 Rennes cedex,** Tel 99362651
Université de Saint-Étienne, Centre Mendès-France, 12, avenue de Paris, 42300 Roanne Tel 77448900

Université Toulouse 1, 33, avenue du 8 Mai 1945m , **12006 Rodez cedex,** Tel 65671046

Université du Droit et de la Santé (Lille II), Rond-point de l'Europe,
59060 Roubaix cedex 01, Tel 20731310
Université Paris-Nord (Paris XIII), Place du 8 Mai 1945, **93206 Saint-Denis cedex 01**
Tel (1) 49406101

Université Jean Monnet (Saint-Étienne), 28, avenue Léon Jouhaux,
42023 Saint-Étienne cedex 2, Tel 77349999,
Université Joseph-Fourier (Grenoble I), Domaine universitaire, BP 67,
38402 Saint-Martin d'Hères cedex, Tel 76825300
Université de Nantes, 58, rue Michel-Ange, BP 420, **44606 Saint-Nazaire cedex**
Tel 40178159

Université Paris XII, Lycée professionnel, Place Eugène Courbet, 27, avenue de l'Europe
77176 Savigny-le-Temple, Tel (1) 64419291
Université Paris-Sud (Paris XI), 8, avenue Cauchy, **92330 Sceaux,** Tel (1) 46600683
Université Louis Pasteur (Strasbourg I), 3, rue Saint-Paul, **67300 Schiltigheim**
Tel 88812412, Fax 88811600
Université Robert Schuman (Strasbourg III), 72, route du Rhin,
67400 Illkirch-Graffenstaden, Tel 88676300
Université Paul Sabatier (Toulouse III), 1, rue Lautréamont, BP 1624, **65016 Tarbes cedex**
Tel 62444202

Université Toulouse-Le Mirail (Toulouse II), 5, allées Antonio Machado
31058 Toulouse cedex, Tel 61504503
Université Paul Sabatier (Toulouse III), 115, route de Narbonne, **31077 Toulouse cedex**
Tel 62258000

Université François Rabelais, 29, rue du Pont-Volant, **37023 Tours cedex,** Tel 47367504
Université de Reims, 9, rue du Québec, BP 396, **10026 Troyes cedex,** Tel 25820667
Université des Sciences Sociales (Grenoble II), 51, rue Barthélémy de Laffemas, BP 2123
26021 Valence cedex, Tel 75437254
Université du Hainaut-Cambrésis, Le Monte-Houy
59326 Valenciennes cedex, Tel 27141252
Université de Haute-Bretagne (Rennes II), 8, rue Montaigne, BP 1104,
56014 Vannes cedex, Tel 97632609
Université de Versailles-Saint-Quentinen-Yvelines, 10-12, avenue de l'Europe
78140 Vélizy, Tel (1) 39463838, Fax (1) 39463046
Université de Besançon,, Avenue Lac-de-Vaivre, **7000 Vesoul,** Tel 8475[illegible]800
Université Paris X-Nanterre, 1, chemin Desvallières, **92410 Ville-d'Avray**
Tel (1) 47097000

Université des Sciences et Techniques de Lille-Flandres-Artois (Lille I)
Cité scientifique, BP 179, **59653 Villeneuve-d'Ascq cedex,** Tel 20434164
Université Nancy 1, Le Montet, **54600 Villers-lès-Nancy,** Tel 83912208
Université Paris-Nord (Paris XIII), Avenue Jean-Baptiste Clément, **93430 Villetaneuse**
Tel (1) 49403128

Université Claude Bernard (Lyon I), 43, boulevard du 11 November 1918,
69622 Villeurbanne cedex, Tel 78948800
Université Claude Bernard (Lyon II), 17, rue de France, **69100 Villeurbanne,**
Tel 78034343

MAJOR RESEARCH ESTABLISHMENTS

ADEME

Agence de l'Environnement et de la maitrise de l'Energie

Environment and Energy Management Agency

ADEME Contributes to national energy control policy and also sponsors research and practical demonstrations.

ADEME , 27, rue Louis vicat, **75737 Paris cedex 15,** Tel 47652488, Telex 203712 Fax 46455236

AFNOR

Association Francaise de Normalisation French Standards Association

AFNOR assesses the need for new technology standards and coordinates standardization efforts by centralizing proposals, adopting standards, and promoting their use.

AFNOR

Tour Europe, Cedex 7, **92080 Paris La Defense** , Tel 42915555, Telex 611974, Fax 47748490

ANVAR

Agence Nationale de valorisation de la Recherche

National Agency for the Promotion of Research.

ANVAR's purpose is to encourage successful industrial innovation by small and medium-sized companies.

ANVAR

43, rue de caumartin, **75436 Paris cedex 09,** Tel 40178300, Telex 230298, Fax 42660220

BNM

Bureau National de Métrologie National Bureau of Metrology

BNM maintains, improves, and disseminates national measurement standards in five primary laboratories, operates calibration systems with 200 accredited laboratories, and ensures that all units of measure can be traced to national standards. It represents France at the International Conference for Weights & Measures and has cooperative agreements with the U.S. National Institute of Standards and Technology concerning national standards.

BNM

22, rue Monge, 75005 Paris, Tel 46344816, Telex 204313, Fax 46344863

BRGM

Bureau de Recherches Géologiques et Minières Bureau of Geological and Mining Research

BRGM, the French geological service and top authority on soil and the substratum, sponsors cartographic, geophysical, environmental, and civil engineering research. With 25 territories and 30 offices abroad, the Bureau also heads a diversified international mining conglomerate, assuming the risks of exploratory operations.

BRGM

Tour Mirabeau, 39-43, quai André Citroën, 75739 **Paris cedex 15,** Tel 40588900, Telex 780258 Fax 40588933

CEA

Commissariat à l'Energie Atomique

Atomic Energy Commission

Founded at the end of the Second World War, CEA is the research agency that defined the French nuclear apparatus. Today, France produces 75% of its electricity with nuclear reactors and possesses an autonomous nuclear deterrent force. CEA sponsors research in nuclear physics (fusion by magnetic confinement, nuclear safety, and waste management), theoretical physics, astrophysics, materials, electronics, robotics, chemistry, geochemistry, biomolecular and biomedical research, and even plant physiology. It also heads a diversified industrial conglomerate.

CEA

31-33, rue de la Fédération, 75752 **Paris,** Tel 40561000, Telex 200671, Fax 40562970

CEMAGREF

Centre d'Etudes du Machinisme Agricole, du Génie Rural, des Eaux and des Forêts

National Centre for Agricultural Machinery, Rural Engineering, Rivers and Forests

CEMAGREF conducts scientific and technological research, development, and technology transfer related to rural development. Fields of expertise include water resource management (hydrobiology, water quality, agricultural hydraulics, and aquaculture), management and protection of renewable natural resources (forests, mountainous areas and endangered zones) and developments of machinery for agriculture, forestry, and aquaculture. Transfering French technology abroad, especially to developing nations, is a priority.

CEMAGREF

Parc de Tourvoie

92160 **Antony,** Tel 40966121, Telex 204565, Fax 46663744

CIRAD

Centre de Coopération Internationale en Recherche Agronomique pour le Dévelopement

Centre for International Cooperation in Agriculture and Development.

Specializing in tropical and subtropical agriculture, CIRAD works closely with African, and Latin American countries, contributing to development through research, experiments, training, and dissemination of scientific and technical information.

CIRAD

42, rue Scheffer, **75166 Paris,** Tel 47043215, Telex 620871, Fax 47551530

CNAM

Conservetoire National des Arts et Métiers

CNAM is a State-run establishment of a scientific, cultural and professional nature. Its principal aims are to ensure higher and further education for adults. It is also a centre of fundamental, applied and industrial research as well as a centre of scientific and technological information thanks to its technological museum (the largest in the world) and its library. CNAM is organised in "departments" (industrial material, economics and management, mathematics and computer science, chemistry, etc.) "institutes and specialised centres". It awards it's own diplomas. Certain DEA may be prepared as well as doctorates (chemistry, process automation, mechanics, ergonomics, staff management...).

292, rue Saint-Martin, **75141 Paris cedex 03,** Tel 40272000, Telex 240247

CNES

Centre National d'Etudes Spatiales

National Space Research Centre

CNES, the French National Space Agency, implements the space programmes approved by the French government, comprising research and technology, space science, applications programmes, and launcher development. Based in Paris, CNES operates a launch vehicle office at Evry, a Technical Centre in Toulouse and launch facilities at Kourou, French Guyana.

CNES
2, Place Maurice Quentin
75039 Paris cedex 1
Tel 45087500, Telex 214674, Fax 45087676

CNET

Centre National d'Etudes des Télécommunications

National Centre for Telecommunications Studies

The research branch of France Télécom, the publicly-owned operator of French telecommunications, CNET sponsors basic and applied research for development of telecommunication networks, publishes specifications and provides technical assistance and expertise.

CNET
30-40 rue du Général Leclerc
92131 Issy-les-Moulineaux
Tel 45294444, Telex 250317, Fax 45295878

CNRS

Centre National de la Recherche Scientifique

National Centre for Scientific Research

CNRS, the largest public research organisation in Europe, is dedicated primarily to fundamental research in mathematics, physics, chemistry, astronomy, biology and medicine, social sciences, the humanities and engineering; interdisciplinary programmes explore energy, natural resources, and the environment. In addition to 370 laboratories of its own, CNRS operates 1000 laboratories in conjunction with French universities, schools of engineering, and research agencies. 59 cooperative agreements with foreign countries enable CNRS experts to work abroad. The centre exchanges researchers with the National Science Foundation and the National Institutes of Health in the U.S. for example.

CNRS
3, rue Michel-Ange, **75016 Paris**
Tel 44964650, Fax 44965002

Collège de France

One of the most prestigious institutions, the "Collège de France" plays an important part in a great number of sciences

* The lectures are open to the public and free. The laboratories however are open only to persons having an authorization from the Professor/laboratory Director.
* It prepares for no examinations, and confers no degrees or titles.
* Each professor chooses every year the subject of his course. The scientific research thus enjoys a good deal of independence and autonomy.

Collège de France
11, Place Marcelin Berthelot
75231 Paris cedex
Tel 44271211, Fax 44271109

CSI

Cité des Sciences et de l'Industrie

City of Science and Industry

CSI develops themes and topics of interest to the public, demonstrates the workings of science, technology and industry; reintroduces history into science and technology; and develops projects with educational and training programmes.

CSI
30, avenue Corentin Cariou
75930 Paris cedex 19
Tel 40057000, Fax 40057344

CSTB

Centre Scientifique and Technique du Bâtiment

National Centre for Construction Research

CSTB sponsors economic, social, and technical research related to construction and housing. Fields of interest include structural dynamics, quality control of equipment and materials, fire safety, acoustics, lighting, environmental effects, "smart" buildings, and construction in developing countries as well as in intemperate zones.

CSTB
4, avenue du Recteur Poincaré
75782 Paris cedex
Tel 40502828, Fax 4525615

EHESS

Ecole des Hautes Etudes en Sciences Sociales

It has replaced the sixth section of the "Ecole Pratiques des Etudes".

Its aims are a high level of scientific research (and teaching) in the field of social sciences.

National degrees for 3rd cycle studies and School degrees are awarded:

* enrolment is only possible on presentation of a dossier containing a research project
* the normal duration of studies is 3 years.

EHESS
54, boulevard Raspail
75006 Paris
Tel 49542525, Fax 45449311

EPHE

Ecole Pratique des Hautes Etudes

The EPHE aims at advancing science in fundamental research and applied research in subjects covered by its three sections:

* Earth Sciences and Energy.
* Historical and Philological Sciences.
* Religious Sciences.

It welcomes and trains research-workers and prepares students for the school diploma and for national third cycle study diplomas.

* Enrolment as an occasional student is not subject to any age limit, possession of a specific University qualification, or specific nationality, but acceptance from the tutor must be obtained
* After 2 years studies and presentation of research work regular students may obtain the degree awarded by the school.

EPHE
12-14, rue Corvisart

75013 Paris
Tel 44085151, Fax 44085152

FNSP
Fondation Nationale des Sciences Politiques
National Foundation of Political Science
The National Foundation of Political Science aims at promoting and diffusing in France and abroad political, economic and social sciences.
It manages specialised documentation services and administrates different research services.
FNSP
27, rue Saint Guillaume, **75341 Paris cedex 7,** Tel 45495050, Fax 42223126

IFREMER
Institut Français de Recherche pour l'Exploitation de la Mer
French Oceanographic Research Institute
IFREMER conducts basic research in geoscience, biology, chemistry, physical oceanography, and mathematical modeling. High-technology IFREMER developement, for their own purposes and on behalf of science and industry, have included high-tech fishing trawlers, robots, submersibles, sensors, and acoustic-imaging equipment. Directing the nation's oceanographic fleet and campaigns, the Institute also operates the French coastal observation network, which monitors water quality in shellfish producing areas.
IFREMER
155, rue Jean-Jacques Rousseau
92138 Issy-Les-Moulineaux
Tel 46482100, Telex 631912, Fax 46482248
IGN
Institut Géographique National
National Geographical Institute
IGN implements in France, geodetic and levelling networks, aerial surveys and updated topographic and derived maps. It conducts remote sensing for geographical purposes, creates and publishes documents, manages a library of documents and photographs, and supervises land surveys. It also controls the French Geographic Sciences Colleges.
IGN
136 bis, rue de Grenelle
75700 Paris
Tel 43988000, Fax 45550785
INED
Institut National d'Etudes Démographiques
National Demographic Institute
INED was founded in 1945 for the scientific and technical study of all aspects of demographics. It collects documentation, does surveys and polls, carries out experiments, follows experiments in other countries and disseminates demographic information.

INED
27, rue du Commandeur, **75675 Paris cedex,** Tel 43201345, Fax 43277240

INRA
Institut National de Recherche Agronomique

National Institute for Agricultural Research
INRA's mission is agricultural research, development and technology transfer. The Institute sponsors programmes on physical and chemical changes in soil, rational management and protection of national resources, improving plant and animal species, biotechnology development, and processing agricultural products into foods. INRA also sponsors social science programmes aimed at comprehending rural and agricultural areas as well as the transformations they are undergoing.
INRA
147, rue de l'Université, **75111 Paris cedex 7,** Tel 42759000, Fax 47059966

INRETS
Institut National de Recherche sur les Transports et leur Sécurité
National Institute for Transport and Safety Research
The objective of INRETS is to improve public transportation and traffic patterns through technical, economic and social research on technological development. It provides consulting services, promotes technology transfer, disseminates scientific information and sponsors personnel training through research in France and abroad.

INRETS
2, avenue du Général Malleret-Joinville
94114 Arcueil
Tel 47407000, Fax 45475606
INRIA
Institut National de Recherche en Informatique et Automatique
National Dataprocessing and Automation Research Institute
INRIA conducts research, produces experimental systems and promotes technology transfer in the fields of parallel-machine architecture, computer languages, artificial intelligence, automation and robotics and man-machine communication.
INRIA
Domaine de Voluceau-Rocquencourt B.P. 105
78153 Le Chesnay cedex
Tel 39635511, Fax 39635330

INSEE
Institut National de la Statistique et des Etudes Economiques
National Institute of Statistics and Economics
Under the auspices of the Ministry of Economy and Finance, INSEE operates 38 national, regional, and inter-regional centres to collect, disseminate, and utilize statistical information of a demographic, social and economic nature; it coordinates Frech statistical systems in all fields; and develops statistical as well as economic expertise through teaching, research, and technical assistance to developing nations.
INSEE
18, boulevard Adolphe Pinard
75675 Paris cedex 14
Tel 45401212, Fax 45407476

INSERM
Institut National de la Santé et de la Recherche Médicale

National Institute for Health and Medical Research
INSERM conducts R&D on the physical, mental, and social factors that condition the health of the individual and society as a whole, biology, medicine, and all disciplines related to health and medical progress as well as all means of intervention for the prevention and treatment of diseases and their consequences and for the improvement of the health of the population. Approximately 2000 researchers employed by other institutions are involved in INSERM research projects.

INSERM
101, rue de Tolbiac
75654 Paris cedex 13
Tel 44236000, Fax 45856856

Institut Curie
Curie Institute
The Curie Institute, a non-profit foundation, was formed by merger of the Radium Institute (founded by Marie Curie and Claudius Regaud in 1911) and the Curie Foundation (founded in 1920 for medical applications of radiation). It is made up of 3 divisions (Medicine and Hospitals, Biology, Physics and Chemistry) dedicated solely to basic and applied research on the prevention, diagnosis, and ionizing radiation on normal and pathological tissue; as well as the study of radioactive bodies and oncology.

Institut Curie
26, rue d'Ulm
75231 Paris cedex 5
Tel 43299667, Fax 43255271

Institut Pasteur
Pasteur Institute
Founded in 1886 by public grant, the Pasteur Institute is a centre for fundamental research in microbiology, virology, immunology, molecular and cellular biology; applied research in human and veterinary medicine, hygiene, agriculture and industry; higher education in microbiology, immunology, epidemiology and other fields.
The Pasteur network of affiliates extends from Lyons and Lille in France to the French territories of Guadeloupe and New Caledonia as well as Greece, Tunisia, Algeria, Morocco, Senegal, the Central African Republic, the Ivory Coast, Madagascar, Iran and Vietnam.

Institut Pasteur
25-28, rue du Docteur Roux
75724 Paris cedex 15
Tel 45688000, Fax 43069835

ICPC
Laboratoire Central des Ponts and Chaussées
Central Public Works Laboratory

LCPC deals with scientific and technical questions related to the environment, urban engineering, and civil engineering. Under the auspices of the Ministry in charge of public works, housing, transportation and the sea, LCPC provides technical assistance to a network of laboratories, including 7 regional centres and 6 specialized research centres.

LCPC
58, boulevard Lefebvre

75732 Paris cedex 15
Tel 40435000, Fax 40435498

MHN
Muséum d'Histoire naturelle
Natural History Museum
The Natural History Museum is the active centre of research concerning natural sciences. The courses, which are open to the public and free of charge, are given by eminent professors.
MHN
57, rue Cuvier 75231 Paris cedex 5 Tel 40793000, Fax 43435473
MSH
Maison des Sciences de l'Homme
Its task is to promote the study of human society. It strives to develop the means of collective work and to bring together the various research centres. It also encourages collaboration between specialists of different disciplines, organizes symposiums and publishes books and journals.
MSH
54, boulevard Raspail 75210 Paris cedex 6 Tel 49542000, Fax 45488353
Observatoire de Paris
Paris observatory
The departments with their headquarters in Paris do research in visual and photographic astronomy, statistics, instrumental astronomy, etc. The international office of time is to be found here.
The departments with their headquarters in Meudon are specialised more in solar research, the planets, the comets and radioastronomy.
It also includes rich libraries, a historic and scientific museum, a documentation centre.
Observatoire de Paris 61, avenue de l'Observatoire 75014 Paris Tel 40512221, Fax 43541804

ONERA
Office National d'Etudes et de Recherches Aérospatiales
National Institute for Aerospace Studies
Dedicated to basic and applied aerospace research, ONERA has played a major role in the development of Concorde, Airbus, Mirage, Rafale, the Dauphin helicopter used by the US Coast Guard, Ariane and Hermès. It also promotes technology transfer and applications outside the aerospace field, offering technical support to industry in aerodynamics, flight systems, testing and computers. ONERA cooperates with NASA, the US Air Force, US Army Laboratories, and the NATO Advisory Group for Aerospace Research and Development (AGARD).
ONERA
29, avenue de la Division Leclerc
92320 Châtillon, Tel 46571160, Fax 46562523

ORSTOM

Institut Français de Recherche Scientifique pour le Dévelopment en Coopération
French Scientific Research Institute for Cooperative Development
ORSTOM conducts research in physics, biology and human sciences aimed at promoting economic progress in developing nations.
Forty percent ORSTOM researchers work outside France in 50 research centres located

in 30 tropical and Mediterranean countries.
ORSTOM 213, rue La Fayette **75480 Paris cedex 10** Tel 48037777, Fax 48030829

Palais de la Découverte
The "Palais de la Découverte" aims at presenting Fundamental scientific experiments to all audiences. Subjects proposed are: mathematics with astronautics and computer science, astronomy and outer space, earth sciences, physics and nuclear physics, electricity, chemistry, biology, medicine and the history of science.

It includes a planetarium, a library, a photo library and a cinema. It organises visits and lectures and publishes "La Revue du Palais de la Découverte".
Palais de la Découverte Avenue Franklin D. Roosevelt **75008 Paris** Tel 43591821, Fax 40748181

TAAF
Terres Australes et Antarctiques Françaises
French Southern and Antarctic Territories
TAAF maintains French sovereignty on the four Antarctic districts of Terre Arelic, Amsterdam, Kergnelen and Crozet. Its permanent mission is to conduct research activities in geophysics, biology and oceanology.
TAAF 34, rue des Renaudes **75017 Paris** Tel 47669241, Fax 47669123
Studies in Dental Surgery
The State Degree in Dental Surgery is awarded at the end of five years of study, to students who clear all the examinations and defend a thesis.
The University Degree in Dental Surgery is awarded to foreign students under the same conditions as those applicable to the state degree. However, it does not entitle them to practise in France.
The First year syllabus is the same as that of the 1st year of medical studies (PCEM1).

As in the case of medical studies, admission into the second year is subject to conditions of grading and number of places granted.
Studies in the following four years take plạce in one of the 16 odontology departments. They include theory and practice, group work, clinical and hospital training.
Any student who has failed the second-year examinations four times, is permanently excluded from dental studies.
At the end of the fifth year, students must present a thesis which entitles them to a doctor's degree in dental surgery.
Third cycle
Holders of the Degree of Doctor of Dental Surgery may prepare for either specialization or research:
* **The Higher Studies in Dental Surgery Certificates-CES** (A and B). One year preparation for each is necessary. These degrees increase student's knowledge of different branches of dental art. They confirm an aptitude for applied research techniques
* **The Certificate of Special Clinical Studies Marked Orthodontics-CECSMO.** Training (practical and theoretical) lasts four year.
* **The Doctorate.** Doctoral studies include the preparation of a DEA (1 or 2 years) and the Doctorate (2 to 4 years).
* The title of Doctor is conferred after the candidate defends an original work of a very

high level.

Studies in Pharmacy

Studies leading to the State Degree of Doctor in Pharmacy include: First cycle-2 years. Admission into second year is through a highly competitive examination. No one may enrol more than twice in first year studies.

Second cycle-2 years.

Third cycle

One year training in hospital, university and

* either one more year of professionally-oriented training with a thesis that has to be defended (General pharmacy)
* or, for students having succesfully passed examinations of the pharmacy "internal", four years of specialisation during which they present a thesis to get the Specialized Studies Degree (DES). This thesis may be used to obtain the State Degree of Doctor in Pharmacy.

Scholarships

French language

A certain number of scholarships and fellowships are offered every year by the French Government to Indian nationals for high level French studies, in accordance with the bilateral agreement signed between the two countries. The "University Grants Commission", New Delhi, conducts the selection of candidates for the scholarships and fellowships.

The selection process for the award of scholarships/fellowships begins in January/February each year.

Application forms may be obtained from the middle of January from the:

University Grants Commission

Bahadurshah Zafar Marg New Delhi 110002

Selected candidates will be given air passage. Tuition fees for the course selected in the University or specialized institution and social security cover as well as monthly allowance will be paid by the French Government.

Scholarships-12 months, renewable

They are meant for teachers or students of French holding an MA degree in French who intend to enrol for a

* "Diplôme d'études approfondies" (DEA)
* "Diplôme d'études supérieures spécialisées" (DESS)
* Diploma or Degree for the teaching of French as a foreign language (Maîtrise du FLE)
* Degree in translation or interpretation.

Fellowships-1 to 3 months

These fellowships are reserved for teachers of French with an M.A. in French who wish to

* Submit a thesis/high level research in a French University
* Take part in a summer course on teaching methodology
* Gather documents not available in India for research work.

Seminars and Workshops

The Centre for the Development of French Studies in India (CEDEFSI) organizes every year a one-month national seminar for teachers of French from all over India, it is followed up with regional seminars and workshops.

These seminars and workshops are meant to train teachers of French in methodology and pedagogy. They will learn the latest teaching techniques for the teaching of French as a foreign language.

Other training sessions are organized from time to time in different fields for example: French as a speciality language such as French for the Hotel and Tourism industry, French for

Business and Commerce, French for International relations, etc. in different parts of the country.

Whom to contact

Please contact the regional offices whose addresses are given below. They will be able to answer all your questions about the teaching of French in their respective regions.

L'Attaché Linguistique
Consulat Général de France
Datta Prasad Building, Nawroji Gamadia Cross Rd No 10, **Bombay 400026**

L'Attaché Linguistique,
Consulat Général de France, 26 Park Street, **Calcutta 700016**

L'Attaché Linguistique, **Alliance Française,** 38, rue Suffren
Pondicherry 605001

L'Attaché Linguistique, **Alliance Francaise**
Adarsh Nagar, **Hyderabad 500483**

For further information, you may contact:

CEDEFSI
French Embassy, 2, Aurangzeb Road
New Delhi 110011
Tel 3014682, Fax (91-11) 3016441

A few scholarships for Social Sciences are offered by the French Government every year through the department of education, Indian Ministry of Human Resources Development. The duration of these scholarships is one academic year.

Under the Indo-French Exchange Programme, collaboration in Social Sciences exists between UGC, ICSSR, ICHR and

Maison des Sciences de l'Homme (MSH)
54, boulevard Raspail **75270 Paris cedex 6** Tel 45443849

For further information on these grants, kindly contact:

University Grants Commision
Bahadurshah Zafar Marg New Delhi 110002 Tel 3310059, 3312429, 3313390, 3312305 Telex 31-66180 AIU IN
Gram ASINDU

Indian Council of Social Science Research
35 Ferozeshah Road New Delhi 110001 Tel 387517, 381571, Fax 388037

Indian Council of Historical Research
35 Ferozeshah Road New Delhi 110001 Tel 386033, 388747

Painting, Sculpture, Graphics

Three scholarships, of two to three months' duration, are available every year for young Indian artists holding a BFA or an equivalent degree from a recognized institution. The selection is made in consultation with the Department of Culture, Ministry of Human Resources Development, New Delhi. Candidates with practical knowledge of the French language are given priority. The selected candidates will go to a French college of art and work under the guidance of a professor. International air passages and all expenses in France of the selected candidates are borne by the French Government.

Architecture

One scholarhip of 12 months duration is available. Minimum qualification required is a B.

Arch. degree. Knowledge of French language is compulsory, as it is the medium of instruction in French schools of architecture. Other conditions remain the same as for the fine arts scholarships described above.

Theatre

Two scholarships are available for training in acting, direction, mime, art direction, etc. The duration is usually of 3 months. A practical knowledge of the French larguage is necessary. Students of the National School of Drama (NSD), New Delhi, are given priority. The selected candidates will go to France for a practical training either in a school of drama or with a professional performing troupe. Other conditions remain the same as for the fine arts scholarships described above.

Fashion/design

Three scholarships are available under this category. All aspects of fashion such as modelling, designing, marketing, fashion forecasting are covered. Knowledge of French is desirable. Students of the National Institute of Fashion Technology (NIFT), New Delhi, and the National Institute of Design (NID), Ahmedabad, have priority. Other conditions remain the same as for the fine arts scholarships described above.

For further information, please contact: Cultural Attaché, the French Embassy.

Journalists in Europe, a non-profit making organisation, admits foreigners into its sessions (October-June). Each year, the programme brings together some 30 journalists from around the world who spend eight months researching and writing on European affairs using Paris as their base.

Since its creation in 1974, 507 journalists from 79 countries have taken part.

Participants have the opportunity to learn first-hand about the countries of Europe, to explore the relations between them as well as between Europe and the rest of the world and to examine the workings of the European Community and its institutions.

The programme includes seminars given by experts in politics, economics and culture as well as reporting assignments in the field. Both are designed to equip journalists with a working knowledge of the key issues affecting Europe today. Programme participant write for the Journalists in Europe's quarterly magazine. They are at liberty to continue working for their own media when time permits and can use the information gathered during the course of the programme for their own articles.

Applicants should be between 25 and 35 years of age and have at least 4 years experience as full-time journalists. A working knowledge of French and English is required: both must be read, understood and spoken, one of the two must be written

The Journalists in Europe Indian Committee is responsible for screening all applications from Indian journalists before sending the dossiers to Paris for selection by the board of administrators of journalists in Europe.

A substantial amount of information is required for the selection procedure. For further details and application forms, interested journalists are advised to contact:

Mr. Jaya Raj, Secretary, Journalists in Europe Indian Committe
8/6 WEA, Karol Bagh, New Delhi 110005, Tel 5720096, 2252402

Complete dossiers must be received by the above mentioned before January 31st.

Journalists in Europe 33 rue du Louvre, **75002 Paris** Tel (1) 45088671, Fax (1) 45081518

FEMIS--The French Film and Television Institute--offers Summer courses for foreign students (below 30 years) who would like to study French cinema and its methods.

The course content is neither specialised nor technical. It includes several discussions which help in understanding the role and the duties of the people involved in creating a film. The duration of the course is 8 weeks with 5 days of intensive classes per week. Since it is not possible to know in advance the level of interested students nor their individual requirements, a general outline of the course is given below.

The class sessions comprise of theory and aesthetics as well as practicals which would require the participants to work in teams to make 10 -minute documentary films on a video format (Beta system).

Main subjects

The main subjects are as follows:

* Projection and analysis of French classics and modern films, followed by discussions with teachers or sometimes those who worked on the film (director, script writer, camera man, editor, etc.)
* Script writing in French cinema
* Effects of light and frame (cinema and video). Painting and Cinema
* Direct sound recording, dubbing and mixing. Analog and digital techniques
* Documentaries filming the "real"
* Cultural policy in France with respect to cinema, financing of films, copy rights
* Practical work--filming a documentary--in 3 or 4 teams, post-production work (produced with the means provided by FEMIS). Each team deals with all the aspects of production by rotation.

Personalities from the French cinema are sometimes invited for discussion during general lecture sessions (producers, directors, script writers, art director, etc.). Visits to museums, laboratories, etc. are also organised to study technical and aesthetic aspects such as special effects.

Other activities could be considered towards the end of the course. These depend on the interests of the participants, the technical and financial means available, etc.

Participants are invited to Film Festivals which take place in France during their stay.

Who can apply

Maximum number of participants are restricted to 12 per year from all over the world. Selection is done on the basis of application (CV, motivation, etc.). Knowledge of French (written and spoken) is compulsory as all the course activities are in French.

One or two scholarships are offered each year by

Audiovisual Section, French Embassy
2, Aurangzeb Road
New Delhi 110011

A few scholarships are offered to Indian nationals for training in public administration at ENA and IIAP. They are reserved for civil servants and the preselection is done by the

Ministry of Personnel
Public Grievances and Pensions, Department of Personnel and Training
North Block, New Delhi 110001

ENA's aim is to train civil servants for top executive positions in the French administration. There is a 16-month study cycle reserved for foreign civil servants recommended by their government. A shorter course of 8 months duration is also offered.

Ecole Nationale d'Administration (ENA)
13, rue de l'Université, 75007 Paris, Tel 49264545, Fax 42602695

Institut International d'Administration Publique, (IIAP)
2, avenue de l'Observatoire, 75006 Paris, Tel 43264900, Fax 46332638

IIAP's aim is to train and perfect foreign civil servants as well as to contribute to the spread of French administrative science and techniques abroad. Foreign civil servants must be recommended by their Government. Long duration courses in specialized areas of public administration are also offered.

1. FIVE LEADING FRENCH "GRANDES ECOLES" OFFER A TWO-YEAR MASTER'S IN MANAGEMENT (HEC PARIS-ESSEC PARIS-ESCP PARIS-ESC LYON-CERAM-NICE)

This Master's programme is designed to train future senior managers for European and international companies. Students are expected to acquire a holistic approach to business management.

Eligibility

Applicants must have successfully completed a Bachelor's degree or its equivalent, obtained after at least 3 years of post-secondary study outside France.

Application Procedure

Application forms available from CIAM (French Graduate Management Admissions Board), together with required documents must be returned to CIAM not later than 1st February of the year during which admission is sought.

Admission Tests

Eligible applicants will receive all documents regarding admission tests. New Delhi is the test centre for India. These tests are usually conducted every year in April.

Management Programme in French

Written tests

* Either the Graduate Management Admission Test-GMAT. Taken not later than January of the year desired and
* The "Certificat Pratique de Français Commercial et Economique" conducted by the Paris Chamber of Commerce or French tests conducted by CIAM.

or

* The MAGE: "Mesure des Aptitudes aux Etudes de Gestion" (3 hours)- French equivalent of GMAT (information from CIAM).

Oral test

(45 minutes)

A personal interview with a panel of examiners to evaluate the applicant's maturity, motivation and aptitude for an international management career.

The jury will take into account the results of the above examinations as well as the applicant's record (academic and extra-curricular activities).

Special management programme in English

(HEC—International Track)

Written tests

* The Graduate Management Admission Test-GMAT
  Not later than January of the current year.
* The Test of English as a Foreign Language-TOEFL
  Not later than January of the current year.

Oral test

(45 minutes)

General information

Tuition expenses vary according to schools ranging from FF 25,000 to FF 39,000-roughly equivalent to between Rs 125,000 and Rs 195,000 per year.

Living expenses for each student (accommodation, meals and miscellaneous) could range from FF 30,000 to 40,000-roughly equivalent to between Rs 150,000 and Rs 200,000 per year.

Finance: Candidates are strongly advised to seek educational loans and/or scholarships through national or international institutions.

***Academic year*:** Graduate courses are conducted from mid-September to the end of June.

Scholarships

Some scholarships are offered every year, after admission is secured, by the
Office of the Counsellor for Cultural, Scientific and Technical Cooperation
French Embassy
2 Aurangzeb Road
New Delhi 110011
Tel 3014682, Fax 3016441

For application forms and further information, kindly contact:
CIAM/French Graduate Management Admissions Board Groupe HEC
78351 Jouy-en-Josas cedex
Tel 39677368/39677443, Fax 39677440

THE ECOLE NATIONALE DES PONTS ET CHAUSSÉES (ENPC) OFFERS AN INTERNATIONAL MBA CALLED MIB

The Ecole Nationale des Ponts et Chaussées (French National School of Bridge and Highways), is widely recognized as one of the most prestigious and elite Civil Engineering Institutes in France. Created in 1747, it is the oldest of the French National Schools of Engineering. It has the mission of training talented students not only in the most advanced sciences, engineering, and technology but also in developing future leaders and managers of industry and government.

The Master in International Business (MIB) at this school is a 13 to 15-month intensive MBA programme for English speaking candidates with top university degrees and, preferably, professional experience, desiring to pursue a career in international business.

Admissions

Candidates for the Masters in International Business should have a good working knowledge of English and have a University or equivalent level degree.

* For candidates for the French system, this is normally a "Diplôme d'Ingénieur" or equivalent, "Ecole de Gestion", "DEA", "DESS".
* For candidates from other systems, this corresponds to a BSc, BA, MA, or MSc degree.
* Candidates who apply while still undergoing studies will be considered on an individual basis taking into account their professional or business experience.

Selection Procedure

The Admissions Committee will make a provisional selection based on:

* grades obtained for the university degrees
* GMAT (Graduate Management Admission Test) results
* TOEFL (Test of English as a Foreign Language) results for non-native English speakers
* completed application and three letters of recommendation

The Admissions Committee makes its final selection of candidates based on an individual interview and on further evidence of the candidate's motivation and aptitude to follow the programme of the Ecole Nationale des Ponts et Chaussées, and to succeed in an international business career.

For information on MIB

The academic year begins in October.
Approximate cost of the programme, Tuition: 95000 FF
Registration fees: 600 FF
Living and travelling expenses, health insurance, etc. is additional.
Some scholarships are offered by the French government to Indian nationals for this

programme.
For further information, contact:
MIB Admissions Office
Ecole Nationale des Ponts et Chaussées
28, rue des Saints-Pères
85007 Paris
Tel 42603413 (ext. 1162), Fax 40159347

The Institute de Management Hôtelier International (IMHI)

Offers a 21-month programme starting from October every year at Cergy-Pontoise, in the close vicinity of Paris. Admission is very selective and competitive.

IMHI is jointly administered by two leading schools of higher learning

* The Ecole Supérieure des Sciences Economiques et Commerciales (ESSEC), one of Europe's most prestigious business schools.
* Cornell University's School of Hotel Administration, a world leader in the area of hotel and restaurant management education.

Admission Requirements

* Bachelor's degree (First division) in any subject from an accredited University, or a diploma (First Class) in Hotel Management and Catering Technology from a recognised Institute.
* Work experience in the Hospitality Industry. The longer and more varied the experience, the better the possibility of admission.
* Candidates must be fluent in written and spoken English as it is the primary language of instruction. Fluency in French is not required for admission to IMHI but is considered as a major advantage.

The final selection is based on:

* GMAT score (test to be taken no later than January of the current year)
* Examination of the candidate's application form and supporting documentation with special emphasis on previous academic performance, letters of recommendation and work experience
* An aptitude test and a personal interview with a representative of IMHI conducted in New Delhi in the first quarter of every year. Outstation candidates have to come to Delhi at their own expense.

For more information, please contact:
IMHI
7 Le Campus
95033 Cergy-Pontoise
Tel (1) 30300002, Fax (1) 34431701

Scholarships

A limited number of French Government scholarships are offered to those candidates who are selected by IMHI. The scholarship covers living expenses of the candidate amounting to 5,000 FF per month.

Tuition fees of around 48,000 FF/year for a period of two years as well as the to and fro travel costs have to be borne by the candidate or his/her hotel group.

Please note that French legislation does not permit foreign students to seek part-time employment in France for financing their studies.

Candidates who fulfill the admission requirements and are willing to meet their tuition and travel costs may collect a copy of the IMHI application form from

The Office of the Counsellor for Cultural, Scientific and Technical Cooperation

French Embassy 2, Aurangzeb Road New Delhi-110011
Tel 3014682, Fax (9111) 3016441

Pursuant to an agreement reached in 1985 between the Government of India and the Government of France, the Indo-French Centre for the Promotion of Advanced Research was established for catalysing, coordinating and sponsoring collaborative Research in Science and Technology between India and France. It is an autonomous body, registered as a society under the Indian Societies Registration Act. The Department of Science and Technology (DST) of the Government of India and the French Ministry of Foreign Affairs are the designated nodal agencies coordinating the affairs of the centre. IFCPAR started its activities in 1987.

Objectives

The principal objectives of IFCPAR are:

* promotion of cooperation in advanced areas of fundamental and scientific research between India and France;
* development of cooperation through identification of scientists and scientific institutions of the two countries likely to cooperate in a profitable way;
* provision of assistance in the form of grants and equipment as well as other appropriate means of support for the pursuit of advanced research;
* organisation of workshops/seminars and other types of fora on topics of mutual interest
* organisation of training in various fields for scientists and researchers of both the countries.

Organisation

IFCPAR is managed by a Governing body of five Indian members and five French members, nominated by their respective Governments. The Secretary, Department of Science and Technology, Government of India, and the Director, Direction du Développement et de la Coopération Scientifique, Technique et Educative of the French Ministry of Foreign Affairs, are the Co-Chairmen of the Governing Body. The Governing Body is responsible for the conduct of the Centre and is empowered to approve support for all cooperation undertaken within the framework of the Centre.

IFCPAR has a Scientific Council with four eminent scientists from each of the two countries as its members. The Scientific Council identifies thrust areas of research, selects research themes for support by the Centre and evaluates proposals for joint research, training and other scientific activities as may be desired by the Governing Body.

The Director of IFCPAR is a scientist, who is an Indian national appointed by the Governing Body. He is responsible for the implementation of the decisions of the Governing Body and is in charge of the normal activities and obligations of the Centre.

Scientific Programmes

IFCPAR supports collaborative research projects, Indo-French Seminars/workshops, preparation of State-of-the-Art Reports, training programmes, etc. All collaborative programmes are based on the recommendations of the Scientific Council of the Centre.

Research Projects

The Centre supports collaborative research projects undertaken jointly by Indian and French scientists. Proposals for such projects are submitted in a prescribed proforma, which can be obtained from the Centre. Proposals should be jointly formulated and submitted by Indian and French scientists. The proposals should bring out clearly, *inter alia,* details of the scientists and institutions involved, particulars of the work to be carried out and a detailed budget of the fund required.

Proposals for collaborative research are taken up for consideration by IFCPAR twice very year, due dates for their receipt being April 1 and October 1. All proposals received are evaluated by expert referees in India and in France before a final recommendation is made by the Scientific Council.

The essential criteria for selection of collaborative research programmes are "Quality", "Continuity", "Critical Mass" and "Complementarity". Any programme to be acceptable should also be relevant to the scientific and technological priorities of the two countries. The maximum duration of a collaborative research project is three years.

Implementation of the projects recommended by the Scientific Council is subject to approval by the Governing Body and clearance by both the Governments.

Thrust Areas

The Scientific Council identifies, from time to time, thrust areas for being supported by the Centre. The list of thrust areas is reviewed periodically based on the evolving needs and interests. Proposals for collaborative research should normally be in topics which fall under any of the thrust areas.

The current list of thrust areas is as follows

* Pure and Applied Mathematics;
* Theoretical Computer Science, Natural Language Processing, Computer Systems
* Cellular and Molecular Biology/Genetics, Genetic Engineering, Biotechnology (including applications to Medicine and Agronomy);
* Medical Sciences: Epidemiology, Immunology, Virology, Development of new vaccines and new drugs, Bio-medical Engineering (e.g. design of artificial aids);
* Chemistry of natural products with special reference to biologically active compounds, Agro-chemicals;
* Catalysis-Science and Engineering;
* Liquid Interface Science;
* Material Science and Engineering, Advanced Ceramics, Composites, Polymers;
* Rare Earths;
* Astro-Physics and Radio Astronomy;
* Geophysics, Geosphere-Biosphere;
* Remote Sensing;
* Water Resources;
* Semi-conductor Physics, Opto-electronics, Micro-electronics;
* Separation Science and Technology;

Workshops and Seminars

IFCPAR also organises Indo-French Workshops/Seminars on topics of current interest. Proposals for organisation of workshops/seminars may be submitted in the prescribed proforma which can be obtained from the Centre.

For further information, please contact

Dr. P.G.S. Mony, Director, **Indo-French Centre for the Promotion of Advanced Research,** 13, Olof Palme Marg, Vasant Vihar, New Delhi 110057

Tel 6106829/6107379, Fax: 6883832

The French Ministry of Higher Education and Research offers a fellowship programme for internationally renowned scientists and high-level foreign researchers, forms for which may be obtained by writing to the address given below.

Procedure

The files must be prepared and presented by the receiving laboratory in France. They should contain the following documents

* an application form duly filled (to be obtained from the address given below)

* a complete bio-data
* a list of published papers and research work
* an invitation letter from the receiving French Laboratory.

Candidates with an invitation programme of over three month duration should get long term visa from the French Embassy or nearest French Consulate in their country of origin. These followship are not available to foreign scientists/researchers already staying in France.

Duration and Finance

Fellowships are awarded for a period of 1 to 6 months with no possibility of renewal. The amount of the fellowship is decided according to the age, experience, qualifications, and salary of the candidate in his country of origin. Travel expenses are not paid by the French ministry.

Selection of Candidates

Files should be sent to the below mentioned address at least four months before the commencement of the programme in France together with the receiving laboratory. They are examined by a selection committee which meets every 3 months.

For further information, write to

Délégation aux Affaires Européennes, Internationales et à la Francophonie

Ministère de l'Enseignement Supérieure et de la Recherche

1, rue Descartes, **75231 Paris cedex 5,** Tel 463418, Fax 43541060

These fellowships are hardled directly by

* Council of Scientific and Industrial Research-(CSIR) Rafi Marg, New Delhi 110001
* **Centre Nationale de la Recherche Scientifique-(CNRS)**

3, rue Michel-Ange, **75016 Paris,** Tel 44964650, Fax 44965002

The French Embassy is informed but not involved in the selection(s).

For these types of fellowships, it is essential that the Indian researcher be affiliated to a laboratory of the CSIR and that the Research Centre to which he is going in France be affiliated to the CNRS.

Details can be obtained from the Head, International Collaboration CSIR, Rafi Marg, New Delhi 110001.

SHORT TRAINING PROGRAMMES

The Agence pour la Coopération Technique Industrielle et Economique-ACTIM-was created in order to organise short training programmes for professionals and to promote technical and industrial cooperation between France and other countries.

ACTIM's training courses take place in France under programmes established with the help of the concerned French organisations (companies, private and public sector, technical organisation/institutions, French specialists in technical areas of the training courses, etc.)

Average duration: two months with or without a preliminary language course.

Engineers, managers and foreign specialists desirous to go to France under the sponsorship of ACTIM can present their projects and obtain all necessary information and suggestions on this subject by writing to :

The Counsellor for Economic and Commercial Affairs

Embassy of France

2/50 E Shantipath, Chanakyapuri, New Delhi 110021, Tel 6104300

The French Ministry of Education has indicated the conditions to be fulfilled by foreign candidates for the following three interuniversity degrees of specialisation in medicine and pharmaceutics:

(i) **Diplôme Interuniversitaire de Spécialization-DIS**
(University Medical Specialisation Degree)

(ii) Attestation de Formation Spécialisée-AFS
(Attestation of Specialised Medical Training)
(iii) Attestation de Formation Spécialisée Approfondie-AFSA
(Attestation of Advanced Specialised Medical Training)

Candidates will undergo elimination exams and have to fulfil certain conditions to be eligible.

(i) DIS

The candidate will be tested for proficiency in the French language either by the cultural service of the Embassy of France in the country where he/she is a residen, or by the interregional coordinator of the degree he/she is applying for, if residing in France. The test will consist of multiple choice and essay questions. Once a certificate of proficiency has been obtained, the committee conducting the test will assign the posting of the candidate, probably in the university of his/her choice, depending on the number of seats available.

The DIS students will follow the same courses as the equivalent French degree students, which will be of a duration of 4 or 5 years. They will also be remunerated during their internship.

The dossiers of the candidate must include an official document issued by a government authority of his/her country of origin stating that this degree will receive recognition there. The candidate must also send an attestation declaring that he/she is aware that the DIS does not give him/her the right to practise in France. Those who have already specialised, in India or abroad, or already completed a DIS are not entitled to apply for this course. Candidates cannot change disciplines at mid-term.

(ii) AFS & AFSA

AFS—This course is intended for foreign doctors or phamacists doing their specialisation who seek to come to France only as part of their training. The course is for a period of 2 to 4 semesters.

AFSA—This advanced course is for 1 or 2 semesters, and is meant for doctors or pharmacists who have already completed their specialization and wish to do further training.

Enrolment conditions

* In their dossiers, the candidates must include a declaration attesting that they are aware that their postings may not be remunerated. However, all these posts will be in the concerned department which conduct the training courses for the French third cycle students.
* For the AFS, head of the Institution where the candidate is doing his/her specialization must specify the pedagogic objectives expected from this extended training in France. For the AFSA, the candidate must explain the objectives of the training he/she is pursuing.
* To be eligible for the course, the candidate must obtain an attestation of proficiency in the French language from the office of the Counsellor Cultural Scientific and Technical Cooperation of the Embassy of France in his/her country.

List of the French Universities offering pharmaceutics :

Aix-Marseille II, Amiens, Angers, Besançon Bordeaux II, Caen, Clemont-Ferrand I, Dijon, Grenoble I, Lille II, Limoges, Lyon I, Montpellier I, Nancy I, Nantes, Poitiers, Reims, Rennes I, Rouen, Strasbourg I, Toulouse II, Tours, Paris V, Paris XI.

List of the French Universities offering medicine :

Aix-Marseille II, Amiens, Angers, Besançon Bordeaux II, Brest, Caen, Clemont-Ferrand I, Dijon, Grenoble I, Lille II, Limoges, Lyon I, Montpellier I, Nancy I, Nantes, Nice, Poitiers, Reims, Rennes I, Rouen, St.-Etienne, Strasbourg I, Toulouse III, Tours, Paris V, Paris, Paris VI, Paris VII, Paris XI, Paris XII, Paris XIII.

Please note

Only candidates whose proficiency in French meets the required level and whose country recognises the above degrees are eligible to apply for the available posts.

The Institut National de la Santé Et de la Recherce Médical INSERM-

(French National Institute of Health and Medical Research)

Offers to foreign research scholars the possibility of training in INSERM or some other French laboratories, for a duration of;

* 1 to 3 months
* 3 months to 1 year

Under no circumstances can the duration of these stays be extended.

1 to 3 months

Meant for qualified foreign research scholars who wish to establish contacts or to collaborate with French laboratories dealing in their speciality.

Living expenses granted to the research scholars are in relation to their age, experience, qualifications and availability of finances. They correspond, in principle, to the remunerations received by other research scholars of the same level working at INSERM. INSERM does not cover travelling expenses of the candidate from his country of origin to France.

Applications should be submitted in two copies in the prescribed forms supplied by the *Mission des Relations Internationles* of INSERM. They must be returned to the same office through the Director of the host laboratory, three months before the date of arrival of the candidate.

3 months to 1 year

Meant for

* young research scholars with some research experience who wish to complete their work in a particular field;
* confirmed research scholars who could undertake work included in the research programme of the host laboratory ; and
* research scholars on annual leave.

Living expenses granted to the research scholars are in relation to their age, experience, qualifications, and availability of finances. They correspond, in principle, to the remunerations received by other research scholars of the same level working at INSERM. During their stay in France, foreign research scholars get the social security benefits granted to French candidates. INSERM does not cover the travelling expenses of the candidate from his country of origin to France.

Applications should be submitted in two copies in the prescribed forms supplied by the *Mission des Relations Internationales* of INSERM.

They must be returned to the same office through the Director of the host laboratory before:

* 15th March for recruitments taking place on 1st January of the following year
* 15th October for recruitments taking place on 1st July of the following year.

For further information, write to:

Mission des Relations Internationales

Institute National de la Santé et de la

Recherche Médical, 101, rue de Tolbiac

75654 Paris cedex 13, Tel (1) 44236000, Fax (1) 45856856

The Claude Bernard Association for the development of biological and medical research in hospitals offers about ten scholarships per year in the concerned 20 research centres as part of the "Assistance Publique" scheme.

These scholarships are meant for high level research scholars who wish to:

* undergo training for completion of fundamental and clinical research;
* participate in ongoing research programmes at their host centre;
* contribute to the creation of scientific ties between the laboratories involved for development of common research programmes.

Normally, candidates are chosen from amongst those with post-doctoral experience. They should preferably have a good knowledge of French.

Scholarships are awarded for a period of one year, beginning on 1st September every year, and the monthly allocation is 8,000 French Francs (about Rs 40,000). Travel expenses are not met by the Association.

Interested candidates should directly communicate with the Head of the French research centre at which they would like to train .

Detailed information can be obtained from

Secrétariat de l'Association Claude Bernard

3, Avenue Victoria, **75100 Paris,** Tel (1) 42771122

Applications should reach before 1st March of the year desired, in the form of a dossier containing:

* the application form of the "Association Claude Bernard," duly filled
* a bio-data
* a detailed work plan
* list of published works
* consent letter from the Director of the chosen French Centre in the event of the candidate being chosen by the Association's selection committee, which normally meets in May.

Collège de Médecine des Hôpitaux de Paris

Since 1956, young medical doctors from outside France are received every year as resident doctors in the hospitals of Paris. Their number has risen from 14 to 60 per year. The scheme is sponsored by the French Ministry of Foreign Affairs, the Ministry of Cooperation and the 'Assistance Publique'.

This training enables young doctors to gain high level practical experience and has met with a lot of success with foreign doctors, considering that there are more than 180 applicants every year, from over 50 countries.

Their status is as follows:

* They are considered as "Senior residents" in Paris hospitals, having completed or being in the process of completing their specialisation (clinical or biological).
* They are nominated by the Director General of the "Assistance Publique" on the proposal ofo the "Collège de Médecine" whose scientific commission examines the educational qualifications and hospital experience of the applicants.
* The duration of the training is one year, non-renewable, starting usually in November.
* They exercise the same functions as the French residents and have the same rights and duties in the hospitals. They must have a good command of the French language so as to be able to communicate easily with patients as well as to prepare medical reports.
* The applicants should be less than 35 years of age at the beginning of the programme.

Procedure for application

* Applicants should first contact the Chief of the Hospital of their choice and obtain his approval.

* Once this approval is obtained, they should request for an application to Collège de Médecine.

These applications should be completed and sent back before 31st December of the year desired.

For further information, write to:

Collège de Mèdecine des Hôpitaux de Paris
45, quai de la Tournelle, **75005 Paris,** Tel (1) 43257076

Details on French education may be obtained from:

Centre for Documentation on Universities, Science and Technology
Embassy of France, 2 Aurangzeb Road, New Delhi-110011
Tel: (011) 3014682/3015631/3793891, Fax: (011) 3793892

Germany

Studying in Germany

Germany has a long tradition in education, science and research. The history of many higher education institutions extends back over many centuries. Following the destruction caused by the Second World War, an education and research landscape has evolved in Germany which, and particularly so since German unification, has never before been as extensive as it is today. 300 and more higher education institutions are located throughout Germany. Those interested in studying in Germany can choose between universities and institutions with university status, such as the technical universities, the *Fachhochschule* institutions, and the colleges of Art and Music. All state-maintained higher education institutions are open to students of all nations.

When you decide in favour of studying in Germany, you really should take the time to find the answers to the following questions so that you can be sure of the ideal studying conditions for yourself:

* What type of German higher education institution is right for you ? Are you perhaps more interested in a shorter and more practice-orientated degree course at a *Fachhochshule* institution or would you like to attend a college of art or music ? Then consult the two specials broachures within the "Studying in Germany" series.
* Do you intend to complete a full degree course in Germany or do you only want to complete part of your studies in Germany (for example, one year) without gaining a degree here ?
* Or have you perhaps already graduated in your home country and would now like to take a postgraduate course in Germany ?
* Will a German Diplom or *Magister* degree, or a State Examination qualification, or a German *Fachhochschule* Diplom degree be recognised as a professional qualification in your home country ?

You should only chart the course for your chosen German higher education institution once you are quite clear about your course back at your home country, about what career prospects your chosen degree courses will give you, and about how you intend to fund your study stay in Germany. We want your studies at a German higher education institution to open up opportunities for you and not to stand in the way of these opportunities.

The University

Since the days of the higher education reformer Wilhelm von Humboldt (1767-1835) the principle of the "indivisibility of research and teaching" has prevailed at universities in Germany. Accordingly, German universities are not merely institutions which provide education and training, but are also always places at which independent, pure and applied research is pursued. "Pure education and science" itself demands that students engage in strict academic work. Consequently, the length of studies is higher than in many other countries.

Universities award the academic degrees of *Diplom* and *Magister Artium* as well as the doctorate. They have the right to confer the habilitation, the professorial teaching qualification, and can qualify university professors.

University faculties and departments incorporate the following study orientations: medicine, science, engineering, arts and humanities, law, theology, economics and social sciences, and agriculture and forestry. The broad range of disciplines offered within the faculties and departments facilitates interdisciplinary study or respectively specialization, right up to the advanced theoretical fields of a particular science. Many universities have significant libraries and archives which support student studies and personal focuses.

Although university studies are based on firm regulations, most disciplines do provide opportunities for students to pursue independent and individual research interests.

Technical Universities

Originally, and as the name implies, the technical universities restricted their teaching to technical and engineering disciplines. However, in the course of time, they have developed into extensive higher education institutions. Hence, students can now also study arts and humanities degree courses at the technical universities. Nevertheless, the focus of their activities continues to be directed towards engineering and science.

Fachhochschule Institutions

Students are increasingly deciding to study at one of Germany's *Fachhochschule* institutions, particularly because the studies are shorter and are more practice-oriented there than is the case at a university. The DAAD has produced a brochure specifically dedicated to Fachhochschule study in its "Studying in Germany" series.

Colleges of Art and Music

The education and training provided by the colleges of Art and Music in Germany aim to qualify graduates for careers in applied art or as teachers of artistic subjects or as professional artists. Studies at a college of music or art differ substantially from those at a university. Further information is contained in DAAD's brochure on the colleges of art and music published in the "Studying in Germany" series.

Other Institutions with University Status

Apart from the above-mentioned types of higher education institution, Germany also has colleges of education at which teachers are trained for primary schools, lower secondary schools, special needs schools, standard secondary schools and the lower grammar school levels. In general, however, teacher training has been integrated into the university structure.

The comprehensive universities developed when a university, a teacher training college, a *Fachhochschule* institution and, in some cases, a college of art and music were merged to form a single institution. Consequently, comprehensive universities provide students with an opportunity to change their degree courses and degrees whilst they are still studying.

Germany also has a number of higher education institutions which specialize on very specific subject areas, such as the Medical and Veterinary Institutions of Higher Education in Hanover and the Medical University in Lübeck. The German University of Sports Sciences and the College of Media Studies in Cologne train highly-qualified experts, whilst the College of Administrative Sciences in Speyer offers postgraduate degree courses for German civil servants and for educators from developing countries.

In addition to the state-maintained universities, there are also several, in most cases smaller universities supported by other funding organisations, for example, the church-maintained institutions of higher education. And last but not least, students can choose to attend a small number of privately-maintained universities which generally charge study fees.

Admission Requirements

German: the Language of Instruction

With the exception of some postgraduate courses which are held in English or another foreign language, the language of instruction at German universities is German. Hence it is imperative that you gain a proficiency in the German language whilst you are still in your home country. Furthermore, your language proficiency will also play an important role in determining whether or not you feel at home during your stay in Germany. If you do not have a Goethe Institute or a university German Department offering German courses nearby, then you should use other possibilities of learning German.

DSH Language Proficiency Test

You must take the DSH language proficiency test for admission to higher education (*Deutsche Sprachprüfung für den Hochschulzugang ausländischer Studienbewerber—DSH*) prior to commencing your studies. Applicants can only be exempted from this requirement, if they gained their *Abitur* (general higher education entrance qualification) in Germany or at one of the recognised German schools abroad, or if they hold certain language certificates issued by the Goethe Institute or the Level II language certificate of the Conference of Ministers of Education and Cultural Affairs of the *Länder*. Each university sets its own dates for the DSH test. Please contact the foreign student office at the university of your choice at your earliest convenience for details on the DSH test. The regulations governing the DSH test are the same at all German universities. The test may be repeated twice.

DSH Preparatory Courses

Most universities offer language courses which prepare applicants for the DSH. However, the capacity is generally not sufficient to meet the demand for places. Moreover, one of the conditions for acceptance into such a preparatory course is that you have already acquired a certain level of proficiency in the German language. The success of your studies and also your personal experience in Germany will depend decisively on how good your knowledge of German is. You should only commence your journey once you are relatively confident that you will be able to cope with the language requirements.

Proficiency in Other Languages

For some degree course, especially at the faculties of philosophy, students must not only be proficient in German, but must also have a knowledge of Latin or French, for instance. If you do not already meet these requirements, you will generally be able to acquire such knowledge in special courses offered during the studies. Please remember that this will result in a substantial loss of time for your personal schedule.

The Higher Education Entrance Qualification and the Assessment Test (Feststellungsprüfung)

Whether you are directly admitted to study your chosen subject will above all depend on whether or not your school-leaving certificate is recognised as being equivalent to the German Abitur (general higher education entrance qualification). Regarding details on whether or not your school-leaving certificate entitles you to be admitted directly to study in Germany or whether you must first take an assessment test, the *Prüfung für die Feststellung der Eignung ausländischer Studienbewerber für die Aufnahme eines Studiums an Hochschulen in der Bun-desrepublik Deutschland,* or, in short, *Fest - stellungsprüfung,* before you can register. The foreign student office at your chosen university will be pleased to advise you.

The assessment test includes the DSH language proficiency test.

Special conditions may apply regarding admission to a German university if you have already spent several semesters studying in your home country. Generally, you will be directly admitted to studies in Germany if you have successfully completed two study semesters in your home country. Again, we would advise you to contact the foreign student office which will best be able to advise you.

Applicants who must take the assessment test are urgently advised to take a preparatory course, the *Studienkolleg*, before sitting for the assessment test.

Preparatory Course *(Studienkolleg)*

The Studienkolleg prepares foreign students for the assessment test, the *Feststellungsprüfung*. Although attendance is not mandatory, foreign students who are required to take the assessment test are advised in their own best interest to make use of this opportunity, since the assessment test may otherwise prove to be a great obstacle. Before being accepted for the preparatory course, you will also be required to provide proof of a good knowledge of German (Goethe Institute—*Mittelstufe* II [Intermediate Level II]). The Studienkollegs generally offer preparatory German courses which fulfil the language requirement for acceptance at the Studienkolleg. Courses for absolute beginners are seldom offered. Please bear in mind how much time you still need before you finally reach your goal, namely acceptance at a university.

The addresses of the Studienkollegs and the application deadlines are listed in the annex.

Acceptance to the Studienkolleg means that you are on your way to studying your chosen subject. Depending on choice of discipline, you are specifically prepared in language and subject matter for your studies. Hence, preparation is provided in various courses: the so-called T-course prepares you for technical, mathematics and science degree courses; the M-course for medicine, pharmacology, biology and related degree courses, the W-course for economics and social sciences degree courses, the G-course for German studies-related, history and philosophy degree courses; and the S-course for all language-related degree courses, with the exception of German.

In contrast to the teaching at university, teaching at the Studienkolleg is still of a school-like nature. You complete your courses as a member of a specific class. Attendance is compulsory. Your weekly course commitment comprises 32 hours. The summer vacation is six weeks long, with two weeks for Christmas and New Year and another three week break in spring.

The preparatory course generally lasts two semesters or one year. Under certain circumstances, each semester may be repeated once. The course ends with the assessment test in which German is always tested, along with other subjects from the relevant course focus:

T-course: mathematics, physics/chemistry;

M-course:biology-chemistry, physics-mathematics; W-course: mathematics, economics;G-course: history, German literature, respectively, English or social studies/geography; S-course: a second foreign language, history or social studies/ geography, or German literature.

The DAAD has produced a brochure called "Study Preparation at Germany's Studienkollegs—Universities" which will provide further information.

Admissions Restrictions

Some disciplines are so popular that the seats available fall short of demand. German and foreign students applying for these disciplines must complete a selection procedure in which the grade point average of the *Abitur* or of the equivalent higher education entrance qualification is decisive for admission to university study. Some disciplines are subject to nation-wide admission restrictions, whilst others are only restricted on a local level or at some few higher education institutions.

Great importance is attached to foreigners studying at Germany's universities. Hence, a specified percentage of the study places in the Numerus clausus subjects is reserved for foreign applicants. This should encourage foreign applicants to apply for these disciplines as well.

Central Admissions Procedure

Admission to certain degree courses is not arranged by the respective German university itself, but rather by the Central Admissions Office, the

Zentralstelle für die Vergabe von Studien-plätzen,
***ZVS.* Sonnenstrasse, D-44128 Dortmund, Germany.**

Please contact the foreign student office at your chosen university to inquire whether or not your chosen discipline is subject to the central admissions procedure. This may well change from one semester to the next. Hence, it is important that you inform yourself in good time. Please contact the higher education institution(s) of your choice at the beginning of the semester prior to the one in which your studies are scheduled to commence. If your degree course is included in the ZVS procedure then you will only have to apply to the ZVS if you hold the status of a citizen of a European Union member country or are a foreigner holding a German higher education entrance qualification (so-called *Bildungsinländer* who have passed through the German education system). All other applicants must apply direct to the foreign student office at the university of their choice.

Admissions Requirements for Advanced Studies

The requirements which you must fulfil, if you wish to take postgraduate or doctoral degree courses at a German university are far more a matter for the discretion of the respective university than is the case for a full degree programme as described above. Please consult the DAAD booklet *"Postgraduate Courses in Germany"*, which will inform you about the range of study opportunities. You should then contact the university of your choice and inquire after the specific admissions requirements which you will be expected to meet. Under certain circumstances, you will be expected to take a placement test (*Kenntnisprüfung*). Depending on the result of the placement test, you may be required to produce proof of further study and examination achievements. All applicants must prove that they are sufficiently proficient in the German language.

Application and Registration

The Application Form

In order to be able to study at a German university, you must apply to the relevant foreign student office at the higher education institution of your choice, regardless of whether you have already studied in your home country (for exceptions please consult the section on the "Central admissions procedure").

You should already detail your personal qualifications (higher education entrance qualification, knowledge of languages, previous studies and study achievements) in your initial inquiry so that the university foreign student office is able to advise you of the conditions which you must meet for admission.

Early Application Recommended

Studies in an unfamiliar country require a great deal of planning and organization. Experience has shown that foreign students require about one year from initial inquiry to the commencement of their studies in Germany. Please make the best use of this time by informing yourself thoroughly with the help of the DAAD brochures and booklets, the local German embassy, or the foreign student office at the university of your choice.

If you intend to commence your studies in the winter semester, you must generally have submitted a full set of application documents to the university to which you are applying by 15th July. The deadline for the summer semester is 15th January.

Studies Commence: Winter Semester or Summer Semester

In most degree courses, you will be able to choose whether you commence your studies in the winter or in the summer semester. However, please note that some degree courses can only be commenced in the winter semester; you should inquire in good time as to when you can commence your degree courses, since this will considerably affect your personal schedule.

Registration

Once you have received your notification of admission (*Zulassungsbescheid*) from the foreign student office and have passed the language proficiency test, you are entitled to register at your chosen higher education institution using the registration number (*Matrikelnummer*) stated in your admission notification, which also specifies by when you must have fulfilled the registration formalities. In most cases, this deadline is relatively short. In almost all cases you must go in person to the student secretariat office or the registration office. Ask the student secretariat office for the information leaflet which specifies the documents which you must present. You will also be required to prove that you have paid the *Studentenwerk* social contributions (*Sozialgebübren*) and that you have health insurance cover. Upon completion of the formalities, you will be given the student pass (*Studentenausweis*) and a study book (*Studienbuch*) in which all the courses you have taken are recorded. You are then officially a student in Germany and can congratulate yourself.

Registration is always valid for just one semester. It is imperative that you re-register (*Rückmeldung*) in good time each semester, otherwise you will soon lose your student status.

As a registered student you are entitled to attend lectures and courses at the university and to take the examinations and tests specified for your degree course and, finally, to gain an academic degree. You are also entitled to use all the university facilities (library, sports facilities, computer facilities, etc). As a registered student you also have the active and passive right to vote at the elections to the student union or parliament. Last but not least, the student pass entitles you to claim certain price reductions, for example, discount fares on local public transport and reduced-rat tickets for cultural events, and so on. You can also use the refectory *(Mensa)* and other *Studentenwerk* facilities.

More detailed information is available in the DAAD brochure entitled "Living and Studing in Germany".

Study Guidance and Counselling

At times, the path to and through a German university will seem like a labyrinth. You should certainly not proceed along it without appropriate guidance and counselling. A whole range of guidance and counselling offices are available to help you and answer your questions. Do not be afraid to use them. It is also important that you talk and exchange ideas with your fellow students; after all, they will often be experiencing quite similar problems.

Your most important contact is in all cases the foreign student office (*Akademisches Auslandsamt*), followed by the guidance and counselling office in your faculty or department, and the student society for your subject. These and further offices providing guidance and counselling are listed in the DAAD brochure "Living and Studying in Germany".

Entry and Residence Regulations

When do you need a Visa ?

Foreign students wishing to enter the Federal Republic of Germany require a residence permit visa for educational purposes issued by a diplomatic representation of the Federal Republic of Germany (embassy or consulate) in the student's country of origin and entered into the passport. This regulation does not apply to study applicants and students from EU countries and from countries with whom differing regulations have been agreed. This currently applies to Honduras Iceland, Liechtenstein, Monaco, Norway, San Marino, Switzerland, and the United States.

Citizens from a number of other countries can also enter Germany without a visa, if they only want to stay in Germany for a maximum of three months. However, once this three-month period is over, they will require a visa for educational purposes which they can only apply for in their home country. This means that such students must first leave the country, which may possibly be expensive in terms of money and time.

You are urgently warned against entering the country as a tourist. A tourist visa cannot be retrospectively converted into a visa or residence permit for educational purposes.

Bureaucratic formalities take time the world over, which in this case means your time. So that you do not unnecessarily lose time, we would advise you to contact the German embassy or consulate as soon as possible about which documents you need for the visa application.

Required Documents

You will need the following documents in order to be able to apply to the German embassy or consulate for an entry visa for educational purposes in the Federal Republic of Germany:

* a valid passport and numerous passport photographs;
* a higher education entrance qualification recognised in Germany (this is the Abitur certificate or an equivalent qualification);
* proof of your previous study achievements;
* proof of sufficient financial funds; and
* the notification of admission from the university of your choice or an applicant confirmation notification certifying that the full set of required application documents

and papers have been received by the university.

Visa for Study Applicants

If you have not been able to contact any German university from your home country, then there is a second visa format, in addition to the visa for educational purposes, with which you will initially be able to enter Germany without formal application to or admission from an institution of higher education or preparatory course (*Studienkolleg*). This visa, the so-called study applicant visa (*Studienbewerber-Sichtvermerk*), allows you a stay of up to three months in Germany in which you can inform yourself about study opportunities in the Federal Republic of Germany, fulfil any conditions which are still required for application or for acceptance to a study programme, and which can then be extended as a residence permit for the Federal Republic of Germany without you first having to leave the country. The necessary papers and documents are the same as above, but without the notification of admission.

Financial Requirements

Most foreign students study in Germany without a scholarship or grant. Hence, you are strongly advised to assess your financial resources soon and realistically. The German foreign missions or aliens' registration authorities must be convinced that you have sufficient financial funds at your disposal to cover your cost of living for the whole study duration in Germany. At the time of going to press (1997) this amounted to at least DM 1,300—per month. The chapter on expenses and scholarships will give you a breakdown of the cost of living.

Do not Plan on Funding your Studies by Working

You must not plan on financing your studies by working in Germany. The German authorities adhere strictly to the employment related legislation applicable to foreign students in Germany. Any violation may lead to immediate expulsion from Germany. Although students from EU countries may work in Germany, unemployment is a major problem in the country and such students will hardly find a job. Scholarship holders and foreign students who are not citizens of an EU country may only earn a kind of pocket-money; such work is carefully monitored. Please ensure that you give serious consideration to the proof of financial resources.

Scholarships and Grants

Generally, German institutions of higher education do not themselves award any scholarships or grants. Hence, there is little point in submitting a scholarship application (*Stipen-dienantrag)* to the institution of higher education. Yet, there are several institutions which do award scholarships and grants. The most extensive German scholarship programme is that organised by the German Academic Exchange Service (DAAD). However, only advanced students may apply for DAAD scholarships, or, in some cases, depending on country of origin and the disciplines, only graduates. The conditions which must be met for other scholarship awarding institutions vary.

Support for a full study programme, that is from the first semester to the completion of studies, is not possible from the DAAD and is also generally not possible with other scholarship sources.

Scholarships are primarily awarded on the basis of achievement criteria. The applicant's financial status only plays a subordinate role. The German foreign diplomatic missions and other German offices abroad, such as the Goethe Institute or offices of the DAAD abroad will provide information on the possibilities of gaining a scholarship or a grant. Information can also be gained from the professors, lecturers and *Lektors* which the DAAD has placed on teaching assignments at foreign higher education institutions. They will all provide details on application requirements and deadlines and will also advise you as to where the application be submitted.

A summary of the DAAD scholarship programmes is contained in the brochure "Studies and Research in Germany: Scholarships and Funding for Foreign Students, Graduates and Academics" (please consult the "Recommended Reading" section in the annex).

UNIVERSITY FOREIGN STUDENT OFFICE ADDRESSES

RWTH Aachen, Akademisches Auslandsamt, Ahornstraße 55
D-52056 Aachen, Tel. 0241/80-4108, e-mail: international@aaa.rwth-aachen.de
Universität Augsburg
Akademisches Auslandsamt, Universitätsstraße 2D-86159 Augsburg
Tel 0821/598-5208, Universität Bamberg
Akademisches Auslandsamt
Markusstraße 6, D-96045 Mamberg, Te. 0951/863-1049
e-mail: heidemarie.klenner@zuv.unibamberg.de
Universität Bayreuth
Akademisches Auslandsamt, Universitätsstraße 30, D-95447 Bayreuth
Tel. 0921/55-5241/5242, e-mail: heinz.poehlmann@uvw.unibayreuth.de
richard.kastner@uvw.unibayreuth.de, E.A.P. Europäische Wirtschaftshochschule
Berlin e.V., Europa Center, D-10789 Berlin, Tel. 030/254802-0
Technische Universität Berlin,
Academisches Auslandsamt
Straße des 17. Juni 135, D-10623 Berlin , Tel. 030/314-24694
Humboldt-Universität zu Berlin
Akademisches Auslandsamt Unter den Linden 6, D-10099 Berlin
Tel. 030/2093-2155/2565, e-mail: doerthe=muecke@verwaltung. hu-berlin.de
Akademisches Auslandsamt der Freien Universität Berlin
Brümmerstraße 52, D-14195 Berlin, Tel. 030/838-73900
e-mail: aaa@fu-berlin.de, Universität Bielefeld, Akademisches Auslandsamt
Universitätsstraße 25, D-33615 Bielefeld, Tel. 0521/106-4088
Ruhr-Universität Bochum Akademisches Auslandsamt
Universitätsstraße 150, D-44780 Bochum, Tel. 0234/700-5483
e-mail: sprun@dez2.uv.ruhr-uni-bochum.de
Universität Bonn Akademisches Auslandsamt Poppelsdorfer Allee 53
D-53113 Bonn, Tel. 0228/73-7626,-7694, Technische Universität zu Braunschweig
Akademisches Auslandsamt, Rebenring 18, D-38106 Braunschweig
Tel. 0531/391-4331, Fax 0531/391-4273
Universität Bremen, Akademisches Auslandsamt
Bibliotheksstraße 1, D-28359 Bremen, Tel. 0421/218-2732,
e-mail: eharjes@vwg.uni-bremen.de, Technische Universität Chemnitz-Zwickau
Akademisches Auslandsamt, Straße der Nationen 62
D-09107 Chemnitz, Tel. 0371/531-7218,-7229,
Technische Universität Clausthal, Akademisches Auslandsamt
Adolph-Römer-Straße 2a, D-38678 Clausthal, Tel. 05323/72-3103,-2231
e-mail: astrid.meier@tu-clausthal.de, erika.el.hussein@clausthal.de
Brandenburgische Technische Universität Cottbus

Akademisches Auslandsamt
Universitätsplatz 2, D-03044 Cottbus, Tel. 0355/692803
e-mail: brandenb@rz.tu-cottbus.de, Technische Hochschule Darmstadt
Akademisches Auslandsamt, Hochschulstraße 1, D-64289 Darmstadt
Tel. 06151/16-5120,-5320, e-mail: @apvw.th-darmstadt.de
Universität Dortmund, Akademisches Auslandsamt
Emil-Figge-Straße 66, D-44227 Dortmund, Tel. 0231/755-1
e-mail: schmidt@verwaltung.uni-dortmund.de
Technische Universität Dresden, Akademisches Auslandsamt
Mommsenstraße 12, D-01069 Dresden, Tel. 0351/463-5358
e-mail: mader@pop3.tu-dresden.de
Universität Düsseldorf Akademisches Auslandsamt
Universitätsstraße 1, D-40225 Düsseldorf, Tel. 0211/81-12238,-12503
e-mail: haas@verwaltung.uni-duesseldorf.de,
janssen@verwaltung.uni-duesseldorf.de
Gerhard-Mercator Universität-Gesamthochschule Duisburg
Akademisches Auslandsamt, Lotharstraße 65
D-47048 Duisburg, Tel. 0203/379-2459,-2458, e-mail: jaritz@uni-duisburg.de
Katholische Universität Eichstätt Akademisches Auslandsamt
Ostenstraße 26, D-85072 Eichstätt, Tel. 08421/93-1283
Pädagogische Hochschule Erfurt-Mühlhausen
Referat Auslandsbeziehungen, Nordhäuser Straße 63
D-99089 Erfurt, Tel. 0361/737-1009
Universität Erlangen-Nürnberg, Akademisches Auslandsamt
Schloßplatz 3, D-91054 Erlangen, Tel. 09131/85-4800
Universität Gesamthochschule Essen Akademisches Auslandsamt
Universitätsstraße 2, D-45117 Essen, Tel. 0201/183-2032,-2022
Bildungswissenschaftliche Pädagogische Hochschule Flensburg
Mürwiker Straße 77, D-24943 Flensburg, Tel. 0461/3130-104
Universität Frankfurt, Akademische Auslandsstelle
Bockenheimer Landstraße 133, D-60325 Frankfurt am Main
Tel. 069/798-22306,-22263,-25021
Europa-universität Viadrina Frankfurt/Oder Akademisches Auslandsamt
Große Scharrnstraße 59, D-15230 Frankfurt/Oder, Tel. 0335/5534-328
e-mail: klugert@euv-frankfurt-o.de TU Bergakademie Freiberg
Akademisches Auslandsamt, Akademiestraße 6, D-09596 Freiberg
Tel. 03731/39-2941, e-mail: finken@zuv.tu-freiberg.de
Pädagogische Hochschule, Freiburg im Breisgau, Akademisches Auslandsamt
Kunzenweg 21, D-79117 Freiburg, Tel. 0761/682-1,-237
Universität Freiburg Akademisches Auslandsamt,
Heinrich-von-Stephan-Straße 25, D-79085 Freiburg, Tel. 0761/203-4375
Universität Gießen Akademisches Auslandsamt, Gutenbergstraße 6
D-35390 Gießen, Tel. + Fax 0641/99-12140, 12141
e-mail: akademisches.auslandsamt@admin.
uni-giessen.de Universität Göttingen, Akademisches Auslandsamt
Wilhelmsplatz 4, D-37073 Göttingen, Tel. 0551/39-4457, -4455
Universität Greifswald Akademisches Auslandsamt
Domstraße 11, D-17487 Greifswald, Tel. 03834/86-1118

e-mail: rappold@rz.uni-greifswald.de
Fernuniversität-Gesamthochschule Hagen, Studentisches Auslandsamt
D-58084 Hagen, Tel. 02331/2447, -4608, Fax 02331/987-399
e-mail: ute.zimmermann@fernuni-hagen.de
monika.heil@fernuni-hagen.de, Universität Halle-Wittenberg
Akademisches Auslandsamt, Selkestraße 9/Haus E
D-06122 Halle, Tel. 0345/552-1313
e-mail: n2p@zuv4.verwaltung.uni-halle.de
Hochschule für Wirtschaft und Politik, Hamburg
Studentensekretariat, Von-Melle-Park 9, D-20146 Hamburg,
Tel. 040/4123-2189, e-mail: ptimmann@rr2.uni-hamburg.de
Universität der Bundeswehr Hamburg, Holstenhofweg 85
D-22043 Hamburg, Tel. 040/6541-2704, Universität Hamburg
Akademisches Auslandsamt, Edmund-Siemers-Allee 1
D-20146 Hamburg, Tel. 040/4123-3305-3310-4472-3884
Technische Universititat Tat Hamburg -Hamburg
Akademisches Auslandsamt Sel, loBriuhlendamm 32
D-21073 Hambury, Tel: 040/7718-3158, E-mail: wilberg@tu-harburg.d400.de
Universität Hannover, Akademisches Auslandsamt
Welfengarten 1a, D-30167 Hannover, Tel. 0511/76-2548,-2550,-4080
e-mail: thomas@aaa.uni-hannover.de, Tierärztliche Hochschule Hannover
Bünteweg 2, D-30559 Hannover, Tel. 0511/856-7555
Medizinische Hochschule Hannover, Carl-Neuberg-Straße 8
D-30625 Hannover, Tel. 0511/532-3303
Hochschule für Jüdische Studien Heidelberg, Friedrichstraße 9
D-69117 Heidelberg, Tel. 06221/22576, Pädagogische Hochschule Heidelberg
Keplerstraße 87, D-69120 Heidelberg, Tel. 06221/477-118
Universität Heidelberg, Akademisches Auslandsamt, Seminarstraße 2
D-69117 Heidelberg, Tel. 06221/54-2336, -2337,
e-mail; aaa@sun1.zuv.uni-heidelberg.de
Universität Hildesheim, Akademisches Auslandsamt, Marienburger Platz 22
D-31141 Hildesheim, Tel. 05121/883-539, e-mail-aaa@rz.uni-hildesheim.de
Universität Hohenheim
Akademisches Auslandsamt Schloß Hohenheim, D-70593 Stuttgart
Tel. 0711/459-2020, e-mail: aaa@ruhaix1.rz.uni-hohenheim.de
Technische Universität Ilmenau Akademisches Auslandsamt
Max-Planck-Ring 14, D-98693 Ilmenau, Tel. 03677/69-2518
e-mail: andrea.bauer@zv.tu-ilmenau.de
Universität Jena Akademisches Auslandsamt
Fürstengraben 1, D-07740 Jena, Tel. 03641/63-0537,-2454
e-mail: hhj@sokrates.verwaltung.uni-jena.de
Universität Kaiserslautern, Akademisches Auslandsamt, Erwin-Schrödinger-Straße, D-67663 Kaiserslautern, Tel. 0631/205-2050,
e-mail: watgen@rhrk.uni-kl.de
Pädagogische Hochschule Karlsruhe Bismarckstraße 10, D-76133 Karlsruhe
Tel. 0721/9254072, e-mail: @ph-karlsruhe.de
Universität Karlsruhe, Akademisches Auslandsamt, Karlstraße 42-44
D-76133 Karlsruhe, Tel. 0721/608-4911,-4948

Universität-Gesamthochschule Kassel
Akademisches Auslandsamt, Mönchebergstraße 19, D-34109 Kassel
Tel. 0561/804-2103, e-mail: aaa@hrz.uni-kassel.de
Universität zu Kiel, Akademisches Auslandsamt, Christian-Albrechtsplatz 4
D-24098 Kiel, Tel. 0431/880-3715
Universität Koblenz-Landau, Akademisches Auslandsamt
Hegelstraße 59, D-55122 Mainz, Tel. 06131/374600
Wissenschaftliche Hochschule für, Unternehmensführung Koblenz
Otto-Beisheim-Hochschule, Burgplatz 2, D-56179 Vallendar
Tel. 0261/6509-0, e-mail: axel schumacher@whu.koblenz.de
Universitätzu Köln, Akademisches Auslandsamt, Kerpener Straße 4
D-50923 Köln, Tel. 0221/470-2332
Deutsche Sporthochschule Köln, Auslandsamt, Carl-Diem-Weg 6
D-50933 Köln, Tel. 0221/4982-209
Universität Konstanz, Akademische Abt. Auslandsreferat
Universitätsstraße 10, D-78464 Konstanz, Tel. 07531/88-2484
e-mail: ausref@uni-konstanz.de
Universität Leipzig, Akademisches Auslandsamt, Goethestraße 6
D-04109 Leipzig, Tel. 0341/9732020
e-mail: poller@verwaltung-uni-leipzig-d400.de
Handelshochschule Leipzig, Internationale Beziehungen, Jahnallee 59
D-04109 Leipzig, Tel. 0341/9851-626, e-mail: hhl@hhl. uni-leipzig.de
Pädagogische Hochschule Ludwigsburg, Akademisches Auslandsamt
Reuteallee 46, D-71634 Ludwigsburg, Tel. 07141/140-372
Medizinsche Universität zu Lübeck, Akademisches Auslandsamt
Ratzeburger Allee 160, D-23538 Lübeck, Tel. 0451/500-3012
Universität Lüneburg, Akademisches, Auslandsamt, Scharnhorststraße 1
D-21332 Lüneburg, Tel. 04131/78-1071
Universität Magdeburg Akademisches Auslandsamt, Universitätsplatz 2
D-39016 Magdeburg Tel. 0391/67-18514
e-mail: AKAA@uni-magdeburg.d.400.de
Universität Mainz Akademisches, Auslandsamt Forum Universitatis 1+2
D-55099 Mainz, Tel. 06131/39-2281-2525,
e-mail: aaa@verwaltung-uni-mainz.de
Universität Mannheim, Akademisches Auslandsamt, L9, 6
D-68131 Mannheim, Tel. 0621/292-5507
e-mail: berg@verwaltung.uni-mannheim.de
Universität Marburg, Akademisches Auslandsamt, Biegenstraße 12
D-35032 Marburg, Tel. 06421/28-6176-6120
e-mail: auslamt@mailgate.verwaltung.Uni-Marburg.de
Universität der Bundeswehr München Werner-Heisenberg-Weg 39
D-85579 Neubiberg, Tel. 089/6004-1
Universität München Auslandsamt, Ludwigstraße 27, D-80539 München
Tel. 089/2180-2823, http://www.uni-muenchen.de/lmu/auslandsamt/
Technische Universität München, Akademisches Auslandsamt
Arcisstraße 19, D-80290 München, Tel. 089/289-25822
e-mail: ritter@hp1.abt5.zv.tu-muenchen.de
Universität Münster Akademisches Auslandsamt, Schloßplatz 2a

D-48149 Münster, Tel. 0251/832-2227-2226
European Business School Oestrich-Winkel Schloß Reicharshausen
D-65375 Oestrich-Winkel, Tel. 06723/69-0
Carl-von-Ossietzky Universität Oldenburg Akademisches Auslandsamt
Ammerländer Heerstraße 121, D-26111 Oldenburg
Tel. 0441/798-2478, e-mail: akahiwi@admin.uni-oldenburg.de
Universität Osnabrück, Akademisches Auslandsamt, Neuer Graben 19/21
D-49069 Osnabrück, Tel. 0541/969-4126,-4106,
e-mail: bschluck@rz.uni-osnabrueck.de
Universität-Gesamthochschule Paderborn, Akademisches Auslandsamt
Warburger Straße 98, D-33100 Paderborn, Tel. 05251/60-2450
e-mail: drovs@zv.uni-paderborn.de
Universität Passau, Akademisches Auslandsamt, Heuwieserstraße 1
D-94032 Passau, Tel. 0851/509-1161, e-mail: elise.vonrandow@uni-passau.de
Universität Potsdam,Akademisches Auslandsamt, Am Neuen Palais 10
D-14469 Potsdam, Tel. 0331/977-1676, e-mail: hunger@rz.uni-potsdam.de
Universität Regensburg, Akademisches Auslandsamt, Universitätsstraße 31
D-93053 Regensburg, Tel. 0941/943-2373,
e-mail: marianne.sedlmeier@verwaltung.
uni-regensburg.de Universität Rostock, Akademisches Auslandsamt
Universitätsplatz 1, D-18051 Rostock, Tel. 0381/4981209
e-mail:dagmar.ronnecker@verwaltung. uni-rostock.de
Universität des Saarlandes, Akademisches Auslandsamt
Im Stadtwald, Gebäude 28, D=66041 Saarbrücken, Tel. 0681/302-3624,-4487
e-mail: stemper@rz.uni-sb.de,
Pädagogische Hochschule, Schwäbisch-Gmünd, Oberbettringer Straße 200
D-73525 Schwäbisch-Gmünd, Tel. 07171/606-1
Universität-Gesamthochschule Siegen, Akademisches Auslandsamt
Sohlbacher Straße 20, D-57068 Siegen-Geisweid, Tel. 0271/740-3903
e-mail: eickbusch@aaa.uni-siegen.d400.de
Hochschule für Verwaltungswissenschaften, Speyer, Freiherr-vom-Stein-Straße 2
D-67324 Speyer, Tel. 06232/654-250
Universität Stuttgart, Akademisches Auslandsamt, Keplerstraße 7
D-70174 Stuttgart, Tel. 0711/121-2274,
e-mail: study.info@uni-stuttgart.de
Universität Trier, Akademisches Auslandsamt, Universitätsring 15
D-54286 Trier, Tel. 0651/201-2806-09, e-mail: haungs/freihoff/
mansion@pcmail.uni-trier.de
Universität Tübingen, Akademisches Beratungszentrum, Wilhelmstraße 11
D-72074 Tübingen, Tel. 07071/297-2937
Universität Ulm, Dezernat II, Studium und Lehre, Robert-Koch-Str.2/1
D-89081 Ulm, Tel. 0731/502-2057,
e-mail: reinhold. luecker/brigitte.kemmler@
rektoramt.uni-ulm.de Hochschule Vechta Driverstraße 22
D-49377 Vechta, Tel.04441/15-340
Gustav-Siewerth-Akademie Weilheim, Oberbierbronnen 1,
D-79809 Weilheim-Bierbronnen, Tel. 07755/699
Hochschule für Architektur and Bauwesen, Weimar Akademisches Auslandsamt

Coudraystraße 7, D-99421 Weimar, Tel. 03643/582362,-63
Pädagogische Hochschule Weingarten, Kirchplatz 2, D-88250 Wiingarten
Tel. 0751/501-1
Universität Witten/Herdecke, Alfred-Herrhausen-Straße 50, D-58448 Witten
Tel. 02302/669291, e-mail: krause@natwi.natwi.uni-wh.de
Universität Würzburg, Akademisches Auslandsamt, Ottostraße 16
D-97070 Würzburg, Tel. 0931/31-2298
Bergische Universität-Gesamthochschule, Wuppertal, Akademisches Auslandsamt
Gaußstraße 20, D-42097 Wuppertal, Tel. 0202/439-2406
e-mail: bieck@wrcs1.urz.uni-wuppertal.de
Internationales Hochschulinstitut Zittau, Markt 23, D-02763 Zittau
Tel. 03583/7715-0,-12

University Studienkolleg Addresses

Aachen

Studienkolleg für ausländische Studierende an der Rheinisch-Westfälischen Technischen Hochschule Aachen, Lochnerstraße 4-20, D-52056 Aachen,
Tel. (0241) 804334

Berlin

Studienkolleg für ausländische Studierende der Freien Universität Berlin
Brentanostraße 50, D-12163 Berlin, Tel. (030) 8241989 Studienkolleg der Technischen Universität Berlin , Ackerstraße 71-76 D-13355 Berlin Tel. (030) 31472720

Bochum

Studienkolleg des ökumenischen Studien-werks e.V. für ausländische Studierende in, Bochum, staatlich genehmigt, Girondelle 80, D-44799 Bochum Tel. (0234) 9388231

Bonn

Studienkolleg für ausländische Studierende an der Universität Bonn
Adenauerallee 10, D-53113 Bonn, Tel. (0228) 737550

Darmstadt

Studienkolleg für ausländische Studierende, Poststraße 5
D-64293 Darmstadt, Tel. (06151) 84838

Frankfurt/M.

Studienkolleg für ausländische Studierende, Bockenheimer Landstraße 76
D-60323 Frankfurt am Main, Tel. (069) 728508

Freiberg

Studienkolleg der TU Bergakademie Freiberg, Gustav-Zeuner-Straße 6
D-09596 Freiberg, Tel. (03731) 39-3239

Greifswald

Staatliches Studienkolleg an der Ernst-Moritz-Arndt-Universität Greifswald, Kapaunenstraße 5-7, D-17489 Greifswald, Tel. (03834) 86-1190,-1191

Halle-Wittenberg

Studienkolleg Für ausländische Studierende, des landes Sachsen-Anhalt am Institut, für Fremdsprachenvermittlung der, Martin-Luther-Universität Halle-Wittenberg, Ländersudienkolleg, Universitätsplatz 11, D-06009 Halle Tel. (0345) 552-4486

Hamburg

Studienkolleg für ausländische Studierende an der Universität Hamburg
Holstenglacis 6, D-20355 Hamburg, Tel. (040) 355-13800

Hannover

Niedersächsisches Studienkolleg für aus-, ländische Studierende der Universität
Hannover, Bismarckstraße 2, D-30173 Hannover, Tel. (0511) 7628440

Heidelberg

Universität Heidelberg/Internationales Studienzentrum, Studienkol eg
Im Neuenheimerfeld 684, D-69120 Heidelberg, Tel. (06221) 485268/69

Karlsruhe

Studienkolleg für ausländische Studierende an der Universität Karlsruhe
Karlstraße 42-44, D-76133 Karlsruhe, Tel. (0721) 6084922

Kassel

Studienkolleg für ausländische Studierende der UGH Kassel
Wilhelmshöher Allee 73, D-34109 Kassel, Tel. (0561) 804-6384/87

Köln

Staatliches Studienkolleg für ausländische Studierende an der Universität zu Köln,
Albertus-Magnus-Platz, D-50923 Köln, Tel. (0221) 435768

Leipzig

Studienkolleg Sachsen an der Universität Leipzig, Lumumbastraße 2-4
D-04105 Leipzig , Tel. (0341) 9730240

Mainz

Staatliches Studienkolleg an der Johannes-Gutenberg-Universität
Saarstraße 52, D-55122 Mainz, Tel. (06131) 374780

Mettingen

Studienkolleg für luso-brasilianische Studierende, Sunderstraße 15-17
D-49497 Mettingen, Tel. (05452) 2358

München

Studienkolleg bei den Wissenschaftlichen, Hochschulen des Freistaates Bayern
Pfänderstraße 6-10, D-80636 München, Tel. (089) 187457

Münster

Studienkolleg für ausländische Studenten an der Universität Münster
Robert-Koch-Straße 31, D-48149 Münster, Tel. (0251) 838413

Nordhausen

Staatliches Studienkolleg Land Thüringen, Weinberghof, D-99734 Nordhausen
Tel. (03631) 902929

Potsdam

Studienkolleg für ausländische Studierende der Universität Potsdam
Postfach 601553, D-14415 Potsdam, Tel. (0331) 2755070

Saarbrücken

Studienkolleg der Universität des Saarlandes, Am Markt/Zeile 6
D-66125 Saarbrücken, Tel. (06897) 798-260

Wismar

Studienkolleg für ausländische Studierende an der Hochschule Wismar
Philipp-Müller-Straße, D-23966 Wismar, Tel. (03841) 753236

Whilst foreign students will have no problems imagining what a university or technical college is, *Fachhochschulen* is a German speciality, with only a very short tradition to look back on. Nevertheless, the Fachhochschulen are enjoying a rapid increase in popularity; a quarter of all students now decide to begin their higher education career at a *Fachhochschule*. The number of students studying at the Fachhochschulen is already five times as higher than when they were founded. Thirtyfive per cent of all higher education graduates now come from a Fachhochschule. In some areas, such as engineering, more than half of the graduates came from a Fachhochschule.

ADDRESSES OF THE FACHHOCHSCHULEN (FOREIGN STUDENT'S OFFICES)

Aachen, Fachhochschule
Akademisches Auslandsamt, Kalverbenden 6, D-52066 Aachen
Tel.: 0241/6009-1019, e-mail: aaa@fh-aachen.de
Aalen, Fachhochschule, Akademisches Auslandsamt, Beethovenstraße 1, D-73430 Aalen,
Tel.: 07361/576-125, e-mail: bminde@fh-aalen.de
Albstadt-Sigmaringen, Fachhochschule Akademisches Auslandsamt
Anton-Günther-Straße 51, D-72488 Sigmaringen, Tel.: 07571/732-236
e-mail: @ aaa-fh-alb.sieg.de
Altmark, Fachhochschule, Am Dom 13, 39576 Stendal, Tel.: 03931/217-214
Amberg-Weiden, Fachhochschule, Kaiser-Wilhelm-Ring 23 (Hallpl. 2)
D-92224 Amberg, Tel.: 09621/482101
Anhalt, Fachhochschule, Bernburg-Dessau-Köthen, Akademisches Auslandsamt
Bernburger Straße 52-57, D-06366 Köthen, Tel.: 03496/67-298
e-mail: mehner@hrz-koe.aaa.fh-anhalt.de
Augsburg, Fachhochschule Akademisches Auslandsamt, Baumgartnerstraße 16
D-86161 Augsburg, Tel: 0821/5586-204,-205
e-mail: ausland@verwaltung.fh-augsburg.de
Berlin, Evangelische Fachhochschule-Fachhochschule für Sozialarbeit und Sozialpädagogik, Reinerzstraße 40-41, D-14193 Berlin, Tel.: 030/829908-0
Berlin, Fachhochschule für Sozialarbeit und Sozialpädagogik, Alice-Salomon
Akademisches Auslandsamt, Karl-Schrader-Straße 6, D-10781 Berlin
Tle.: 030/21730-286, e-mail: beiderwieden@sonet.asfh-berlin.de
Berlin, Fachhochschule für Technik und Wirtschaft Akademisches Auslandsamt
Treskowallee 8, D-10313 Berlin, Tel.: 030/5019-2591,
e-mail: roehr@nsvl.vb.fhtw-berlin.de
Berlin, Fachhochschule für Wirtschaft, Akademisches Auslandsamt
Badensche Straße 50-51, D-10825 Berlin, Tel. 030867-1
Berlin, Katholische Fachhochschule, Köpenicker Allee 39-57
D-10318 Berlin, Tel.: 030/5010 10-14
Berlin, Technische Fachhochschule Akademisches Auslandsamt
Luxemburger Straße 10, D-13353 Berlin, Tel.: 030/4504-2950,-2768
e-mail: ausland@tfh-berlin.de
Biberach, Fachhochschule, Karlstraße 11, D-88400 Biberach
Tel.: 07351/582-101, e-mail: bruschke@mx.500.fh-biberach.de
Bielefeld, Fachhochschule Akademisches Auslandsamt,
Kurt-Schumacher-Straße 6, D-33511 Bielefeld, Tel.: 0521/106-2609
e-mail: perlick@zv.fh-bielefeld.de
Bingen, Fachhochschule, Akademisches Auslandsamt, Rochusallee 4
D-55411 Binger, Tel.: 06721/70537

Bochum, Fachhochschule, Akademisches Auslandsamt, Universitätsstraße 150
D-44707 Bochum, Tel.: 0234/700-6055
Bochum, Technische Fachhochschule für Rohstoffenergie und Umwelt
Georg Agricola, Herner Straße 45, D-44787 Bochum
Tel.: 0234/968-3358
Bochum, Evangelische Fachhochschule, see Rheinland-Westfalen-Lippe
Bonn, Fachhochschule für das öffentliche, Bibliothekswesen,
Wittlsebacherring 9, D 53115 Bonn, Tel.: 0228/7258-168
Brandenburg, Fachhochschule Magdeburger Straße 53, D-14770 Brandenburg an der Havel, Tel.: 03381/355-104,-106, e-mail: riedel@fh-brandenburg.de
Braunschweig-Wolfenbüttel, Fachhochschule Zentralstelle für Auslandskontakte
Salzdahlumer Straße 46/48, D-38302 Wolfenbüttel, Tel.: 05331/939-790, 791
e-mail: h.zimpel@zafrap. fh-wolfenbuettel.de Bremen, Hochschule
Akademisches Auslandsamt, Neustadtswall 30, D-28199 Bremen,
Tel.:0421/5905-148
Bremerhaven, Hochschule, Akademisches Auslandsamt, An der Karlstadt 8
D-27568 Bremerhaven, Tel.: 0471/4823-103
Coburg, Fachhochschule, Akademisches Auslandsamt, Friedrich-Streib-Straße 2
D-96450 Coburg, Tel.: 09561/317-247, e-mail: stegemann@cris.fh-coburg.de
Darmstadt, Evangelische Fachhochschule Kommission für Internationale Beziehungen,
Zweifalltorweg 12, D-64293 Darmstadt, Tel.: 06151/8798-0
Darmstadt, Fachhochschule Referat Auslandsbeziehungen Haardtring 100
D-64295 Darmstadt, Tel.: 06151/16-8014, 8019
Deggendorf, Facchochschule Franz-Josef-Strauß-Straße 7, D-94469 Deggendorf
Tel.: 0991/37069-0, http://www.ft-deggendorf.de
Dieburg, Fachhochschule Deutsche Telekom AG, Auslandsamt, Postfach 1155, D-64801
Dieburg, Tel.:06071/28-2020, e-mail: m.duepre@t-online.de
Dortmund, Fachhochschule Akademisches Auslandsamt, Postfach 105018
D-44047 Dortmund, Tel. : 0231/9112-266,-345,
e-mail: desjardins@th-dortmund.de, moser@fh-dortmund.de
Dortmund, International School , of Management ISM, Otto-Hahn-Straße 37
D-44227 Dortmund, Tel.: 0231/75796, e-mail: 101460.1627@compuserve.com
Dresden, Evangelische Fachhochschule, für Sozialarbeit Voßstraße 2
D-01219 Dresden, Tel.: 0351/4690211
Dresden, Hochschule für Technik und Wirtschaft (FH), Akademisches Auslandsamt
Friedrich-List-Platz 1, D-01069 Dresden, Tel.: 0351/462-3377
e-mail: auslandsamt@htw-dresden.de
Duisburg, Universität-Gesamthochschule Akademisches Auslandsamt Lotharstraße 65,
D-47048 Duisburg, Tel.: 0203/379-2458
e-mail: jaritz@uni-duisburg.de
Düsseldorf, Fachhochschule, Akademisches Auslandsamt, Universitätsstraße
Gebäude 23.31/32, D-40225 Düsseldorf, Tel.: 0211/811-3545
Eberswalde, Fachhochschule, Alfred-Möller-Straße 1, D-16225 Eberswalde
Tel.: 03334/65431
Emden, see Ostfriesland Erfurt, Fachhochschule Akademisches Auslandsamt
Alonaer Straße 25 a, D-99085 Erfurt, Tel.: 0361/6700-0
Essen, Fachhochschule für Oekonomie und Management (FOM), Herkulesstraße 32,
D-45143 Essen, Tel.: 0201/81004-400

Essen, Universität-Gesamthochschule, Akademisches Auslandsamt, Universitätsstraße 2, D-45117 Essen, Tel.: 0201/183-2032
Esslingen, Fachochschule für Sozialwesen, Akademisches Auslandsamt
Flandernstraße 101, D-73732 Esslingen, D-0711/397-49
Esslingen, Fachhochschule für Technik, Akademisches Auslandsamt
Kanalstraße 33, D-73728 Esslingen, Tel.: 0711/397-3080
Flensburg, Fachhochschule, Akademisches Auslandsamt, Kanzleistraße 91-93
D-24943 Flensburg, Tel.: 0461/805-313
Frankfurt/Main, Fachhochschule Referat Auslandsbeziehungen
Nibelungenplatz 1, D-60318 Frankfurt/Main, Tel.: 069/1533-2735
e-mail: kuf@aa.fh.frankfurt.de
Frankfurt/Main, Hochschule für bankwirtschaft (HfB), Sternstraße 8
D-60318 Frankfurt/Main, Tel.: 069/959460
Freiburg, Evangelische Fachhochschule für Sozialwesen, Religionspädagogik und Gemeindediakonie, Bugginger Straße 38, D-79114 Freiburg
Tel.: 0761/47812-26
Freiburg, Katholische Fachhochschule für Sozialwesen und Religionspädagogik
Wölflinstraße 4, D-79104 Freiburg, Tel.: 0761/200-491
Freising, see Weihenstephan Fresenius, Facchochschule Limburgerstr. 2
D-65510 Idstein, Tel.: 06126/93520
Fulda, Fachhochschule Referat für Auslandsangelegenheiten
Marquardstraße 35, D-36039 Fulda, Tel.: 0661/9640-147,-148
e-mail: christina.langsdorf@verw.fh.fulda.de
Furtwangen, Fachhochschule, Akademisches Auslandsamt, Postfach 28
D-78113 Furtwangen, Tel.: 07723/920-269
Gelsenkirchen, Fachhochschule, Akademisches Auslandsamt
Neidenburger Straße 10, D-45877 Gelsenkirchen, Tel.: 0209/9596-446,-451
e-mail: wolf@fh-ge.de
Gießen-Friedberg, Fachhochschule Referat für Auslandsbeziehungen
Wiesenstraße 14, D-35390 Gießen, Tel.: 0641/309-262
e-mail: almuth.rhode@verw.fh-giessen.de, Göttingen, Private Fachhochschule
Weender Landstraße 3-5, 37073 Göttingen, Tel.: 0551/54700-0
Hamburg, Evangelische Fachhochschule für Sozialpädagogik der Diakonenanstalt des Rauhen Hauses, Horner Weg 170, D-22111 Hamburg, Tel.: 040/65591-180
Hamburg, Fachhochschule, Akademisches Auslandsamt Winterhuder Weg 29
D-22085 Hamburg, Tel.: 040/2988-3625
Hannover, Evangelische Fachhochschule, Postfach 690363, D-30612 Hannover
Tel.: 0511/5301-0
Hannover, Fachhochschule, Akademisches Auslandsamt
Ricklinger Stadtweg 118, D-30459 Hannover, Tel.: 0511/9296-406
e-mail: beate.gerken@verw.fh-hannover,de
Harz, Fachhochschule, Akademisches Auslandsamt, Friedrichstraße 57-59
D-38855 Wernigerode, Tel.: 03943/359-104
Heide, see Westküste Heidelberg, Fachhochschule der Stiftung
Rehabilitation, Postfach 101409, D-69004 Heidelberg, Tel.: 06221/882-258
Heilbronn, Fachhochschule Akademisches Auslandsamt Max-Planck-Straße 39
D-74081 Heibronn, Tel.: 07131/504-263
Hildesheim-Holzminden, Fachhochschule, Akademisches Auslandsamt

Goslarsche Str. 19, D- 31134 Hildesheim, Tel.: 05121/13010-1,2,-3
Hof, Fachhochschule Wirthstraße 51, D-95028 Hof, Tel.: 09281/409301
Idstein, see Fresenius Ingolstadt, Fachhochschule Akademisches Auslandsamt
Goldknopfgasse 7, D-85049 Ingolstadt, Tel.: 0841/9348-121
Iserlohn, Märkische Fachhochschule Akademisches Auslandsamt
Frauenstuhlweg 31, D-58644 Iserlohn, Tel.: 02371/566-210,
e-mail: mfh@mfh-iserlohn.de
Isny, Fachhochschule der Naturwissenschaftlich-Technischen Akademie
Seidenstraße 12-35, D-88316 Isny, Tel.: 07562/9707-55
Jena, Fachhochschule Tatzendpromenade 1 b, D-07745 Jena, Tel.: 03641/643488
Kaiserslautern, Fachhochschule, Akademisches Auslandsamt, Morlauterer Straße 31, D-67657 Kaiserslautern, Tel.: 0631/3724-133
Karlsruhe, Fachhochschule, Akademisches Auslandsamt, Moltkestraße 30
D-76133 Karlsruhe, Tel.: 0721/925-1090, -1088,
e-mail: gertrud.schenk@fh-karlsruhe.de
schneider-koerber@fh-karlsruhe.de Kempten-Neu-Ulm, Fachhochschule,
Hochschule für Technik und Wirtschaft, Akademisches Auslandsamt
Immenstädter Straße 69, D-87435 Kempten, Tel.: 0831/2523-117
e-mail: peter.roth@htw-kempten.de, bernd.holzhauser@htw.kempten.de
Kiel, Fachhochschule, Akademisches Auslandsmat, Sokratesplatz 1
D-24149 Kiel, Tel.: 0431/21018-00,-01
Kiel, Fachhochschule für Kunst und Gestaltung Muthesius-Hochschule
Lorentzendamm 6-8, D-24103 Kiel, Tel.: 0431/5198400
Koblenz, Fachhochschule Akademisches Auslandsamt Am Finkenherd 4
D-56075 Koblenz, Tel.: 0261/9528-202
Köln, Fachhochschule Akademisches Auslandsamt Claudiusstraße 1
D-50678 Köln, Tel.: 0221/8275-3110
Köln, Katholische Fachhochschule, see Nordrhein-Westfalen
Köln, Rheinische Fachhochschule Hohenstaufenring 16-18, D-50674 Köln
Tel.: 0221/2030211
Köthen, see Anhalt
Konstanz, Fachhochschule, Akademisches Auslandsamt, Brauneggerstraße 55
D-78462 Konstanz, Tel.: 07531/206-297, e-mail: ballance@fh.konstanz.de
Krefeld, see Niederrhein Landshut, Fachhochschule Akademisches Auslandsamt
Am Lurzenhof 1, D-84036 Landshut, Tel.: 0871/506-0
Lausitz, Fachhochschule, Akademisches Auslandsamt, Postfach 1538
D-01958 Senftenberg, Tel.: 03573/85-0, e-mail: piper@fh-lausitz.de
Leipzig, Deutsche Telekom AG, Fachhochschule Leipzig, Akademisches Auslandsamt, Postfach 71, D-04251 Leipzig, Tel.: 0341/3062-110
e-mail: aaa@fh-telecom-leipzig.de
Leipzig, Hochschule für Technik, Wirtschaft und Kultur (FH), Akademisches Auslandsamt, Postfach 66, D-04251 Leipzig, Tel.: 0341/3076512
Lemgo, see Lippe Lippe, Fachhochschule, Akademisches Auslandsamt
Liebigstraße 87, D-32657 Lemgo, Tel.: 05261/702-0
e-mail: klee@adm.fh-lippe.de Lübeck, Fachhochschule Akademisches Auslandsamt, Stephensonstraße 3, D-23562 Lübeck, Tel.: 0451/500-5098
Lüneburg, see Nordostniedersachsen Ludwigsburg, Evangelische Fachhochchsule
für Diakonie der Karlshöhe Ludwigsburg Paulusweg 24, D-71638 Ludwigsburg

Tel.: 07141/9650
Ludwigshafen, Evangelische Fachhochschule für Sozialwesen Maxstraße 29
D-67059 Ludwigshafen, Tel.: 0621/59113-27
Ludwigshafen, Fachhochschule, Akademisches Auslandsamt
Ernst -Boehe-Straße 4, D-67059 Ludwigshafen, Tel.: 0621/5203-187
Magdeburg, Fachhochschule Am, Krökentor 2, D-39104 Magdeburg
Tel.: 0391/6702
Mainz, Fachhochschule, Akademisches Auslandsamt, Seppel-Glückert-Passage 10, D-55166 Mainz, Tel.: 06131/2392-17
Mainz, Katholische Fachhoschule für Sozialarbeit, Sozialpädagogik und Praktische Theologie, Postfach 2340, D-55013 Mainz, Tel.: 06131/289440
Mannheim, Fachhochschule für Sozialwesen Lodolf-Krehlstr. 7-11
D-68167 Mannheim, Tel.: 0621/3926-132
Mannheim, Fachhochschule für Technik und Gestaltung Akademisches Auslandsmat, Windeckstraße 110, D-68163 Mannheim, Tel.: 0621/292-6447
e-mail:flack@fh-mannheim.de
Merseburg, Fachhochschule, Akademisches Auslandsamt Geusaer, Straße 38
D-06217 Merseburg, Tel.: 03461/46-2249
e-mail: gretel.joachim@aas.fh-merseburg. de
Mittweida, Hochschule für Technik und Wirtschaft (FH) Büro für Auslandsbeziehungen, Technikumplatz 17, D-09648 Mittweida
Tel.: 03727/58-0, e-mail: doberenz@htwm.de
Moritzburg, Evangelische Fachhochschule für Religionspädagogik und Gemeindediakonie, Bahnhofstraße 9, D-01468 Moritzburg, Tel.: 035207/81427
München, Fachhochschule, Akademisches Auslandsmat, Lothstraße 34
D-80335 München, Tel.: 089/1265-1461,-1456,-1464
e-mail: merz@tb.fh-muenchen.de goeller@tb.fh-muenchen.de
München, Katholische Stiftungsfachhochschule, Preysingstraße 83
D-81667 München, Tel.: 089/48092-286
Münster, Fachhochschule, Akademisches Auslandsamt, Hüfferstraße 27
D-48149 Münster, Tel.: 0251/83-4289, e-mail: sinsbeck@fh-muenster.de
Neubrandenburg, Fachhochschule, Akademisches Auslandsamt
Postfach 1902, D-17009 Neubrandenburg, Tel.: 0395/569-30
Niederrhein, Fachhochschule, Akademisches Auslandsamt Postfach 2850
D-47728 Krefeld, Tel: 02151/822-625
e-mail: margot.timmer@kr.fh-niederrhein.de
Norddeutschland, Katholische Fachhochschule, Abteilung Vechta Driewerstr. 23, D-49377 Vechta, Tel.: 04441/92260
Nordostniedersachsen, Fachhochschule Akademisches, Auslandsamt
Bardowicker Straße 27, D-21335 Lüneburg, Tel.: 04131/390066
e-mail: barbara-fritzsche@fh-lueneburg.de
Nordrhein-Westfalen, Katholische Fachhochschule Wörthstraße 10
D-50668 Köln, Tel.: 0221/7757-0
Nürnberg, Evangelische Fachhochschule, Akademisches Auslandsamt
Burgschmietstraße 10, D-90419 Nürnberg, Tel.: 0911/3727931
Nürnberg, Georg-Simon-Ohm-Fachhochschule, Akademisches Auslandsamt
Postfach 210320, D-90121 Nürnberg, Tel.: 0911/5880-136
Nürtingen, Fachhochschule, Akademisches Auslandsamt, Neckarsteige 6-10

D-72622 Nürtingen, Tel.: 07022/33270
Nürtingen, Fachhochschule für Kunsttherapie der Freien Kunstschule
Sigmaringer Straße 15, D-72622 Nürtingen, Tel.: 07022/33270
Offenburg, Fachhochschule, Akademisches Auslandsamt, Badstraße 24
D-77652 Offenburg, Tel.: 0781/205-218, e-mail: heller@fh-offenburg.de
Oldenburg, Fachhochschule, Akademisches Auslandsamt, Ofener Straße 19
D-26121 Oldenburg, Tel.: 0441/7708-114
Osnabrück, Fachhochschule, Akademisches Auslandsamt, Caprivistraße 1
D-49076 Osnabrück, Tel.: 0541/969-2966,
e-mail: aaa@hermes.rz.fh-onsabrueck.de
Ostfriesland, Fachhochschule, Akademisches Auslandsamt, Constantiaplatz 4
D-26723 Emden, Tel.: 04921/807-641,-639,-640
e-mail: walden@perseus.fho-emden.de
Ottersberg, Freie Kunst-Studienstätte, Am Wiestebruch 66-68, D-28870 Ottersberg
Tel.: 04205/596
Paderborn, Fachhochschule der Wirtschaft, Fürstenallee 3-5, D-33102 Paderborn
Tel.: 05251/301-02, e-mail: casper@pb.bib.de
Paderborn, Universität-Gesamthochschule, Akademisches Auslandsamt
Warburger Straße 100, D-33098 Paderborn, Tel. 05251/60-3210
e-mail: veit@zv.uni-paderborn.de
Pforzheim, Fachhochschule, Hochschule für Gestaltung, Technik und Wirtschaft
Akademisches Auslandsamt, Tiefenbronner Straße 65, D-75175 Pforzheim
Tel.: 07231/28-6145 (mornings),-6222 (afternoons)
Pinneberg, Nordakademie An der Muhlenau 14, D-25421 Pinneberg
Tel.: 04101/512991
Potsdom, Fachhochschule Pappelallee 8-9, D-14469 Potsdam,
Tel.: 0331/580-2010, e-mail: kotulla@fh-potsdam.de
Ravensburg-Weingarten, Fachhochschule Akademisches Auslandsamt
Postfach 1261, D-88241 Weingarten, Tel.: 0751/501-592
e-mail: hamer@verw.fh-weingarten.de
Regensburg, Fachhochschule, Akademisches Auslandsamt, Prüfeninger Straße 58
D-93049 Regensburg, Tel: 0941/943-1067
Reutlingen, Evangelische Fachhochschule für Sozialwesen Ringelbachstraße 221,
D-72762 Reutlingen, Tel.: 07121/24140
Reutlingen, Fachhochschule für Technik und Wirtschaft, Akademisches Auslandsamt,
Alteburgstraße 150, D-72762 Reutlingen, Tel.: 07121/271-488
e-mail: baldur.veit@fh-reutlingen.de
Rhein-Sieg, Fachhochschule, Rathausallee 10, D-53757 Sankt Augustin
Tel.: 02241/865-622, e-mail: silke.halle@fh-rhein-sieg.de
Rheinland-Westfalen-Lippe, Evangelisch Fachhochschule Immanuel-Kant-Straße 18-20
D-44803 Bochum, Tel.: 0234/36901-133
Rosenhei, Fachhochschule, Akademisches Auslandsamt, Marienberger Straße 26
D-83024 Rosenheim, Tel.: 08031/805-272', e-mail: reiner@fh-rosenheim.de
Rottenburg, Hochschule für Forstwirtschaft (FH) Schadenweilerhof
D-72108 Rottenburg, Tel.: 07472/951-203, e-mail: bort@fh-rottenburg. de
Saarbrücken, Fachhochschule für Bergbau, Trierer Straße 4
D-66111 Saarbrücken, Tel.: 0681/405-2486
Will close October 1997, therefore no admission Saarbrücken, Hochschule für Technik, und

Wirtschaft des Saarlandes Auslandsamt Goebenstraβe 40
D-66117 Saarbrücken, Tel.: 0681/5867-109
Saarbrücken, Katholische Hochschule für Soziale Arbeit, Rastpfuhl 12 a
D-66113 Saarbrücken, Tel.: 0681/97132-14
Sankt Augustin, see Rhein-Sieg, Schmalkalden, Fachhochschule
Akademisches Auslandsamt, Blechhammer, D-98574 Schmalkalden
Tel.: 03683/688-130, e-mail: heide@verw.fh-schmalkalden.de
Schwäbisch Gmünd, Fachhochschule für Gestaltung, Rektor-Klaus-Straße 100
D-73525 Schwäbisch Gmünd, Tel.: 07171/602603
e-mail: sekretariat@hfg-gmuend.de
Senftenberg, see Lausitz, Siegen, Universität-Gesamthochschule, Akademisches Auslandsamt, D-57068 Siegen, Tel.: 0271/740-3903
e-mail: eickbusch@aaa.uni-siegen.d400.de
Sigmaringen, see Albstadt Stendal, see Altmark Stralsund, Fachhochschule
Große Parower Straße 145, D-18435 Stralsund, Tel.: 03831/367533
Stuttgart, Fachhochschule für Bibliothekswesen, Feuerbacher Heide 38-42
D-70192 Stuttgart, Tel.: 0711/227420, e-mail: office@hbi-stuttgart.de
Stuttgart, Fachhochschule für Technik Akademisches Auslandsamt Schellingstraße 24, D-70174 Stuttgart, Tel.: 0711/121-2694
e-mail: kruppa@saturn.rz.fht-stuttgart.de
Stuttgart, Merz-Akademie Hochschule für Gestaltung, Teckstraße 58
D-70190 Stuttgart Tel.: 0711/26866-20, e-mail: 100566.3420@compuserve.com
Trier, Fachhochschule, Akademisches Auslandsamt, Schneidershof
D-54293 Trier, Tel.: 0651/8103-378
Ulm, Fachhochschule Akademisches Auslandsamt, Prittwitzstraße 10
D-89075 Ulm, Tel.: 0731/502-8272, e-mail: bruns@fh-ulm.de
Vechta, see Norddeutschland Wedel. Fachhochschule, Auslandsamt
Feldstraße 143, D-22880 Wedel, Tel.: 04103-8048-0
e-mail: sekretariat@fh-wedel.de
Weihenstephan, Fachhochschule, Akademisches Auslandsamt, D-85350 Freising
Tel.: 08161/71-4532
Weingarten, see Ravensburg Wernigerode, see Harz Westküste, Fachhochschule, Hochschule, für Wirtschaft und Technik, Akademisches Auslandsamt
Rungholtstraße 9, D-25746 Heide, Tel.: 0481/8555-68
Wiesbaden, Fachhochschule Auslandsreferat Kurt-Schumacher-Ring 18
D-65197 Wiesbaden, Tel.: 0611/9495-128
Wildau, Technische Fachhochschule Friedrich-Engels-Straße 63, D-15742 Wildau
Tel.: 03375/507197
Wilhelmshaven, Hochschule, Akademisches Auslandsamt, Friedrich-Paffrath-Straße 101, D-26389 Wilhelmshaven, Tel.: 04421/985-386
e-mail: menn@ze.fh-wilhelmshaven.de
Wismar, Fachhochschule für Technik, Wirtschaft und Gestaltung, Akademisches Auslandsamt, Postfach 1210, D-23952 Wismar, Tel.: 03841/753-390
Wolfenbüttel, see Braunschweig Worms, Fachhochschule, Akademisches Auslandsamt, Erenburger Straße 19, D-67549 Worms, Tel.: 06241/509-168
Wuppertal, Bergische Universität Gesamthochschule, Akademisches Auslandsamt
Gaußstraße 20, D-42119 Wuppertal, Tel.: 0202/439-2406

Würzburg-Schweinfurt-Aschaffenburg Fachhochschule, Akademisches Auslandsamt, Münzstraße 12, D-97070 Würzburg, Tel.: 0931/304-172
e-mail: bender@fh-wuerzburg.de, ulsamer@fh-wuerbburg.de
Zittau-Görlitz, Hochschule für Technik, Wirtschaft und Sozialwesen (FH)
Akademisches Auslandsamt, Postfach 261, D-02755 Zittau
Tel.: 03583/611-444, e-mail: kuehne@verwaltung.htw.zittau.de
Zwickau, Hochschule für Technik und Wirtschaft (FH), Akademisches Auslandsamt, Postfach 201037, D-08012 Zwickau, Tel.: 0375/536-1061
e-mail: elke. kunze@banjan.th.zwickau.de

Assessment of foreign secondary school leaving certificates

Admission to studies at a German institution of higher education depends on how the foreign student's secondary school-leaving certificate is assessed in the Federal Republic of Germany.

Students coming from a country must generally take the assessment test before admission to studies.

Exceptions ("exemptions") are generally only made for students with school-leaving certificates from German schools abroad.

Admission to the assessment test is often only possible with a specific school-leaving certificate from the respective country and frequently only after the fulfilment of certain conditions (grade point average, study period in the home country).

India

Admission to the assessment test only for applicants who can prove that they have a secondary school leaving certificate awarded after 12 years of schooling.

Applicants who provide proof of successful participation in the entrance examination for the Indian Institutes of Technology will be exempted from the assessment test.

Aims, Functions and Programmes of the DAAD

The German Academic Exchange Service (Deutscher Akademischer Austauschdienst, DAAD) is an academic exchange and support organization jointly founded by the German instituions of higher education. The purpose of the DAAD is to promote relations between these German institutions and higher education institutions in foreign countries, primarily through the exchange of students and academics. Its programmes are open to all countries and disciplines and to foreigners as well as Germans. The DAAD also supports the higher education institutions' international activities with a number of services such as information programmes, publications, and counselling and advising. Because of its organizational competence, the DAAD also plays a significant supporting role in the development and implementation of German cultural policy abroad.

The higher education institutions' exchange service was first established in 1925 on the basis of an initiative from academic circles. It was dissolved in 1945 and refounded in 1950 as a registered organisation under private law. The DAAD's full member are, if they apply, the higher education institutions represented in the German Rectors' Conference (*Hochschulrekto-renkonferenz, HRK)* and their student bodies. Currently there are a total of 222 institutions and 130 student bodies from various types of higher education institutions in the DAAD.

The DAAD has the following functions:

- to allocate scholarships to foreign and German students, student trainees, junior academic staff and professors, in order to promote international experience in education and further education as well as in research;

- to recruit, place and support German academic teaching staff from all disciplines for short or long-term teaching assignments at foreign institutions of higher education (especially "Lektoren", young academics who teach German language and literature and contemporary German studies);
- to provide information on study and research opportunities at home and abroad through leaflets and brochures, oral and written advice to individuals and through information visits of foreign and German academics and student groups;
- or maintain follow-up contacts with former scholarship holders especially those abroad, through a reinvitation program, follow-up meetings and publications, e.g. the "DAAD Letter".

The EU programmes SOCRATES (general education), LEONARDO DA VINCI (vocational training) and TEMPUS (cooperation with central and Eastern Europe) are a special variant of structured programmes for mobility and co-operation. In the programmes of SOCRATES which deal with higher education and are called ERASMUS since 1987, the DAAD functions at a "national agency". It receives scholarship funding for Germany and distributes partial scholarships among German institutions of higher education. In addition, it provides detailed information about the programmes. Furthermore, the DAAD assumes the role of a national information and counselling centre for the EU programme part of LEONARDO DA VINCI concerning the cooperation of higher education and industry and for the TEMPUS programme.

DAAD Addresses in Germany and abroad

Head Office Bonn Bad Godesberg

Deutscher Akademischer Austauschdienst, Kennedyallee 50, D-53175 Bonn, Postfach 200404, D-53134 Bonn, Tel. (0228) 882-0, Fax (0228) 882-444, Tele: 885515 daad d, e-mail: postmaster@daad.de

Berlin Office

Deutscher Akademischer Austauschdienst, Jägerstraße 23, D-10117 Berlin
Postfach 240, D-10106 Berlin, Tel. (030) 202208-0, Fax (030) 2041267
Telex 304760 daad d

Arbeitsstelle Berlin-Mitte

Deutscher Akademischer Austauschdienst, Breite Straße 11, 10178 Berlin Postfach 86, 10122 Berlin, Tel. (030) 247590-0, Fax (030) 24759020 Telex: 307911 dabm d

London Office (since 1952)

German Academic Exchange Service, 34 Belgrave Square, GB-London SW1X 8QB, Tel. (0044/171) 235 1736, Fax (0044/171) 235 9602
e-mail: info@daad.org.uk

Cairo Office (since 1960)

German Academic Exchange Service, 11 Sh. Saleh Ayyoub Cairo-Zamalek, Egypt, Tel. (0020/2) 3402726, Fax (0020/2) 2420722 e-mail: daadcairo@frcu.eun.eg

New Delhi Office (since 1960)

German Academic Exchange Service, 176, Golf Links, New Delhi 110003, India, Tel. (0091/11) 4615-148, 4615-009, Fax (0091/11) 4690-99, Telex: 081-31-6 6471 daad in,
e-mail: daad@doe.ernet.in

Paris Office (since 1963)

Office Allemand d'Echanges Universitairis, 15, rue de Verneuil, F-75007 Paris

Tel. (0033/1) 4261-5757, Fax (0033/1) 4286-9442

New York Office (since 1971)

German Academic Exchange Service, 950 Third Avenue, 19th floor New York, N.Y. 10022, USA, Tel. (001/212) 758-3223 Fax (001/212) 755-5780, e-mail: daadny@daad.org

Rio de Janeiro Office (since 1972)

Serviço Alemão de Intercâmbio Acadêmico, Rua Presidente Carlos de Campos. 417 22.231-080 Rio de Janeiro-RJ, Brasilien, Tel. (0055/21) 553-3296 Fax (0055/21) 553-9261 e-mail: daad.rj.@nc-rj.rnp.br

Nairobi Office (since 1973)

German Academic Exchange Service, Regional Office for Africa
(P.O. Box 14050, Nairobi, Kenya), Bishops House, 1st Floor
Bishops Road, Upper Hill, Nairobi, Kenia, Tel. (00254/2) 729741, 722660
Fax (00254/2) 716710, Telex: 0987-22953 daad ke, e-mail: daadnrb@arcc.or.ke

Tokyo Office (since 1978)

Deutscher Akademischer Austauschdienst, Akasaka 7-5-56, Minato-ku Tokyo 107, Japan, Tel. (0081/3) 3582-5962, Fax (0081/3) 3582-5554 e-mail: daad@gmd.co.jp

San Jose Office (since 1985)

Servicio Alemán de Intercambio Académico , c/o CONARE, Apdo. 374
2050 San Pedro Montes de Oca, Costa Rica, Tel. (00506) 2531922, 2343066
Fax (00506) 2839433, e-mail: mschulze@cariari.ucr.ac.cr

Jakarta Office (since 1990)

DAAD Jakarta Office, Jl. Jend. Sudirman, Kav. 61-62, Summitmas I, lt. 19
Jakarta 12190, Indonesien, Tel. (0062/21) 5200870, 5252807
Fax (0062/21) 5252822, e-mail: daadjak@rad.net

Moscow Office (since 1993)

Deutscher Akademischer Austauschdienst, Leninskij Prospekt, 95a
117313 Moscow—Russian Federation, Tel. (007/095) 1322429
Fax (007/095) 1324988, e-mail: daadmsk@glas.apc.org

Beijing Office (established 1994)

Deutscher Akademischer Austauschdienst, c/o Beijing Waiguoyu Daxue
P.O. Box 8110-46, Xisanhuanbeilu Nr. 2, 100081 Beijing, PR of China
Tel. (0086/10) 684567-02 and 03, Fax (0086/10) 684567-04
e-mail: daad@iuol.cn.net

Organisations affiliated with the DAAD

Deutsch-Französisches Hochschulkolleg, Deutsches Sekretariat
Schillerstraße 11, D-55116 Mainz, Tel. (06131) 23 16-97,-98
Fax (06131)236701, Maison Heinrich Heine, Maison de l'Allemagne dans la Cite Internationale Universitaire de Paris, 27C, bd. Jourdan, F-75014 Paris
Tel. (0033/1) 44.16.13.00, Fax (0033/1) 44.16.13.01

DAAD New Delhi

The New Delhi office, established in 1960, administers primarily DAAD-funded programmes and activities for India, Bangladesh, Bhutan, Nepal and Sri Lanka. It provides information about German universities and "Fachhochschulen" and distributes publications about study, research,

Germany to Indian nationals, and on Indian university study and research opportunities to Germans. DAAD New Delhi is also the liaison office for the Alexander von Humboldt Foundation (AvH), the German University Presidents' and Vice-Chancellors' Association (HRK), the German Research Society (DFG), and the Max Planck Society (MPG). It has a close working relationship with the South-Asia Institute New Delhi (SAI) of the University of Heidelberg and the Society for Technical Cooperation (GTZ).

DAAD's Indian Partners

Most of DAAD's programmes with India are jointly sponsored by the Department of Education, Ministry of Human Resource Development (HRD), the University Grants Commission (UGC), the Council of Scientific and Industrial Research (CSIR), Department of Science and Technology (DST), others by the Indian Council for Cultural Relations (ICCR), and the Indian Institutes of Technology (IITs).

Programmes in India

DAAD grants and fellowships are available to *resident* India faculty and scholars as well as doctoral candidates and postgraduates, for participation in a wide variety of academic programmes. Short descriptions of these programmes and the minimum, formal application requirements for each are listed here. Unless otherwise stated, participants in DAAD programmes must be citizens of India and full-time faculty members or scholars working or enrolled at Indian colleges, universities, national laboratories or other recognised research institutes, at the time of application.

Application Procedure

Application forms for DAAD programmes described here may be obtained, where applicable, through the Indian partners indicated in the relevant rubric below, or by writing to DAAD, New Delhi. Requests for application forms must reach DAAD's partners by the dates given in their own announcements of the fellowships in question. Requests addressed to DAAD must reach the New Delhi office at least two weeks prior to the respective deadlines.

For further information on any aspect of DAAD's grant and fellowship programmes, please contact the New Delhi Office.

DAAD FELLOWSHIP/SCHOLARSHIP PROGRAMMES

Fellowship Programmes for Indian Postgraduates

Essential Prerequisites

- Candidates for 1.1.1 Research Fellowships for Young Scholars and Recent Post-docs, and for 1.1.2 Sandwich-model Fellowships for Ph.D. Scholars, must possess at least a Master's degree from an accredited institution of higher education in India or abroad (provided the latter is recognised by the appropriate authorities in the Federal Republic of Germany).
- Candidates for 1.1.3 Sandwich-model Scholarships for M.S. (Research) and M. Tech. Students at Indian Institutes of Technology must be enrolled in an M.S. (Research) or an M. Tech. programme *and* must be registered for course work at an IIT according to the regulations of the IIT.
- Candidates must be residing in India at the time of application.
- Candidates must sign a *bond* vis-a-vis their government/university guaranteeing their return to India after their stay in Germany. Employed candidates must produce proof

of their employers' undertaking to re-employ them upon return.

- Candidates must have a recent-dated letter of placement from a faculty member at a German university or from an equivalent mentor at a research institute/laboratory.
- Applications must be routed through proper channels, where required.

Long-term Fellowships ("Jahresstipendien")

These fellowships are offered primarily through DAAD's partner organisations in India, as part of the Cultural Agreement between the Government of India and the Federal Republic of Germany: The Department of Education, Ministry of Human Resource Development, New Delhi (HRD), the University Grants Commission, New Delhi (UGC), and the Council of Scientific and Industrial Research, New Delhi (CSIR). They will announce the fellowships in July/August 1998, after which application forms will be available from them.

Highly qualified candidates with a letter of nomination from a former DAAD or AvH fellowship holder, who fulfill the application requirements below *and* rank at the top of their discipline/profession, may apply to DAAD New Delhi directly. The deadline for submission of complete applications to DAAD New Delhi is October 15, 1998.

Fellowships are, initially, for one year preceded by a two-to-six, most commonly four-month German language course in Germany arranged and funded by DAAD. Upon application and proper documentation, they are extendable upto another 12 months.

Applications are invited in the fields of:

Agriculture, Communication/Information Sciences, Computer Science, Engineering, Forestry, Horticulture, German Language and Literature/German Studies, Humanities, International Law, Linguistics, Mathematics, Natural Sciences, Social Sciences, Veterinary Science, and Sports.

These long-term fellowships are of three kinds:

Research Fellowships ("Forschungssti - pendien") for Young Scholars and Recent Post-docs

Open to junior scholars at Indian universities or regional institutes of university standard (deemed universities), research institutes of national importance in India, and the Indian Institutes of Technology (IITs).

Specific Eligibility Requirements and Provisions:

- *Age Limit:* Candidates may not be more than 32 years old at the inception of the scholarship period (i.e. born on or after October 01, 1966).
- *Prior Experience:* Candidates must have at least two years of teaching and/or research experience after obtaining their Master's degree.
- *Employment:* Candidates who are permanently employed will be given preference. Exceptions will be considered on an individual basis.

Sandwich-model Fellowships for Ph.D. Scholars ("Sandwich-Stipendien" für Doktoranden)

Open to junior scholars registered for doctorate degrees in India. They may carry out research alternately in India and Germany, under the--previously agreed--joint supervision of an Indian and German mentor. Failure to obtain such prior agreement will disqualify the candidate from the competition for this type of fellowship.

Specific Eligibility Requirements:

- *Age Limit:* Candidates may not be more than *36* years old at the time of the inception of the scholarship period (i.e. born on or after October 01, 1962).

- *Registration:* Candidates must be registered for their Ph. D. degree *in India* at the time of application.

Sandwich-model Scholarships for M.S. (Research) and M.Tech. Students at Indian Institutes of Technology

DAAD offers "Sandwich-Model" scholarships to students registered for Masters-degrees at an Indian Institute of Technology. The "Sandwich-Model" for Masters students is a multi-phases scheme in which candidates carry out their required course work in India and the research portion in Germany, under the supervision of a guide from the respective Indian Institute of Technology as well as a mentor from one of 5 participating German technical universities (Technische Hochschulen, Technischen Universitaeten, at Aachen, Berlin, Darmstadt, Karlsruhe, and Stuttgart), according to a schedule previously drafted out.

Candidates must be enrolled in an M.S. (Research) or an M.Tech. programme and must be registered for course work at an IIT according to the regulations of the IIT. After successfully completing the course requirements they are offered a scholarship under one of the following schemes:

(A:) One-year programme for "Master of Science by Research" students at IIT Delhi and Madras

- 4-week language course in Germany.
- 9 months (equivalent to 2 semesters) research work for the Masters thesis to be carried out at a German University.
- 4 to 8 weeks of practical training/internship in German industry may be arranged upon request and availability of placements.

(B:) 9-months programme for "Master of Technology" student from all IITs

- 4-week language course
- 6 months research work as in scheme A above,
- 4 to 8 weeks of practical training/internship of German industry may be arranged upon request and availability of placements.

Students in both categories will return to their home institutes to complete the degree requirements and obtain their degrees there.

Applications are to be submitted to the concerned, Dean/Deputy Director of the IIT in question, for nomination to DAAD. DAAD together with representatives from the participating German universities make the final selection and confirm placement.

Scholarships are awarded only after definitive placement has been obtained at one of the participating universities.

For further information and application forms, please contact the concerned Dean/ Deputy Director at your IIT.

IIT Bombay	:	Dean of Academic Programmes
IIT Delhi	:	Dean of Postgraduate Studies and Research
IIT Kanpur	:	Deputy Director
IIT Kharagpur	:	Dean of Postgraduate Studies
IIT Madras	:	Dean of Academic Courses

1.2 Short-term Fellowships ("Kurzstipendien")

These fellowships are primarily offered through the University Grants Commission (UGC), New Delhi, to scholars registered for a Ph.D. at universities or research institutes in India, to enable them to collect material in Germany for the completion of their doctoral thesis. The fellowships are for two to six months, (no extension possible) in the fields of Economics, Education, History, Philosophy, Mathematics, and the Natural Sciences. For the special programme for Junior scholars of German Studies (Language, Literature, Culture, and Society), see Section 4.2 in this part.

UGC will announce the availability of these fellowships in July/August 2000 and set its own deadline for the submission of applications. Applications to DAAD New Delhi directly are also possible. DAAD's deadline for submission of complete applications is:

October 15, 2000

Specific Eligibility Requirements:

- *Age Limit:* Candidates must not be older than *32* years, (i.e. born on October 01, 1968 or later) and the time of the inception of the fellowship period
- *Registration:* Candidates must be registered for their Ph.D. with a university or research institute of university standard.
- *Research Status:* Candidates' research must be at an advanced stage at the time of application.

2.Scholarships for Postgraduate Courses with Relevance to Developing Countries ("Stipendien fuer entwicklungslaenderbezogene Aufbaustudiengaenge")

Essential Prerequisites

- Candidates must possess at least a Master's degree from an accredited institution of higher education in India or abroad (provided the latter is recognised by the appropriate authorities in the Federal Republic of Germany).
- Candidates must be residing in India at the time of application.
- Candidates must sign a bond vis-à-vis their government/university guaranteeing their return to India after their stay in Germany Employed candidates must produce proof of their employers' undertaking to re-employ them upon return.
- Candidates applying for fellowships must be recommended by the university of "Fachhochschule" in question.
- Applications must be routed through proper channels, where required.

Universities and "Fachhochschulen" in Germany offer postgraduate degree or certificate courses with special relevance to developing countries, some of which are offered in English. They are open to qualified applicants (at least a B.Tech., B.Engg., or B.Arch. First Class) regardless of DAAD support. Applications for admission only may be addressed to the German institutions directly, or via DAAD New Delhi.

DAAD offers a small number of scholarships to those admitted for participation in those courses which are listed in DAAD's brochure "Scholarships in Germany for Postgraduate Courses with Relevance to Developing Countries 1999/2000". This brochure has been distributed to the relevant agencies in India.

Special Note: These scholarships are also offered in Bhutan.

Specific Eligibility Requirements for DAAD Scholarships

- Degree: Candidates must have a Master's degree in the relevant subject (Unless expressly stated otherwise, Ph.D. holders are not encouraged to apply).
- Prior Work Experience: Candidates must have two years of professional experience after obtaining the core qualification.
- Employment/Sponsorship: Candidates must be permanently employed and must be sponsored by their employers.

- Age Limit: For most courses, candidates may not be older than 36 years at the time of application. For exceptions to this rule, please inquire at the DAAD New Delhi office.

Note: Participation in these courses does *not* lead, and DAAD fellowships offered under this programme *cannot* be used or changed to lead, to a Ph.D. degree in Germany.

3. Fellowship Programmes for Indian Faculty and Scholars

Essential Prerequisites

- Only scholars and faculty on active duty can be considered. Emeriti are *not* eligible.
- Applicants must have recent-dated correspondence--not older than 6 months--from their counterparts at German universities, "Fachhochschulen", or research institutes agreeing to the proposed plan of research and the suggested time schedule.
- At least two-thirds of the stay is to be spent at *one* particular institute in Germany.

Study Visits ("Studienaufenthalte")

DAAD supports short study and research visits of *one to three months* by Indian scholars and faculty to universities, "Fachhochschulen", and research institutes in Germany. Invitations are extended with a grant to cover maintenance and, where applicable, domestic travel in Germany.

The international airfare is to be borne by the Indian side.

Candidates for this programme are normally proposed by the University Grants Commission (UGC), New Delhi, who will advertise this programme through its own channels and set its own deadlines. Applications to DAAD New Delhi directly are also possible.

Applications have to reach DAAD New Delhi by *October 15, 1998.*

Successful candidates will be notified only in January/February of 1999.

(Wherever possible, special arrangements will be made for scholars whose visit is scheduled to begin in the first few months of the year.)

CSIR (India)-DAAD Exchange of Scientists Programme ("Indisch-Deutsches Wissens chaftler austauschprogramm")

This programme is open to CSIR scientists for visits of between two and three months to research institutes or universities/ "Fachhochschulen" in Germany, to carry out specific research projects.

Conversely, German scientists suggested by their Indian counterparts or nominated by DAAD may be sponsored for visits of between 14 days and three months to CSIR institutes in India (see Section 6.3 of this part).

Under the provisions of this reciprocal programme, the sending side takes charge of international airfare, and the receiving side shoulders the costs related to local hospitality.

Specific Eligibility Requirements and Additional Provisions

- Interested faculty must be nominated or endorsed by CSIR.
- DAAD requires 10 to 12 weeks notice before being able to issue the formal letter of invitation.

* *Note:* Direct application to DAAD New Delhi is *not* possible.

3.1. *Study Visit and Exchange of Scientists for IIT Faculty*

Upon nomination by the Director of IIT qualified faculty from any department may apply for shorterm study visit grants, for a period of upto three months each, to Germany.

The international airfare is borne by the IIT in question. DAAD provides a stipend for maintenance.

- *Note:* Direct application to DAAD New Delhi is *not* possible.

3.2 International Long Term Guest Lecturership for Faculty from Abroad ("Auslaendische Gastdozenten an deutschen Hochschulen")

With a view to strengthening the international dimension of teaching in German higher education, DAAD supports longterm appointments of qualified full-time faculty from abroad at German universities and Fachhochschulen, for periods of six months to two years, in any field of specialisation (except languages). The courses, which are an integral part of the curriculum of the department in question, should be taught in the incumbents' native language--or the language most commonly used in academic teaching in their home country--but in any event in a language other than German.

Interested Indian faculty should consult with the DAAD New Delhi Office about the parameters of this programme. They should also contact their counterparts at German institutions of higher education and inquire about possible openings. They must have an outstanding teaching and research record and be in active service at the time of application.

- *Note :* Direct applications for participation in this programme are *not* possible. The German host institution decides on inviting an Indian faculty member and subsequently applies to DAAD Bonn for support.

4. Special Fellowship Programmes for Indian University Teachers and Junior Scholars of German

Essential Prerequisites

- Nominees must supply recent-dated correspondence--not older than six months--with the German counterparts in question agreeing to the proposed plan of research and the suggested time schedule.

4.1 Study Visit Grants for Teachers of German ("Deutschlehrer-Programm")

For teachers of German Language and Literature/German Studies at Indian universities, institutes deemed to be universities, and Indian Institutes of Technology, DAAD offers the opportunity to visit Germany for a period of three months, to collect material for further research and teaching.

The offer is made through the University Grants Commission (UGC) who will announce this programme and set its own criteria for pre-selection. In exceptional cases, direct application to DAAD, New Delhi is possible. Please consult the office before applying.

Applications must be addressed to UGC, at the deadlines given in their announcement. Direct applications have to reach the office of DAAD New Delhi by *October 15, 2000*

Specific Eligibility Requirements

- Degree/Language Proficiency: Nominees should have at least a Master's Degree and a distinctly above-average current proficiency in German.
- Prior Experience/Employment: Nominees must have a teaching experience of at least two years and be permanently employed at an Indian institution of higher education, at the time of application.

4.2 Grants For Junior Scholars of German ("Kurzstipendien fuer Nachwuchsgermanisten")

Primarily through UGC, DAAD offers 3 to 6 month grants to junior Indian scholars of German language, literature, culture, and society enrolled at Indian universities, to enable them to collect material for their M.Phil. or Ph.D. thesis under the guidance of professors at universities in ???

5. Follow-up Programmes for Former DAAD Fellowship Holders from India

5.1 Re-invitation Programme

Former *long-term* (minimum: 1 year) DAAD fellowship holders on active duty may apply for *research visits* to Germany for a maximum period of 3 months at a time. At least two-thirds of the stay should be spent at a particular institute.

There are separate re-invitation programmes for former DAAD fellowship holders from CSIR institutes, as well as for former AvH fellowship holders. Scientists from these institutes and AvH-fellows may apply through those channels only.

All applications for re-invitation visits from eligible candidates should reach DAAD New Delhi by October 15, 1998

Eligibility Requirements

- *Time frame:* At least 3 years must have elapsed since the applicant's return from the stay in Germany supported by a long-term DAAD fellowship.
- *Contact:* Applicants should have remained in regular scientific contact with their counterparts in Germany after their return to India.
- *Placement:* Applicants should submit copies of correspondence with their German counterparts-not older than 6 months--agreeing to the proposed research plan and the suggested time schedule.
- *Leave:* Applicants must submit a certificate from their employers granting paid research leave for the duration of their visit.

Germany, or to enroll there for short refresher and/or specialisation courses. In exceptional cases, direct applications to DAAD; New Delhi are possible. Please consult the office before applying.

Applications must be submitted to the UGC after their announcement of this programme. Direct applications must reach DAAD New Delhi by *October 15, 2000*

Eligibility Requirements

- Degree/Status: Applicants should be M.Phil. or Ph.D. students currently enrolled at Indian universities.
- Sponsorship: Applications should be accompanied by a recommendation of the Indian university/thesis advisor.

5.2 Grants for Books, Journals, and Equipment

Former long-term DAAD fellowship holders may apply for donations of books or subscriptions to journals published in Germany (publications from elsewhere will be considered in exceptional cases). The value should not exceed DM 400 per year. Requests indicating author, title, year, and publisher should be forwarded directly to DAAD New Delhi.

Applications for the supply of scientific equipment and other material related to a specific research project, which should have a practical orientation and be part of a teaching and/or research programme, are also possible. The value of the equipment and material, including transportation from Germany to the port of entry, should not exceed DM 40,000. The grant will be in the name of the university or institute of the former fellowship holder and administered by the Society for Technical Cooperation (GTZ) in close cooperation with DAAD New Delhi.

DAAD New Delhi.

The recipient institutes must undertake to install, maintain, and repair the equipment at their own cost and to bear relevant fees accruing in India. Whenever possible a representative of DAAD should be invited to inaugurate the installation of the equipment on site.

6. Fellowship and Grant Programmes for German Scholars in India

6.1 *German Postgraduates, Doctoral Candidates, and Recent Ph.D.s ("Vertiefungs-und Kurzstipendien fuer Deutsche")*

The Indian Council for Cultural Relations (ICCR), co-sponsored and co-founded by DAAD, offers a number of fellowships for *German* postgraduates for study and research in India.

For further information on the profile of the scholarships, eligibility requirements, application procedures and deadlines, please consult the DAAD brochure "Studium, Forschung, Lehre-Foerderungsmoeglichkeiten im Ausland fuer Deutsche 1999/2000" which is available free of charge at all Akademische Auslandsaemter of the German universities and "Fachhochschulen" as well as from DAAD Bonn. Photocopies of relevant pages can be made available to interested candidates residing in India--or to departments at Indian universities wishing to host a German scholar--by DAAD New Delhi, upon request.

6.2 German Guest Lecturership Programme ("Langzeit-und Kurzzeitdozenturen")

Under the Indo-German Cultural Agreement, visits of German professors and scientists to universities and research institutes as long-term (2 to 5 years) and short-term (1 to 3 months) guest-teachers in all disciplines, with full teaching assignments according to the host university's specifications and conditions, can be sponsored by DAAD. A contribution from the host university is expected.

The host Indian university/institute is expected to obtain the necessary clearance of the Government of India for the guest professor. Applications must be directed to the UGC, New Delhi, with a copy to the Department of Education, Ministry of Human Resource Development, Government of India.

Further information and application forms may be obtained from DAAD, New Delhi upon written request by Heads of Departments, Deans, or Vice-Chancellors.

Complete applications take between 4 and 6 months to process.

6.3 DAAD/CSIR Exchange of Scientists *("Deutsch-Indischer Wissenschafftleraustausch")*

Under this programme--which is the German portion of the programme described in full under Section 3.1.1. of this part--German scientists from disciplines corresponding to those represented by the CSIR laboratories in India, may be invited, with the concurrence of DAAD and CSIR, for periods of between 14 days and three months, to do joint collaborative research with their Indian counterparts.

Note: Direct application to DAAD New Delhi is *not* possible.

6.4 German Teachers of German/German Studies and of German as a Foreign Language ("Lektoren fuer die Deutsche Sprache" und "Praktikanten fuer

Deutsch als Fremdsprache")

6.4.1 DAAD-Teachers of German/German Studies

For many years, DAAD has been helpful in placing German teachers of German Language and Literature/German Studies at universities in India, on a cost-sharing basis. Among those were universities where the Department of German or the German Section in a Department of Foreign Languages is particularly strong and, as a rule, has a Masters Degree as well as an M.Phil. and/or Ph.D. programme in German. Currently, there are ten such DAAD teachers of German/German Studies employed at Indian universities with the support of the UGC. The network is likely to be increased.

Heads of German and/or Foreign Language as well as Humanities Departments, Deans, and Vice-Chancellors may inquire for details at the DAAD New Delhi Office.

- *Note*: Applications by Indian faculty members without an administrative function for the services of DAAD teachers are not possible. Qualified German nationals may apply in response to public advertisements in the German media, and through DAAD Bonn only.

6.4.2 DAAD-Praktikanten "DaF"

German Departments or German Section of Foreign Language Departments which do not have a Master Degree, M.Phil. or Ph.D. programme, but are in need of assistance by native teachers of German, may inquire about the placement, through DAAD, of native German advanced and specially qualifiied student interns ("Praktikanten"). Their academic specialisation, pursued at selected professional institutes for second language acquisition in Germany, is "German as a Foreign Language" ("Deutsch als Fremdsprache"-DaF). Their appointment may be for one semester or, at most, one academic year.

7. Grants for Practical Training/Internships for Indian and German Students ("Praxisbezogene Ausbildung"/"Hochschulpraktika")

Indian and German students whose course of study requires a period of practical training (internship) abroad, *and* who have a good command of German or English, respectively, may apply for logistical assistance from DAAD, to establish contact with an appropriate employer in the host country and to obtain the necessary clearances. A small number of DAAD stipends towards international travel costs is available.

DAAD also is the German Chapter of the International Association for the Exchange of Students for Technical Experience (I.A.E.S.T.E.) which arranges internships for Indian and German students from the Engineering disciplines, Agriculture and Forestry in German or Indian universities and research institutes as well as in industry.

For further information on eligibility requirements and procedures, please contact DAAD, New Delhi.

8. Grants for Study and Information Visits by Groups of Young Indian and German Scholars

DAAD offers grants for study and information visits to Germany by groups of Indian students from all disciplines and, vice-versa, to groups of German students to India, under the direction of an accompanying faculty member. The visits are intended to familiarize the participants with the latest developments in their respective fields and/or with the current political, economic and cultural affairs in the host country.

Visits are possible for groups of between 10 and 30 qualified participants, for the duration of a week to a maximum of 21 days. For Indian participants, knowledge of German is desirable but not essential.

For Indian groups, the international airfare and transportation within Germany will have to be borne by the Indian side. DAAD arranges the programme and supplies an English speaking guide. Application forms are obtainable from DAAD, New Delhi. Complete applications take approximately 4 months to process.

German groups may apply through DAAD Headquarter in Bonn only.

II. FELLOWSHIPS IN ACADEMIC NETWORKING AND INDOGERMAN PROJECTS

1. Institutional and Departmental Links ("Hochschulpartnerschaften")

In the interest of strengthening academic cooperation between institutions of higher education in developing countries and in Germany, DAAD supports institutional and/or departmental links between universities and Fachhochschulen in India and their German counterparts. These links are intended to enhance academic exchanges on all levels, help in developing joint curricula in areas of high priority to both partners, and in establishing technology transfer centres in fields with particular relevance to global development.

Interested Indian institutions of higher education should inquire at the DAAD, New Delhi Office for information on the parameters of this new programme.

- *Note:* Direct applications for participation in this programme are *not* possible. The Indian institutions' German partner will apply to DAAD Bonn for support under this programme.

2. Indo-German Project-based Persons' Exchange Programme (PPP)

With effect from March 1998, DAAD and the Department of Science and Technology (DST), Government of India, has been offering exchange opportunities for Indian and German senior and junior scientists and faculty who are engaged in, or plan, research within the framework of Indo-German projects in Science and Technology. The support offered will cover international travel and local hospitality only.

For more information and proformas for application, eligible Indian scientists and faculty should contact the International Division of the DST. German scientists must apply through DAAD, Bonn.

- *Note:* Direct applications by Indian scientists to DAAD New Delhi are *not* possible.

III. DAAD SUPPORTED STUDY OPPORTUNITIES IN GERMANY

Special Undergraduate and Postgraduate Courses for German and International Students ("Auslandsorientierte Studiengaenge")

Each academic year a number of German universities are offering several undergraduate and postgraduate courses ("Master Plus"), primarily in the fields of Technology and Management, Jointly, to German and International students. They are taught either consecutively in English and German, or simultaneously in German and another foreign language (in principle: English). No prior knowledge of German is required. They lead to internationally recognised Bachelors' or Masters' degrees.

DAAD has selected a number of these courses for special institutional support, primarily intended to assist international students in adapting to the German higher education system and studying techniques, and in learning German while enrolled.

Two special brochures obtainable free of charge from DAAD New Delhi, describe the programmes offered in a given year.

1. Undergraduate Degree Programmes in English.

2. Postgraduate Degree Programmes in English and German

IV. PROGRAMMES OF OTHER INSTITUTIONS CO-ADMINISTERED BY DAAD NEWDELHI

1. Alexander von Humboldt-Stiftung

Jean-Paul Str. 12, D-53173 Bonn, Germany, Tel.: 0049/228/833-0 Fax: 0049/228/833-119, Telex: 885 627

For applicants: select@alex.avh.uni-bonn.de

For former fellows: followup@alex.avh.uni-bonn.de, *Internet:* www.avh.de

1.1 *Humboldt Research Fellowships*

The Alexander von Humboldt Foundation (AvH) offers fellowships to highly qualified scholars world-wide, from all academic disciplines, to carry out research projects of their choice at universities and research institutes in Germany. There is no special quota for Indian nationals. Initially awarded for a period of 6 to 12 months, the grants can be extended upto 24 months upon application. Upto 6 months of the grant period may be spent at institutions in other European countries.

Applications (marked "AvH") may be submitted to DAAD, New Delhi for processing at any time. They may also be submitted directly to AvH in Bonn.
AvH selection committee meetings are held every March, June/July, and November.

Complete applications take approximately 4 to 6 months for proper processing and adjudication. Successful candidates will be notified approximately one month after the respective selection committee meetings.

Eligibility Requirements

- An academic degree comparable to a doctorate degree (Ph.D).
- High quality academic publications in prestigious, international refereed journals.
- A specific research plan.
- A good command of the German language (for applicants in the Humanities and Social Sciences), and of English (for those in the Natural, Medical, and Engineering Sciences).
- Applicant must be less than 40 years old (i.e. born on October 01, 1960 or later).
- Applicants should be permanently employed.

1.2 Humboldt Research Awards

Upon combined nominations by eminent German and international scholars, these awards are granted to scholars of the rank of Full Professor or Senior Scientist on active duty, with extensive, distinguished, internationally recognized research records. Award winners are invited to spend a research stay of 4 to 12 months at German institutes of their choice. There is no age limit and no special quota for Indian nationals.

- *Note:* Direct applications for these awards are not accepted.

1.3 Humboldt Follow-up Programme

The Alexander von Humboldt Foundation, with the logistical assistance of DAAD, New Delhi, maintains contact with its grantees after their return to India by:

- inviting them to spend further short periods to conduct research in Germany;
- donating academic literature and scientific equipment;
- awarding grants towards the cost of attending academic conferences in Germany, and towards printing costs of significant scientific publications (books and monographs).

Applications by former AvH fellowship holders for any of these programmes may be made via DAAD, New Delhi at any time.

- *Note:* Former AvH fellowship holders are *not* eligible for *DAAD* follow-up programmes.

2. Max Planck Society (MPG) Research Awards for International Cooperation (Through AvH)

These MPG awards are granted through the Alexander von Humboldt Foundation to internationally recognised non-German and German scholars enabling them to carry out long-term, project-oriented joint research up to three years. The awards carry a maximum value of DM 250,000.

Nominations may be made to AvH only by heads of German universities or parent organisations of non-university research institutes at any time, for scholars from all disciplines.

- *Note:* Applications directly from individual scholars or research teams are not accepted.

3. South-Asia Institute (SAI), New Delhi South-Asia Institute

New Delhi Branch 3, Kasturba Gandhi Marg New Delhi 110001Te.: 91-11-3326001 Fax: 91-11-3716684

As part of the cultural agreement between the Government of India and the Federal Republic of Germany, the State of Baden-Wuerttemberg, through the University Grants Commission (UGC), offers annually one six-month or two three-month fellowships to qualified Indian scholars, to conduct research at the South-Asia Institute of the University of Heidelberg in Germany. Applications are to be directed to UGC, after their announcement of the fellowship.

Eligibility Requirements and Provisions

- *Degree*: Applicants must have a Ph.D degree or its equivalent.
- *Employment:* Applicants must be employed at an Indian university.
- *Sponsorship:* Applicants should be endorsed by their universities and be treated as "on duty" while in Germany, i.e. entitled to their full regular compensation.
- *Placement:* Applicants should be able to produce recent dated correspondence--not older than 6 months-with faculty members of SAI, Heidelberg agreeing to their proposed research plan and suggested time schedule.
- *Age Limit:* None.

Further information is available from SAI New Delhi. Application forms may be obtained from UGC, in due time.

V. GENERAL INFORMATION ON STUDYING IN GERMANY (FOR NON-SPONSORED STUDENTS)

The German system of higher education is quite different from the Indian model. It does, in principle and historically, not follow the Anglo-American system, although Bachelors and Masters Degrees have recently been introduced.

At a German university or "Fachhochschule", you can study for one of the first degrees-- "Diplom" or "Magister" (M.A.) the designation varies according to disciplines-or, at universities only, for a doctoral degree (equivalent of the Ph.D.), for which one of the first degrees is a prerequisite. While the universities and "Fachhochschulen" (Universities of Applied Sciences) have equal academic and legal standing, the "Fachhochschulen" are more practice-oriented and require internships in industry and/or commerce, prior to and during academic studies.

You are advised to find out from the Association of Indian Universities (AIU House, 16, Kotla Marg, New Delhi-110012) whether and which German degrees are recognised in India, prior to enrolment at a German institution of higher education.

The medium of instruction, principally, is German. Please study the relevant materials describing the courses of your interest to verify the language(s) of instruction.

For some undergraduate and postgraduate courses especially designed for international students from developing countries, some courses for undergraduates from Germany and abroad, or courses on English language and literature are mostly conducted in English. For these, a minimum TOEFL score of 550 points is required.

Although there are *no tuition fees* in Germany, the cost of living is relatively high. You should have enough funds to cover your entire cost of living for the entire study duration. You should count on monthly expenses of no less than DM 1200 (As per the current rate of exchange, this amounts to about Rs. 25,000 per month).

Compensating for the lack of funds through work is not an option, because your student visa and residence Permit do no allow you to be gainfully employed for more than three months in a given year, and student/campus jobs are practically not available.

There are no scholarships/fellowships offered from German sources for international beginning students or undergraduates. A Master's degree is the minimum qualification required for a scholarship, except for the special programme for IIT students to German Technical Universities

Germany does not offer in principle, employment for international students after graduation, even if they have obtained a German degree. But, in exceptional cases, German employers may request the services of a foreign national in Germany or, more frequently, in one of the foreign subsidiaries of German firms, all over the world.

For general information on Germany and visa requirements:

Embassy and Consulates of the Federal Republic of Germany in India

Embassy of the Federal Republic of Germany
6/50G, Shantipath, Chanakyapuri New Delhi - 110021
Tel.: General Number: (011) 6871831; Consular Section: 6871891

Consular jurisdiction: Arunachal Pradesh, Assam, Haryana, Himachal Pradesh, Jammu and Kashmir, Manipur, Meghalya, Mizoram, Nagaland, Punjab, Rajasthan, Sikkim, Tripura, some districts of Uttar Pradesh (Uttarkashi, Chamoli, Pithoragarh, Tehri-Garhwal, Garhwal, Almora, Nainital, Bijnor, Moradabad, Badaun, Rampur, Bareilly Pilibhit, Shajahanpur, Dehra Dun, Saharanpur, Muzaffarnagar, Meerut, Bulandshar, Aligarh, Mathura, Agra, Etah, Mainpuri, Farrukhabad, Etawah) Chandigarh, Delhi, Andaman and Nicobar, Lakshadweep, Minicoy and Maladives. Bhutan.

Consulate General of the Federal Republic of Germany Hoechst House, 10th Floor, 193, Backbay Reclamation, Nariman Point Bombay-400021.
Tel.: (022) 2832422, 2832517

Consular jurisdiction: Daman, Diu, Goa, Gujarat, Madhya Pradesh, Maharashtra.

Consulate General of the Federal Republic of Germany 1, Hastings Park Road, Alipore Calcutta-700027
Tel.: (033) 4791141, 4791142

Consular Jurisdiction: Bihar, Orissa, some districts of Uttar Pradesh (Kanpur, Fatepur, Allahabad, Jhansi, Jalaun, Hamirpur, Banda, Kheri, Sitapur, Hardoi, Unnao,

Lucknow, Rae Bareli, Bahraich, Gonda, Bara Banki, Faizabad, Sultanpur, Pratapgarh, Basti, Gorakhpur, Deoria, Azamgarh, Jaunpur, Ballia, Ghazipur, Varanasi, Mirzapur) and West Bengal.

Consulate General of the Federal Republic of Germany
MICO Building, 22, Ethiraj Road
Chennai-600105 Tel.: (044) 8271747, 8273593

Cousular Jurisdiction: Andhra Pradesh, Karnataka, Kerala, Tamil Nadu and Pondicherry.

For information on German language studies in India, please contact:

Max Mueller Bhavans in India

Max Mueller Bhavan, 3, Lavel Road, P.O.Box. 5058
Bangalore-560001
Tel.: (080) 2214964, 2275435; Fax: (080) 2215255, Max Mueller Bhavan
Prince of Wales Museum Annexe, Off Mahatma Gandhi Marg
Mumbai-400001
Tel.: (022) 2027710, 2022085; Fax: (022) 2873826
Max Mueller Bhavan, 8, Pramatesh Barua Sarani
Calcutta-700019
Tel.: (033) 4759424, 4759398; Fax: (033) 4747188 Max Mueller Bhavan
13, Khader Nawaz Khan Road, Off Nungambakkam High Road
Channai-600006
Tel.: (044) 8261314, 8262343; Fax: (044) 8282565
Max Mueller Bhavan, 3, Kasturba Gandhi Marg
New Delhi-110001
Tel.: (011) 3329506, 3329890; Fax: (011) 3325534; 3722573
Max Mueller Bhavan, 14/3-B, Boat Club Road Pune-411001
Tel.: (0212) 624945, 621042; Fax: (0212) 620542 contact: For private sector programmes, please

Offices of the Indo-German Chamber of Commerce in India

Indo-German Chamber of Commerce, Maker Tower "E", 1st Floor
Cuffe Parade Mumbai-400005 P.O. Box: 11092 Mumbai-400020
Tel.: (022) 2186131 (9 lines); Fax: (022) 2180523
Indo-German Chambers of Commerce
German House, 2, Nyaya Marg, Chanakyapuri
New Delhi-110021
Tel.: (011) 6878721, 6871730; Fax: (011) 6118664
Indo-German Chamber of Commerce
3, West Range Calcutta-700017
P.O.B.: 2504 Calcutta-700001
Tel.: (033) 2474147, 2405645; Fax: (033) 2476165
Indo-German Chamber of Commerce
Temple Tower, 4th Floor, "B" Block, 476, Anna Salai, Nandanam
P.O. Box: 3501 Channai-600035
Tel.: (044) 4348161, 4348027; Fax: (044) 4344816
Indo German Chamber of Commerce

403, Shah Sultan, P.O. Box 144, Cunningham Road

Bangalore-560052

Tel.: (080) 2265650; Fax: (080) 2203797

DAAD provides detailed information on

German education free of cost. Their address is:

German Academic Exchange Service (DAAD)

176, Golf Links, New Delhi-110003, Tel. : (011) 4615148, 4615009

Fax : (011) 4690919, e-mail : daadnd@delz.vsnl.net.in

Greece

Universities and Faculties
University of Athens
Ethnico and Kapodistriako Panepistimio Athinon
Founded in 1837, Panepistimiou 30, 10679 Athens
Tel.: + 301 3620020, 3620003, Fax: + 301 3602145

School of Theology
Panepistimioupoli, 15702 Athens, Dept. of Theology, Tel.: 7795177
Dept. of Social Theology, Tel: 7795177
School of Law, Economics and Political Sciences Dept. of Law
Solonos 57, 10672 Athens, Tel.: 3607607, 3610112
Dept. of Political Science and Public Administration
Omirou 19, 10672 Athens, Tel.: 3628745
Dept. of Economics
Pesmatzoglou 8, 10559 Athens, Tel.: 3223187, 3609004
School of Arts, Panepistimioupoli, 15702 Athens
Dept. of Greek Literature
Dept. of History and Archaeology, Tel.: 7239718
Dept. of Philosophy, Psychology and Education, Tel.: 7249009
Program in Phychology
Dept. of English Language and Literature, Tel.: 7239718
Dept. of French Language and Literature, Tel.: 7291490
Dept. of German Language and Literature, Tel.: 7291490
Dept. of Foreign Cultures, Tel.: 7239718, 7246066
School of Medicine
M. Asias, 11527 Goudi, Tel.: 7791699
School of Science
Panepistimioupoli, 15702 Athens
Dept. of Physics, Tel.: 3614311, 7230172
Dept. of Chemistry, Tel.: 7242906
Dept. of Mathematics, Tel.: 7240453-4
Dept. of Biology, Tel.: 7253780, 7284248
Dept. of Geology, Tel.: 7237475
Dept. of Computer Studies, Tel.: 7248154

Independent Departments of Health Science
Dept. of Dentistry, Tetrapoleos 4-6, 11527 Goudi, Tel.: 7785587
Dept. of Pharmacy, Panepistimioupoli, 15702 Athens, Tel.: 7284351
Dept. of Nursing (Hospital Care), M. Asias, 11527 Goudi, Tel.: 7774149

Independent Departments

Dept. of Science of Physical Education and Sports
Vas. Olgas av. 41, 17237 Dafne, Tel.: 9750569, 9715315
Dept. of Primary Education, Navarinou and Mavromichali 13
10680 Athens, Tel.: 3639735
Dept. of Pre-school Education, Ippokratous 33, 10680 Athens, Tel.: 3627277
Dept. of Communications and Mass Media Studies, Stadiou 5, 10562 Athens
Tel.: 3220820
Dept. of Music Studies, Panepistimioupoli, 15702 Athens, Tel.: 7248305
Dept. of Theatre Studies, Panepistimioupoli, 15702 Athens, Tel.: 7291490
Department of Philosophy, and History of Science, Panepistimioupoli, 15702 Athens, Tel.: 7209119, 7257681

NATIONAL TECHNICAL UNIVERSITY OF ATHENS

Ethnico Metsovio Polytechnio Athinon Founded in 1887
Herron Polytechniou 9, 15773 Zografou Athens
Tel.: + 301 7722046-8, Fax: + 301 7721866

Dept. of Civil Engineering, Tel.: 3691287, 3691415
Dept. of Mechanical Engineering, Tel.: 3608854, 3691210
Dept. of Electrical and Computer Engineering, Tel.: 3691421, 3609970
Dept. of Architecture, Tel.: 3611522, 3691262
Dept. of Chemical Engineering, Tel.: 7724211, 7724214
Dept. of Rural and Surveying Engineering, Tel.: 7790148
Dept. of Mechanical and Mineral Engineering, Tel.: 7719287
Dept. of Naval Architecture and Marine Engineering, Tel.: 7728073-4
General Department, Tel./Fax: 7784750

ARISTOTLE UNIVERSITY OF THESSALONIKI

Aristotelio Panepistimio Thessalonikis, Founded in 1925
Panepistimioupoli, 54006 Thessaloniki
Tel.: + 3031 996000, Fax: + 3031 206138

School of Theology

Dept. of Theology, Tel.: 996980-8354006
Dept. of Pastoral and Social Theology,Tel.: 996682

School of Law, Economics and Political Sciences

Dept. of Law, Tel.: 995251
Dept. of Economic, Tel.: 995254

School of Arts

Tel.: 995233-4, Dept. of Classical Greek Literature
Dept. of History and Archaeology, Tel.: 995217
Dept. of Philosophy and Education, Tel.: 995201-6
Dept. of Psychology, Tel.: 996887
Dept. of English Language and Literature, Tel.: 997479
Dept. of French Language and Literature, Tel.: 995176
Dept. of German Language and Literature, Tel.: 997557

Dept. of Italian Language and Literature, Tel.: 997582

School of Science

Dept. of Physics, Tel.: 998120, 998130
Dept. of Chemistry, Tel.: 997640, 997920
Dept. of Biology, Tel.: 998250, 998260
Dept. of Mathmatics, Tel: 997910, 997920
Dept. of Geosciences, Tel.: 998450, 998460
Dept. of Computer Science, Tel.: 998423

School of Health Science

Dept. of Medicine, Tel.: 999283
Dept. of Dentistry, Tel.: 999477
Dept. of Pharmacy, Tel.: 997623

School of Geotechnical Science

Dept..of Agricultural Science, Tel.: 995187
Dept. of Forestry and Natural Environment, Tel.: 995195
Dept. of Veterinary Medicine, Tel.: 995227

School of Technology

Dept. of Civil Engineering, Tel.: 995612
Dept. of Architecture, Tel.: 995595
Dept. of Mechanical Engineering, Tel.: 996072
Dept. of Electrical and Computer Engineering, Tel.: 996392
Dept. of Chemical Engineering, Tel.: 996186
Dept. of Agronomy and Surveying, Tel.: 995832
Dept of General Departmant, Tel: 995924

School of Fine Arts

Dept. Pictorial and Applied Arts, Tel.: 995074
Dept. of Music Studies, Tel.: 995075
Dept. of Drama, Egnatia 122 54622 Thessaloniki,

School of Education

Dept. of Primary Education, Tel.: 995056
Dept. of Pre-school (Nursery) Education, Tel.: 995064

Independent Departments

Dept. of Science of Physical Education and Sports, Tel.: 219482
Dept. of Journalism and Mass Media Studies, Tel.: 234424

Branches

Branch of Education 53100 Florina, Dept. of Primary Education, Tel.: + 30385 22471
Dept of Pre-school (Nursery) Education, Tel.: + 30385 22475
Branch of Science of Physical Education and Sports, Dim. Miaouli 43, 62122 Serres, Tel.: + 30321 67135

ATHENS UNIVERSITY OF ECONOMICS AND BUSINESS

Iconomiko Panepistimio Athinon, Founded in 1920,
Patission 76, 10434 Athens
Tel.: + 301 8237361, 8228419, Fax: + 301 8226204

Dept. of Economics, Tel.: 8231725, 8238249
Dept. of International and European Economic Studies, Tel.: 8214122
Dept. of Business Administration, Tel.: 8214510, 8230966
Dept. of Management Science and Marketing, Tel.: 8228816, 8225677
Dept. of Applied Informatics, Tel.: 8230940, 8226105
Dept. of Statistics, Tel.: 8230488

AGRICULTURAL UNIVERSITY OF ATHENS

Georgiko Panepistimio Athinon Founded in 1920
Iera Odos 75, 11855 Athens, Tel.: + 301 5294891, 5294893, Fax: + 301 5294802
Dept. of Agriculture, Tel.: 5294893
Dept. of Animal Production, Tel.: 5294414
Dept. of Agricultural Biology and Biotechnology, Tel.: 5249893
Dept. of Agricultural Economics, Tel.: 5249893
Dept. of Agricultural Industries, Tel.: 5294362
Dept. of Land Reclamation and Agricultural Engineering, Tel.: 5294052
General Deparment, Tel.: 5249122

UNIVERSITY OF PIRAEUS

Panepistimio Piraeus, Founded in 1938
Karaoli and Dimitriou 80, 18534 Piraeus Tel.: + 301 4120751-5, Fax: + 301 4179064
Dept. of Economics, Tel.: 4116377
Dept. of Business Administration, Tel.: 4137189
Dept. of Statistics and Insurance Science, Tel.: 4136974
Dept. of Banking and Financial Management, Tel.: 4121458
Dept. of Industrial Management, Tel.: 4221231
Dept. of Maritime Studies, Tel.: 4220158
Dept. of Informatics, Tel.: 4220160

UNIVERSITY OF MACEDONIA

Founded in 1948 , Egnatia 156, 54004 Thessaloniki
Tel.: +3031 891295, Fax: + 3031 844536

Dept. of Economics, Tel.: 891210-1
Dept. of Business Administration, Tel.: 891212, 891214
Dept. of International and European,
Economical and Political Studies, Tel.: 891464
Dept. of Accounting and Finance, Tel.: 891461
Dept. of Applied Informatics, Tel.: 891218
Dept. of Educational and Social, Tel.: 891218

UNIVERSITY OF IOANNINA

Panepistimio Ioanninon, Founded in 1970
Dompoli 30, 45110 Ioannina, Tel.: + 30651 41800, Fax: + 30651 44112

School of Science

Dept. of Physics, Tel.: 41805
Dept. of Chemistry, Tel.: 40549
Dept. of Mathematics, Tel.: 41855
Dept of Informatics, Tel.: 42914

Independent Departments

Dept. of Medicine, Tel.: 41802, 40577
Dept. of Primary Education, Tel.: 43826, 43723
Dept. of Pre-school Education, Tel.: 40552

DEMOCRITOS UNIVERSITY OF THRACE

Democritio Panepistimio Thrakis, Founded in 1973

Democritou 17, 69100 Komotini, Tel.: + 30531 39000, Fax: + 30531 26660

School of Engineering

Vas. Sofias st. 67100 Xanthi, Dept. of Civil Engineering , Tel.: + 30541 20319
Dept. of Electrical and Computer Engineering, Tel.: + 30541 23878 Fax: + 30541 20275
Dept. of Environmental Engineering, Tel.: + 30541 22013, Fax: + 30541 20275

Independent Departments

Dept. of Medicine Kavyri 6, 68100 Alexandroupoli Tel.: + 30551 20483, Fax: + 30551 31289
Dept. of Law, Panagi Tsaldari 1, 69100 Komotini, Tel.: + 30531 25206 Fax: + 30531 35331
Dept. of Science of Physical Education and Sports 7th km. Ethn. Odou Komotinis-Xanthis, 69100 Komotini Tel.: + 30531 29696, Fax: + 30531 26908 Dept. of Primary Education, Nea Chili 68100 Alexandroupoli, Tel.: + 30551 39627, Fax: + 30551 39630
Dept. of Pre-school (Nursery) Education, Nea Chili 68100 Alexandroupoli, Tel.: + 30551 39623, Fax: + 30551 39624
Dept. of History and Ethnology Panepistimioupoli, 69100 Komotini Tel.: + 30531 32707, Fax: + 30531 25212
Dept. of Greek Literature, Dimocritou 17, 69100 Komotini Tel.: + 30531 37043, Fax: + 30531 27016 Dept. of Social Administration (in progress) P. Tsaldari 1, 69100 Komotini, Tel.: + 30531 37628

UNIVERSITY OF CRETE

Panepistimio Kritis, Founded in 1974

Dimitrakaki 17, 74100 Rethymno, Tel.: + 30831 25313, 24069, Fax: + 30831 27956

School of Science

Ambelokipi, 71409 Heraklio, Dept. of Physics, Tel.: + 3081 394003
Dept. of Chemistry, Tel.: + 3081 235014, Dept. of Biology, Tel.: + 3081 235014

Dept of Mathematics

Tel. +3081235014

Dept. of Geology

Dept. of Computer Science, Tel.: + 3081 235014

School of Heaeth Science

Ampelokipi, 71409 Heraklio , Dept. of Medicine, Tel.: + 3081 232156

Dept. of Dentistry

Dept. of Nursing and Health Specializations,

School of Education

Perivolia Rethymnou, 74100 Rethymno, Dept. of Primary Education Tel.: + 30831 27809
Dept. of Pre-school, Nursery Education, Tel.: + 30831 27935

TECHNICALUNIVERSITYOFCRETE

Polytechnio Kritis, Founded in 1977, Terma Ag. Markou, 73100 Chania Crete
Tel.:+30821 41928,41930,Fax:+30821 53571

Dept. of Mechanical Engineering
Dept. of Chemical Engineering
Dept. of Electronic and Computer Engineering, Heroon Polytechniou 37
73100 Chania, Tel.: + 30821 41920
Dept. of Production and Management Engineering
Terma Ag. Markou, 73100 Chania, Tel.: + 30821 59926
Dept. of Mineral Resources Engineering, El. Venizelou 127
73100 Chania, Tel.: + 30821 54370
General Department, Terma Ag. Markou, 73100 Chania, Tel.: + 30821 58090

UNIVERSITY OF AEGEAN

Panepistimio Aegacou, Founded in 1984

Voulgaroktonou 30, 11472 Athens, Tel.: + 301 6400194-6, Fax: 301 6400197, 6437129
School of Social Sciences, Karantoni 17, 81100 Mytilini, Dept. of Environmental Science,
Tel.: + 30251 29579, 21286, Fax: + 30251 23783
Dept. of Social Anthropology, Tel.: + 30251 29579, 21286, Fax: + 30251 23783
Dept. of Anthropogeography, Tel.: + 30251 29579, 21286, Fax: + 30251 23783

Independent Departments

Dept. of Business Administration, Michalon 8, 82100 Chios,
Dept. of Mathematics, Karlovassi, 83200 Samos, Tel.: + 30273 33896, 33914
Dept. of Primary Education, Dimokratias av, 85100 Rhodes
Tel.: + 30241 37015, Fax: + 30241 37100,
Dept. of Pre-school (Nursery) Education Dimokratias av 85100 Bhodes
Tel.: + 30241 37015, Fax: + 30241 37100

IONIANUNIVERSITY

Ionio Panepistimio, Founded 1984

Deligiorigi 55-59, 10437 Athens, Tel.: + 301 5228715, 5248287, Fax: + 301 5248313
Dept. of Foreign Languages Translation and Interpreting Megaro Kapodistria
49100 Corfu, Tel.: + 30661 22993-4, 45614, Fax: + 30661 22549
Dept. of Music Studies, Megaro Kapodistria, 49100 Corfu
Tel.: + 30661 24995, 22993-4, Fax: + 30661 24995, 22549
Dept. of History, I. Theotoki, 49100 Corfu, Tel.: + 30661 35147, 35149 Fax: + 30661 35197
Dept. of Archive and Library SciencesI. Theotoki st.
49100 Corfu, Tel.: + 30661 48181-3, Fax: + 30661 48184

UNIVERSITY OF THESSALY

Panepistimio Thessalias, Founded in 1983

Kolokotroni 44, 10560 Athens, Tel.: + 301 3249682 Fax: + 301 3249195
School of Humanities, Ktirio Proin Papastratou, Argonafton and Filellenon
38221 Volos,
Dept. of Primary Education, Tel.: + 30421 26488, 24005, Fax: + 30421 34826
Dept. of Pre-school (Nursery) Education, Tel.: + 30421 26488, 24005, Fax: + 30421 34826
Dept. of Education for Children with Special Needs (in progress)
Dept. of History (in progress)
Dept of Archaeology (in progress)

Dept. of Laography (in progress)

General Department

School of Technological Science

Pedion tou Areos 38334 Volos

Dept. of Crop and Animal Production Tel.: + 30421 69782, Fax: − 30421 63383

Dept. of Regional Development and Planning Tel.: + 30421 69783-4, Fax: + 30421 63793

Dept. of Mechanical and Industrial Engineering Tel.: + 30421 69781-4, Fax: + 30421 69787

Dept. of Civil Engineering Tel.: + 30421 69781-4, Fax: + 30421 62660

School of Health Science

Dept. of Medicine, Papakyriazi 22, 41222 Larissa, Tel.: + 3041 53250, Fax: + 3041 255420

Dept. of Dentristry (in progress)

Papakyriazi and Asklipiou 36, 41222 Larissa

Dept. of Veterinary Medicine Terma Trikalon 43100 Karditsa

Tel.: + 30441 75245, Fax: + 30441 70906

Independent Departments

Dept. of Science of Physical Education and Sports, Matsopoulou Park

42100 Trikala, Tel. : + 30431 75731-4, Fax : + 30431 75732

Dept. of Mathematics and Informatics (in progress)

CHAROKOPIO UNIVERSITY OF HOME ECONOMICS

Charokopio Panepistimio Ikiakis Ikonomias

Founded in 1992, El. Venizelou 30, 17671 Kallithea

Tel.: + 301 9577051-5, Fax: + 301 9577050

Dept. of Home Economics, Dept. of Dietics

T.E.I. OF ATHENS

Ag. Spyridonos and Dimitsanas, 12210 Egaleo

Tel.: 301 5909002-4, 5909015-7, Fax: + 301 5911596 5448673

Faculty of Graphic Arts and Design Tel.: 5907896

Departments:

Technology of Graphic Arts

Decorative Arts Restoration of Archeological Findings and Works of Art

Photography Graphic Design

Faculty of Administration and Economics Tel.: 5907895

Departments:

Librarianship, Business Administration, Health and Care Unit Administration

Marketing, Tourist Industry

General Department of Foreign Languages and Physical Training

Faculty of Health and Caring Professions Tel.: 5989897

Departments:

Aesthetics, Baby/Infant Care, Public Hygiene, Home Health Care, Occupational Therapy,

Medical Laboratory Studies, Social Work, Midwifery, Nursing A, Nursing B,

Dental Mechanics, Optics, Radiology-Actinography, Physiotherapy,

General Department of Basic Medical Subjects

Faculty of Technological Applications Tel.: 5989858

Departments:

Energy Technics, Electronics, Mechanical Engineering, Shipbuilding. Informatics, Civil Works Technics, Medical Instrument Technology. Topography, General Department of Mathematics. General Department of Physics, Chemistry and Material Technology.

Faculty of Food Technology and Nutrition, Tel.: 5907897

Departments:

Ocnology and Spirit Technology Food, Technology

T.E.I. OF HERAKLIO

Stavromenos, 71500 Heraklio Crete, Tel.: + 3081 250611-3, Fax: + 3081 250548

Faculty of Aministration and Economics Tel.: 254237, Fax: 254103

Departments:

Accounting, Cooperative Organizations and Holdings, Tourist Industry General Department of Foreign Languages and Physical Training.

Faculty of Health and Caring Professions Tel.: 254103

Departments: Social Work, Nursing

Faculty of Agricultural Technology Tel.: 254103

Departments: Greenhouse Growing and Floriculture, Grop Production

Faculty of Technological Applications Tel.: 254103

Departments: Electrical Engineering Mechanical, Engineering, Civil Engineering Technology, General Department of Applied Sciences.

BRANCH OF CHANIA

Partheniou Kelaidi 24, 73136 Chania, Tel.: + 30821 99188

Dept. of Electronics Technology

T.E.I. OF THESSALONIKI

P.O. Box 14561, 54110 Thessaloniki, Tel.: + 3031 791111, fax: + 3031 799152

Faculty of Administration and Econimics Tel.: 791181

Departments: Librarianship, Marketing, Accounting, Tourist Industry General Department of Foreign Languages and Physical Training

Faculty of Health and Caring Professions Tel.: 791352

Departments: Aesthetics, Baby/Infant Care, Midwifery Medical Laboratory Studies, Nursing, Physiotherapy

Faculty of Agricultural Technology Tel.: 791321

Departments: Farm Administration, Animal Production, Crop Production

Faculty of Technological Applications Tel.: 791251

Departments: Automation, Electrical Engineering, Electronics Technology Mechanical Engineering, Vehicle Technology, Informatics Civil Works Technology, General Department of Applied Sciences

Faculty of Food Technology and Nutrition Tel.: 791361

Departments: Nutrition, Food Technology

T.E.I. OF KAVALA

Ethnikis Antistasis SG. 65403 Kavala, Tel.: + 3051 834848-9, Fax: + 3051 230779

Faculty of Administration and Economics Tel.: 246038

Departments: Business Administration, Accounting, General Department of Foreign Languages

Faculty of Technological Applications Tel.: 246030

Departments: Electrical Engineering, Mechanical Engineering, Petroleum Technology, General Department of Applied Sciences

BRANCH OF DRAMA

Proastio, 66100 Drama, Tel.: + 30521 37707, 33308,
Dept. of Forestry, T.E.I. OF KOZANI, *Kila, 50100 Kozani*
Tel.: + 30461 40161-4, Fax: + 30461 39682

Faculty of Administration and Economics

Departments: Business Administration, Accounting
General Department of Foreign Languages and Physical Training

Faculty of Technological Applications

Departments: Electrical Engineering, Mechanical Engineering, Mining Technology
General Department of Applied Sciences

BRANCH OF FLORINA

Palia Georgiki Scholi, (Terma Kontopoulou, 53100 Florina
Tel.: 430385 23302. Fax: 430385 29997

Departments:
Animal Production, Crop Production

T.E.I. OF LARISSA

T.E.I. of Larissa, 41110 Larissa, Tel.: + 3041 611061, Fax: + 3041 610803

Faculty of Administration and Economics

Departments: Business Administration, Accounting, Tourist Industry
General Department of Foreign Languages

Faculty of Health and Caring Professions

Departments: Medical Laboratory Studies, Nursing

Faculty of Agricultural Technology

Departments: Agricultural Machinery and Irrigation, Animal Production Plant Production

Faculty of Technological Applications

Departments: Electrical Engineering, Mechanical Engineering, Civil Works Technology, General Department of Applied Sciences

BRANCH OF KARDITSA

Terma Trikalon, 43100 Karditsa, Tel.: + 30441 71752, 44230, Dept. of Forestry

T.E.I. OF LAMIA

30th km. of Ethn. Odos Athinon-Lamias, 35100 Lamia, Tel./Fax: + 30231 33945

Faculty of Health and Caring Professions

Departments: Nursing, Physiotherapy

Faculty of Technological Applications

Departments : Electrical Engineering, electronic engineering, General Department of Foreign Languages and Physical Training

T.E.I. OF MESSOLOGI

Nea Ktiria, 30200 Messologi, Tel.: + 30631 26121-6, Fax: + 30631 25183

Faculty of Administration and Economics Tel.: 26121

Departments: Accounting, Cooperative Organizations and Agricultural Operations General Department of Foreign Languages and Physical Training

Faculty of Agricultural Technology

Tel.: 26121

Departments: Pisciculture and Fisheries, Agricultural Machinery and Irrigation, Conservatory Growing and Floriculture

T.E.I. OF HEPEIROS

P.O. Box 110, 47100 Arta, Tel.: + 30681 26880, Fax: + 30681 32292

Faculty of Agricultural Technology

Departments: Plant Production, Animal Production, Floriculture and Landscape Architecture

BRANCH OF IOANNINA

40th km. Ethn. Odou, 45500 Ioannina, Tel.: + 30651 38667, fax: + 30651 45453

Faculty of Health and Caring Professions

Departments: Baby/Infant Care, Nursing, General Department of Foreign Languages and Physical Training

BRANCH OF KARPENISSI

36100 Karpenissi, Tel.: + 3023723282

Dept. of Forestry,

T.E.I. OF PATRA, *Koukouli, 26335 Patra*

Tel.: + 3061 325001, 321881, fax: + 3061 313770

Faculty of Aministration and Economics

Tel.: 321881

Departments: Business Administration, Accounting, Tourist Industry, General Department of Foreign languages and Physical Training

Faculty of Health and Caring Professions Tel.: 329943

Departments: Social Work, Nursing

Faculty of Technological Applications Tel.: 313775

Departments: Electrical Engineering, Mechanical Engineering, Civil Works Technology

T.E.I. OF KALAMATA,

Anticalamos Messinias, 24100 Kalamata, Tel.: + 30721 69589

Faculty of Administration and Economics

Departments: Health and Care Unit Administration, Local Government Administration

Faculty of Agricultural Technology

Departments: Plant Production, Conservatory Growing and Floriculture

T.E.I. OF PIRAEUS

P. Ralli and Thivon 250, 12244 Egaleo, Tel.: + 301 5450951, Fax: + 301 5450962

Faculty of Administration and Economics Tel.: 5451128, 4826082-3

Departments: Business Administration, Accounting, General Department of Foreign Languages

Faculty of Technological Applications

Tel.: 5623851

Departments: Automation, Electrical Engineering, Electronics Technology Electronic Computer Systems, Textile Engineering Technology, Mechanical Engineering, Civil

ENgineering Technology, General Department of Physics, Chemistry, and Material Technology, General Department of Foreign Languages and Mathematics

T.E.I. OF SERRES

Ipsilantou 1, 62123 Serres, Tel.: + 30321, 26556, Fax: + 30321 22740

Faculty of Administration and Economics Tel.: 26522

Departments: Business Administration, Accounting, General Department of Foreign Languages, and Physical Training

Faculty of Technological Applications Tel.: 26556

Departments: Mechanical Engineering, Civil Engineering Technology

T.E.I. OF CHALKIDA

34400 Psachna, Tel.: + 30228 22887, 23507

Faculty of Administration and Economics

Departments: Business Administration, Accounting, General Department of Foreign Languages and Physical Training

Faculty of Technological Applications

Departments: Electrical Engineering, Mechanical Engineering, General Department of Applied Sciences *Immigration rules for students.* After a student gets scholarship, the student is given a student visa.

An introduction to scholarships

The Onnassis scholarships are open for applications once per year.

IKY scholarships are given each year to teachers and students for specific summer programmes. Greek Government scholarships are also given.

Pre-requirements for admission

The pre-requirements for admission to the universities varies from university to university. Therefore, for details write to the university directly.

Useful address in India:

Embassy of Greece, 16 Sunder Nagar, New Delhi-110003

Tel: 00-91-11-4617800, 4617854, Fax: 00-91-11-4601363 E-mail: hellemb@del2.vsnl.net.in

Hungary

Hungarian Institutions of higher learning which admit foreign students

College International

College International is representing world-wide the institutions of higher education in Hungary listed below. Activities include recruitment and student service.

- Full time English language degree programs at the following Hungarian universities:
  Semmelweis University of Medicine, Budapest (*Doctor of Medicine or Dentistry, Master of Pharmacy*)
  University of Veterinary Science, Budapest (*Doctor of Veterinary Medicine*);
  Albert Szent-Györgyi University of Medicine, Szeged (*Doctor of Medicine, Master of Pharmacy*
  Hungarian University of Physical Education, Budapest (*MA in Physiotherapy, MA in Physical Education, BA in Coaching*);
  Roland Eötvös University of Liberal Arts and Sciences (*MA in Biology, BA in Psychology*)
- An American undergraduate BA program in Economics and Business Administration in Hungary (4 semesters) and in the United States (4 terms) in cooperation with Western Maryland College, Westminster MD.

Passport and Visa for Hungary

A passport valid for Hungary and at least for two years is necessary. Students arriving to study to Hungary must apply for a student TM 6 visa after obtaining their letter of acceptance from the institution they wish to study at. Only having this TM 6 student visa you can apply for a residence permit which will enable you to stay in Hungary as a student. The officially appointed College International representative in your country or the Embassy of the Hungarian Republic will provide details and assistance. If there is no representative or Embassy of the Hungrain Republic, please contact College International, Budapest.

Custom regulations are relatively strict in Hungary. Foreign citizens are required to pay deposit on valuable goods for their own use: car, Hi-Fi system, record player, video recorder, cameras, etc. College International is not in the position to give students financial or any other guarantee.

Application Requirements

Application form and all supporting materials should be presented by September 15th to the officially appointed representative in your country or directly to College International.

These include:

1. Secondary School Certification from an accredited secondary school. The school leaving certificate and transcript of courses must be submitted with an authorized English translation.

2. Official Transcripts (or attested copy) of your academic record at secondary school. Unofficial transcripts may be submitted to facilitate evaluation but acceptance into the program is conditional, pending receipt of all official transcripts or attested copies.

Authorized English translation of the transcripts should also be attached.

3. Letters of Recommendation. Letters in English from secondary school principal or instructors are preferred.

4. Curriculum Vitae in English.

5. Medical Certificate. Certification of good health based on complete physical examination and parasitology test no later than three months before classes begin. Results of an HIV test should be attached.

6. Completed Application form with Application Fee US$ 50 (non refundable).

7. Signed Photographs. 4 passport size photos.

Applications Procedure

After the College International leaderships and faculty review the application materials and determine that the applicant appears qualified and potentially able to complete the program, applicants will be notified about the decision not later than September 20th. Obviously you can apply early (spring, summer) and as soon as College International receives your documents decides on acceptance. There is no entrance examination. Late applications can be considered in case of vacancies.

Costs of the Program for two Semesters

Tuition:		US$	5300
+ Application fee:		US$	50
+ Registration fee:		US$	50
Payable as follows:			
	at application –	US$	50
	before Ocbtober 1st – (tuition + registration)	US$	2950
	before February 1st –	US$	2400

One academic year consists of 8 months.

Note: Make cash or certified check payable in US$ directly to:

"INTERNATIONAL STUDIES, PREP
Account No. 501-12152-4105-4012"
Hungarian Foreign Trade Bank Ltd.
Budapest V., Szent István tér 11. H-1821

This fee includes registration, tuition fee, the mid-year examinations, but does not include the cost of text-books, auxiliary materials and health insurance. No dormitory facilities can be offered but College International will help with your accommodation.

For details contact:

College International
H-1114 Budapest, XI., Villĭanyi út 11-13., Hungary
Phone: (36-1) 1669740; 1666306, Fax: (36-1) 2092328

Western Maryland College

Western Maryland is a private college of the Liberal Arts and Sciences founded in 1867. It is located 30 miles (48 kilometres) northwest of Baltimore and 56 miles (90 kilometres) north of Washington, D.C., the nation's capital. The College overlooks Westminster, Maryland, Carroll County's largest town and county seat.

Well established for more than a century, Western Maryland is fully accredited by the Middle States Association of Colleges and Schools, and it is listed as one of the 142 Selective Liberal Arts Colleges in the nation by the Carnegie Foundation for the Advancement of Teaching.

WMC is internationally recognized for its graduate programs is Education. The College enrolls 1500 students from 23 states and 19 foreign coutnr es, 45 per cent are men, 55 percent women. The average class size is 20.

Western Maryland College has enrolled international students since 1890. The College continues a commitment to the broadest educational and social experience, particularly in bringing together students from diverse backgrounds.

Students must meet the following requirements during four years of study to earn a B.A. degree:

- Complete successfully at least 128 semester credit-hours. The 128 credit-hours are distributed among major requirements, basic liberal arts subjects, electives, and at least one January Term Course;
- Complete the requirements of at least one academic major with an overall Grade Point Average of 2.00 or above in all major courses;
- Complete the College's Basic Liberal Arts Requirements (BLARs);
- Complete at least one January Term;
- Maintain an overall Grade Point Average (GPA) of at least 2.0 on a 4.0 system

Special Students

Those meeting formal requirements for admission are welcome to enroll as special non-degree seeking students for individual courses offered on the curriculum.

Admission and Application Requirements

Continuing its nearly century-long tradition of enrolling students from all around the globe, Western Maryland College welcomes all applications for admission. WMC BUDAPEST seeks students with appropriate academic qualifications, a good command of English and a strong motivation to study.

Studying at WMC BUDAPEST offers many advantages. The WMC BUDAPEST student can:

- Master English before transferring to the home campus in Westminster, Maryland, and also prepare for the required Test of English as a Foreign Language (TOEFL);
- Save substantially on tuition fee and travel expenses in the first two years;
- Get acquainted with American academic standards and practice, earn American college credits;
- Remain in Europe and within proximity to family and friends in the initial two years of study.

Application Requirements

To apply to WMC BUDAPEST, complete a Western Maryland College application and attach the following:

1. *Photocopy or official transcript of Secondary School Record,* Certificate of Final Examination, Diploma of Graduation, or other certificates demonstrating that you have completed secondary education and are qualified for entry into an institution of higher education; test scores of American college-bound exams (SAT, ACT) if you have graduated from high school in the United States, and an exact and faithful English translation of all documents originally issued in other languages.

2. *Two Letters of Recommendation* in English from the Principal or instructors of the secondary school you have graduated from;

3. *Four passport-size photos:*
4. *Check or money order* for US$ 100 (non-refundable)
5. *A medical certificate* in English verifying that you do not suffer from any chronic diseases, and are physically and mentally captable to undertaking studies at an institution of higher education:
6. *Curriculum Vitae* in English (attach separate page).

All materials should be sent to

The Director
Western Maryland College Budapest, H-1518 Budapest, P.O.B. 121

Deadline of application

May 31 each year (Late applications may be considered on special request.)

Important Note ! Those attending secondary school in the United States should bear in mind the following:

Prospective applicants should pursue a broad secondary school program. Sixteen high school units are usually considered the minimum preparation for college. one, or preferably two years of Algebra, or equivalent taken at high school is a must for those wishing to choose Business Administration as their major field.

All candidates for admission must take either the College Board Scholastic Aptitude Test (SAT) or the American College Testing (ACT) Assessment Test. High school counselors can advise students about the dates, times and locations for these tests.

COSTS OF THE FOUR-YEAR PROGRAM

Costs for each academic year in Budapest

Tuition and fees	US$	6,600*
Housing /Food	US$	2,500-5,500

(depending on the type of accommodation required)

•*Payable as follows:*

Registration fee when accepted	US$	600

(Deducted from the first instalment. Refunded only if cancellation is made before August 15th)

Before September 1	US$	3,600
Before February 1	US$	3,000

PLEASE NOTE ! At registration for classes, students must present proof of payment in full for tuition.

Payments should be made in cash or by certified (bank) check at the office of WMC BUDAPEST, or by transfer to:

The Hungarian Foreign Trade Bank Ltd., Budapest H-1821
Szent István tér 11, for the bank account:

"INTERNATIONAL STUDIES, WMC
Account No: 10300002-50116381-41004019"

Cost of one course in Budapest

Tuition for one semester	US$	825

Preparatory course

Tuition	US$	5,300

Current costs for one academic year in Westminster

for WMC BUDAPEST students enrolling there for the third academic year:

Tuition		17,730
		– 3,000*
	US$	14,730
Room (double occupancy)	US$	2,540
Board (17 meals a week)	US$	2,810

- Special reduction for all WMC BUDAPEST students meeting basic academic requirements.

REMARK: Modest annual increase in tuition, room and board may be expected.

Financial Aid

There are several grants and scholarships available for WMC BUDAPEST students to facilitate their transfer to Westminster for the upper two years. The primary criterion of any financial aid awarded by the College is demonstrated need. A l financial aid awards will be made on a one-year basis, and will be renewable with demonstrated need. Requests for financial aid or scholarship will assessed on the basis of academic merit. The minimum requirement for any financial aid is an overall Grade Point Average of at least 2.00.

Useful address in India.

Hungarian Information and Cultural Centre

Embassy of the Republic of Hungary,

1/A, Janpath, New Delhi-110011, Ph: (91-11) 3014992, 3011152. 301 4497

Fax: (91-11) 3793161, E-mail: hun cultc @ nda.vsnl. net. in

Ireland

Ireland is an island of just over 32,000 square miles with the Atlantic Ocean to the west and the Irish Sea and the larger island of Great Britain to the east. The Republic of Ireland, a parliamentary democracy and a country of 3.5m people, comprises over 80 per cent of the land area while Northern Ireland, a separate area in the north-east, is administered by Great Britain. Because of its location Ireland has long been a gateway between East and West-a position greatly enhanced over the past 25 years by its very active membership of the European Union.

Ireland is a country of great antiquity. Its earliest surviving monument is the megalithic tomb at Newgrange which was built over 5000 years ago and today draws scholars from all parts of the world. Its museums house gold and silver artefacts from ancient sites only partly excavated and manuscripts from earliest times, the most renowned of which is the Book of Kells, have been preserved to demonstrate the scholarship and craftsmanship which lent Ireland the epithet "The Island of Saints and Scholars".

Ireland is English speaking but has a rich cultural heritage which has retained its own distinctive language (Gaeilge), music, literature and sports. Ireland is a very literate and literary country and has produced some of the finest and most internationally acclaimed writers in the English language: such as Joyce, Beckett, Yeats and Wilde. In mus too Ireland has made its mark through the world renowned flautist, James Galway, the tenor John McCormack and popular artistes like the Chieftains, U2, Sinead O'Connor, Enya and many others.

Ireland is beautiful--it is green, environmentally clean, has a mild climate and is very hospitable. Much of the countryside is still unspoilt providing an excellent natural habitat for a flourishing plant, animal and bird life and, despite its increasing urbanisation and the conflict associated with Northern Ireland, personal safety is very high and there is a low level of violent crime. As a result tourism is one of the biggest industries with over 4m people visiting the country each year.

Ireland, from being predominantly an agricultural country up to the 1950s, is today thoroughly modern nation with well developed manufacturing and international services sectors and the highest economic growth rate in the European Union-hence the title "Celtic Tiger". This transformation has been brought about through investment in physical and technological infrastructure and by the availability of an articulate and well educated workforce. Thus it stands as a testimony to the quality of the Irish education system at all levels.

The Irish Education System

Ireland has a long and honourable tradition in education dating back to the middle ages when its monks were amongst the principal education provides to the western world. This tradition is carried on to the present day and is reflected in the wide international recognition afforded Irish education qualifications and the increasing number of students from overseas studying in Ireland.

Primary

Years 1-8

English Language Training	Secondary Years 1-3 Junior Cycle Year 4 Transition Year Years 5-6 Senior Cycle

Primary and Secondary Education

In Ireland the school year runs from September to June. The school system comprises eight years of primary school followed by a six year secondary cycle at the end of which students sit for the National Leaving Certificate Examination. Typically students take six, seven or even eight subjects and performance in this examination determines access to further and higher education.

Higher and Further Education

In Ireland the academic year runs from September to June. There are nine universities, the oldest of them Trinity College Dublin formed in the late 16th century. There are also ten Colleges of Technology, two Institutes of Technology and a number of teacher training colleges. All are funded by the Ministry of Education and offer a range of programmes at undergraduate and postgraduate level in the Arts and Humanities, Medicine, Engineering, Science and Technology, and Business. In addition there are a number of independent colleges recognised by the Ministry.

Entry Requirements

Irish higher education qualifications are widely recognised internationally as being of excellent quality. Access to higher education is very competitive and the standard required of students is high. A national State examination generally governs access to undergraduate programmes for Irish students and overseas students' academic transcripts are considered individually on their merits for all levels. In addition to academic entry requirements overseas students whose first language is not English must prove their proficiency in that language.

English Language and University Access Programmes

For those students who do not meet the basic entry requirements noted above there are many schools and institutes offering English language programmes tailored to individual students' needs. In addition there are a number of high schools offering one and two-year programmes leading to the national high school examinations.

Details on these options are available on request from the International Education Board Ireland.

Coming to Ireland

All universities and colleges in Ireland have an international student office which acts as a resource pre departure, on arrival and for the duration of the programmes. They are there to ensure that students have the most rewarding time possible during their stay in Ireland both on and off campus. The closest point of entry to Ireland is London (one hour away) and, once here, the country is easy to get around and the public transport system is good.

Accommodation

Most students stay in self catering accommodation, in halls of residence on campus or in privately run apartments and houses off campus. Alternatively accommodation with an Irish family can be arranged. Information and help in making accommodation arrangements is provided by the International Offices of the universities and colleges.

Money and Expenses

The Irish Pound (£ or Ir£) often called the Punt, is worth approximately US$1.50. Tuition fees vary according to the programme of study: typically Humanities and Business

Studies are £5,000-6,000 per year, Engineering and Science £6,000-7,000 per year and Medicine13,000 per year. Living expenses average approximately £5,000 per year. Some student health services are provided on campus: however students are advised to make their own arrangements for health insurance cover.

For more Information

For further more detailed information on specific programmes contact the university or college of your choice (details at the back of this publication). For more general information on education opportunities in Ireland, including pre-university programmes and English language training contact:

International Education Board-Ireland
IPC House, 35-39 Shelbourne Road, Dublin 4, Tel: + 353-1-6144836
Fax: + 353-1-6144839, E-Mail: enquiries@iebi.ie

IRISH UNIVERSITIES

UCC
University College, Cork, Tel: 353-21-276871 Fax: 353-21-273C72, Ms Anne Gleeson Admissions

UCD
University College, Dublin 4, Tel: 353-1-7061414
Fax: 353-1-7061165, Ms Nora Murphy, International Office

UCG
University College Galway
Tel: 353-91-750304, Fax: 353-91-525051
Mr Seamus O'Grady, International Office

TCD
Trinity College, Dublin 2, Tel: 353-1-7021396, Fax: 353-1-6771698
Dr Ivan Filby, International Office

DCU
Dublin City University, Dublin 9, Tel: 353-1-7045574
Fax: 353-1-7045504, Dr Anthony Glynn, International Office

MAY
St Patricks College, Maynooth, Co Kildare Tel: 353-1-6285222, Fax: 353-1-6289063
Dr Peter Carr Registrar

QUB
Queens University Belfast Tel: 44-1232-245133, Fax: 44-1232-247895
Mr Stirling Wisener Admissions

UL
University of Limerick, Limerick Tel: 353-61-333644, Fax: 353-61-330316
Mr Barry Sharkey
Admissions

UU
University of Ulster, Coleraine, Co Derry, Tel: 44-1265-324133,
Fax: 44-1265-324930
Dr Michael Green
International Office

RCSI
The Royal College of Surgeons in Ireland
123 St Stephen's Green Dublin 2,Tel: 353-1-4022100

Fax: 353-1-4022458, Ms Orla Sheerin, Admissions

IRISH COLLEGES OF TECHNOLOGY

DIT

Dublin Institute of Technology, Fitzwilliam House
30 Upper Pembroke Street, Dublin 2
Tel.: 353-1-4023000, Fax: 353-1-4023399, Dr Declan Glynn, International Office

ATHLONE

Athlone RTC, Co Westmeath, Tel: 353-902-24400
Fax: 353-902-24417, Ms Mary Duffy, Admissions

CARLOW

Carlow RTC, Tel. 353-503-70400, Fax: 353-503-43787, Mr Jim McEntee
Development Office

CORK

Cork RTC, Tel: 353-21-326100, Fax: 353-21-545343
Ms Fiona Kelly, Registrar's Office

DUNDALK

Dundalk RTC, Co Louth, Tel: 353-42-70200, Fax: 353-42-33505
Mr Stephen McManus, Registrar

GALWAY

Galway RTC, Galway, Tel.: 353-91-753161, Fax: 353-91-751107
Mr Andrew D'Arcy, International Office

LKENNY

Letterkenny RTC Co Donegal, Tel.: 353-74-24888, Fax: 353-74-24879
Mr Jack O'Herlihy, Development Office

Limerick

Limerick RTC, Limerick, Tel: 353-61-327688, Fax: 353-61-327696
Ms Anne O'Donovan, Admissions

SLIGO

Sligo RTC, Sligo, Tel: 353-71-55222, Fax: 353-71-44096, Mr P Cuffe, Admissions

TALLAGHT

Tallaght RTC, Dublin 24, Tel: 353-1-4042000, Fax: 353-1-4042700
Ms Stella Brown, Admissions

TRALEE

Tralee RTC, Co Kerry, Tel: 353-66-24666, Fax: 353-66-25711
Ms Mary Stritch, Admissions

NCAD

National College of Art and Design, 100 Thomas Street, Dublin 8
Tel: 353-1-6711377, Fax: 353-1-6711748, Prf. Noel Sheridan, Director.

WATERFORD

Waterford RTC, Waterford, Tel: 353-51-302000, Fax: 353-51-378292
Mr. Patrick Downey, Registrar

DCAD

Dunlaoghaire College of Art and Design, Kill Avenue, Dunlaoghaire, Co Dublin
Tel: 353-1-2801138, Fax: 353-1-2803345, Ms Roisin Hogan, Principal

Approved Independent Colleges

DBS, Dublin Business School, 13-14 Aungier Street, Dublin 2
Tel: 353-1-4751024, Fax:353-1-4751043
Mr Diarmuid Moroney, President

GRIFFITH
Griffith College, South Circular Road, Dublin 8
Tel: 353-1-4545640, Fax: 353-1-4549265, Mr Leo O'Brien, International Office
LSB
LSB College, 6-9 Balfe Street, Dublin 2, Tel: 353-1-6794844
Fax: 353-1-6794205, Ms Dympna Donlon, International Office
NCIR
National College of Industrial Relations, Sandford Road, Dublin 6
Tel: 353-1-4060500, Fax:353-1-4972200, Dr. Joyce O'Connor, President
PORTOBELLO
Portobello College, South Richmond Street, Dublin 2, Tel: 353-1-4755811
Fax: 353-1-4755817, Mr John McGee, Academic Director
AMERICAN
American College in Dublin, 2 Merrion Square, Dublin 2, Tel: 353-1-6768939
Fax: 353-1-6768941, Ms Bid O'Connor-Mullins, Administration Director
SCHM
Shannon College of Hotel Management, Shannon, Co Clare
Tel: 353-61-471444, Fax: 353-61-475160, Ms Anna Cunningham
BURREN
The Burren College of Art Newtown Castle, Ballyvaughan Co Clare
Tel: 353-65-77200, Fax: 353-65-77201, Ms Mary Hawkes-Green, Director

Iceland Visa Information

The granting of an Irish visa is, in effect, only a form of pre-entry clearance. It does not grant permission to enter Ireland. Immigration Officers have authority to grant or deny admission. Visa holders are subject to normal immigration control at the port of entry. They should therefore carry with them, for possible presentation to Immigration Officers, the originals or copies of the documents submitted with their applications.

Visa applicants require a valid visa each time they enter the State, including entry via the UK.

This also applies to persons who have current permission to reside in the State.

A visa does not grant permission to stay in Ireland. The date of validity shown on the visa indicates only the date before which it must be presented to an Immigration Officer. The length of stay is decided by an Immigration Officer at the port of entry. Irish law does not provide for a permanent residence visa.

A visa holder who remains in the State longer than the permitted period and/or who submitted false or misleading information in support of his/her application may become liable for prosecution and/or subject to deportation.

Travel tickets should not be booked or paid for by applicants until their applications have been approved.

IMPORTANT–PLEASE READ CAREFULLY

Applications

1. Please type or write clearly in *BLOCK CAPITAL LETTERS.* Illegibility may prevent applications from being processed. Application forms must be *signed* by applicants.
2. *All* questions must be answered and *originals* of all documents submitted. Failure to do so may result in delays.
3. Each application is given a *reference number* which should be quoted if an enquiry is made.
4. Applications must normally be made through the Irish Embassy or Consulate in the applicant's

COURSES
ART AND DESIGN

	TCD	UCD	QUB	UU	UCC	DCU	MAY	DIT	Athlone	Carlow	Cork	Galway	Limerick	L'Kenny	Sligo	Tallaght	Tralee	Waterford	DCAD	NCAD
Certificate																				
A/V Communications																*				
Design-Film/TV																			*	
Design-Display								*												
Design-Industrial														*						
Design-Presentation								*												
Modelmaking/SFX																			*	
Commercial Photograph																			*	
Print Media Comms.											*									
Diploma																				
Art/Design								*			*		*		*			*	*	
Design												*								
Design-Comms.								*	*				*	*				*	*	
Design-Environmental								*												
Design-Fashion													*							
Design-Industrial											*				*					
Design-Printing								*			*						*			
Design-Product								*			*		*							
Graphic Repro.								*			*									
Painting-European	*																			
Video Production								*				*								
Bachelors																				
Art																				*
Art-Design				*																
Art-Design Education																				*
Art-Fine				*							*		*							*
Art-Fine & Applied				*																
Art-History	*																			*
Art-Hist/Craft Design																				*
Art-Hist-Fashion Design																				*
Art-Hist/Textile Design																				*
Art-Hist/Vis Comms.																				*
Ceramics											*		*							
Craft																				*

	TCD	UCD	QUB	UU	UCC	DCU	MAY	DIT	Athlone	Carlow	Cork	Galway	Limerick	K'Kenny	Sligo	Tallaght	Tralee	Waterford	DCAD	NCAD
Design-Fashion													*							*
Design-Graphic								*					*							
Design-Industrial											*									*
Design-Technology				*																
Design-Textile																				*
Design-Textile/Fashion				*																
Film & Video Studies																			*	
Visual Communications				*																*
PG Cert.																				
Fine Art				*																
PG Diploma																				
Art & Design Education											*		*							*
Fine Art				*																
Film Production								*												
Masters																				
Art History		*																		
Fine Art				*																
Interactive Media								*												

BUSINESS

	TCD	UCD	QUB	UU	UUC	UCG	UL	DCU	MAY	DIT	Athlone	Carlow	Cork	Dundalk	Galway	Limerick	L'kenny	Sligo	Tallaght	Tralee	Waterford
Certificate																					
Auctioneering										*	*										
Business Admin.														*					*		
Business Studies										*	*	*	*		*	*	*	*		*	*
-Accounting												*						*	*		
-Agribusiness															*						
-Bar Management										*											
-Front Off. Admin.											*										
-Hotel Accom/Lang															*						
-Hotel/Catering Mgt											*				*						
-Hotel/Catering Sup										*	*		*								
-Hotel Reception										*					*						
-Lang. & Marketing																		*	*	*	
-Marketing										*				*							
-Office IT											*	*	*	*	*		*	*		*	
-Recreation/Leisure												*									
-Retailing										*											
-Security										*											
-Small Bus Enterpr																					*
-Transport/Dist.Mgt										*											*
-Travel & Tourism										*			*		*						
Legal Studies																	*				*
Adv. Cert.																					
Business Studies													*	*						*	
-Accounting													*	*							
Diploma																					
Auctioneering										*											
Business Studies					*					*				*			*			*	
-Accounting				*						*	*		*	*				*	*	*	
-Catering Mgt										*											
-Computer Apps																		*			
-Euro Bus/Lang										*	*							*			
-Export Law																					*
-Finance Info Sys	*																				

	TCD	UCD	QUB	UU	UUC	UCG	UL	DCU	MAY	DIT	Athlone	Carlow	Cork	Dundalk	Galway	Limerick	L'kenny	Sligo	Tallaght	Tralee	Waterford
B/Studies continued..																					
-Financial Services																					*
-Hotel/Catering Mgt										*	*				*						
-IT Management																				*	
-IT										0	0						0				
-Int Bus/Languages												0								0	
-Lang & Marketing											0										0
-Lang & Office IT												0									
-Mgt/Finance											0								0		
-Marketing										0		0	0	0	0			0			
-Printing Mgt										0											
-Property Mgt															0						
-Recreation/Leisure										0								0			0
Hospitality Mgt				0																	
Int Business		0																			
Legal Studies																	0				
Bachelors																					
Accounting		0	0	0	0			0						0						0	
Accounting/Finance	0	0						0			0									0	
Actuarial/Fin Studies								0													
Banking & Finance				0				0													
Business Admin				0				0													
Business Economics																					
Bus/Financial Studies																					0
Business Info Studies						0															
Bus & Legal Studies		0																			
Bus/Econ/Soc Studies	0							0													
Business Studies	0			0	0	0	0	0		0	0	0		0	0			0			0
-Acc/Economics																					
-Acc/Finance																				0	
-Banking																					
-Computing				0				0													
-Japanese				0			0	0													
-Marketing							0	0	0											0	
-Personnel							0	0													
Business Duropean				0						0											
Business Internationl		0				0				0											
Business Studies		0																			
Business Strategy				0																	

	TCD	UCD	QUB	UU	UUC	UCG	UL	DCU	MAY	DIT	Athlone	Carlow	Cork	Dundalk	Galway	Limerick	L'kenny	Sligo	Tallaght	Tralee	Waterford
Co-Op Studies					0																
Database Mkt & IT										0											
Economics		0			0	0			0												
-Rural Development						0															
Entrepren Studies		0					0			0											
Finance/Economics			0																		
Health/Soc Serv Mgt				0																	
Hotel Operations										0											
Human Resource Mgt																					
Irish Heritage Mgt				0																	
Information Mgt					0																
Int. Marketing/Lang			0							0											
Info. Technology									0												
Mgt. (Advanced)		0																			
Media Mgt										0											
Mgt Eng/Science	0																				
Marketing				0				0		0											
Marketing Practice		0			0																
Networked Systems										0											
Purch/Supply Mgt				0																	
Sport/Leisure Studies				0			0														
Reg/Local Develop.										0											
Soc/Voc Rehab Stud.		0																			
Systems Analysis						0															
Tourism				0			0		0	0											
Masters																					
Accounting		0	0	0				0													
Accounting (Europ)					0																
Accounting/Finance				0																	
Admin/Legal Studies			0																		
Agric Econ & Mgt	0	0			0	0		0													
Business Studies	0	0			0	0		0													
-Acc/Fin/Mgt/IT					0																
Business (European)				0																	
Business Strategy				0																	
MBA	0	0		0																	
MBA (Int Business)		0		0																	
Economics		0			0	0		0	0												
Entrepreneurship					0		0														

	TCD	UCD	QUB	UU	UUC	UCG	UL	DCU	MAY	DIT	Athlone	Carlow	Cork	Dundalk	Galway	Limerick	L'kenny	Sligo	Tallaght	Tralee	Waterford
Finance			0					0													
Health/Soc Serv Mgt				0																	
Hotel/Catering Mgt				0																	
Hotel/Tourism Mgt				0																	
Hum Resource Mgt				0																	
Info. Studies		0																			
IT						0				0											
IT/Strategic Mgt										0											
Irish Heritage Mgt					0																
Management Practice	0																				
Management Science	0	0																			
Marketing		0		0				0		0											
Market. Studies				0				0													
Organ. Behaviour	0																				
Public Admin					0																
Public Policy/Mgt				0																	
Purch/Supply Mgt				0																	
Sport/Exerc/Leisure				0																	
Strategy/Competition					0																
Strategic Mgt	0																				
Systems Analysis						0		0													
Rural Development						0															

ENGINEERING

	TCD	UCD	QUB	UU	UUC	UCG	UL	DCU	MAY	DIT	Athlone	Carlow	Cork	Dundalk	Galway	Limerick	L'kenny	Sligo	Tallaght	Tralee	Waterford
Certificate																					
Construction Studies										0	0	0	0	0	0	0	0	0		0	0
-Architect. Graphics												0									
-Build. Maintenance										0											
Engineering										0	0	0	0	0	0	0	0	0	0	0	0
-Agricultural																				0	
-Building Services										0			0								
-Civil										0	0	0	0	0	0	0	0	0		0	0
-CA Precision																		0			
-Electrical													0								
-Electro Mechanical																0	0				
-Electronics				0							0	0	0	0	0	0	0	0	0		0
-Environmental																					0
-Glass Technology																					0
-Industrial															0						
-Manufacturing													0								
-Mechanical										0	0	0		0	0		0	0	0	0	0
-Mech/Elec																				0	
-Plastics											0										
-Production																					0
-Geo/Surveying										0											0
-Transport										0											
Technology										0	0	0	0	0	0	0	0	0	0	0	0
-Tech Maintenance										0	0	0	0	0	0	0	0	0	0	0	0
-Printing										0											
-Furniture															0						
Diploma																					
Arch. Technician													0		0						0
Construction Studies				0						0		0	0	0	0	0	0	0		0	0
-Architecture				0						0											
-Building Mgt												0			0						
-Building Surveying														0							
-Construction Econ.													0					0			0
-Construction Tech										0										0	
-Fire Technology																0					

	TCD	UCD	QUB	UU	UUC	UCG	UL	DCU	MAY	DIT	Athlone	Carlow	Cork	Dundalk	Galway	Limerick	L'kenny	Sligo	Tallaght	Tralee	Waterford
Site Management																0					
Engineering				0						0	0	0	0	0	0	0	0	0	0	0	0
-Agricultural																				0	
-Autom & Control																0					
-Building Services										0			0								
-Civil				0						0	0	0	0	0		0	0			0	0
-Electron/Electrical				0						0		0	0	0	0	0	0		0		0
-Electronics & IT											0										
-Environmental																					0
-Geosurveying										0											
-Glass Technology																					0
-Highways/Traffic				0							0										
-Info Studies	0																				
-Indus. Automation																		0			
-Manufacturing										0	0			0					0		
-Marine & Plant													0								
-Mechanical				0						0		0	0	0							
-Meneral											0										
-Plastics											0										
-Production										0				0	0					0	
-Tool Design																		0			
-Transport										0											
-Water																		0			
Technology																		0			0
-Manufacturing																					0
-Quality Control																		0			
Bachelors																					
Aeronautical			0				0														
Agric/Technology		0					0														
Architecture		0	0	0						0											
Building Surveying											0			0		0					
Building Mgt Servs										0						0					
CAM																					0
Chemical		0	0																		
Civil	0	0	0	0	0	0												0			
CA Mechanical			0																		0
Computer	0		0				0	0													
Construction Mgt																					0
Electrical		0			0					0											

	TCD	UCD	QUB	UU	UUC	UCG	UL	DCU	MAY	DIT	Athlone	Carlow	Cork	Dundalk	Galway	Limerick	L'kenny	Sligo	Tallaght	Tralee	Waterford
Electronic	0	0	0	0	0	0	0	0		0			0								
Elec/Electronic	0	0	0	0	0																
Elec & Software			0					0													
Electr. Prod Manuf							0														
Food Process					0																
Industr/Info Systems						0	0														
Industrial Mgt			0																		
Info Systems	0																				
Manufacturing Systems				0																	
Manufacturing Tech			0				0								0						
Mech & Manuf	0		0							0											
Mechanical	0	0	0	0		0	0			0			0								
Metal & Eng Techn							0														
Polymer											0										
Prod Tech/Eng							0					0									
Production Mgt							0														
Quantity Surveying				0						0						0					
Structural										0											
Software	0							0			0										
Telecoms							0	0		0											
Valt at on Surveying										0						0					
Wood Sc & Technol							0														
PG Cert.																					
Arch (Prof Practices		0																			
PG Diploma																					
Civil			0																		
CA Mech Eng Des			0																		
Computer							0														
Comp Mod/Simul	0																				
Construct/Proj Mgt				0																	
Electronics				0			0	0													
Elec/Signals Proc				0																	
Electronic Systems								0													
Engineering						0															
Eng Computation			0																		
Eng Hydrology						0															
EnvMonitor/Contro	0					0		0													
Fire Safety				0																	

	TCD	UCD	QUB	UU	UUC	UCG	UL	DCU	MAY	DIT	Athlone	Carlow	Cork	Dundalk	Galway	Limerick	L'kenny	Sligo	Tallaght	Tralee	Waterford
Highway Technology	0										0										
Information Eng			0																		
Mgt for Eng & Sc	0																				
Manufacturing Sys			0		0																
Man Tech (Advanced)								0													
Microelectronics					0																
Optoelectronics			0					0													
Pharmac Technology	0																				
Physical Planning	0																				
Polymer Sc/Eng			0	0																	
Project Mgt	0																				
Public Admin Engs	0																				
Quality Assurance	0					0															
Safety & Ergonomics							0														
Town/Country Plann			0																		
Masters																					
Aerospace Struct																					
Agric/Food Eng Tech		0																			
Architecture		0	0																		
Arch Landscape		0																			
Chemical		0																			
Civil	0	0	0			0															
Civil/Environmental					0																
CA Mech Eng Des			0																		
Computer Systems							0														
Computer Manuf						0															
Const/Proj Mgt				0																	
Electronic/Electrical		0	0																		
Electronic Systems		0						0													
Electr/Signals Proc				0																	
Elec/Microelec					0																
Eng Computation			0																		
Engineering Design						0															
Engineering	0	0			0	0															
Environmental		0																			
Envir Monit/control							0														
Fire Safety				0																	
Hydrology						0															
Human Factors Eng						0															

	TCD	UCD	QUB	UU	UUC	UCG	UL	DCU	MAY	DIT	Athlone	Carlow	Cork	Dundalk	Galway	Limerick	L'kenny	Sligo	Tallaght	Tralee	Waterford
Human Factors Eng						0															
Industrial		0					0														
Manufacturing	0																				
Manufact. Mgt				0																	
Manufact. Systems	0		0																		
Man Tech (Advanc)							0														
Materials (Advanc)							0														
Mechanical		0																			
Mech Eng Des Anal						0															
Microelectronics					0																
Ops Research (App)						0															
Optoelectronics			0					0													
Polymer Sc/Eng			0	0																	
Regional/Urban Plan		0																			
Safety/Ergonomics							0														
Software Re-engin							0														
Structural		0																			
Town/Country Plan			0																		
Urban/Build Constr		0																			
Water		0																			

HUMANITIES

	TCD	UCD	QUB	UU	UUC	UCG	UL	DCU	MAY	DIT	Athlone	Carlow	Cork	Dundalk	Galway	Limerick	L'kenny	Sligo	Tallaght	Tralee	Waterford
Certificate																					
Journalism													0								
Social Studies (App)										0	0		0					0			0
Soc Stud/Pre School										0											
Diploma																					
Addiction Studies	0																				
Archeology						0															
Counselling	0																				
Folk Theatre Studies																				0	
Journalism													0								
Law/EU Studies																			0		
Soc Stud/Sch Care						0												0			0
Recreation/Cult Stud														0							
Women's Studies						0															
Bachelors																					
American Studies			0	0																	
Ancient Hist/Archeol	0		0																		
Anthropology			0																		
Arabic		0																			
Archeology		0			0	0															
Biblical/Theol Studies	0		0						0												
Celtic Civilization		0	0		0	0			0												
Classical Civilization	0	0	0			0															
Communications				0			0	0		0											
Drama/Theatre Stud	0	0		0																	
Early Childcare					0																
Economics	0	0	0	0	0	0		0	0												
Education																					
English	0	0	0	0	0	0			0												
European Studies	0		0	0	0		0	0													
Finance									0												
Folklore					0																
French	0	0	0	0	0	0	0	0	0												
Geography	0	0	0	0	0	0			0												
German	0	0		0	0	0	0	0	0												

	TCD	UCD	QUB	UU	UUC	UCG	UL	DCU	MAY	DIT	Athlone	Carlow	Cork	Dundalk	Galway	Limerick	L'kenny	Sligo	Tallaght	Tralee	Waterford
Greek	0	0	0			0			0												
Greek/Roman Civiliz		0			0				0												
History	0	0	0	0	0	0			0												
Hebrew	0	0	0																		
Insurance/Euro Stud							0														
Irish	0	0		0	0	0		0	0												
Irish Studies			0	0					0												
International Studies				0																	
Italian	0	0	0		0	0															
Japanese				0			0	0													
Journalism								0		0											
Languages (App)				0			0	0													
Lang/Cult Studies					0			0													
Latin	0	0	0		0	0			0												
Law	0	0	0					0													
-with Accounting			0				0														
-with Economics				0																	
-with Euro Legal St		0					0	0													
-with Government				0																	
-with Politics			0	0																	
Law-Corporate						0		0													
Law-Civil/Common	0	0	0		0																
Legal Science						0															
Legal/Bus Studies																					0
Linguistics	0	0		0				0													
Logic						0															
Mathematics	0	0	0	0	0	0		0	0												
Maths (Applied)		0	0			0		0													
-with Physics	0	0	0		0	0		0	0												
Media Stud/Journalism				0				0													
Music	0	0	0	0	0				0	0											0
Peace/Conflict Studies				0																	
Philosophy	0	0	0	0	0	0			0												
Politics	0	0	0	0		0															
Physical Education				0			0														
Communications			0	0	0	0	0														
-Applied Comms				0	0																
-Technical Comms							0														
Counselling					0																
Development Studies		0																			

	TCD	UCD	QUB	UU	UUC	UCG	UL	DCU	MAY	DIT	Athlone	Carlow	Cork	Dundalk	Galway	Limerick	L'kenny	Sligo	Tallaght	Tralee	Waterford
Drama Studies		0																			
Ecumenics	0																				
Economics (Applied)				0	0				0												
Education	0	0			0	0		0	0												
-Administration					0																
-Adult/Community									0												
-Art & Design																0					
-Business							0														
-Compen/Remedial		0			0	0															
-Curriculum Studies					0																
-Management								0	0												
-Nursing Studies				0				0													
-Techers for Deaf		0																			
-TEFL		0	0	0			0														
English			0		0																
Equality Studies		0																			
Gestalt					0																
Therapy																					
Guidance/Counselling					0																
Irish Folklore		0																			
Irish Heritage Mgt					0																
Irish History									0												
Irish Lang/Literature		0																			
Japanese Studies							0														
Journalism										0											
Law			0	0						0											
-Arbitration										0											
-European		0																			
Legal Studies										0											
Library/Info Systems		0																			
Linguistics		0																			
Mathematics		0				0			0												
Medieval Studies		0			0																
Music/Music Educ							0			0											
peace Studies	0			0																	
Philosophy			0			0															
Prof Development				0																	
psychology					0																
Psychotherapy		0			0																
Public Relations										0											

	TCD	UCD	QUB	UU	UUC	UCG	UL	DCU	MAY	DIT	Athlone	Carlow	Cork	Dundalk	Galway	Limerick	L'kenny	Sligo	Tallaght	Tralee	Waterford
Soc Services Admin																					
Social Stud (A;;)		0																			
Social Policy		0			0				0												
Social work				0	0																
Statistics		0																			
Women's Studies		0					0														
Youth/Comm Work					0																
Masters																					
Admin/Legal Studies				0																	
Anglo Irish Lit/Drama	0	0		0																	
Anthropology			0						0												
Archeology		0	0		0	0															
Archival Studies		0																			
Arts (Applied)				0																	
Celtic Studies						0			0												
Celtic Languages		0	0						0												
Childcare Studies	0				0																
Classical Studies		0	0			0			0												
Communications			0	0			0	0													
Drama/Theatre Stud		0			0																
Economics		0		0	0				0												
Econ & Finance									0												
Ecumenics	0																				
Education	0	0			0	0			0												
-Adult/Community									0												
-Management	0			0				0													
English		0	0			0															
-Amer Literature		0																			
-European Literat			0																		
-Irish Writing			0				0														
-Old/Middle English		0																			
-Med/Ren/Victorian			0		0																
TEFL			0	0			0														
Equality Studies		0																			
Ethical/Cult Studies						0															
European Studies		0	0				0														
Ethnochoreography							0														
Ethnomuscicology			0				0														
Film/Drama/Theatre		0						0													

	TCD	UCD	QUB	UU	UUC	UCG	UL	DCU	MAY	DIT	Athlone	Carlow	Cork	Dundalk	Galway	Limerick	L'kenny	Sligo	Tallaght	Tralee	Waterford
French		0	0		0	0		0	0												
Geography		0				0			0												
German		0	0		0	0		0	0												
Greek		0				0			0												
Greek/Roman Civiliz					0				0												
Guidance/Counselling		0			0																
Health Promotion						0															
Hispanic Studies			0																		
History	0	0	0		0	0			0												
-Ancient		0	0																		
-Local					0				0												
-Medieval	0	0			0																
-Modern		0							0												
-Reform/Enlighten	0																				
Human Rights			0																		
Humanistic Therapy					0																
International Studies							0														
Irish-Early-Mediev		0																			
Irish Heritage Mgt					0																
Irish History		0	0		0																
Irish Politics		0	0																		
Irish Studies		0	0			0			0												
Social Policy		0																			
Social Studies		0			0				0												
Social Science		0	0		0																
Sociology		0				0			0												
Community Develop						0															
Community Health	0																				
Development Studies		0																			
Youth/Comm Work					0																
Spanish		0			0	0		0													
Statistics	0	0			0																
Translation Studies					0			0													
Women's Studies	0	0			0		0	0													
Welsh		0																			

MEDICINE

	TCD	UCD	QUB	UU	UcC	UCG	RCSI
Diploma							
Dental Hygiene					0		
Bachelors							
Dentistry	0		0		0		
Medicine	0	0	0		0	0	0
Medical Sciences					0		
Nursing & Nursing Studies		0		0	0	0	
Occupational Therapy				0			
Optometry				0			
Pharmacy	0		0				
Physiotherapy	0	0		0			
Radiography	0	0		0			
Speech & Language Therapy	0						
Veterinary Medicine		0					
Postgraduate							
Short							
Anaesthesia							0
Dentistry							0
Meedical Science (Basic)							0
Nursing							0
Opthalmology							0
Otolaryngology							0
Paediatric Refresher							0
Radiology							0
Surgery-Basic							0
Surgery-Clinical							0
Surgery-Head & Neck Restorative							0
Surgery-Higher Training							0
Trauma & Life Support (Advanced)							0
PG Cert							
Audiology							
Dental Health							
Gynaecology & Obstetrics							
International Health							0
Nursing	0	0				0	0
Nurshing & Advanced Midwifery		0		0			

	TCD	UCD	QUB	UU	UcC	UCG	RCSI
Nursing & Public Health					0		
Respiratory Studies (Advanced)		0					
TropicalMedicine							0
Masters							
Clinical Laboratory Medicine	0		0				
Dentistry-Surgery			0				
Dentistry-Surgery & Cell Biology			0				
Dentistry-Paediatric & preventative			0				
Dentistry-Restorative			0				
Diagnostics & Interventional Cardiology	0						
Medical Science	0	0	0	0	0	0	
MCH/MAO/MD	0	0	0		0		0
Nursing	0	0	0				
Advanced Nursing & Midwifery				0			
Pathology		0	0				
Public Health	0	0					
Sports Medicine	0				0		
Ultrastructural Anatory & Pathology			0				
Doctoral							
Medical Sciences				0			

SCIENCE AND TECHNOLOGY

	TCD	UCD	QUB	UU	UUC	UCG	UL	DCU	MAY	DIT	Athlone	Carlow	Cork	Dundalk	Galway	Limerick	L'kenny	Sligo	Tallaght	Tralee	Waterford
Certificate																					
Agricultural Science																			0		
Aquaculture																				0	
Biology (Applied)											0	0	0	0	0	0	0	0	0	0	0
Catering Technology										0	0										
Chemistry (Applied)												0	0	0	0	0	0	0	0	0	0
Chem & Computing											0										
Computing											0	0	0	0	0	0	0	0	0	0	0
Commercial Science																			0		
Industrial Science																			0		
Diet Cooking										0	0										
Fish Farming																	0				
Food Qual Assur										0											
Food Science														0				0			
Food Process Tech										0											
Healthcare Tech										0											
IT Skills																	0				
Instrument Physics															0						
Med Lab Sciences										0			0		0						
Pharmaceutical Sc																			0		
Physics (Applied)												0									
Phys/Instrum (App)													0								
Phys/Elect (App)																				0	
Physiol/Health (App)												0									
Diploma																					
Aquatic Science															0						
Analytical Science												0					0			0	
Bioanalysis																				0	
Bakery Production										0											
Biology										0		0	0			0					
Biomedical Science										0											
Biotechnology																			0		
Catering Technology										0											
Chemistry (App)										0	0				0				0		0
Chem-Analytical											0					0		0	0		
Chem Technology													0								

	TCD	UCD	QUB	UU	UUC	UCG	UL	DCU	MAY	DIT	Athlone	Carlow	Cork	Dundalk	Galway	Limerick	L'kenny	Sligo	Tallaght	Tralee	Waterford
Computing										0		0	0	0	0	0	0	0	0	0	0
Comp/IT																0					
Environ Res Mgt										0											
Fine Chem/Pharm															0						
Food Process/Tech										0											
Food Qual Assur										0										0	
Food Sc & Technol										0		0	0			0					
Healthcare Technol										0											
Nautical Science													0								
Phototonics												0								0	
Phys & Instrum													0								
Pollution Ass/Cont																		0			
Physics										0											
Quality Assurance																					0
Safety/Health																		0			
Toxicology											0										
Tech Instrumentation															0						
Bachelors																					
Agriculture		0	0																		
Agric Prod Technol							0														
Anal Chem/QA								0					0								
Analytical Science								0													
Anatomy		0	0		0																
Astrophysics	0		0																		
Aquaculture																					
Biochemistry	0	0	0	0	0	0	0	0													
Biochem-Industr							0	0													
Biology/Bio Science		0	0	0	0	0		0	0												
Biol/Qual Mgt																					
Biology-Cell		0																			
Biology-Environm	0	0	0																		
Biology-Industrial												0									
Biology-Molecular		0	0			0															
Biomedical Science			0	0	0					0			0								
Maths/Physics		0	0		0	0			0	0											
Maths/Statistics		0																			
Meteorology						0															
Microbiology						0															
Nutritional Science				0	0																

	TCD	UCD	QUB	UU	UUC	UCG	UL	DCU	MAY	DIT	Athlone	Carlow	Cork	Dundalk	Galway	Limerick	L'kenny	Sligo	Tallaght	Tralee	Waterford
Nutrition-Human				0						0											
Oceanography						0															
Optometry				0						0											
Physics		0			0			0		0											
Physics-Applied							0	0					0								
Physics-Expenm	0	0				0	0	0	0												
Physiology	0	0	0		0	0															
Pharmacology		0			0	0															
Polymer Technology											0										
Quality Assurance																	0				
Science Education							0														
Software Develop								0		0		0			0						
Sports Science							0														
Statistics		0			0			0													
Toxicology													0								
Transport Technol				0																	
Zoology	0	0	0		0	0															
PG Cert																					
Exercise Science				0																	
River Flow Modell						0															
PG Dip																					
Agricultural Science			0																		
Aquaculture					0	0															
Biomedical Science				0																	
Biological Science				0				0													
Biotechnology				0	0			0													
Chemistry-Analyt					0	0		0													
Chem-Pure/Applied			0																		
Computer Sc/IT		0	0	0	0		0		0		0	0									0
Comp Animation	0			0						0											
Comput Methods		0																			
Environ Analysis					0																
Health Mgt				0						0											
Equine Studies		0																			
Food Sc/Technology			0		0					0											
Genetics-Molecular	0																				
Geology-Sediment		0																			
Hydrology						0															

	TCD	UCD	QUB	UU	UUC	UCG	UL	DCU	MAY	DIT	Athlone	Carlow	Cork	Dundalk	Galway	Limerick	L'kenny	Sligo	Tallaght	Tralee	Waterford
IT									0												
Instrum Analysis								0													
Mathematical Sc		0			0	0			0												
Microbiology						0															
Micropropogation					0																
Model/Num Comput					0																
Nutritional Science					0																
Nutrition-Human				0																	
Occup Health/Hyg						0															
Physics (Applied)			0		0			0	0												
Plant Disease Mgt					0																
Quality Control	0																				
Radiation Science				0																	
Safety & Health		0																			
Sports Exerc/Leis				0																	
Statistics		0																			
Masters																					
Agricultural Science		0	0																		
Aquaculture					0	0															
Biological Science				0				0													
Biomedical Science	0		0	0																	
Biotechnology				0	0	0		0													
Chemistry (Anal)					0			0													
Chem-Mat Sc					0																
Chemical Technol										0											
Clin Biochemistry	0																				
CBL			0																		
Comp & Design				0																	
Comp & IT				0		0		0													
Comp & Maths						0		0	0												
Computer Science	0		0		0			0	0	0											
Computat Science			0																		
Environmental Sc	0	0	0																		
Environ Anal Chem					0																
Environ Anal Chem																					
Environ Protection																		0			
Environ Res Mgt		0																			
Equine Studies		0																			
Food Science		0	0		0																

	TCD	UCD	QUB	UU	UUC	UCG	UL	DCU	MAY	DIT	Athlone	Carlow	Cork	Dundalk	Galway	Limerick	L'kenny	Sligo	Tallaght	Tralee	Waterford
Food Technology			0		0																
Geophysics						0															
Horticulture		0																			
Hydrology								0													
Instrument (Adv)								0					0								
Maths/Maths Phy.		0							0												
Maths-Ind & App								0													
Maths/Comp Sc					0		0														
Maths/Science		0							0												
Nutrition				0	0																
Nutrition-Human				0																	
Occup Hlth/Ergon						0															
Oceanography						0															
Optoelectronics						0		0													
Physics	0	0																			
Plant Protection		0																			
Quality/Reliability						0															
Radiation Science		0		0																	
Safety & Health		0																			
Sensor Technology								0													
Science		0																			
Sports Science				0																	
Stats/Comp Science		0			0																
Stats/App Maths					0																

country of *permanent* residence and applicants may be required to attend for personal interview. If there is no Irish Embassy or Consulate, through the applicant is reference in Ireland or direct by post to the *Visa Office, Department of Foreign Affairs, 69-71 St. Stephen's Green, Dublin 2, Ireland* [Tel. (3531) 4780822].

5. Applicants who have permission to remain in Ireland may apply for re-entry visas by post or by calling in person to the Visa Office on any weekday between the hours of 10 a.m. and 12 noon. *Please note, however, that same-day service is not and cannot be guaranted.* Certificates of Registration ("Green Book") must be submitted with applications.
6. *Passports* must be submitted whether applications are being made by post, through an Irish Embassy or Consulate or at the Visa Office in Dublin. Visas cannot be issued unless passports are submitted. In cases where the applicant in unable to submit his/her passport with the application s/he must state the reason and indicate from which Irish Embassy or Consulate she proposed to collect the visa. *In those cases only,* photocopies of *all* pages of the passports must be submitted with the application.
7. Applicants' passports should be valid for at least 6 months after the intended date of *departure from* Ireland following visits.
8. *Three r ecently-taken passport-size colour photographs* must also be submitted with applications.
9. *Children under 16 years of age accompanying* a parent or legal guardian do not require visas to enter Ireland However, they must have passports/travel documents or be named on those of their parents/legal guardians. Papers proving parentage or legal guardianship of such children must also be in the possession of the parents/legal guardians, for inspection by Immigration Officers at ports of entry. Children may remain in Ireland only as long as their parents/legal guardians do so.

Other Original Documents to be Submitted with Visa Applications

10. *On Business / to Attend a Conference*
    (A) Letter of invitation from Irish company stating the reason for and duration of proposed visit and responsibility for the applicant's accommodation/maintenance costs;
    or
    (B) Letter from conference host setting out details including nature, duration and programme of conference and responsibility for accommodation/maintenance costs.
11. *For Visit / Holiday*
    (A) Confirmation of hotel booking or letter from reference in Ireland undertaking to provide the applicant with accommodation during his/her stay; and
    (B) Evidence that the applicant has sufficient funds to maintain him/her stay (e.g. recent bank statement) or letter from reference in Ireland undertaking to support the applicant financially during his/her stay; and
    (C) Evidence of obligations in the applicant's country of permanent residence, e.g. letter from employer/college certifying intention to return there after the visit.
12. *For Study/Training/Examination Purpose*
    (A) Letter of registration from college/school verifying the duration/nature of the course or examination; and
    (B) Evidence that the requisite fees have been paid in full; and
    (C) Evidence that the applicant has sufficient funds to maintain him/herself for the period of his/her proposed stay.

Processing Time/Decisions

13. While many applications are decided quickly (for example those of Government officials, well travelled business people and persons with residence rights in Ireland or Europe or with valid visas for other EU or Schengen Member States) others, such as those from people intending to work,

study or come as tourists, may have to be referred for decision to the Department of Justice, Equality and Law Reform in Dublin. In all cases, therefore, applicants should apply at least three weeks (five weeks if by post) in advance of the intended date of departure for Ireland. Minimum communication costs, of which details are available from them, will be charged by Irish Embassies and Consulates from applicants who wish to have their applications expedited. *Consulates have to refer all applications to a supervising Embassy or to Dublin.*

Application Fees

14. Details of application fees are available from Irish Embassies and Consulates and from the Visa Office in Dublin. Applications made direct to the Visa Office should be accompanied by the relevant fee in Irish pounds (*bank drafts only,* payable to Department of foreign affairs, Dublin). Application fees are *non-refundable.*

Applicants who are *married to EU citizens* are exempt from fees.

Change of status

15. In general, persons granted visas for particular purposes (e.g. visit; study; accompanying spouse; examination) are *not permitted* under Irish law to involve themselves in any other activity or to remain in the State for any purpose other than that for which the visa was specifically granted. A person wishing to undertake any activity in Ireland other than that for which his/her visa was granted (including re-sitting an examination) must leave the State and then apply for a new visa. The applicant may not return to Ireland while awaiting a decision on his/her new application. *The Visa Office cannot accept applications for re-entry visas involving change of status in Ireland. Enquiries about change of status must be directed to the Immigration and Citizenship Division, Department of Justice, Equality and Law Reform, 72-76 St. Stephen's Green, Dublin 2 [tel: (3531) 6028202).*

Appeals

16. Should an application be refused, the applicant may apply to have it reconsidered by the *Visa Appeals Officer, Department of Justice, Equality and Law Reform, 72-76 St. Stephen's Green, Dublin 2* [tel: (3531) 6028202]. Any further information or additional documentation which it is wished to have taken into account should be sent to the Visa Appeals Officer. This can be done direct or through the Irish Embassy or Consulate through which the application was made. The application reference number must be quoted. *Appeals cannot be dealt with over the telephone.*

Registration

17. A visa holder proposing to remain in Ireland for longer than three months is required to register with the Gardai (police) in the area in which s/he resides. Registration establishes permission to reside. For the greater Dublin area, the relevant office is the Aliens Registration Office, Harcourt Street, Dublin 2 (tel: (3531) 4755555). Items required for registration are:

(a) passport; (b) four recently-taken passport-size photographs;

(c) documentation relating to entry, such as work permit, business permission, evidence of funds, letter from college.

The period of permission given is determined by the duration of the course or the validity of the work permit. On registration, the person is given a Certificate of Registration (Green Book) and is required to keep his/her permission to reside in Ireland up-to-date for the duration of his/her stay in the State.

Visa Applications-Additional Information

Applicants are reminded to read the instructions carefully; failure to comply with all the requirements set down will cause delays and may lead to the rejection of the application.

Passports

Where the original passport is not submitted with the application applicants, are reminded that photocopies of all pages of the passport must be submitted with the application.

Visa Applications for Examination Purposes

Applicants are required to submit evidence of obligations in country of permanent residence, e.g., letter from employer/college certifying intention to return there after the visit, in addition to other requirement for visa application.

Visa Applications for Business Purposes

Applicants are required to submit a letter from the applicants company/organisation indicating the purpose of travel to Ireland.

For more details on Irish education, contact:
Embassy of Ireland, 230 Jor Bagh, New Delhi-110003
Tel: 462-6733/41/43, Fax: 469-7053, Telex: 3165546 NDEI IN

Israel

Israel in 1948 was a small sliver of land with a minuscule population, overwhelmingly concerned with the problems of daily survival, and struggling to create the framework for an independent and viable state. Fifty years on, it is home to a thriving and vibrant cultural life embodying manifold forms of human expression.

It has developed from an inward-looking, introverted and culturally self-absorbed people, into a universalist, extrovert and dynamic, multi-cultured world-embracing force. Its artists, writers, dancers and musicians have made an impact far beyond their number, while an increasing variety of international festivals and events, such as the Israel Festival, the Jerusalem International Book Fair, the International Poetry Festival, the Karmiel Dance Festival and many others, have become notable events in the world's cultural calendar. In Israel itself, the constant search for cultural identity is expressed by dynamic creativity in a broad range of art forms, appreciated and enjoyed by a great many people—not as an activity for the privileged few, but as an essential part of daily life.

Education

Education in Israel begins at a very young age in order to provide children with an augmented 'head start,' particularly in terms of socialization and language development.

Many two-year-olds and almost all three and four-year-olds attend some kind of preschool framework. Most programs are sponsored by local authorities, some within day-care centres operated by women's organizations; others are privately owned. The Ministry of Education allocates special resources for preschool education in disadvantaged areas.

Kindergarten for five-year-olds is free and compulsory. The curriculum aims to teach fundamental skills, including language and numerical concepts, to foster cognitive and creative capacities and to promote social abilities. The curricula of all preschools are guided and supervised by the Ministry of Education to ensure a solid and well-rounded foundation for future learning.

School System

School attendance is mandatory from age 6 to 16 and free to age 18. Formal education starts in primary school (grades 1-6) and continues with intermediate school (grades 7-9) and secondary school (grades 10-12). About nine per cent of the school population aged 13-18 attends boarding schools.

The multi-cultural nature of Israel's society is accommodated within the framework of the education system. Accordingly, schools are divided into four groups: *state schools,* attended by the majority of pupils; *state religious schools,* which emphasize Jewish studies, tradition and observance, *Arab and Druze schools,* with instruction in Arabic and special focus on Arab and Druze history, religion and culture; and *private schools,* which operate under various religious and international auspices.

In recent years, with the growing concern of parents over the orientation of their children's education, some new schools have been founded, which reflect the philosophies and beliefs of specific groups of parents and educators.

Curriculum

Most hours of the school day are devoted to compulsory academic studies. While the subject matter to be covered is uniform throughout the system, each school may choose from a wide range of study units and teaching materials, provided by the Ministry of Education, which best suit the needs of its faculty and pupil population. With the aim of enhancing pupils' understanding of their society, each year a special topic of national importance is studied in depth. Themes have included democratic values, the Hebrew language, immigration, Jerusalem, peace and industry.

Administration and Structure

The Ministry of Education is responsible for school curricula, educational standards, supervision of teaching personnel and construction of school buildings. Local authorities are charged with school maintenance as well as with acquisition of equipment and supplies. Teaching personnel at the kindergarten and primary school level are Ministry employees, while those in the upper grades are employed by local authorities, which receive funding from the Ministry according to the size of the school population. The government finances 72 pe rcent of education, while the rest comes from local authorities and other sources.

Secondary Education

The majority of secondary schools offer academic curricula in science and in the humanities leading to a matriculation certificate and higher education.

Certain secondary schools offer specialized curricula which lead to a matriculation certificate and/or vocational diploma. Technological schools train technicians and practical engineers on three levels, with some preparing for higher education, some studying towards a vocational diploma and others acquiring practical skills. Agricultural schools, usually in a residential setting, supplement basic studies with subjects relating to agronomy. Military preparatory schools, in two different settings, train future career personnel and technicians in specific fields required by the Israel Defence Forces; both programs are residential, one open to boys only, the other is coeducational. Yeshiva high schools, mainly boarding schools, with separate frameworks for boys and girls, complement their secular curricula with intensive religious studies and promote observance of tradition as well as a Jewish way of life. Comprehensive schools offer studies in a variety of vocations, ranging from book keeping to mechanics, electronics, hotel trades, graphic design and more. Apprenticeship programs are provided by the Ministry of Labor in schools affiliated with vocational networks. Lasting three to four years, these programs consist of two years of classroom study followed by one/two years during which students study three days a week and work at their chosen trade on the other days. Trades range from hairstyling and cooking to mechanics and word processing.

Higher Education

Higher education plays a pivotal role in the economic and social development of the country. Almost a quarter of a century before the state came into being, the Technion—Israel Institute of Technology in Haifa was opened (1924) to train engineers and architects needed for the rebuilding of the country, and the Hebrew University of Jerusalem was founded (1925) as a centre of higher learning for youth in the Land of Israel and to attract Jewish students and scholars from abroad. When Israel attained independence in (1948), enrolment at the two universities totaled about 1,600. Today about 149,000 students attend the country's institutions of higher learning. Of these 97,000 attend colleges, while some 24,000 participate in courses through the Open University.

Being accorded full academic and administrative freedom, Israel's institutions of higher education are open to all those who meet their academic standards. New immigrants and students lacking the necessary qualifications may attend a special preparatory program, which upon successful completion enables them to apply for admission.

Council for Higher Education

Institutions of higher education operate under the authority of the Council for Hihger Eudcation, which is headed by the Minister of Education, Culture and Sport and includes academics, community representatives and a student representative. It grants accreditation, authorizes the awarding of academic degrees and advises the government on the development and financing of higher education and scientific research.

The Planning and Grants Committee, composed of four senior academics from different fields and two public figures from the business or industrial sectors, is the intermediary body between the government and the institutions of higher education regarding financial matters, submitting budget proposals to both bodies and allocating the approved budget. Public funds provide 70 percent of the budget for higher education, 20 per cent is derived from tuition and the rest from various private sources. The Committee also promotes cooperation among the various institutions.

Students

Most Israeli students are over the age of 21 years when they begin their studies, due to three years compulsory military service for men and almost two years for women. Until the early 1960s, students pursued higher education mainly to acquire knowledge, while in recent years they have been more career-oriented, with larger numbers enrolled in the wide range of professional studies now offered. At present, well over half of Israelie in the 20-24 years age group are enrolled in one of the country's institutions of post-secondary or higher education.

THE HEBREW UNIVERSITY OF JERUSALEM

Mount Scopus, 91905 Jerusalem; Tel. (02) 882111, Fax. (02) 322545

In July 1918, the foundation stone of the Hebrew University of Jerusalem was laid on Mount Scopus by Dr. Chaim Weizmann. The University was officially opened in 1925, when the first Board of Governors, composed of leading figures such as Sigmund Freud, Martin Buber, and Albert Einstein, expressed their threefold objective for the new university: (1) to be an internationally respected institution of higher learning and research; (2) to play a prominent role in the development of the Jewish state; and (3) to be the University of the Jewish people. From the nucleus of three research institutes that existed in 1925—Chemistry, Microbiology, and Jewish Studies—the Hebrew University has grown into a multidisciplinary institution spreading over four campuses at Mount Scopus, Givat Ram, Ein Kerem, and Rehovot.

Overseas students have attended the Hebrew University since its earliest days. Special programs for overseas students were instituted in 1955 and continually expanded. In 1971 the School for Overseas Students was opened in order to coordinate the various programs and activities for overseas students, to facilitate their integration into the academic and social fabric of the Hebrew University and Israeli society, to expand the scope of existing programs and to develop new ones. On its tenth anniversary in 1981, the School was dedicated as the Rothberg School for Overseas Students.

Programs for Overseas Students

The Rothberg School for Overseas Students offers the following programs of study to qualified students:

The Four Year/Preparatory Program

The Four Year/Preparatory Program prepares secondary school graduates from abroad for regualr undergraduate studies at the Hebrew University and other Israeli institutions of higher education. The first year of study in the program is offered at the Rothberg School for Overseas Students. Upon completion of the year, students who meet the general Hebrew Univesity and specific faculty and/or departmental admission requirements may continue to study at the University for another three years in pursuit of their bachelor's degree.

Two trends are available: Humanities/Social Sciences and Mathematics/Science. Two alternate sessions of study are offered for each trend: one commencing in August and the other in February. Both sessions open with an intensive Hebrew language course (*Ulpan*). The latter session is intended for students who have some prior knowledge of Hebrew and English.

Courses are offered in Hebrew, English, French, Spanish and Russian. Introductory courses in the Humanities and Social Sciences and courses in Mathematics and Science are taught in Hebrew during the second semester; credit is granted by the appropriate faculties/departments at the Hebrew

University for these courses.

Admission Requirements: Applications are considered on an individual basis. Admission is based on the candidate's complete secondary school record and scores on either the NITE Psychometric Entrance Test or the Scholastic Aptitude Test (SAT).

The Freshman Program

The Freshman Program is designed primarily for students from North America who have completed high school abroad and wish to come to Israel for a year of study. The program includes courses in Hebrew, Jewish and Israel studies, and introductory courses in the Humanities, Social Sciences and Science. Upon completion of the program, participants generally return to their home country for further studies or apply for admission as regular degree students at an Israeli university. They will usually be admitted to North American universities as sophomores.

The One Year Program

The One Year Program is designed to provide visiting undergraduate and graduate students with a diversified academic experience at the Hebrew University, while earning credits which may be transferred to their home college or university. Most of the courses fall under the wider disciplines of the Humanities and Social Sciences, and may provide credit in such departments as Jewish Studies, Middle East Studies, Archaeology, History, Linguistics, Literature, Philosophy, Russian Studies, Economics, International Relations, Political Science, Psychology, Religious Studies, Sociology and Urban Studies. Qualified students may engage in independent study, under the supervision of an instructor.

Most courses in the program are offered in English, with a few given in Hebrew. Students with sufficient proficiency in Hebrew are encouraged to attend regular classes in the faculties of Humanities, Social Sciences, and Science.

Admission Requirements: Candidates must have completed at least one year at an accredited college or university with at least a "B" average. Some Canadian students must fulfill special admission requirements, such as two years of CEGEP (PQ-completion of DEC) or six Grade 13 or Ontario Academic courses (OAC). Prior knowledge of Hebrew is into a prerequisite.

Graduate Division: Students who hold a bachelor's and/or master's degree from abroad may study one year at the Hebrew University in one of the following capacities:

- Visiting Student—a student who holds a bachelor's degree.
- Visiting Graduate Student—a student enrolled in a master's degree program abroad.
- Visiting Research Student—a student enrolled in a doctoral program abroad.

Students accepted as Visiting Graduate or Research students are allowed relative freedom in drawing up their programs, but their status does not guarantee admission to any particular course. The Institute of Life Sciences, through the One Year Program, offers supervised visiting research opportunities for English-speaking graduate students in the areas of biological chemistry, botany, developmental biology, ecology, genetics, neuro-biology and zoology.

Semester Programs in Jewish and Israel Studies

Two special semester programs in Jewish and Israel Studies are offered to qualified high school graduates: the "Nativ" Program in the fall semester and the British and Australian Semester Program in Jewish and Israel Studies (BASP) in the spring.

The Nativ Program is specially designed for North American students belonging to United Synagogue Youth (USY) who are attending the year-long Nativ Leadership Training Institute in Israel. The students study at the Hebrew University during the fall semester, while participating in various cultural and social activities within Nativ. The remainder of the academic year is spent working and studying on a kibbutz.

BASP is designed for mantriculants who have successfully completed A-levels, HSC/VCE, or equivalent matriculation examinations, the program strives to foster a better understanding of Judaism, Jewish history, the Jewish people and the State of Israel.

Summer/Winter Ulpan

The *Ulpan* is an intensive, full-time Hebrew language course designed to prepare new students for study at the Hebrew University. Classes are held on six levels, ranging from beginners to advanced. The courses concentrate on specific language skills and terminology and place particular emphasis on the reading of journal articles and scientific texts. The Summer Ulpan consists of approximately 200 hours of study and usually extends over a nine-week period in August-September. The Winter Ulpan consists of 100 hours and extends over a four-week period around February. Candidates not registered at the Hebrew University may apply to study as external students if they havė completed at least one year of study at a recognized institution of higher education.

Summer Courses

Summer Courses provide visiting students with an academic program primarily in Judaic, Middle Eastern and Israel Studies. language instruction is offered in Modern and Biblical Hebrew, Literary and Spoken Arabic, and Yiddish. Many courses include field trips to enhance the learning experience. Except for language courses, the language of instruction is English. Two sessions, each three weeks long, are held in July and August. Most of the language courses extend over both sessions. Summer Courses are open to visiting undergraduate and graduate students, as well as to adults with an academic background. Credits can generally be transferred to the student's home university or college.

The following programs are also offered by the Hebrew University to overseas students:

International Master of Public Health Program

The Hebrew University-Hadassah School of Public Health and Community Medicine offers a special international program, taught in English, leading to a Master of Public Health (M.P.H) degree. The intensive program, which extends over twelve months, commences in late October. The overall objective of the course is to provide basic knowledge of the theory and practice of public health for workers either already engaged in one or another branch of this discipline or wishing to enter it in their future work.

For more information and application forms, contact the Coordinator, International M.P.H. Course, School of Public Health and Community Medicine, POB 1172, 91010 Jerusalem, Israel. Applications may also be obtained from Israeli diplomatic or consular representatives in the applicant's country of origin.

Samuel Mendel Melton Center for Jewish Education in the Diaspora

The Melton Center for Jewish Education in the Diaspora, established by the School of Education and Institute of Contemporary Jewry, represents the Hebrew University's commitment to the study and improvement of Jewish education around the world. In addition to its regular M.A. and Ph.D programs, the Center offers two special programs for participants from abroad.

- The Senior Educators Program is designed for senior educators seeking to enrich their educational and Jewish backgrounds during a year of study at the Hebrew University. Proficiency in the Hebrew language is required.
- The Summer Institute for Jewish Educators brings together teachers, principals and community workers from all over the world to participate in seminars which enrich Judaic knowledge and impart didactic skills and classroom methods. Courses are offered in both Hebrew and English.

For further information and application forms, contact the Friends office in your country of origin (see addresses below) or the Melton Center for Jewish Education in the Diaspora, School of Education, the Hebrew University of Jerusalem, Mount Scopus, 91905 Jerusalem.

Division for External Studies of the Faculty of Agriculture

This division offers courses taught in English to holders of B.Sc. degrees or higher. Courses offered in the past include the following:

- Horticulture Crop Production in Subtropical and Tropical Climates (7 weeks)
- Workshop on Curriculum Development and Evaluation for Agricultural Schools and Institutions (3 weeks)
- International Post-Graduate Course in the Exploration, *Expoloition* and Management of Groundwater Resources (4 months)

Inquiries pertaining to these and other courses should be directed to the Coordinator, Division for External Studies, Faculty of Agriculture, POB 12, 76100 Rehovot, Israel; Tel: (08) 481285; Fax: 972-8-462181.

Religious Services

Houses of worship are located throughout Jerusalem. There is a synagogue on each campus, where daily and Sabbath services are held. The Beit Midrash program at the University's Hecht Synagogue, for the informal study of traditional sources, offers students from all backgrounds unique a opportunity to widen their Jewish horizons. Informal religious advising is available to members of all denominations. The Student Christian Forum serves as a chaplaincy for Christian students.

Housing

The Hebrew University dormitories can accommodate over 5,500 students. Single students admitted to programs at the Rothberg School for Overseas Students are first-year students from abroad who make their reservations on time are generally guaranteed dormitory space. Quarters for married students are limited. The University is currently in the process of renovating and building new dormitories. Kitchen facilities are available for light cooking. supermarket, day-care center for students' children, bank, post office, laundry, and other facilities are available on campus.

Financial Aid

Overseas students who need financial aid should apply to the Friends of the Hebrew University in their home country, where their request will be reviewed.

For further information about programs at the Hebrew University, contact:

In Israel

Office of Overseas Students Admissions, Hebrew University of Jerusalem
Goldsmith Building, Mount Scopus, 91905 Jerusalem, Israel
Tel.: (02) 882607; Fax: 972-2-827078

In the United States

Office of Academic Affairs, American Friends of the Hebrew University
11 East 69th Street, New York, NY 10021, Tel.: (212) 472-2288

In Canada

Canadian Friends of the Hebrew University, 3080 Yonge Street, Suite 5024
Toronto, Ont., M4N 3P4, Tel.: (416) 485-8000, 1-800-668-3956

In Great Britain

Friends of the Hebrew University, 3 St. John's Wood Road, London NW8 8RB, England
Tel.: (071) 286-1176

In Australia and New Zealand

Australian Friends of the Hebrew University, 584 St. Kilda Road
Melbourne, Victoria 3004, Tel.: (03) 529-4611

In South Africa

Friends of the Hebrew University, P.O. Box 4316

Johannesburg 2000, Tel.: (01) 333-6632, 333-6668

THE TECHNION ISRAEL INSTITUTE OF TECHNOLOGY

Technion City, 32000 Haifa; Tel. (04) 292111, Fax (04) 221581

The Technion—Israel Institute of Technology is Israel's most comprehensive technological university and ranks among the leading institutions of its kind in the Western world. The campus was officially opened in 1924, the first institute of higher education in Israel. The Technion has played and continues to play a vital role in Israel's growth and security as a major source of the country's scientists, engineers, managers, architects, and physicians. The Technion Research and Development Foundation is the largest applied research center is Israel. The Foundation offers consultative services to Israeli and foreign clients, including many private industries and governmental agencies.

The Technion City campus is located on the slopes of Mount Carmel in Haifa. The 300-acre site offers a commanding view of the Lower Galilee and the Haifa Bay area. There are more than 100 buildings on campus, housing the various departments, laboratories, and student facilities.

Programs for Overseas Students

Special Program for Overseas Students

A special program for Overseas Students is offered by three departments: Aerospace Engineering, Agricultural Engineering, and Industrial Engineering and Management. The program is designed for undergraduate students who wish to spend their junior year at the Technion and earn credits transferable to their home universities. Students may enroll for either the winter or spring semester or for both.

All courses are given in English. In addition to courses in aerospace engineering, agricultural engineering, and industrial engineering and management, the program offers classes in the humanities, social sciences and Hebrew.

Students proficient in Hebrew may participate in regular courses offered at the Technion.

The Centre for Pre-Academic Studies

The Centre's program is intended to prepare students for entrance to the Technion. The fields of study include mathematics, physics, chemistry, English (if necessary), and Hebrew for new immigrants. In addition to classroom lessons, small group and individual tutoring sessions are held.

There are programs that last for six, eight, or ten months, depending on the student's qualifications. The final dates of the courses correspond to the entrance examination dates of the Technion. Admission requirements are twelve years of schooling, an examination in mathematics, and the NITE Psychometric Entrance Test.

Admission to the preparatory program does not guarantee admission to the Technion. In view of space limitations, qualifying examinations are competitive, and all students, native or foreign, must take them.

In view of the Technion's requirements, the overseas undergraduate candidate is advised to send a transcript of his or her high school record, listing courses taken and the grades received. On the basis of this record, the Technion will advise the candidate whether he or she can qualify for admission and on what terms, or suggest that he or she come to the Technion for a preparatory year of study.

Candidates must demonstrate a certain level of proficiency in Hebrew. Candidates who qualify in all other respects are advised to come to Israel prior to commencement of the academic year to attend an Ulpan to improve their Hebrew ability.

THE OPEN UNIVERSITY OF ISRAEL

POB 39328, Tel Aviv; Tel. (03) 6460460, Fax.. (03) 6423639

The Open University of Israel was established in 1974. Designed to transcend such obstacles to higher education as time and distance and to make academic studies accessible to broader populations throughout Israel, the Open University has become a multi-campus university offering a broad spectrum of programs and formats of study, in accordance with the needs and interests of the student.

Authorized by the Council for Higher Education to confer bachelor's degrees, the Open University of Israel offers about 250 courses. More than 16,000 students are enrolled.

Admission Requirements

Adhering to the principle that everyone has the right to pursue academic studies, the Open University has no formal admission requirements. It has been proven that students possessing matriculation do not succeed better in Open University courses than those who do not. The Open University's open admission policy makes studies available to those who wish to try.

Studies outside of Israel

Several hundred students take Open University of Israel studies abroad. These students are proficient in Hebrew and take courses and exams in Hebrew. Open University studies abroad are conducted by mail directly between the University tutor and the individual student. Assignments are submitted by mail, corrected and graded in Israel and then returned to the student. Arrangements are made for supervised exams abroad.

For further information in the United States, contact:

American Friends of the Open University of Israel
330 West 58th St., Suite 4A, New York, NY 10019, Tel.: (212) 713-1515 Fax: (212) 974-0769

BEN-GURION UNIVERSITY OF THE NEGEV

84105 Beer Sheba, Tel. (057) 461111, Fax. (057) 31463

Beer Sheba, home of the Ben-Gurion University of the Negev, is the capital of Israel's Negev, an arid area covering over 50 per cent of the State of Israel.

Since the establishment of the State, the policy of the Government of Israel has been to encourage population dispersion. In line with this policy, various industries, such as quarries, chemicals, electronics, and textiles, were set up in Beer Sheba and the neighboring development towns to provide sources of employment. The resulting increase in population quickly led to the creation of service and commercial enterprises.

The founding of the Ben-Gurion University of the Negev in 1964 by a group of prominent citizens in the region was a historic event in Israeli education. The founders believed that the best scholarship should be brought to bear on the nation-building efforts to develop a modern society in the Negev.

Programs for Overseas Students

The semester and year program, which is taught in English, offers a full range of courses in Jewish studies, Israel society, politics and Zionism, desert studies, Hebrew language, natural sciences, mathematics and computer science, management and business administration, English language and literature/linguistics, and art.

Special courses which take advantage of the desert surroundings include History of the Negev, Bedouin Society, Desert Art and Ecology. In addition, more standard courses are offered in Hebrew of Zionism, politics, and computers.

Ben-Gurion University, in conjunction with Pinhas Sapir Regional College, offers special programs, such as the College Kibbutz Program. This one-semester program combines academic studies on the kibbutz with actual experience in kibbutz life.

A special summer archeology program at Tel Nizzana is also offered.

Preparatory Programs for New Immigrants

The following preparatory programs for new immigrants are offered:

The Multiple-Purpose Preparatory Program is designed for new immigrants possessing a matriculation certificate. The objectives of the program are to impart a knowledge of Hebrew to the students, to improve their knowledge of English (where necessary), and to prepare them for University studies. The duration of the program is nine months (October-June).

The Engineering and Natural Sciences Preparatory Program is designed for new immigrants possessing a matriculation certificate who would like to study in the faculties of Engineering Sciences and Natural Sciences. The duration of the programs is nine months (February-November).

Candidates who do not live in Israel can apply through the emissary (*shaliach*) of the Jewish Agency in their country.

Financial Aid

A limited number of graduate assistantships are available to outstanding students. For additional information, write to the chairman of the department of your choice.

Student Life

Students are organized into a Student Association which is apolitical in character. Student officers are elected annually according to departments and as individuals. Student representatives participate in most university bodies, such as the Board of Governors, the Executive Committee, and the Senate.

Many cultural activities are held for students. Once a week there is a concert and/or a lecture on current topics. Often there are films and plays. Activities in the student dormitories include lectures, performances, community singing, folk dancing and the like.

The student newspaper, called *Barbaran,* offers students the opportunity to express themselves on student matters and general topics.

The students have access to a synagogue and a *rabbi*, who is responsible for activities related to Jewish studies and traditions.

Students participate in voluntary community service projects. In this way, they devote time and energy for the general good and help to raise the level of children in underprivileged neighbourhoods.

Many sports activities are available. The University has a sports center which includes a gymnasium, six tennis courts, and two swimming pools. Sports clubs exist in various fields such as handball, volleyball, chess, and swimming. Students participate in teams which represent the University in various leagues.

For further information about programs at the Ben-Gurion University of the Negev, contact:

In Israel

Overseas Student Program, Ben-Gurion University of the Negev, P.O. Box 653
84105 Beer Sheba, Tel. (057) 461144

In the United States

Overseas Study Program, American Associates, Ben-Gurion University of the Negev
342 Madison Avenue, Suite 1924, New York, NY 10173

BAR-ILAN UNIVERSITY

52900 Ramat Gan; Tel. (03) 5318111, Fax. (03) 344622

The establishment of a Jewish State in the land of Israel was an event of astounding historical significance for the Jewish people. After almost two thousand years of exile, Torah and nation are again one. To meet the challenges of this new age, to properly and creatively fuse traditional Jewish identity and modern life, to promote a twentieth-century Israel built on 30 centuries of Jewish values and learning, Bar-Ilan University was founded in 1955. In 35 short years, Bar-Ilan has grown from 80 to 10,000 students, distinguished itself as a centre for scientific, professional, and Jewish studies, and become the unchallenged spokesman for national religious thought and orientation in the State of Israel.

Special Programs for Overseas Students

Bar-Ilan's office of the Dean of Students, which is responsible for all overseas student programs, offers a range of special programs for students from abroad.

One Year/One Semester "Torah U'Mada" Programs

Designed to meet the needs of students from religious backgrounds wishing to experience life in Israel, the One Year/One Semester *Torah U'Mada* programs offer courses in both Jewish and general studies that grant credit easily transferable to colleges and universities abroad. Combined with a spectacular array of trips and visits to Israel's historical sights, these programs provide students with a meaningful Israeli experience sure to remain with them for the rest of their lives.

The One Year/One Semester programs contain three components: Jewish studies, Hebrew language instruction, and general studies. Four Jewish studies tracks are offered: men's beginning and advanced tracks and women's beginning and advanced tracks. Beginning tracks are taught in English or other native languages of the students, while advanced tracks are taught in Hebrew. Men study in the University's Institute of Higher Torah Studies—*Machon Hagavoha La Tora*—and women study in its Torah Institute for Women—*Midrasha La'Banot.* All four tracks feature studies in Bible, Talmud, Jewish history, Jewish thought, Israel studies, and individual research, under the personal guidance of men and women with rabbinic and academic credentials. Five Hebrew language *ulpan* levels are offered, and students are carefully evaluated upon entrance to the University. As the year progresses, students may advance from level to level on an individual basis.

General studies in University academic departments are conducted in the afternoon. Dozens of course selections in all faculties are available in English, and students with an adequate knowledge of Hebrew are welcome in most of the 5,000 courses offered in Hebrew each year.

Students on the One Year/One Semester *Torah U'Mada* Program live on campus in the Bar-Ilan dormitories, and every possible effort is made to integrate them into campus life. They may participate in all extracurricular activities and are members of the Israeli Student Organization. They have at their disposal all the facilities and amenities available to the regular Bar-Ilan student. In addition, students are "adopted" by Israeli students and faculty families to facilitate the adjustment process.

Trips, tours, and special Shabbat and *Yom Tov* programs add a distinctive flavor to what is Israel's premier, and certainly most unique, one-year Torah program.

Admission Requirements

Admission to the One Year/One Semester *Torah U'Mada* programs is open to any student possessing a high school diploma who has achieved a grade-point average of at least 3.0 (80-85) and good results on a standardized test, such as the SAT or ACT. Recommendations (one must be from a rabbi) and a personal interview with the director of Academic Affairs (when geographically possible) complete the application process.

Finally, the program is especially designed for students with a strong personal commitment to the observance of Jewish tradition; thus only students with this commitment will be considered for admission. Students from non-observant backgrounds who are seriously interested in rediscovering their heritage, and who are prepared to observe the University's minimum observance requirements, are also welcome.

One Year/One Semester General Programs

Overseas students from non-observant backgrounds may also attend Bar-Ilan University on an "academic studies only" basis, selecting their academic program from general studies and academic Jewish studies courses offered in English or, as outlined above, in Hebrew. The Office of the Dean of Students aids students in designing their academic program.

Although dormitory facilities are not available to students in this program, they may participate in all campus programming, and all regular University services are at their disposal.

All of the above One Year/One Semester Programs are open to freshmen and upper-class students.

Exchange Student Programs for University Juniors

Students in attendance at other universities who wish to spend their junior year at Bar-Ilan University, taking courses in their major field of concentration augmented with Jewish and/or Hebrew language studies, may apply for exchange student status through the Office of the Dean of Students. Special individualized arrangements will be made with the department of choice to provide academic guidance for study and research. All University services for overseas students are available to exchange students as well.

Pre-Academic Preparatory Program

Students from abroad come from a wide variety of social, academic, and religious backgrounds.

All struggle with the challenge of a new language, a new culture, and a new way of thinking and living. Therefore, most students from abroad require special preparation for academic studies in Israel.

The *Mechina* or Preparatory Program consists of an intensive, six-week introductory *ulpan,* followed by two semesters of academic studies designed to prepare the student for entrance into academic departments in the following year.

The *Mechina* year is academically challenging, consisting of the following study components: Hebrew and English language instruction (where required), statistics or mathematics, Jewish studies, Israeli citizenship and culture, and introductory academic courses. The weekly study program ranges from 30 to 40 hours per week in class.

Special Sabbath and holiday programming, guest lectures, and wholesome social programming round out the *Mechina* year.

The Weizmann Institute of Science

76100 REHOVOT; TEL. (08) 342111, FAX. (08) 466966

Situated on 250 acres of lawns and gardens in Rehovot, 14 miles southeast of Tel. Aviv and 35 miles west of Jerusalem, the Weizmann Institutue of Science occupies what is probably the most beautiful campus in Israel - in fact, one of the most attractive anywhere. Today's campus of 40 buildings grew out of the modest Daniel Sieff Research Institute, founded in 1934 by Dr. Chaim Weizmann, the scientist-statesman who was later to become the first President of the State of israel and the first President of the Institute.

The main task of the Feinberg Graduate School, the educational arm of the Weizmann Institute, is the advanced training of new generations of creative and original researchers in the natural sciences and mathematics - in other words, the education of future scientific leaders. Founded in 1958, the School confers M.Sc., and Ph.D. degrees under the authorization of the Israel Council for Higher Education and pursuant to a charter granted by the Board of Regents of the State of New York. Students who exhibit exceptional creativity and initiative are encouraged to enroll in a special direct doctoral program.

The official language of study is English, which enables the large number of foreign students (currently 25 per cent of the enrollment) to participate fully in all of the School's programs. The School admits candidates of all races, colors, and ethnic origins and has students from North America, Europe, Africa, Asia, South America, and Central America. Together with the substantial number of foreign visiting scientists on the campus, they contribute to the Weizmann Institute's international atmosphere.

Admission Requirements and Application Information

- Candidates for M.Sc. degree programs must have a B.Sc. degree with a grade average of at least "Good," or qualifications deemed equivalent by the appropriate Board of Studies.
- Admission is subject to the approval of the Admission Boards, which will notify candidates of their decision.
- The Admission Boards may request a personal interview with the applicant.
- The prerequisite for admission to Ph.D. degree programs is an M.Sc. degree and a sound academic record, or qualifications deemed equivalent by the Admissions Board.
- Early Admission to the Ph.D. Program: Out-standing students in the M.Sc. program at the Graduate School may be admitted to the doctoral program prior to their completion

of all M.Sc. requirements, with the approval of the Dean and the appropriate Board of Studies.

The academic year begins in October. Candidates for M.Sc. programs may register until July 15 of the same year. Applications received after this date will be considered under exceptional circumstances only.

Doctoral candidates may either apply directly to the science department in which they wish to study or contact the Office of the Graduate School. The final decision on admission must be confirmed by the Dean and the appropriate Board of Studies. Ph.D. students may register at any time.

Housing

Dormitory housing at low rates, for single students and married couples without children, is available for a limited number of students. Candidates from abroad who wish to arrange housing for a family must notify the Graduate School well in advance. A special housing allowance, covering only part of the expenses, may be granted.

Financial Aid

As a policy, students receive a fellowship covering tuition and living expenses. The fellowship for Ph.D. candidates is comparable to that at American universities.

For further information in the United States, contact:

American Committee for the Weizmann Institute of Science, 51 Madison Avenue
New York, NY 10010, Tel.. (212)779-2500, Fax: (212)779-3208

University of Haifa

MOUNT CARMEL, 31999 HAIFA; TEL (04) 240111, FAX (04) 342104

Founded in 1963 and accredited as an autonomous institution of higher education, the University of Haifa is the principal center in the north of Israel of higher education in the Humanities, Arts, and Social Sciences. Situated on the heights of Mount Carmel, above the city of Haifa, the University serves as an academic center for Haifa, the settlements of the Galilee, the Jordan and Jezreel valleys and the coastal plain from Hadera to the Labanese border. The 200-acre campus, commanding a breathtaking view of the entire Haifa bay and the valley of Zebulun, was designed by the Brazillian architect Oscar Niemeyer. The University of Haifa has one central library and a centralized physical plant.

Special Programs for Overseas Students

The Department of Overseas Studies at the University of Haifa offers unique opportunities because it is relatively small and intimate, enrolling approximately 80 students per semester, and well integrated with the University and the community. The students live in the University dormitories and room with Israeli students. Classes are small, and most are open to Israeli students as well. Frequent excursions throughout the North and other parts of Israel enhance the student's increasing knowledge of and experience in Israel.

Israeli students take part in the field trips and social programs. Students are offered a family hosting option—another source for interaction with Israelis. The staff of the program is dedicated to working with each individual student and responding to his or her academic and personal needs.

Semester and One Year Programs

The program is designed for students who have successfully completed at least one year of study at a recognized institution of higher education. A student may register for one semester or the entire year. The fall semester runs from October to January and the spring semester from February to June. Additionally, students may enroll in the Ulpan during the summer either before or after the program, and receive 8 credits in Hebrew language for completion of the Ulpan. All courses provide full academic transfer credit to the student's home university.

The academic program focuses on Hebrew and Arabic language and literature; Israel, Jewish, and Middle Eastern studies; and general studies, such as English literature, mathematics, computer science, philosophy, and psychology.

The program is well known for its specialization in a number of specific areas, including:

- Kibbutz studies (classroom and experiential programs)
- Maritime studies (marine archaeology, biology, geography, commerce, history)
- Ethnography/intercultural communication - the peoples of Israel (the various ethnic groups of Israel, including Jewish, Arab, and Druze cultures)
- Development studies - ecologically based regional planning and management of natural resources.

Special academic programs include the International Honors Programn Psychology, archaeological excavations, marine archaeological excavations, and lecture and travel accredited courses (e.g., Ancient and Modern Egypt-excursion to Egypt, Sephardic Jewry - excursion to spain, Turkey, and Portugal, the Impact of the Holocaust-excursion to Poland).

A rich extracurricular program including such activities as folk dancing, folk singing, student newsletter, sports, hiking, and debate group is offered. Students also take several field trips to all parts of Israel.

One of the best ways for a student to learn about Israel in depth and to develop a personal relationship with the country is to volunteer in one of the community action programs. Options include the Perach "student to student" program; the Jewish-Arab Center; the Unit for Bridging the Gap; the Center for a Battered Women; the Matnass (Community Center) Program; and Project Renewal.

Summer Ulpan

The Summer Ulpan is an intensive ten-week Hebrew language program offered on a variety of levels, from beginners through advanced. The Ulpan combines four days (twenty hours) per week of classes with one day each week dedicated to trips and tours of historical, archaeological, and other sites in northern and central Israel. The tours are integrated with the language studies. The program is highly recommended (though not required) for students taking the semester or year program.

Kibbutz University Semester

This program affords students the opportunity to participate in a work-study program, combining one of the most significant social experiments in the contemporary period - the kibbutz-with a full semester (or year) at the University.

Approximately ten weeks prior to the start of the semester, the students begin their kibbutz experience. While on the kibbutz, the students work a five-hour day in one or more of the branches comprising the kibbutz economy. Each student is "adopted" by a kibbutz family, whose primary responsibility is to provide an open door to the inner complexities of kibbutz life, as well as help the student to overcome any integrative difficulties which may arise.

The program involves ten weeks of kibbutz living, Hebrew language instruction (8 credits), field trips, and a special seminar in Jerusalem. Special arrangements for directed reading and research can be made for students with special interests. At the end of the kibbutz experience, the students move from the kibbutz to the University of Haifa campus and, after an orientation, join the regular Overseas Studies program. During the regular semester, students can earn 15-18 credits.

The Kibbutz University Semester takes place in both the fall and spring semesters.

Internship Program

This special opportunity allows students to combine scholarly pursuits with practical field work. Students are placed in their particular field of interest, under academic and professional supervision. Programs are planned according to the student's needs and qualifications. Internships can be arranged in a variety of fields, including education, the physical sciences, women's studies, and Arab-Jewish relations. At least 25 hours per week are dedicated to supervised field work or internship. It is also possible to take an individual tutorial course given by a qualified academic in the field related to the internship, and to participate in regular or Overseas Studies courses provided that the course prerequisites are met.

The program is open to qualified students who have successfully completed at least two full years of university work.

The Pre-Academic Unit

To ensure the integration into academic life of students who wish to study but are not yet fully qualified, the University offers a year-long Pre-Academic Program (Mechina) which teaches preparatory courses in relevant areas of study. Students study Hebrew, English (when necessary), Jewish studies (including history of the Jewsih people, civics, and geography of Israel), and Introduction to the Humanities and Social Sciences.

Housing

The University dormitory accommodations consist of suites with three bedrooms, kitchen facilities, and a bathroom. Six people (two to a room) occupy a suite.

The University offers modern, spacious dormitory rooms on campus and in nearby Romema. There are units for individuals and married couples.

Financial Aid

Students in need of financial assistance may apply to the University of Haifa Overseas Studies Program. Partial scholarships are awarded by the Student Aid Committee on the basis of need and academic achievement.

For further information about programs for Overseas students, contact:

In Israel

Department of Overseas Studies, University of Haifa, 31999 Haifa, Tel.(04)246584
Fax.: (04)254184

In the United States

Kibbutz Aliyah Desk, (University of Haifa Desk), 27 West 20rh, St. (9th floor)
New York, New York 100111, Tel.: (212)255-1338, Tel.: outside New York: 800-444-7007
Fax: (212)929-3459

Tel Aviv University

RAMAT AVIV, 69978 TEL AVIV; TEL. (03) 5450111, FAX (03) 6427556

Located in Israel's cultural, financial, and industrial heartland, Tel Aviv University is a major center of teaching and research, comprising nine faculties, with more than 90 departments and 65 research institutes. Its nucleus was formed in 1956, when three small educational units - the Tel Aviv School of Law and Economics, an Institute of Natural Sciences, and an Institute of Jewish Studies - joined together to form the University of Tel Aviv. At first attached to the Tel Aviv municipality, Tel Aviv University was accredited as an autonomous institution of higher education in 1963, and its campus in the northern residential section of Ramat Aviv was inaugurated the following year.

The Overseas Students Program provides young people from abroad with the opportunity to study at Tel Aviv University for a year, a semester, or a summer. The program, available in English and Spanish, offers a wide choice a corurses.

Other study opportunities for students from abroad are a Graduate Program in Middle Easern Studies sponsored by the Moshe Dayan Center for Middle Easern and African Studies; the Mechina (Preparatory) Program for high school graduates wishing to enroll at Tel Aviv University; a Summer Law Program co-sponsored by Temple University Law School and the Tel Aviv University Faculty of Law; the Sackier School of Medicine New York State/American Program, a four-year M.D. program tought in English; and the Medical New York State/American Programm, a foru-year M.D. Program taught in English; and the Medical Electives Program.

Special Programs for Overseas Students

Overseas Students Program

Tel Aviv University offers one year, semester (spring or fal), and summer programs for overseas students open to all undergraduates, as well as high school graduates. A broad range of courses is offered in English, with a primary focus on course is offered in English, with a primary focus on courses in historic and modern day Israel, Middle East affairs, and Judaica, as well as a wide spectrum of liberal arts subjects, among them labor studies, archaeology, the Holocaust, psychology, and business administration. All courses in the Overseas Students Program are taught in English by members of Tel Aviv University's outstanding faculty and have been designed to quality of full credity at American and Canadian universities. Students in the year or semester program are required to attend the Intensive Hebrew Language Program prior to the start of their studies.

Among the Unique features of the Overseas Student Program (in addition to the regular courses) are the following:

- A voluntary community involvement program, which brings overseas students into the disadvantaged neighbourhoods of the Tel Aviv area to establish a "big brother" relationship.
- The opportunity to assist at the University's Moshe Dayan Center for Middle Eastern and African Studies and become integrated into the research process on current Middle East affairs.
- A course on 'The Kibbutz as a Way of Life," which focuses on a uniquely Israeli life style, both in theory and practice.
- In cooperation with the Nahum Goldmann Museum of the Jewish Diaspora, special seminar sessions combining the study of Jewish subjects with the use of audio-visual aids, films, displays, libraries, and lectures at the Museum for an indepth examination of the Jewish legacy.
- An independent study program for superior students with a recommendation from the dean of their college abroad, to pursue a specific subject under the guidance of a Tel Aviv University tutorial sponsor.
- Honors Seminars in Middle East Studies: Several special honours seminars taught on an advanced level, have been added to the Overseas Student Program curriculum. Participation is limited to a few highly qualified students.
- Graduate Middle East Studies Program: Tel Aviv University's famed Moshe Dayan Center for Middle Eastern and African Studies and the department of Middle Eastern and African History, in cooperation with the Overseas Student Program, offers year and semester programs, granting graduate credit in this field. The program is designed for graduate students who are currently enrolled in an M.A. program in the U.S. or who plan to enter such a program after completing their studies in Israel.

The Overseas Program also includes extracurricular activities, tours, trips, and special seminars throughout the country.

Sackler School of Medicine, New York State/American Program

The New York State/American Program provides a four-year M.D. curriculum chartered by the Education Department of the State of New York. It is open to U.S. and Canadian students with a bachelor's degree who have completed pre-med studies.

Class size is limited to 60 students. The curriculum is modeled after that of U.S. medical schools, and English is the language of instruction. Education in the basic medical sciences takes place on the campus of Tel Aviv University and clinical clerkships are conducted in affiliated hospitals in the greater Tel Aviv area.

Students may take elective clinical clerkships in the U.S. during their fourth year. They re-enter the U.S. medical system upon graduation through participation in the National Resident Matching Program.

Sackler students have achieved outstanding results on the professional examinations, surpassing all other, U.S. and Canadian students studying medicine abroad. Sackler graduates have obtained excellent residencies and fellowships in top American hospitals.

Application for admission, which is competitive, is made through the Scakler School of Medicine offices at 17 East 62nd St., New York, NY 10021; Tel. : (212) 688-8811.

Electives Program for Medical Students

The Electives Program offers clinical electives to visiting medical students in the affiliated teaching departments, located in seven general hospitals, a rehabilitation hospital and six mental health facilities in the greater Tel Aviv area. The departments' physicians have experience in teaching Israeli and American students. Students take part in the routine activities of the department, participate in supervised rounds and bedside instruction, and may participate in departmental seminars and conferences.

Every elective is organized on an individual basis, with each participant in an appropriate department at a Tel Aviv University affiliated hospital or clinic, and working with the department's staff. No theoretical lectures are given as part of this program. Housing is available to the participants.

For further information and application, contact:
Electives Program Committee, Sackler Faculty of Medicine, Tel Aviv University, 69978 Ramat Aviv, Israel (101); Tel.: (03)6423428, Fax:972-3-410173.

Students from the U.S. may also contact: Sackler School of Medicine, 17 East 62nd St., New York, NY 10021; Tel.: (212)688-8811.

International Postgraduate Training in Medicine

The International Postgraduate Training Program in Medicine is a joint venture of the Saekler Faculty of Medicine and the Ministry of Foreign Affairs. The program offers physicians with at least two years of experience from different countries individual clinical training for a period of three months in chosen specialized fields of interest in affiliated departments in seven general hospitals, a rehabilitation hospital, and six mental health centers, located in the greater Tel Aviv area. The departments' physicians have experience in teaching and instructing overseas trainees. The participants take active part in the everyday routine of the department as well as in conferences, seminars, and congresses which take place in Israel during their stay here. Courses begin three times a year: autumn winter and spring. The physicians are covered by malpractice insurance as well as health insurance while in the program. In addition to the daily routine in the hospitals, the program holds general lectures, tours of the country, and social activities.

For further information, contact: International Postgraduate Training in Medicine, Sackler Faculty of Medicine, Tel Aviv University. P. O. Box 39040, 69978 Tel Aviv;

Tel.: (03) 5459797/5, or 412492, Fax: (03) 410173.

Preparatory Program (Mechina)

The *Mechina* is a special one-year preparatory program designed for foreign students who wish to entroll as undergraduates at an Israeli university. Applicants should be qualified high school graduates and may have studied for no more than one academic year at a university abroad.

Since Hebrew is the language of instruction at the University, one of the main objectives of the *Mechina* is to enable students to comprehend university-level Hebrew and achieve proficiency in writing term papers. To that end, all courses in the Mechina are conducted in Hebrew.

There are two major study areas:

The Sciences

(a) Exact Sciences, including course work in mathematics and physics

(b) Life Sciences, including course work in chemistry and biology as well as mathematics and physics.

Liberal Arts

Course work is geared to admission requirements of the faculties of Humanities, Social Sciences, Fine Arts, Law and Management, and the schools of Education and Social Work. In addition to required courses, students must take electives in preparation for study in the department of their choice.

The academic year in the *Mechina* runs from mid-August to July. Classes are held Sunday through Thursday.

The Tel Aviv University Admission Board considers successful completion of the *Mechina* as equivalent to an Israeli matriculation certificate. *Mechina* graduates must also meet all other regular requirements for admission to the University, including Hebrew proficiency, a passing score on the Psychometric Entrance Test, and any departmental requirements. The *Mechina* does not grant academic credit toward degrees at Tel Aviv University or any other university in Israel or abroad.

In order to provide a deeper knowledge of the country and people of Israel, the Mechina offers field trips, educational tours, seminars and a range of social and cultural activities.

For further information about programs for Overseas students, contact:

In Israel

Tel Aviv University, Overseas Students Program, Dormitories, Building B, 69978 Ramat Aviv, Tel.: (03) 5450639, Fax: (03) 5414559

In the United States

Office of Academic Affairs, American Friends of Tel Aviv University, 360 Lexington Avenue, New York, NY 10017, Tel.: (212) 687-5651, Fax: (212) 687-4085

In Canada

Office of Academic Affairs, Canadian Friends of Tel Aviv University, 3910 Bathurst Street, Suite 205, Downsview, Ontario, M3H 5Z3, Tel.: (416) 398-0845, Fax: (416) 398-2137

Fields of Study in the Universities and Degrees Awarded

The Council for Higher Education grants institutions of higher education in Israel the right to award academic degrees in a wide variety of disciplines. The following table lists the fields of study offered by Israel's universities leading to bachelor's, master's, and doctoral degrees. The table also includes areas of specialization which do not lead to a comprehensive academic degree. For further information, please contact the particular university or the Council for Higher Education.

Fields of Study	*Hebrew Univ.*	*Tel Aviv Univ.*	*Technion*	*Bar-Ilan Univ.*	*Halfa Univ.*	*Ben-Gurion Univ.*	*Weizmann Inst.*	*Open University*
Accounting	BA, PhD	BA		BA	BA	BA		
Administration, Public				BA	BA			
African Studies	BA, MA, PhD							
Agriculture Economics and Management	BSc Agr, MSc Agr, PhD							
Agriculture Sciences	BSc Agr, MSc Agr, PhD							
American Studies	MA, PhD				BA			
Ancient Semitic Languages	BA,MA, PhD				BA, MA			
Animal Sciences	BSc Agr, MSc Agr, PhD							
Applied Science and Technology	MSc, PhD						MSc, PhD	
Arabic Language and Literature	BA, MA, PhD	BA, MA, PhD		BA, MA, PhD	BA, MA			
Archeology	BA, MA, PhD	BA, MA, PhD			BA	BA		
Architecture			B Arch, MSc, DSc					
Architecture-Urban Design			B Arch, MSc, DSc					
Architecture-Urban & Regional Planning			B Arch, MSc,DSc					
Archives Studies	MLS, PhD							
Art History	BA, MA, PhD	BA, MA, PhD			BA			BA
Assyiology	BA, MA, PhD							
Astronomy		MSc, PhD						

Fields of Study	Hebrew Univ.	Tel Aviv Univ.	Technion	Bar-Ilan Univ.	Halfa Univ.	Ben-Gurion Univ.	Weizmann Inst.	Open University
Astrophysics							MSc, PhD	
Atmospheric Sciences	MSc, PhD	MSc, PhD						
Behavioral Sciences			MSc,DSc			BA, MA		
Bible Studies	BA, MA, PhD	BA, MA, PhD		BA, MA, PhD	BA, MA, PhD	BA		
Biochemistry	MSc, PhD	MSc, PhD		BSc,MSc,PhD		MSc,PhD	MSc,PhD	
Biology	BSc,MSc,PhD	BSc, MSc, PhD	BA,MSc, DSc	BSc,MSc,PhD		BSc, MSc, PhD	MSc, PhD	BA
Biophysics		MSc		BSc,MSc,PhD			MSc, PhD	
Biotechnology	MSc, PhD	MSc, PhD	MSc, DSc			MSc	MSc, PhD	
Botany	MSc, PhD	MSc, PhD		BSc,MSc,PhD			MSc, PhD	
Business Administration	BA,MA,PhD	BA,MBA,PhD		BA,MA,PhD	BA	BA		
Chemistry	BA,MSc,PhD	BSc,MSc,PhD	BA,MSc DSc	BSc,MSc,PhD		BSc,MSc,PhD	MSc, PhD	BA
Chemistry of Polymers and Textiles	MSc,PhD						MSc, PhD	
Chemistry, Physical	MSc,PhD	MSc,PhD		BSc,MSc,PhD		BSc,MSc,PhD	MSc, PhD	
Classical Studies	BA,MA, PhD	BA,MA,PhD		BA,MA				
Communication Disorders		BA,MA						
Communications	BA,MA,PhD							
Computer Science	BSc,MSc,PhD	BSc,MSc,PhD	BA,MSc, MSc,DSc	BA,MA,PhD	BA,MA,PhD	BSc,MSc,PhD	MSc,PhD	BA
Criminology	MA,PhD			BA,MA,PhD				
Demography	MA,PhD							
Dentistry	B Med Sc,MSc DMD	DMD						
Engineering, Electrical and Electronics		BSc,MSc,PhD	BSc,MSc			BSc,MSc,PhD		

Fields of Study	Hebrew Univ.	Tel Aviv Univ.	Technion	Bar-Ilan Univ.	Halfa Univ.	Ben-Gurion Univ.	Weizmann Inst.	Open University
Engineering, Environmental		BSc,MSc,PhD	BSc,MSc, DSc,			BSc,MSc,PhD		
Engineering, Food & Biotechnology			MSc,DSc					
Engineering, Geodetical			BSc,MSc DSc					
Engineering, Geodetical			BSc, MSc DSc					
Engineering, Industrial and Management		BSc, MSc, PhD	BSc, MSc, DSc,				BSc, MSc, PhD	
Engineering, Information Systems			BSc					
Engineering, Material			BSc, MSc, DSc,				BSc, MSc, PhD	
Engineering, Mechanical		BSc, MSc, PhD	BSc, MSc DSc,			BSc, MSc, PhD		
Engineering, Mineral			MSc, DSc					
Engineering, Nuclear			MSc, DSc			MSc, PhD		
English Language and literature	BA, MA, PhD	BA, MA, PhD		BA,MA,PhD	BA,MA	BA		
Epidemiology						Msc, PhD		
Earth Sciences	BSc, MSc, PhD						MSc,PhD	
East Asian Studies	BA, MA, PhD							
Ecology (Environmental Biology)	MSc ,PhD			BSc,MSc,PhD			MSc.PhD	
Economics	BA, MA, PhD	BA, MA, PhD	BA,BSc, MSc,DSc	BA,MA,PhD	BA, MSc,PhD	BA, MA		BA
Education	BA, MA, PhD	BA, MA, PhD		BA,MA,PhD	BA, MA,PhD	BA, MA		BA

Field of Study	*Hebrew Univ.*	*Tel Aviv Univ.*	*Technion*	*Bar-Ilan Unlv.*	*Halfa Unlv.*	*Ben-Gurion Univ.*	*Weizmann Inst.*	*Open University*
Education in Technology and Science		BSc, Tech	BSc, MSc, DSc				MSc,PhD	
Egyptology	BA,MA,PhD							
Engineering, Aerospace			BSc, MSc DSc					
Engineering,Agricultural			BSc, MSc DSc					
Engineering, Bio-Medical		MSc, PhD	MSc, DSc			MSc, PhD		
Engineering, Chemical			BSc, MSc DSc			BSc, MSc, PhD		
Engineering, Civil			BSc, MSc DSc					
Engineering, Computer			BSc			BSc, MSc, PhD		
Film & Televisison		BA, BFA						
French Language, Literature & culture	BA,MA,PhD	BA, MA, PhD		BA, MA	BA, MA	BA		
General Studies in Humanities	BA	BA			BA	BA		
General Social Sciences				BA				
Genetics	MSc, PhD	MSc						MSc, PhD
Geochemistry								MSc, PhD
Geodesy & Cartography			BA					
Geography	BA,MA,MSc PhD	BA, MAPhD		BA, MAPhD	BA, MA	BA, MA,		
Geology	MSc, PhD	MSc, PhD				BSc, MSc, PhD	MSc, PhD	BA

Fields of Study	*Hebrew Univ.*	*Tel Aviv Univ.*	*Technion*	*Bar-Ilan Univ.*	*Halfa Univ.*	*Ben-Gurion Univ.*	*Weizmann Inst.*	*Open University*
Geophysics		BSc,MSc,PhD					MSc, PhD	
German Language and Literature	BA,PhD							
Herbew Language and Literature	BA,MA,PhD	BA, MA, PhD		BA,MA,PhD	BA, MA	BA		BA
History	BA,MA,PhD	BA, MA, PhD		BA,MA,PhD	BA,MA,PhD	BA, MA		BA
History of the Jewish People	BA,MA,PhD	BA, MA, PhD		BA,MA,PhD	BA,MA,PhD	BA, MA		BA
History and Philosophy of Science	MA	MA, PhD						
History, Military and Diplomatic		MA,PhD						
Immunology						MSc, PhD	MSc, PhD	
Indian,Iranian and American Studies	BA, PhD							
Information Sustems		MSc, PhD		BA				
Instruction Languages		MA						
Instruction, Music and Musical Education		MA		BA				
Instruction,Science	MSc, PhD	MA	BSc		BSc		MSc, PhD	
Internationall Relations	BA,MA,PhD	BA, MA, PhD		MA, PhD	BA, MA,PhD			BA
Isamic and Middle Eastern Studies	BA,MA,PhD			BA,MA,PhD	BA, MA,PhD			
Italian Language and LITERATURE	BA,MA,PhD							
Jewry,Contemporary	MA,PhD			BA, MA				
Jewish Thought	BA,MA,PhD	BA, MA, PhD		BA,MA,PhD	BA, MA	BA, MA		BA
Labour Sdtudies		MA, PhD						
Land of Isrel Studies				BA, MA	BA			
Law	LLB, LLM LLD	LLB,LLM,JSD		LLB, LLM,PhD	LLB			
Law, Jewish		LLM, JSD		LLM, JSD				
Library, Science	MLS, PhD			BA				
Linguistics	BA,MA,PhD	BA, MA, PhD		BA,MA,PhD		BA		BA

Fields of Study	Hebrew Univ	Tel Aviv Univ.	Technion	Bar-Ilan Unl	Halfa Unlv	Ben-Gurion Univ	Weizmann Inst.	Open University
Linguistics, Semitic	BA,MA,PhD	BA,MA,PhD		BA,MA,PhD	BA,MA			
Literatudre, Genjral & Comparative	BA,MA,PhD	BA,MA,PhD		BA,MA,PhD	BA,MA			BA
Management	BA,MA,PhD	BA,MBA		BA,MA		BA,MSc		BA
Management,Health Systems		MHA,PhD						
Maritime Civilizations					MA			
Mathematics	BSc,MSc,PhD	BSc,MSc,PhD	BA,BSc,	BSc,MSc,PhD	BA,MA,PhD	BA,BSc,MSc,PhD	MSc,PhD	BA
			MSc,DSc					
Medical Scdiences	MSc,PhD		BSc,MSc,			B MedSc,MSc		
			PhD					
Medicine	MD,BMed Sc	MD	MD			MD		
Microbiology	MSc,PhD	MDc,PhD		BSc,MSc,PhD		MSc,PhD	MSc,PhD	
Music	BA Mus	BA,MA,						BA
	MA Mus	BMus<Mus						
Musicology	BA,MA,PhD	BA,MA,PhD		BA,MA,PhD				
Ndeurobiology	MSc,PhD					MSc,PhD	MSc,PhD	
Nuclear Science		MSc					MSc,PhD	
Nutrtional Sciences	BSN	BA,MA				B Nurs		
Occuptional Therapy	BOT	BOT	BOT	BOT				
Oceanography	MSc,PhD							
Operations Research		MSc	MSc,PhD					
Pharmacy	BPharm,							
	MScPharm PhD							

Field of Study	Hebrew Univ	Tel Aviv Univ.	Technion	Bar-Ilan Univ.	Halfa Univ	Ben-Gurion Univ	Weizmann Inst.	Open University
Philosophy	BA,MA,PhD	BA,MA,PhD		BA,MA,PhD	BA,MA	BA,MA		BA
Physics	BSc,MSc, PhD	BSc,MSc, PhD	BA,BSc MSc,DSc	BSc, MSc,PhD		BSc,MSc,PhD	MSc,PhD	BA
Physiology	MSc,PhD	MSc,PhD				MSc,PhD	MSc,PhD	
Physiotherapy		BPT				BPT		
Political Science	BA,MA,PhD	BA,MA,PhD		BA,MA,PhD				BA
Psychology	BA,MA,PhD	BA,MA,PhD		BA,MA,PhD	BA,MA,PhD	MA		BA
Public Health	MPH,PhD							
Public Policy		MA,PhD		MA				
Quality Assurance & Reuability			MSc,DSc					
Religion ,Comparative	BA,MA,PhD							
Rommance Studies	MA,PhD							
Russian & Slavic Studies	BA,MA,PhD							
Social Work	BSW,MSW PhD	BSW,MSW PhD		BSW,MSW PhD	BSW,MSW	BSW		
Sociology & Anthropology	BA,MA,PhD	BA,MA,PhD		BA,MA,PhD	BA,MA,PhD	MA		BA
Soil & Water Sciences	MSc,PhD		MSc,DSc				MSc,PhD	
Spanih & Latin American Studies	BA,MAPhD							
Statistics	BA,MA,MSc PhD	BSc,MSc PhD	MSc,DSc	BA,MA	BA,	BA		BA
Talmud (Jewish Oral Traddition	BA,MA,PhD	BA,MA,PhD		BA,MA,PhD				
Theater Studies	BA,PhD	BA.MA,MFA						

		PhD						
Udraban & Regional Studies	MA							
Veterianry Medicine	DVM,PhD							
Virology						MSc,PhD	MSc,PhD	
Western European Studies	MA							
Yiddish	BA,MA,PhD			BA	BA			
Zoology	MSc,PhD	MSc,PhD		BSc,MSc,PhD			MSc,PhD	

REGIONAL COLLEGES ASSOCIATED WITH UNIVERSITIES

Name and Address	Telephone	Fax
1. The Academic College of Tel Aviv-Yaffo (Tel Aviv University) 4 Rehov Antokolski P. O. BOX 16131, Tel Aviv 61162	972-3-5271272	972-3-5271278
2. Achva College (Ben Gurion University) Mobile Post Shikmim Beer Tuvia 79800	972-8-8588044	972-8- 8501626
3. Ashkelon College (Bar Ilan University) 480 Rehov David Braga P. O. BOX 9071 Ashkelon 78211	972-7-6712881	972-7-6710266
4. Eilat College (Ben Gurion University) of the Negev) P.O. BOX 1301 Eilat 88112	972-7-332446	972-7-334837
5. Jezreil Valley (Haifa University) Mobile Post Jezriel 19300	972-6-6423423	972-6-6423400
6. Jordan Valley College (Bar Ilan University) Tsemach Regional Center Jordan Valley 15132	972-6-6773700	972-6-6773705
7. Menashe College (Tel Aviv University) P.O. BOX 2094, Hadera	972-6-6322720	972-6-6322721
8. Sapir College of the Negev (Ben Gurion University of the Negev) Mobile Post Hof Ashkelon 79165	972-7-6712881	972-7-6710266
9. Tel Chai College (Haifa University and Hebrew University) Mobile Post Upper Galilee 12110	972-6-6943731	972-6-6950697
10. Western Galilee College (Bar Ilan University) Acco-Naharia Road Mobile Post Oshrat 25200	972-4-9811687	972-4-9811694
11. College of Judea and Samaria (Bar Ilan University) P.O. Box 3 Ariel 44837	972-3-9065111 972-3-9365850	972-3- 9365901
12. Žfat College (Bar Ilan University)	972-6-6920045	972-6- 6921068

11 Rehov Jerusalem, P.O. Box 160
Zfat 13206

INSTITUTIONS OF HIGHER EDUCATION THAT ARE NOT UNIVERSITITES

Name and address	Telphone	Fax
1. Bezalel Academy of Arts and Design Mount Scopus P. O. BOX 24046 Jerusalem 91240	972-2-5893313	972-2-5823094
2. The Braude ORT College of Technology P. O. BOX 78 Carmiel 20101	972-4-9901911	972-4-9882016
3. The Center For Optical Study 7 Rehov Yad Harutizim Tel Aviv	972-3-382340	972-3-382642
4. The College of Management Academic Studies - Tel Aviv 9 Rehov Shoshana Parsitz Tel Aviv 61480	972-3-6902020	972-3-6990460
5. Hadassah College 37 Rehov Hanevi'm, Jerusalem 91010	972-2-6291911	972-2- 6250619
6. Jerusalem College of Technology – Machon Lev P.O. Box 16031 Jerusalem 91160	972-2-6751111	972-2- 6422075
7. The Jerusalem Rubin Academy of Music and Dance Givat Ram, Jerusalem 91904	972-2-6759911	972-2-6527713
8. Ruppin Institute of Agriculture, Emek Hefer 40250	972-9-8683072	972-9-8683090
9. Shenkar College of Textile Technology and Fashion 12 Rehov Anna Frank Ramat Gan 52536	972-3-7521133	972-3-7521141

TEACHERS' TRAINING COLLEGES

A. Teachers' Training Colleges which offer B.Ed., and are recognized and/or permitted to operate by the Council for Higher Education (4 Year Programs)

Name and Address	Telephone	Fax
1. The A.D. Gordon College of Education 73 Rehov Tchernichovsky Haifa 35705	972-4-8331194 972-4-8333197	972-4-8332040

2. Beit Beri Teachers College Doar Beit Berl Tzofit, Kfar Saba 44905	972-9-7906333	972-9-7906314
3. Center for Technology Studies – Holon, 52 Rehov Golomb Holon 58102	972-3-5026556	972-3-5026550
4. The David Yellin Teachers College, P.O. Box 3578 Beit Hakerem, Jerusalem 91035	972-2-6513111	972-2-6521548
5. Levinsky Teachers College – Tel Aviv, P.O. Box 48130 Tel Aviv 61480	972-3-6902444	972-3-6993546
6. Michlalah - Jerusalem College for Women, P.O. Box 16078 Bayit Vegan, Jerusalem 91035	972-2-6750911	972-2-6750917
7. Oranim-The School of Education of the Kibbutz Movement Kiryat Tivon 36910	972-4-9838811	972-4-9530488
8. ORT Academic College for Teachers in Technology - Jerusalem Givat Ram, Jerusalem 95435	972-2-6724666	972-2-6520610
9. The Ra'am Lipschitz Religious Teachers College 17 Rehov Hillel, P.O. Box 2308 Jerusalem 91022	972-2-6252157	972-2-6259432
10. State Teachers College - Seminar Hakibbutzim, 149 Derech Namir Ramat Aviv, Tel Aviv 62507	972-3-6902323	972-3-6990269
11. Talpiot College – The State Religious Teachers College, 10 Rehov Hazerem P.O. Box 8376, Tel Aviv 68168	972-3-5128555 972-3-5128512	972-3-5128570
12. The Zinman College of Physical Education at, the Wingate Institute Doar Wingate, Netanya 42902	972-9-8639222	972-9-8650960

B. Teachers' Training Colleges which offer a teaching certificate from the ministry of education (3-year Programs)

Name and Address	Telephone	Fax
1. Achva Regional College Beer Tuvia, Mobile post Shikimim 79800	972-8-5880444	972-8-501626
2. Eilat College – Extension of Levinsky College, POB 1301 Eilat 88000	972-7-332446	972-7-334837
3. Beit Midrash for Teachers of Judaic Studies, Rehov HaGra	972-8-9470887	972-8-9471550

POB 1106, Rehovot		
4. Beit Rivka Religious College for Women, Kfar Habad Bet 72915	972-3-9607667	
5. Beit Yaakov Teacher Training Seminary Kikar Harav Levin, P.O. Box 511 Jerusalem	972-2-5318611 972-2-5386821	972-2-5387840
6. Beit Yaacov Teacher Training Seminary, 57 Rehov Malchei Yisrael P.O. Box 6033, Jerusalem	972-2-5382455	972-2-5383012
7. Beit Yaakov Seminary for Kindergarten and Professional Teachers 4 Rehov Yitzchak Elchanan, P.O. Box 29111 Tel Aviv 61290	972-3-5160267	972-3-5172050
8. Beit Yaakov Seminary for	972-4-8665940	972-4-661528

INSTITUTIONS FOR THE STUDY OF THE ARTS

Name and Address	Telephone	Fax
1. Avni Institute-Tel Aviv 6 Rehov Eilat Yaffo 68118	972-3-6817080 972-3-6820549	972-3-6825805
2. Beit Zvi 2 Rehov Shualei Shimshon, Ramat Gan 52386	972-3-5796739	972-3-6195480
3. Hadassa-WIZO Neri Bloomfield College, of Design 12 Rehov Chana Senesh, POB 4131 Haifa 31448	972-4-8383440	972-4-8378638
4. College of Visual Arts – Beer Sheva, 2 Rehov Simcha Assaf Beer Sheva 84225	972-7-6491960	972-7-6491960
5. Emunah College 104 Derech Beit Lechem, P.O.B 10290 Jerusalem 91102	972-2-6732333	972-2-6711372
6. The Jerusalem School of Film 4 Rehov Yad Harutzim Third floor, POB 10636 Jerusalem 91103	972-2-6731950	972-2-6731949
7. Jezriel Valley (Haifa University), Mobile Post Jezriel 19300	972-6-6423423	972-6-6423400
8. The Nissan Nativ Studio of Acting, 4 Yad Rehov Harutzim Jerusalem 91532	972-2-6733414	972-2- 6721133
9. The Nissan Nativ Studio of Acting, 158 Rehov Herzl	972-3-5182410	972-3-5182411

Tel aviv 68101		
10. The Rimon Jazz and Contemporary Music School, 46 Rehov Shmuel Hanagid Ramat Hasharon 47295	972-3-5408882 972-3-5401012	972-3-5496163

INSTITUTIONS OF HIGHER EDUCATION (MISCELLANEOUS)

Name and Address	Telephone	Fax
1. Hadassah School for Hotel Management, Hadassah College 37 Rehov Hanevi'im, Jerusalem 91010	972-2-6291911	972-2-6250619
2. Tadmor School for Hotel Management, 38 Rehov Basel Herzliya 46660	972-9-9589919	972-9-9574560

Address to Contact in India:
Ambassy of Israel, Aurangzeb Road, New Delhi – 110011, Tel: 301-3238, Fax: 301-4298

Italy

In understanding of the Italian education system, in its true perspective, is essential for anyone who wishes to be associated with it in any way, whether at the undergraduate level or at a post-doctoral research programme level.

Until the passing of Law n. 168 of 1989, the entire Italian education system was under the control of the Ministry of Education. It was only in 1989 that the Ministry of Universities and Scientific Research was created to take over the responsibilities of university education and scientific and technological research.

PRIMARY AND SECONDARY EDUCATION:

Primary: 5 years of schooling beginning at the age of 6.

Secondary: 8 years of schooling divided into two levels.

After the completion of the first three years of the secondary level, known as the lower secondary school eduation, the student is awarded a Middle School Certificate (Diploma di Licenza Della Scuola Media).

In the remaining 5 years of the secondary level, called the upper secondary school education, the student is required to select a particular field like: scientific, linguistic, classical, artistic, technical, vocational or teachers training. After the successful completion of these five years the student is awarded a Higher Secondary Certificate (Diploma di Maturità) in the field chosen by him.

UNIVERSITY EDUCATION

Italian university education is organised on 3 different levels:

(1) The 1st level includes:

(a) Corsi di Diploma Universitario – DU (University Diploma Courses),

(b) Courses run by the Scuole Dirette a Fini Speciali – SDAFS (Schools for Special Purpose).

Both these courses lead to the award of a Diploma Universitario. Their main purpose is to provide students with a type of university education and training which, after only 2 or 3 years may enable them to enter certain professions in the public or private sector.

(2) The 2nd level consists only of eorsi di Laurea – the Italian University studies best known abroad – leading to the award of Diploma di Laurea (DL).

As a rule, the average duration of Laurea is 4-5 years, depending on the course selected except for the Faculty of Medicine and Surgery, which is 6 years, as fixed by law.

Admission requirements for (1) and (2):

(i) Italian 5-years diploma di maturita', or a comparable foreign qualification, (12 years of schooling for Indian nationals);

(ii) Knowledge of Italian language

(3) The 3rd level includes:

(a) Courses run by the Scuole di specializzazione-SS(Specialisation Schools), leading to the award of the Diploma di Specialista (DS) (duration two years);

(b) Programmi di Dottorato di Ricerca-DR (Research Doctorate Porgrammes), resulting in the title of Dottore di Ricerca (duration three years);

(c) Corsi di Perfezionamento-CP (Advanced Courses) (duration varied);

(d) Master's Courses (special studies, normally post-Lauream).

(3) (a) The specific role of Scuole di specializzazione consists in the granting of post-Laurea degrees to Laurea degree holders to specialise further in a chosen discipline. The successful candidates are conferred with the title 'Specialista' (Specialist). Most Scuole di Specializzazione operate in the medical sector, thus offering to young graduates in Medicine and Surgery the opportunity of specialising in such branches as pediatrics, orthopedics, psychiatry, etc.

Admission requirements:

(i) the pre-requisite is the Diploma di Laurea or an equivalent foreign degree. Admission is granted on the basis of merit and is restricted to the number of seats available.

(3) (b) In many respects, the Italian Research Doctorate is similar to other Doctorates throughout the world. Mention should be made, however, of some differences such as: candidates competing for a limited number of seats, selection based on national examinations; etc. The granting of the final title is determined by national examiners' commissions composed of qualified university teachers. The training is full-time and fully subsidised with the allocation of study grants. Existing Research doctorate programmes cover such disciplinary areas as agriculture, architecture, economics, pharmacy, law, engineering, humanities, modern languages, education, biomedicine, medicine and veterinary science, natural sciences, physics, mathematics, political science.

Both Italian and foreign nationals holding foreign academic degrees may participate in a Dottorato di Ricerca entrance examination after their degrees have been recognized as equivalent- or at least evaluated as comparable – to the relevant Italian Laurea.

(3) (c) Advanced Courses (Corsi di Perfezionamento): Primarily designed to meet the need for in-depth academic study of certain specific fields, Corsi di Perfezionamento often offer good opportunities for professional updating or re-training, and for continuing education. They are essentially menat to satisfy local requirements.

Admission: The basic requirement is a Laurea degree in a related field; however, there are also Corsi di Perfezionamento accepting holders of lower or even different qualifications (e.g. a 1st degree like a post-secondary non-university qualification), provided they rank at university level.

(3) (d) Master's courses (a special type of post-Laurea studies): Italian State universities, and legally-recognized private Universities, conduct courses and award qualifications different from those regulated by the national law.

Admission: all Master's Courses are subject to numerus clausus restrictions; applicants must qualify a selective entrance examination, which may vary from one Masters programme to another.

INFORMATION SOURCES

(1) Italian Consulates abroad may be contacted for details on how to obtain:

* Pre-enrolment: Since foreign students residing outside Italy have to deliuer their applications to the relevant Italian Consulates by 15-20 May every year, they had better apply to the Consulates before 15 March to obtain all the necessary information.

No pre-enrolement exists in the case of Corsi *de Perfezionamento* and Master's courses. Enrolment for these types of studies takes place directly at he universities concerned; deadline depends on individual institutions.

* Non-European Union nationals should obtain a study visa from the Italian Consulates in their countries.

* Health Assistance. Non-European Union students must hold health insurance policies, which entitle them to the benefits of the Local Health Units (USL) of the Italian National Health Service.

(2) The General Secretarial Offices (Segreteria Studenti) or the Faculty Secretariats concerned (Segreterie di Facolta'), that is the Faculties conducting certain University diploma courses, schools offering Courses for special purposes or Laurea courses also supply information on nature and contents of 1st-and-2nd-level degree courses.

(3) For the 3rd level or post-Laurea studies, candidates are required to apply to the Secretarial Office of the specific Specialization School (Segreteria della Scuola di Specializzazione in.) or the DR Office (Ufficio Dottorati di Ricerca) of the university concerned. Details on Corsi di perfezionamento and Master's courses are available at the Secretarial Offices of the Faculties or at the Schools holding particular courses.

(4) Individual institutions may be contacted for the following types of information: final enrolment deadlines, initial dates of study courses, subdivision of the academic year; dates and contents of the Italian language exam; application deadlines for grants and scholarships; enrolment fees and other financial contributions; housing, meals, working opportunities.

FOREIGN STUDENTS' ADMISSION TO UNIVERSITY STUDIES

Basic requirements

Foreign students asking for enrolment in Italian universities (or in other institutions of higher education):

(a) If residing aborad, they should contact the relevant Italian Consulates in their countries. Applications must be delivered to the nearest Italian Consulate.

(b) If residing in Italy, they should contact a Segreteria studenti (Student secretarial office) or a Ufficio studenti stranieri (Foreign student office) in a university or other higher education institution.

Foreign students must comply with the following requirements:

* They must possess a qualification equivalent to 12 years of school education which enable them to access to university studies of an academic type in their own countries;
  Students holding a US high school diploma must have completed two years of college education;
* They have to qualify an Italian language exam;
* Non-European Union citizens must obtain a study visa from the closest Italian consulate in their countries;
* Non-European Union citizens must demonstrate econom c support in Italy on the basis of their own financial means or through scholarship grants, etc.
* Non-European Union citizens must hold a certain type of health insurance policy entitling them to the benefits of the Italian halth system services: EU citizens enjoy the same services as in their home countries.

Language requirements

All foreign students are required to qualify an exam in the Italian language. Language examinations is usually held at each university in the first half of September, prior to the beginning of the academic year.

Contents and procedures of the language examination may vary considerably from one institution to the other. It usually includes a written and an oral part.

In addition to the language test, some universities hold an additional test to ascertain the cultural awareness of candidates. Such a test may consist in oral and/or written questions of a general character, mainly on Italian civilization, history and culture, and/or current topics.

Students who have not qualified the language (+ cultural) examination cannot be admitted to university courses; failed candidates will not be allowed to repeat the exam until the following academic year.

Foreign students holding the certificates issued by the Universita' per stranieri di Perugia and the Universita' per stranieri di Siena on completion of courses in Italian language and culture may be exempted from the language exam.

Numero programmato regulations

Numero programmato implies selective evalutation criteria to assess students' performance in entry examinations, if any.

Restrictions may be applied in:

* Newly-established institutions (e.g. Universita' della Calabria, Universita' di Roma "Tor Vergata", Universita' di Roma Tre) to all levels and types of studies;
* Laurea degree courses in: Dentistry; Medicine and Surgery; Veterinary Medicine; International studies; environmental sciences; Communication sciences; Education; Engineering; Psychology; etc.
* Newly established Laurea courses;
* Scuole dirette a fini speciali (Schools for special purposes, first level), corsi di diploma universitario (Diploma courses, first level), scuole di specializzazione (specialization schools, 3rd level), Dottorato di ricerca (Research doctorate, 3rd level).

THE ITALIAN LANGUAGE AND CIVILIZATION FOR FOREIGNERS IN ITALY ITALIAN UNIVERSITIES

At each academic institution, courses in Italian, including both language and literature, are offfered to foreign students mainly at the so-called Centri Linguistici di Ateneo (University Language Centres). Some of these courses are reserved for scholarship holders participating in European Union mobility programmes.

In particular two universities, at Perugia and Siena respectively, are specialised in cultural and language courses for foreigners.

Universitia' per Stranieri di Perugia

The University for Foreigners at Perugia carries on teaching and research activities aiming at promoting the knowledge and diffusion of the Italian language, civilization and way of life. Its faculty of Italian Language and Culture organises, for example:

- In-depth courses of Italian for foreign students
- Advanced courses for teachers of Italian abroad
- Courses for interpreters and translators
- Language courses for admission to Italian universities.

In conformity with its Statute, the University for Foreigners of Perugia may confer certificates, diplomas and specialization diplomas; it cooperates with the Italian Ministry for Foreigners Affairs so as to attain its targets also in an international context.

Universita' per Stranieri di Siena

The University for Foreigners at Siena primarily defines itself as a research centre, mainly in the field of the teaching and learning of Italian as a second language as well as in the diffusion of Italian civilization and cultural traditions.

To achieve its institutional purposes, it runs courses in the Italian language and culture for foreigners; language and cultural courses for foreign students seeking enrollment at Italian universities; it also plans and organises refresher or specialization courses – along with training activities – for teachers of Italian as a second language.

The Institution confers the following qualifications: diplomas – at 1st and 2nd level – of knowledge of both the Italian language and culture; specialization diplomas; certificates of attendance and /or diplomas related to special cultural courses.

Societa' dante alighieri

The Society and its Committees, which promotes Italian language and culture, are active not only abroad, but also in such Italian cities or towns as Bologna, Florence, Milan, Naples, Palermo, Pietrasanta (Lucca), Roma, Siena, Trieste, Urbania (Pesaro-Urbino), Venezia. For other details, contact: Italian Embassy Cultural Centre,
50-E, Chandragupta Marg, Chanakya Puri, New Delhi: - 110021
Tel.: 0091-11-6871901, Fax: 0091-6871902, E.Mail: Italcult @del2.vsnl.net.in

ITALIAN UNIVERSITIES

Universita' degli Studi di ANCONA
Via del Bestione, 3
60121 ANCONA
tel.**39-71-2201

Universita' degli Studi di BARI
Piazza Umberto I, 1
70121 BARI
tel.**39-80-5711111

Politecnico di BARI
Via Celso Ulpiani, 11
70125 BARI
tel.**39/80/5460111

Universita' degli Studi di BERGAMO
Via Salvecchio, 19
24129 BERGAMO
TEL.**39/984/4911

Universita' degli Studi di BOLOGNA
Via Zamboni, 33
40126 BOLOGNA
tel.**39/51/259111

Universita' degli Studi di BRESCIA
Piazza Mercato, 15
25121 BRESCIA

Universita' degli Studi di CAGLIARI
Via Università', 40
09124 CAGLIARI
tel. ** 39/70/6751

Universita' degli Studi di CAMERINO
Via del Bastione, 3

Universita' degli Studi di CATANIA
Piazza dell'Universita', 2
95124 CATANIA
tel.**39/95/325333

Universita' degli Studi "Gebriele d''Annunzio
di CHIETI
Via dei Vestini, 31
66100 CHIETI
tel.**39/871/3551

Universita' degli Studi della CALABRIA
Via Brodolini
87036 ROGES DI RENDE
(COSENZA)
tel. **39//532/2931111

Universita' degli Studi di FERRARA
Via Savonarola, 9
44100 FERRARA
tel. ** 39//532/293111

Universita' degli Studi di FIRENZE
Piazza San Marco, 4
50121 FIRENZE
tel.** 39/55/27571

Universita' degli Studi di GENOVA
Via Balbi, 5
16126 GENOVA
tel.** 39/10/2099221-290

Universita' degli Studi di L'AQUILA

62032 CAMERINO
tel.** 39/737/4011

Universita' degli Studi di MOLISE
Via Mazzini, 8
86100 CAMPOBASSO

Universita' degli Studi di CASSINO
Via G. Marconi, 10
03043 CASSINO
776/2991

Libero Istituto Universitario
Carlo Cattaneo
Corso Matteotti, 22
21053 CASTELLANZA
Tel.** 39/331/5721

Politecnico di MILANO
Piazza Leonardo da Vinci, 32
20133 MILANO
Tel. **39/ 2/72341

Universita' Cattolica del Sacro Cuore
Largo Gemelli, 1
20123 MILANO
Tel. **39/ 2/72341

Universita' Commerciale
Luigi Bocconi
Via Sarfatti, 25
20136 MILANO
Tel. **39/ 2/58361

Instituto Universitario di Lingue
Moderne
Via.Filippo da Liscate, 1.2
20143 MILANO
Tel. **39/ 2/582181

Universita' degli Studi di MODENA
Via Universita', 4
41100 MODENA
Tel. **39/ 59/329111

Universita' degli Studi di NAPOLI
Piazza Vincenzo Rivera, 1
671000 L'AQUILA
Tel.**39/862/431111

Universita' degli Studi di LECCE
Viale Gallipoli, 49
73100 LECCE
Tel. **39/832/336111

Universita' degli Studi di MACERATA tel.**39/
Piazza dell'Universita'
62100 MACERATA
Tel. **39/733/2581

Universita' degli Studi di MESSINA
Piazza Pugliatti
98100 MESSINA
Tel.**39/90/716111-2-3

Universita' degli Studi di MILANO
Via Festa del Perdono, 7
20122 MILANO
Tel.** 39/2/58351

Universita' degli Studi di PADOVA
Via VIII Febbaraio, 2
35122 PADOVA
Tel. **39/ 49/8283111

Universita' degli Studi di PALERMO
Piazza della Marina, 61
90133 PALERMO
Tel. **39/ 91/6075111

Universita' degli Studi di parma
Via Cavestro, 7
43100 PARMA

Tel. **39/ 521/2041

Universita' degli Studi di PAVIA
Strada Nuova, 65
27100 PAVIA
Tel. **39/ 382/5041/504202-3

Universita' degli Studi di PERUGIA
Pizza Universita', 1
06100 PERUGIA
Tel. **39/ 75/5851-42621

"Federico II"
Corso Umberto I
80138 NAPOLI
Tel. **39/ 81/5477111-200-202

Seconda Universita' degli Studi di NAPOLI
Via S. Maria di Constantinopoli, 104
80138 NAPOLI
Tel. **39/ 81/296794

Instituto Universitario Navale
Via Ammiraglio Acton, 38
80133 NAPOLI
Tel. **39/ 81/5475111

Instituto Universitario Orientale
Piazza S. Giovanni Maggiore, 30
80134 NAPOLI
Tel. **39/ 81/7605111
Istituto Universitario Pareggiato di Magistero "Suor O. Benincasa"
Corso Vitorio Emanuele, 292
80135 NAPOLI
Tel. **39/ 81/412908

Universita' degli Studi di ROMA "La Sapienza'
Piazzale Aldo Moro, 5
00185 ROMA
Tel. **39/ 6/49911
Universita' degli Studi di ROMA "Tor Vergata"
Via Orazio Raimondo, 8
00173 ROMA
Tel. **39/ 6/72591

Universita' degli Studi di ROMA Tre
Via Ostiense, 159
00154 ROMA
Tel. **39/ 6/573741
Libera Universita' Internazionale degli Studi Sociali "Guido Carli"
Viale Pola, 12

Universita' degli Studi di PERUGIA
Palazzo Gallenga
Piazza Fortebraccio, 4
06122 PERUGIA

Tel. **39/ 75/57461-5746240

Universita'per stranieri di PISA
Lungarno Pacinotti, 45
56100 PISA
Tel. **39/ 50/920111

Scuola Normale Superiore
Piazza dei Cavalieri, 7
56126 PISA
Tel. **39/ 50/509111

Scuola Superiore di Studi Universitari e di Perfezionamento"S. Anna"
Via G. Carducci, 40
56100 PISA
Tel. **39/ 50/883111

Universita' degli Studi della BASILICATA
Via Nazario Sauro, 85
85100 POTENZA
Tel. **39/ 971/474111

Universita' degli Studi di REGGIO CALABRIA
Via Zecca, 4
89125 REGGIO CALABRIA
Tel. **39/ 965/332202-3331701

Universita' degli Studi di TORINO
Via Verdi, 8
10124 TORINO
Tel. **39/ 11/8182111

Politecnico di TORINO
Corso Duca degli Abruzzi, 24
10129 TORINO
Tel. **39/ 11/5646111-300
Universita' degli Studi di TRENTO
Via Belenzani, 12
38100 TRENTO

00198 ROMA
Tel. **39/ 6/67486410

Libera Universita "Maria SS. Assunta"

Via della Traspontina, 21
00193 ROMA
Tel. **39/ 6/6865945-6864443

Libero Istituto Universitario
"Campus Bio-Medico"
Via Emilio Longoni, 83
00155 ROMA
Tel. **39/ 6/225411

Universita' degli Studi di SALERNO
Via Valle dell'Irno,
84084 FISCIANO
Tel. **39/ 89/961111

Universita' degli Studi di SASSARI
Piazza Universita', 12
07100 SASSARI
Tel. **39/ 79/228811-12

Universita' degli Studi di SIENA
Via Banchi di Sotto, 55
53100 SIENA
Tel. **39/ 577/298206-298000
Universita' degli Studi di SIENA
Via Pantaneto, 45
53100 SIENA
Tel. **39/ 577/240111

Universita' degli Studi di teramo
Viale Crucioli, 122
64100 TERAMO
Tel. **39/ 861/2661

Tel. **39/ 461/881111

Universita' degli Studi di TRIESTE
Piazzale Europa, 1

34127 TRIESTE
Tel. **39/ 40/6767111

Scuola Internazionale Superiore
di Studi Avanzati di TRIESTE
Via Beirut, 2.-4
34014 TRIESTE
Tel. **39/ 40/37871

Universita' degli Studi di UDINE
Via Palladio, 8
33100 UDINE
Tel. **39/ 432/556111

Universita' degli Studi di URBINO
Via Saffi, 2
61029 URBINO
Tel. **39/ 722/3051

Universita' degli Studi
"Ca' Forcari" di VENEZIA
Dorsodura, 3246
30123 VENEZIA
Tel. **39/ 41/2578111
Istituto Universitario
di Architettura di VENEZIA
S.Croce – Tolentini, 191
30135 VENEZIA
Tel. **39/ 41/5297711

Universita' degli Studi di VERONA
Via dell'Artigliere, 8
37129 VERONA
Tel. **39/ 45/8098111
Universita' degli Studi dela Tuscia
Via San Giovanni Decollato
101100 VITERBO
Tel. **39/ 761/3571

Jorden

Public Universities in Jordan University of Jordan, Amman, Jordan, Tel : 962-6-843555, Telex : 21629, Fax : 962-6-832318
Yarmouk University , Irbid, Jordan, Tel : 02/271100, Telex : 51533
Fax : 962-02-274725
Mu'tah University, P.O. Box : 7, Karak, Jordan, Tel : 962-6-617860, Telex : 63003, Fax : 962-03-654061
Jordan University of Science and Technology, Irbid, Jordan , Tel : 962-02-295111
P.O. Box : 3030, Fax : 962-02-295123, Telex : 55545 Just Jo
Amman University College for Applied Engineering, P.O. Box : 15008
Amman, Jordan, Tel : 962-6-892342, 892345, 892348, 984291, Fax : 962-6-894292
Zarka University, Liaison Office, Ministry of Higher Education, P.O. Box 35262
Private Universities in Jordan
Amman, Jordan, Tel : 962-6-842700, Fax : 962-6-843864

Private Universities in Jorden

1. Amman National University, Tel : 835167 – 835166, 836101 – Six Lines
Fax : 835169, P.O. Box : 337 – Jubaiha – Jordan
2. Al – Isra University
Tel : 07-51710 / 51830 / 51581, Fax : 07-51505
P.O. Box : 83 , Um-Elamad, Maadaba : 16197
3. Priccess Sumaya University College to Technology
Tel : 844701 / 9, Fax : 844806, Telex : 21276, P.O. Box 925819
Cable Erramah – Amman
4. Zarka Private University, Tel : 998835, P.O. Box : 3331
5. Irbid National University, Tel : 274733, P.O. Box : 794
6. Jordan Academy of Music (Higher Institute of Music)
P.O. Box : 2497, Tel :606234, Amman – Shmeisani
7. College of Educational Science –United Nations
Tel : 826171 – 7, Tele Fax : 826179, Telex : 21170 Jo
8. Applied Science University, P.O. Box : 11931
Fax : 832899, Tel : 837181
9 Philadelphia University – Private University, P.O. Box : 1101 Sweileh
Tel : 832171, Telfax: 832172
Al – Romman, Amman Jarash Rd. Liaison Office
Tel : 698405, Shmesani Queen Noor St.
10. Jordan University for Women, Tel : 715546- 715549, Fax : 715570
P.O. Box : 961343, Amman – Jordan, K. No. 2308
11. Al-Zaytoonah University, Tel : 688303 – 69483/84, P.O. Box 83739
Fax : 690483

For details contact them directly.Useful address in India :
Embassy of the Hashemite Kingdom of Jordan, 1/21, Shanti Niketan,

Netherlands

If you are considering coming to the Netherlands to study at a university, you should be aware of the following:

- the language of instruction is Dutch;
- there is a restriction on the number of places for many fields of study;
- the starting level is high, comparable with that in other Western European countries;
- study must be completed within a prescribed period of time;
- the degrees, like the structure of study, are different from elsewhere;
- in general no financial aid is given to foreign students by the government or any other body;
- living accommodation is difficult to find.

Besides the universities, there are professional colleges which offer specialised courses in the applied arts and sciences. They award a degree roughly equivalent to the bachelor's. This form of higher education is known as HBO ('hoger be-roepsonderwijs'). Much of the above applies also to the HBO colleges, althought admission requirements are different. Competition is stiff, and not all HBO programmes are open to foreign students. Some do not qualify as grounds for being granted a residence permit.

Further information about HBO can be obtained from:
The Netherlands Council of Higher Professional
Education (HBO –raad), Information Office, P.O. Box 123, 2501 CC The Hague
Tel. (070) 3624951

There is a third form of higher education in the Netherlands, known as International Education. This is primarily designed for people from developing countries.

It should be clear by now that being a foreign student in a regular course of study at a Dutch university means overcoming many problems. For this reason, a separate system of international education was developed in the Netherlands.

The international courses are of short duration (generally not longer than one year) and are conducted in English. (A few are given in Spanish or French.) These highly specialised courses are designed primarily for graduates from developing countries who have already had several years of practical experience on the job, although graduates from industrial countries are also admitted. Some of the courses are at post-secondary level, but most qualify as postgraduate. The many subjects that are dealt with include: social sciences, local government, management, health development, food science, housing planning and building, hydraulic and environmental engineering, electronics, telecommunications, aerospace survey and earth sciences, agricultural sciences, radio and television.

Nationals from developing countries can apply for financial support from the Netherlands Fellowships Programme of Development Cooperation of the Dutch government. Detailed information about these courses can be found in a small book entitled 'Basic data on international courses offered in the Netherlands', which can be obtained from Nuffic or any Dutch embassy. This book also contains information about scholarships and fellowships.

Dutch universities are also offering a growing number of international courses conducted in English. Their duration varies from several months to a full four years. These possibilities too are listed in the book 'Basic data on international courses offered in the Netherlands.'

Language

With very few exceptions, lectures at Dutch universities are given in the Dutch lan guage Foreign students must pass a test in this language before they can be admitted to a regular degree programme. It takes approximately one year of intensive language training before a person reaches the level of mastery required for unversity study.

Information about Dutch language courses and language tests can be obtained from the universities themselves, which should be contacted well in advance of the desired enrollment date.

Because study in most fields requires reading literature in languages other than Dutch, passive knowledge of at least two more languages is also essential. These are, in order of preference, English, German and French. A student is expected to know these extra languages before coming to the Netherlands. There will not be enough time to do so after arrival.

Admission requirements

A person's prior education must meet several requirements if one is to be admitted to a Dutch university. The first is a general requirement, and others are specific to the field of study. The general requirement for admission to a university course of study is possession of a diploma from the pre-university programme of a Dutch secondary school, or its equivalent. This diploma makes a person eligible to attend lectures. Permission to sit examinations, however, may require proven mastery in certain subjects, depending on the field. If this was not obtained to the prescribed level in secondary school, the university will administer qualifying tests in the subjects in question. Because pre-university education differs in different countries, foreign students are often required to sit these qualifying tests. Information about requirements can be obtained from the universities.

The starting level of Dutch university education corresponds to that in the other countries of Western Europe. This is one or two years higher than in most other countries of the world. The Netherlands has no special institutions where foreign students can prepare themselves for university entrance if they do not already have the required level of prior education.

Several years of university study outside the Netherlands can be grounds for exemption from one or more parts of the Dutch university curriculum. But the starting level is high, and in general such exemption is difficult to obtain.

Quotas

Because of a shortage of places, a 'numerus fixus' or quota system has been intro duced that affects many fields of study. It is decided each year which fields will have quota and how many places will be available, both nationally and per university. The very popular courses in medicine, dentistry and veterinary science always have special quotas for foreign students. The number of places available for first-year students is very small. Admission at a later stage is virtually impossible.

Structure and length of study

A full university course in the Netherlands takes at least four years and involves two examinations: the first or preliminary ('propaedeutisch') examination at the end of the first year, and the final ('doctoraal') examination at the end of the fourth year.

Students are allowed two extra years to complete the course. The first examination must be passed by the end of the second year, and the final examination within a total of six years. After this time, one may not be registered as a regular student in any field at any Dutch institution of higher education. Exceptions are made, but not often.

This system can pose extra problems for foreign students. If time is lost as a result of the language, for example, it might become impossible to finish within six years and thus to obtain a degree. A foreign student might also have problems getting a residence permit for more than six years of study.

Of the students who pass the 'doctoraal' examination, only a small portion are offered opportunities to take further, professional courses. These include:

1. Training for the profession of physician (general practitioner), pharmacist, dentist, veterinarian, chartered accountant or business manager;
2. Professional training of teachers for secondary schools and institutions of non-university higher education;
3. Advanced training in research and engineering.

These candidates are selected by committees, and the number of places is limited. To qualify for a research-training position, one must already have a residence permit.

The university faculties of medicine do not train specialists. This training is received through hospital internships under the supervision of senior specialists. Only doctors licensed to practise medicine in the Netherlands are eligible for internships, and even then it is virtually impossible for a foreign national to obtain either a position for specialist training, or the work permit that is also required.

Degrees

A person who passes the 'doctoraal' examination in law generally acquires the title 'meester in de rechten (mr.): the title in engineering or agriculture is 'ingenieur' (ir.): and in all other fields the title 'doctorandus' (drs.) is conferred. Since 1986 all university graduates may also use the more internationally familiar title 'Master' (M), followed by initials representing one's field. In several fields a professional title can be obtained only after further training. The title 'doctor' (dr.) is the highest title conferred by Dutch universities. The Ph.D. degree, unknown within the regular university system, is awarded only by a few Dutch institutes for International Education.

Doctorate

Anyone who passes a 'doctoraal' examination is eligible to proceed to a doctorate. The preparation for this takes at least four years, but usually longer, and consists of independent research conducted under the supervision of a 'promotor', who has to agree to perform this task. A candidate for the doctorate is not a student, i.e. he is not registered at the university and is not eligible for a student grant. Normally he has a university appointment as a research assistant ('assistent in opleiding or AIO'), but he might also be working in a research laboratory, or holding another post while doing research in his own time. The results of the research must be laid down in a dissertation ('proefschrift'), which is defended at a public session of the Council of Deans of a university. The dissertation may be written in Dutch, English, French or German; for all other languages special permission is required. Permission is also needed for defending the dissertation in a language other than Dutch.

Financial Support

A foreign student with no dependents must count on having to spend at least Dfl. 13,500 a year for study and living expenses in the Netherlands. It is impossible to manage on less, and in fact a person without this much money might be denied a residence permit for study. This amount includes the annual fee of Dfl. 1850 for tuition and registration. (These figures apply in 1991/92, and could change.)

It is virtually impossible to obtain financial support from the Dutch government. Grants for regular university study are reserved for Dutch citizens. Exception is made for foreign nationals only if they are already permanent residents of the Netherlands and satisfy several other conditions. There are some types of scholarships available to foreign students for short periods of advanced study. These are granted within the framework of cultural conventions or exchange programmes between the Netherlands and other countries. Application must be made in one's home country. Foreign students with a residence permit for the purpose of studying are prohibited from working. Moreover, it is generally considered impossible to combine study and work.

Living Accommodation

Except for the University of Twente, none of the Dutch universities has a campus. This means that students must find their own living accommodation. Rooms can be rented through special organisations (called 'stichting studentenhuisvesting') connected with the universities. Because they have long waiting lists, these organisations must be contacted well in advance of a student's arrival.

Inquiries

Information about admission procedures, and general information about Dutch university study, can be obtained directly from the universities. There are no differences between the universities in terms of quality, and the diplomas from all of them are valued equally.

Admission Procedure

The academic year starys on 1 September. Prospective foreign students must contact their university of choice well in advance, since they must first obtain written permission to sit university examinations. Without the appropriate Dutch secondary-school diploma or one of the other European diplomas recognised as its equivalent, this permission requires a separate declaration from the university's executive board saying that all requirements have been met. Usually this will mean that the applicant must have passed a Dutch language test, plus tests in prerequisite subjects. General requirements are outlined in the Dutch University Education Act, but specific requirements are set by faculty boards of examiners. This is why only the university can provide full information about admission requirements. And since this whole procedure is time-consuming, it is best to contact the university at least one year in advance.

The document granting permission to sit examinations must reach the Central Student Placement Office ('Centraal Bureau Aanmelding env Plaatsing'- CBAP) of the Dutch Ministry of Education and Science by no later than mid-August of the year in which one wishes to begin. Officially, students apply to study a particular field. The CBAP places them at a university. It is therefore impossible to improve one's chances of acceptance by applying to more than one university.

Residence Permit

Every foreign student needs a residence permit to live in the Netherlands. To be eligible for this permit, one must:

- hold a valid national passport;
- be registered in a full-time course of study;
- have enough money to cover study and living expenses;
- be insured for medical costs;
- have enough money to pay for a ticket home.

Citizens of some countries can apply for and obtain residence permits after they arrive in the Netherlands. These countries are: EC member states, Austria, Canada, Finland, Iceland, Monaco, Norway, Sweden, Switzerland, Liechtenstein, and the United States.

Nationals of all other countries must obtain an authorisation for temporary residence ('machtiging tot voorlopig verblijf'-MVV) before coming to the Netherlands. One must apply for this authorisation to the Dutch embassy or consulate in the country where one is a citizen or legal resident. If all of the conditions listed above are met, a special-purpose residence permit is issued, which reads: '... for study (or training) at...'

No residence permits are granted for the sole purpose of attencing a Dutch language course in the Netherlands. If all other requirements for university admission are met, however, a temporary permit for a meximum of 12 months will be granted for the purpose of language-test preparation.

Universities :

- University of Amsterdam
- Free University Amsterdam
- Delft University of Technology
- University of Twente (Enschede)
- University of Groningen
- Leiden University
- University of Limburg (Maastricht)
- University of Nijmegen
- Erasmus University , Rotterdam
- Tilburg University
- Utrecht University
- Wageningen Agricultural University

Addresses for Information

University van Amsterdam (University of Amsterdam)
Informatiecentrum DSW, Nieuwe Doelenstraat 9, 1012 CP Amsterdam,
tel. (020) 5254310.

Faculties

Theology, law, medicine (and dentistry), mathematics and natural sciences (including computer science), humanities, economics, social sciences, philosophy, geography and prehistory, actuarial science and econometrics.

Language laboratory: Tel. (020) 5254310

Vrije Universiteit, Amsterdam (Free University Amsterdam)
Bureau Studentendecanen, De Boelelaan 1105, 1081 HV Amsterdam,
Tel (020) 5482672.

Faculties:

Theology, law, medicine (and dentistry), mathematics and natural sciences (including computer science), humanities, economics (and econometrics), social sciences, philosophy, geography and prehistory, physical education science.

Language laboratory: tel. (020) 5484968.

Technische Universiteit Delft (Delhi University of Technology)
International Office, P.O. Box 5027, 2600 GA Delft, Tel. (015) 786098.

Faculties:

General sciences (engineering mathematics, computer science), civil engineering, geodetical engineering, architecture, mechanical engineering, electrical engineering, chemical engineering, mining engineering, engineering, physics, marine engineering, aerospeace engineering, metallurgical (and materials) engineering, industrial design.

Language laboratory: tel. (015)784124.

Technische Universiteit Eindhoven (Eindhoven University of Technology)
Bureau Studentendecanen, P.O. Box 513, 5600 MB Eindhoven, Tel. (040)472263.

Faculties:

General sciences (engineering mathematics, computing sciences), industrial engineering, engineering physics, mechanical engineering, electrical engineering, chemical engineering,

architecture, structural engineering and urban planning.
Language laboratory: tel. (040) 472889.

Universiteit Twente (University of Twente) Bureau Studentendecanen, P.O. Box 217, 7500 AE Enschede,Tel. (053) 892035.

Faculties:

Mechanical engineering, electrical engineering (not electrical power systems), chemical engineering, engineering physics, industrial management science, Technology and social science, engineering mathematics, (Dutch) public administration, applied educational science, computer engineering:
Language laboratory: tel (053) 892035.

Rijksuniversiteit Groningen (University of Groningen)
Bureau Studentendecanen, Oude Boteringestraat 69, 9712 GG Groningen, Tel.(050) 638004.
Faculties:

Theology, law, medicine, mathematics and natural sciences (including computer science and pharmacy; physics, chemistry and mathematics also offered as engineering options), humanities, economics, social sciences, philosophy, geography and prehistory, actuarial science and econometrics, management science.
Language laboratory: tel. (050) 635802.

Rijksuniversiteit Leiden (Leiden University Bureau Studentendecanen, Stationsplein 234, 2312 AR Leiden, Tel. (071) 278022.

Faculties:

Theology, law, medicine, mathematics and natural sciences (including computer science), humanities, social sciences (including public administration), philosophy.
Language laboratory: tel. (071) 278022.

Rijksuniversiteit Limburg (University of Limburg)

Bureau Studentendecanaat, P.O. Box 616, 6200 MD Maastricht, Tel. (043) 887354.
Faculties:
Medicine, health sciences, law, economics.
Language laboratory: tel. (043) 257052.

Katholieke Universiteit Nijmegen (University of Nijmegen)

Bureau Studentendecanen, P.O. Box 9102, 6500 HC Nijmegen, Tel. (080) 612226.

Faculties:

Theology, humanities, law, medicine (and dentistry), mathematics, natural sciences, computer science, social sciences, philosophy, policy science.
Language laboratory: tel. (080) 612359.

Erasmus Universiteit Rotterdam (Erasmus University, Rotterdam)
Bureau Buitenlandse Vooropleidingen, P.O. Box 1738, 3000 DR Rotterdam, Tel. (010) 4081786.

Faculties:

Economics (including econometrics and computer science), law, social sciences (including public administration and social history), medicine (including health care policy and management), philosophy, management science.
Language laboratory: tel. (010) 4081786 or (010) 4081206.

Katholieke Universiteit Brabant, (Tilburg University)

Dienst Studentenzaken, P.O. Box 90153, 5000 LE Tilburg, Tel. (013) 662135.

Faculties:

Economics (including econometrics), social sciences (sociology and psychology), law, theology, philosophy, linguistics and literature.

Language laboratory: tel. (013) 662508.
Rijksuniversiteit Utrecht (Utrecht University), Afdeling Studentenzaken, P.O. Box 80125, 3508 TC Utrecht, Tel. (030) 532527.
Faculties:

Theology, law, medicine, mathematics and natural sciences (including computer science, geophysics anddeveloped pharmacy), humanities, veterinary medicine, social sciences, philosophy, geography and pre-history.

Language laboratory: tel. (030) 334114.
Landbouwuniversiteit Wageningen (Wageningen Agricultural University Afdeling Studentenzaken, P.O. Box 9101, 6700 HB Wageningen, Tel. (08370) 83433,
Faculties:

Field crops, tropical crops, horticulture, plant breeding, plant pathology, animal production: food technology , human nutrition, environmental sciences, molecular sciences; forestry, landscape architecture, land and water use, tropical land and water use, agricultural engineering , soils and fertilizers; agriculatural economics, rural sociology, home economics: biology.

Language laboratory: Tel. (08370) 82552.

The Netherlands University Fellowships Porgramme

The Netherlands University Fellowships Programme (UFP) is a new scheme that began in August of the academic year 1996-1997. It is one of three components of the Netherlands Fellowships Programme (NFP). Each year some 200 to 250 fellowships can be awarded within this new scheme.

The Training and Fellowships Desk of Nuffic's Department for Human Resource and Institutional Development (Nuffic/OS/BOB) implements the Netherlands University Fellowships Programme. Nuffic also interacts with the Dutch universities that take part in the fellowships programme or wish to do so.

Objectives

The Netherlands University Fellowships Programme enables people belonging to the target group to take a postgraduate-level course at a Dutch university, and thus to acquire knowledge and experience with which they can help to build up their country's capacity for generating and applying scientific knowledge and skills.

Fellowships are provided for enrolment in courses that have been selected by the Netherlands Ministry of Foreign Affairs as having particular relevance for developing countries.

Target group

The Netherlands University Fellowship Programme is aimed at nationals of developing countries who have recently completed higher education or are studying for a postgraduate degree. To be eligible for a grant from the Netherlands University Fellowship Programme, a student or recent graduate must have a good record of achievement and be strongly motivated. He or she must also be between the ages of 21 and 30, and meet the academic requirements for admission to a Dutch university in one of the courses or study programmes designated by the Netherlands Ministry of Foreign Affairs.

Applicants who are recent graduates must have completed a course of higher education at a recognized institution in a developing country no more than two years prior to the date of application. They must have earned at least a bachelor's degree or its equivalent and be able to provide certified copies of a diploma and/or their academic record.

Student applicants must be studying for a master's degree at a recognized higher educa tion institution in a developing country, after having earned a bachelor's degree or its equivalent at a recognized institution in a developing country. They must be able to provide certified copies of their diploma and/or academic record, as well as an official statement from their current academic supervisor verifying the fact that the course or programme they wish to enrol in the Netherlands is relevant to their current studies and will be recognized as part of them.

PhD students are not eligible for grants from the Netherlands University Fellowships Programme.

Country of Origin

To be eligible for a UFP grant applicants must be from one of the countries listed in appendix 1.

Courses and fields of study

Fellowships are awarded for study in fields of specific importance for developing countries, and only at Dutch universities that have the facilities needed to accommodate foreign students. Each year a list of the eligible courses is drawn up by Netherlands approved by the Netherlands Ministry of Foreign Affairs.

Fellowships

Fellowships are awarded for the duration of the course in question. This is never less than three months and in principle not more than 18 months. Persons who accept a fellowshipmust promise that as soon as the course is finished, they will return to the country they came from. Agreements are made with the host institution to help ensure that UFP fellows do not use their time in the Netherlands for purposes other than the proposed study.

A fellowship is mean as a contribution to the costs of living and studying in the Netherlands. Although UFP allowances will not cover any extras, they are supposed to provide the student with enough money to cover the essential expenses. The amounts of the allowances are fixed by the Netherlands Ministry of Foreign Affairs.

The Application Procedure in Brief

1. Applicants obtain UFP application forms from the nearest Netherlands embassy or consulate or from Nuffic.
2. Applicants duly complete the forms and submit them directly to Nuffic.
3. Nuffic examines applications to make sure that they meet the programme criteria and the conditions set by the Netherlands Ministry of Foreign Affairs.
4. Nuffic sends each application to an appropriate university. The course director of the university institution informs Nuffic whether or not the applicant can be acceptable for participation in the course in question.
5. Application may be submitted at any time throughout the year. Fellowships are awarded three times a year, however. Selections are made in January, April and Sep tember. An attempt is made to distribute the fellowships as evenly as possible over the eligible courses (see the factsheet) and the eligible countries of origin; preference is given to women applicants. Fellowship applications that are rejected only because there were more applications than the budget would allow, or because more students applied than could be admitted, are given preference in a subsequent selection. The same is true for successful applicants who were unable to make use of a fellowship for a reason beyond their control.
6. Nuffic awards fellowships to the selected applicants by means of an official letter, which is sent to the applicant via the nearest Netherlands embassy or consulate. If the applicant's medical examination is favourable, and if the Netherlands Ministry of Justice has cleared the applicant, the embassy or consulate issues the appropriate visa

(Machtiging tot Voorlopig Verblijf) and gives the fellow the airline ticket that Nuffic has arranged.

7. Applicants whose applications are rejected receive written notification directly from Nuffic. Nuffic sends copies to the Dutch Universities and the Dutch Embassies in question.

APPENDIX 1 : COUNTRIES OF ORIGIN

To be eligible for the University Fellowships Programme, an applicant must be a national of one of the following countries:

Afghanistan
Albania
Algeria
Angola
Antigua and Barbuda
Argentina
Armenia
Autonomous Palestinian Territories
Azerbaijan
Bangladesh
Belize
Benin
Bhutan
Bolivia
Bosnia-Hercegovina
Botswana
Brazil
Burkina Faso
Burundi
Cambodia
Cameroon
Cape Verde Islands
Central African Republic
Chad
Chile
China
Colombia
Comoro Islands
Congo Brazzaville
Costa Rica
Cuba
Dem. Rep. Congo
Djibouti
Dominica
Dominican Republic
Ecuador
Mauretania
Mauritius
Mexico
Egypt
El Salvador
Equatorial Guinea
Eritrea
Ethiopia
Eip
Gabon
Gambia
Georgia
Ghana
Grenada
Guatemala
Guinea
Guinea Bissau
Guyana
Halil
Honduras
India
Iran
Iraq[2]
Ivory Coast
Jamaica
Jordan
Kazachstan
Kenya
Kiribati
Kyrgyzstan
Laos
Lebanon
Lesotho
Liberia
Macedonia
Madagascar
Malawi
Malaysia
Maldives
Mali
Sri Lanka
St. Kitts and Nevis
St. Lucia

Moldavia
Mongolia
Morocco
Mozambique
Myanmar (Burma)[1]
Namibia
Nepal
Nicaragua
Niger
Nigeria
North Korea
Pakistan
Panama
Papua New Guinea
Paraguay
Peru
Philippines
Rwanda
Sao Tome & Principe
Senegal
Seychelles
Sierra Leone
Solomon Islands
Somalia
South Africa
St. Vincent and Grenadines
Sudan
Surinam[3]
Swaziland
Syria
Tadjikistan
Tanzania
Thailand
Togo
Tonga
Trinidad and Tobago
Tunisia
Turkey
Turkmenistan
Tuvalu
Uganda
Uruguay
Uzbekistan
Vanuatu
Venezuela
Vietnam
West Samoa
Yemen
Zambia
Zimbabwe

[1] Only for candidates proposed by certain NGOs.

[2] Only for candidates proposed by certain NGOs, and other persons who are active in the struggle for human rights and democracy.

[3] Except in case of candidates proposed by certain NGOs, fellowships for nationals of Surinam are funded from sources related to the treaty between Surinam and the Netherlands.

APPENDIX 2: PERSONAL CRITERIA FOR THE NETHERLANDS UNIVERSITY FELLOWSHIPS PROGRAMME

To be eligible for a fellowship, applicants must meet the following criteria:

1. Applicants must submit a duly completed and signed application form, accompanied by a reference. For students, this is a statement from their own academic supervisor indicating that their application has the support of the student's own institution. For recent graduates, this is a letter of recommendation from the university from which they graduated.
2. Applicants must provide evidence of their academic achievements and motivation.
3. Applicants must be nationals of one of the countries on the currently valid list. (See appendix 1.)
4. At the time of application, applicants either should still be studying at a recognized higher education institution in one of the countries on the list or should have completed studies at such an institution no longer than two years prior to the application data. It should also be sufficiently certain that applicants intend to return to their own country.
5. Applicants should be studying, or have studied, in a field related to that of the proposed course.

6. Applicants should not have any other obligations during the entire period for which the proposed course is scheduled.

7. Applicants must offer evidence that they are sufficiently skilled in speaking and writing the language (this is generally English) in which the course will be taught.

8. At the time of application, applicants should be between the ages of 21 and 30.

9. At the time of application, applicants should not be studying, or a have studied, in a country that is not on the currently valid list (see appendix).

Address Nuffic, P.O. Box 29777, 2502 LT The Hague, The Netherlands

Telephone: +31 (0)70 426 02 60, Telefax: +31 (0) 70 426 03 99, E-mail: ufp@nufficcs.nl http://www.nufficcs.nl

Indian address to contact:

Dept. of Press, Culture, and Education, Royal Netherlands Embassy 6/50 F Shantipath, Chanakyapuri, New Delhi–110021

Tel. 00-11-30884951, Fax: 00-11-6884956, E-mail. Rcc.Aarsse@nde.minbuza.hl

New Zealand

If you are applying from overseas to study as a full-fee student in New Zealand, consult the New Zealand Government office in your country about available courses. Applications should be made direct to educational institutions.

Closing dates for applications to polytechnics and colleges of education are available from prospectuses held at New Zealand Government offices overseas. The application form must also be accompanied by all the documentation requested on the form, for example, certified copies of examination results.

If you are applying for admission to a tertiary institution as a full-fee student and you are already attending a New Zealand School, apply directly to the university, polytechnic, college of education or other institution of your choice.

ONCE YOU HAVE BEEN OFFERED A PLACE

All applicants must accept and offer by the date specified on the notification letter received from an institution. An offer of a place does not necessarily guarantee the issuing of a student visa.

FOREIGN STUDENTS LIVING OVERSEAS

If you are not already in New Zealand and you are applying to enter New Zealand to study, you must complete the requirements for the issue of a student visa. You will be given the required forms by the New Zealand Government office (the visa issuing officer) in your country. Requirements for a student visa will normally include:

(a) *VERY IMPORTANT* - A written offer of a place, which notifies you that have been accepted by an educational institution in New Zealand to study there.

(b) *EITHER*

A receipt for payment of course fees (you not required to produce the receipt before your application has been approved in principle)

OR

Evidence that you are exempt from course fees. For example, a New Zealand Government Scholarship.

(c) A completed and signed 'Application for Students Visa' form, with a passport-size photograph. You will be required to pay a non-refundable student visa application fee.

(d) A guarantee of accommodation – a written assurance from an educational institution or other person that suitable residential accommodation is available to you in New Zealand.

(e) Your passport or certificate of identity, which must be valid for the period of time for which you are applying to study.

(f) Evidence that funds are available for your maintenance throughout your stay. One of the following four is acceptable as evidence:

A completed 'Sponsoring a student' form, in which your sponsor gives a financial undertaking that he or she can transfer to New Zealand NZ$7,000 a year – this amount is considered the minimum for a year's living expenses.

A letter from your educational institution confirming that your living costs have already been paid for as part of your fees.

A bank document showing that funds of the amount required will be available to you in New Zealand ($1000 for each month of your stay for short term study, $7,000 a year for long term study).

An award of a full New Zealand scholarship.

If you intend studying in New Zealand for more than 24 months you will need:

(a) Completed New Zealand Immigration Service medical and chest X-ray certificates.

(b) Character clearances, which must be two original character references (if under 17 years of age), or a local police clearance (if you are 17 or over). You will be advised of the procedure for obtaining these by the New Zealand Government office.

All these documents are essential before a student visa is issued. When the New Zealand Government Office overseas is satisfied that your application is complete and in order you will be issued a student visa.

YOUR DEPENDANTS

Your dependants, who may include a spouse, de facto spouse, fiance(e) and children, may accompany you to New Zealand or may join you later. They must apply for the type of visa required, that is, work or student. For school-aged dependants you will need to pay full fees to enrol them in primary and secondary courses.

WORKING WHILE YOU STUDY

If you are studying in New Zealand, you must not work unless allowed to do so by the New Zealand Immigration Service.

If you have a student permit, you may be granted a work permit or a variation of your student permit to allow you to gain practical experience on completion of a three-year course, or over the summer vacation.

Before a certificate can be awarded for some courses, for example, New Zealand Certificate courses on Advanced Vocational Awards, you must do three year's work experience related to your course work.

The training provider will try to help you find suitable employment. There is some flexibility on how this employment may be obtained. For example, the possibility of suitable work post-education or the possibility of its being done in your home country, under qualified supervision.

If your spouse wishes to work while you are in New Zealand an application must be made through the New Zealand Immigration Service.

No definite assurances can be given on whether an application to work will be successful. This depends on whether there are any unemployed New Zealand residents who can do the job which has been offered.

HEALTH BENEFITS

As a full-fee foreign student you are eligible for health benefits if your course is two or more years long. Medical insurance is strongly recommended for those doing courses taking less than two years.

INCOME SUPPORT

A condition of your student visa is that you will be able to meet the full cost of education, accommodation and living expenses, and income support assistance will NOT be given.

LIST OF NEW ZEALAND UNIVERSITIES

THE UNIVERSITY OF AUCKLAND

Manager, International Student's Office, Private Bag 92019 Auckland New Zealand
Tel: 649 373 7513, Fax: 649 373 7405, E mail international @auckland.ac.nz
Website http://www.auckland.ac.nz

MASSEY UNIVERSITY
Manager, International Student's Office, Private Bag 11222 Palmerston North New Zealand
Tel: 646 350 6148, Fax: 646 350 5698, E mail: B.C Graham@massey ac.nz
Website http://www.massey.ac.nz
LINCOLN UNIVERSITY
Director, International, PO Box 94 Canterbury New Zealand
Tel: 0064 3 325 3826, Fax: 0064 3 325 3879
Email Ormandy@lincoln.ac.az, Website http:/www.lincoln.ac.nz
UNIVERSITY OF OTAGO
Manager, Research and International, PO Box 56 Dunedin New Zealand
Tel: 0064 3 479 8344, Fax: 0064 3 479 8367, Email international @otago.ac.nz
Website http://www.otago.ac.nz
THE UNIVERSITY OF WAIKATO
Manager, International Office, Private Bag 3105 Hamilton New Zealand
Tel: 647 838 4439, Fax: 647 838 4269, Email international@waikato.ac.az
Website http://www.Waikato.ac.nz
VICTORIA UNIVERSITY OF WELLIN
Manager, International Student's Office, Po Box 600 Wellington New Zealand
Tel: 64 4 471 5350, Fax: 64 4 495 5056, Email International – Student's @vuw.ac.nz
Website htt://www.uvw.av.nz
UNIVERSITY OF CANTERBURY
Academic Registrar, Private Bag 4800 Christchurch New Zealand Tel: 0064 3 325 3826, Fax: 0064 3 3654 2999, Email: A.Wildmore@regy.canterbury.ac.az
Website:http://www.canterbury.ac.nz

COMMONWEALTH SCHOLARSHIPS IN NEW ZEALAND

The New Zealand government is offering scholarships to men and women students from other parts of the Commonwealth under the Commonwealth Scholarship and Fellowship Plan.

The scholarships aim at providing opportunities for Commonwealth students normally resident in other countries to pursue advanced courses or undertake research in a New Zealand university. They are intended for persons of high intellectual promise who may be expected to make a significant contribution to life in their own countries on their return from study abroad.

Eligibility

1. Candidates must be Commonwealth citizens or British protected persons resident in countries of the Commonwealth other than New Zealand.
2. Candidates must be graduates of a University or College in their own countries or holders of an equivalent qualification.
3. Applicants for Ph.D. study must have a minimum standard of upper second class honours and applicants for other courses should have a minimum standard of Bachelors degree with at least an average of B; or they should be expected to achieve these results in coming examinations.
4. To be eligible for selection, applicants should have completed a relevant qualification within the last five years preceding the year of application. For those applicants who completed an appropriate qualification.

Tenure of awards

1. Awards for a two-year postgraduate course will be made to cover two academic years and the intervening summer. Awards may also be made for a shorter period for a programme

of study which takes less than two years. Awards for Ph.D. study will be made for three years in the first instance with provision for an extension of up to one further year. The academic year in New Zealand commences at the beginning of March but it may be possible for a research student to commence studies some months earlier if suitable-arrangements can be made.

2. Each award will be made on the understanding that it will be continued for the period of the programme of study or research for which it is granted provided that the scholar's progress and conduct are satisfactory, but no award shall last for more than four years.

Value of awards

The Value of the award has been set so that under normal circumstances the living allowance and other benefits will cover the scholar's expenses of travel living and study during tenure of the scholarship.

The following payments will be made:-

1. Travel to and from New Zealand by the most direct, economical route, as arranged in conjunction with the New Zealand Vice-Chancellors' Committee. (A scholar will be responsible for paying the airfares for spouse or dependants to New Zealand).
2. Approved tuition, laboratory, and examination fees.
3. A personal maintenance allowance at the rate of NZ$950.00 a month from the date of arrival in New Zealand.
4. A refund of actual and reason able expenditure on necessary books up to $450.00 a year subject to the bocus on the list being certified by the scholar's supervisor as necessary for the scholar's course. A scholar may apply, with the support of his or her supervisor, to use part of the grant for the purchase of a calculator.
5. Establishment grant of $575.00
6. Medical and hospital expenses with the exception of the following: (i) hearing aids; (ii) spectacles; (iii) any form of dental treatment.
7. Dependants' allowance for a scholar accompanied by spouse and/or children (provided that the spouse neither holds a scholarship nor is in paid employment). $200 per month for first dependant, $65 per month for second dependant, $40 per month forward dependant, and $30 per month for fourth dependant.

Note 1. The dependant's allowance is provided as a contribution towards the support of a scholar's spouse and family in New Zealand, Immigration authorities will require evidence that a scholar has sufficient financial resources to support his or her spouse and family in New Zealand before entry visas for the spouse and family will be issued.

Note 2. Original documents relating to any qualifications a spouse may have should also be brought to New Zealand.

8. Where a scholar has a spouse to support and the spouse has not been able to earn while in New Zealand, the cost of travel home of the spouse at the most economical rates.
9. Assistance with preparation of thesis of up to $1000.00 for PhD students and $500 for Masters students.
10. The Scholarships Committee, on the recommendation of the Head of Department in which the scholar is working, may make grants in aid of internal travel and held expenses connected with the scholar's programme of up to $550.00 a year.

The allowances named above are not taxed in New Zealand. Values shown for allowances are at 1995 rates.

Placement

Every effort will be made to place selected candidates in the univers ty of their choice, but, if this is not possible an alternative university offering opportunities for the proposed course of study will be chosen.

General conditions of award

1. The scholar MUST return to his or her own country at the end of the scholarship.
2. Unless the scholar receives special permission he or she may not take paid employment during the tenure of his or her scholarship or serve on the staff of his or her country's official representative in New Zealand.
3. The scholar shall follow a full-time course of study approved for him or her and shall abide by the rules of the university in which he or she is placed.
4. Any periods of leave must be approved by the university and in accordance with the purposes of the Commonwealth Scholarship. It is expected that leave will normally be spent in New Zealand, but the university may approve a short period spent overseas.

A student wishing to travel overseas for an extended period would first need to establish medical or compassionate grounds before immigration clearances could be obtained. Expenses for such travel are not included in the scholarship.

5. The scholarships are tenable in New Zealand universities and research will normally be carried out in New Zealand. If appropriate it may be possible for a limited amount of research to be carried out in the scholar's home country. Financing of such an arrangement would be the responsibility of the scholar. Registration and study requirements vary between the universities, but generally only short periods of study off campus are permitted.
6. A New Zealand scholarship under the Commonwealth Scholarship and Fellowship Plan cannot normally be held with any other award.
7. Candidates for scholarships must have a good knowledge of written and spoken English. (The Committee reserves the right to request evidence of having passed an accredited English language test).
8. Applicant are required to be of sound health and awards are subject to successful applicants satisfying a prescribed medical examination.
9. An award may be terminated at any time for unsatisfactory conduct, for a breach of any condition of the award, or for failure to make satisfactory progress.

General information

Further information about New Zealand Universities and courses available may be obtained from:-

(1) the Commonwealth Universities Yearbook, published by The Association of Com monwealth Universities, John Foster House, 36 Gordon Square, London WC1 0PF, Britain. (Each candidate's nominating agency should have copies of the section concerning New Zealand).

(2) by writing to individual universities in New Zealand, at the addresses overleaf.

Applications

1. Applications will not be considered unless they are made through the appropriate agency in the country of a candidate's residence.
2. All applicants for a New Zealand award must submit six copies of the application form provided for the purpose together with six copies of all supporting documents except the birth certificate, of which only one is required.
3. A detailed official academic transcript showing courses taken each year and the grade or mark obtained must be included. A photocopy is not acceptable unless certified by the Registrar as being a true copy.

Address
COMMONWEALH SCHOLARSHIPS AND FELLOWSHIPS COMMITTEE
NEW ZEALAND VICE-CHANCELLORS' COMMITTEE PO BOX 11-915
WELLINGTON, NEW ZEALAND
Ph: (64 4) 801 5091 Fax: (64 4) 801 5089 E-Main: schools@nzvcc.ac.nz
For more details, contact:
New Zealand High Commission, 50-N, Nyaya Marg, Chanakyapuri, New Delhi-110021

Norway

Norwegian Universities, University of Oslo, Office for Foreign Students, Post Box 1081 Blindern, N – 0317 Oslo 3, Norway.
University of Bergen, Foreign Student Adviser, Harald Horfagresgate 4 N – 5014 Bergen, Norway.
University of Tromso, Post Box 635, N – 9001 Tromso, Norway
University of Trondheim, N – 7055 Dragvoll, Trondheim, Norway.
(FOR INFORMATION, KINDLY WRITE TO THEM DIRECTLY)

Immigration

Possibility for immigration to Norway is very limited, restricted to foreign nationals with close family ties to Norway or who are granted work (within certain categories) before entry into the country.

Work permit may be accorded to specialists, skilled workers or persons with special qualifications, when this competence is deemed absolutely necessary for the activity in question, and the post cannot be filled with resident labour.

Before applying for work permit on this ground, you must have a concrete offer of employment from an employer in Norway.

For further details, contact:

Royal Norwegian Embassy, 50 C Shantipath, Chanakyapuri, New Delhi–110021
Tel: 91 11 6873532, 6873138, Telex: 81 82 071 ambn in, Telefax: 91 11 6873814
Cable: Noramb.

Philippines

UNIVERSITIES IN THE PHILIPPINES

1. The Registrar

UNIVERSITY OF THE PHILIPPINES, Diliman, Quezon City, Philippines

2. The Registrar

ATENEO DE MANILA, Loyola Heights, Quezon City, Philippines

3. The Registrar

DE LA SALLE UNIVERSITY, 240 Taft Avenue, Metro Manila, Philippines

4. The Registrar

UNIVERSITY OF STO. TOMAS, Espana, Sampaloc, Metro Manila, Philippines

5. The Registrar

UNIVERSITY OF THE EAST, 2219 Claro M. Recto Avenue, Sampaloc, Metro Manila Philippines

6. The Registrar

FAR EASTERN UNIVERSITY, Nicanor Reyes Sr. Street, Sampaloc, Metro Manila Philippines

7. The Registrar

MANILA CENTRAL UNIVERSITY, EDSA, Caloocan City, Metro Manila, Philippines

8. The Registrar

PHILIPPINE WOMENS UNIVERSITY, Taft Avenue, Malate, Metro Manila, Philippines

9. The Registrar

Adamson University, 900 San Marcelino Street, Metro Manila, Philippines

10. The Registrar

LYCEUM OF THE PHILIPPINES, Muralla Street, Intramuros, Metro Manila,Philippine

For details regarding courses and admission requirement contact them directly:

Contactable Indian address: Embassy of the Philippines, 50 – N, Nyaya Marg, Chanakyapuri, New Delhi – 110021, Tel: 601120, Fax: 6876401

Poland

Poland lies in Central Europe and covers an area of 312, 00 km^2 . The country's borders extend for 3582 km, of which 528 run along the coastline of the Baltic Sea. Poland has borders with seven countries: Russia, Lithuania, Belarus, Ukraine, Slvakia, the Czech Republic and Germany. The longest borders separates it from the Czech Republic (790 km), while the shortest - from Lithuania (103 km). Poland is a lowland country, with some 75% of the area below 200 m above sea level. Of the country's total area 60% is arable land, 28% forests, and almost by 22 national parks. The climate of Poland is moderate, with average annual temperatures ranging from 6 to 8.8 degrees Celsius.

Poland is divided into 49 voivodships (provinces) and 2,468 gminas (communities). The regional administration consists of:

- regular regional organs of the central administration (voivodship offices and district offices embracing several gminas);
- special regional organs of the central administration;
- organs of local governement (gmina offices and local assemblies).

Currently the government is working on a project aimed at introducing a middle rank of regional administration, situated above the gminas: the poviats (counties). Last March a simulation study was completed in order to define competencies, budgets, and start-up costs of the proposed poviats.The capital of Poland is Warsaw, with 1.642 million inhabitants. Other big cities in Poland include: Lódz (831,000), Kraków (746,000) Wroclaw (643,000), Poznan (583,000) Gdansk (464,000), Szczecin (418,000), Bydgoszcz (385,000), Katowice (359,000), Katowice (359,000) and Lublin (352,000).

1. Silesian University, 40-007 Katowice, ul. Bankowa 12, Republic of Poland
   Fax: (48-32) 599605
2. Nicolaus Copernikus University, 87-100 Torun,
   ul. J. Gagarina 11, Republic of Poland
3. Warsaw University, ul. Krakowskie Przedmiescie 26/28, 00-927 Warszawa, Republic of Poland
4. Adam Mickiewicz University, 61-712 Poznan, ul. H. Wieniawskiego 1, Republic of Poland
5. University of Gdansk, ul. J. Bazynskiego 1a, 80-952, Gdansk, Republic of Poland
6. Wyzsza Skola Informatyki I Zarzania im. Jozefa, Tyszkiewcza – 43 – 509, Bielsko-Biala, al. Armi ixi Krajowaj 336, Republic of Poland, tel/fax; (0-33) 145852
7. Skola Glowna Handlowa, 02-554 Warszawa, al. Niepodlelosci 162, Rep. of Poland
   tel. (0-22) 495061
8. Akademia Ekonomiczna w Krakowie, Krakow, ul. Rakowicka 27, Republic of Poland, tel: (0-12) 210568
9. Akademia Eknomiczna im. Karola, Adamieckiego w Katowicah,
   40-287 Katowice, Rep. of Poland, tel: (0-32) 598 421
10. Wyasza Szkola Marketinu i Biznesu, 90-950 Lodz,

ul. pilsudzkiebo 8 x.p. –Rep. Of Poland, tel. (0-42) 368978

11. Wyzsza Szkola Zarzdzania i Bankowosci, 60-854 Poznan,ul. R. Strzalkowskiego 5, Rep. of Poland, tel/fax: (0-61) 47 47 98

Szkota Gtowna Handlowa Warszawa

(Warsaw School of Economics –Warszawa), Al. Niepodleglosci 162, 02-554 Warszawa
Tel.: (48-22)495076, 491251 ext. 202, Fax: (48-22)495312, Tlx: 816031 sgpis pl
Rector: Aleksander Müller, Pro-rector for research: Wojciech Roszkowski
Pro-rector for teaching: Marek Rocki, Pro-rector for teaching staff and international cooperation: Ryszard Gajecki, Professor and Assistant Professors: 175
Lecturers: 647, Teachers total: 824, Staff total: 1500, Number of Polish Students: 8383

University Financed and supervised by Ministry of National Education

The school was established in 1906 after reorganization of three-year commercial education courses into the Higher School of Commerce which in 1921 gained full academic rights. In 1933 its name was changed into the Warsaw School of Economics which in 1949 was renamed into the Central School of Planning and Statistics. From May 14, 1991 the school regained its original name of the Warsaw School of Economics. It is the biggest higher school of economics in Poland. Its many outstanding professors include Oskar Lange, Michat Kalecki and Leszek Balcerowicz. The academy offers graduate studies in business administration, economics, finance and banking, international economics, marketing and public economy. The main fields of the academy's scholarly research and expertise encompass: accounting, agrobusiness, current economic and social surveys, data processing, demography, developing countries, econometrics, economic history, economic systems, feasibility studies, finance, computer systems, international business, international economic relations, labour studies, law, local economy, management, marketing, social policy, statistics, theory of organization, transport systems and tourism. Over the past five years the academy has contributed three applications of original solutions and registered five patent t applications. Members of the faculty have received 20 awards of the Minister of National Education, have organized UNIDO courses and special study programmes for American students. The school has recently opened a Polish – Canadian Management Center and is an active participant in three TEMPUS programs. In the 1991 academic year there were 8,074 students enrolled in the school, 1,023 graduated with the Master of Economic Sciences Degree. The main library collection comprises some 1,800,000 volumes. The school's foreign partners include leading U.S. and European educational institutions.

Towards a cooperation scheme the academy offers marketing services, consulting services, elaboration of technology and completion of research and development projects to foreign orders. It invites foreign investors to join a development project to be located in its attractive real estate in downtown Warsaw.

Fields of Study:

301200 Economics (Commerce and Services)
301200 Economics (Foreign Trade)
301200 Economics (Production)
342600 Business Data Processing and Programming
343600 Banking
343600 Finance (National Economy)
301200 Economics (Transport)
301200 Economics (Human Resources)
340000 Business Administration and Management (National Economy)
342600 Business Data Processing and Programming (Organization)
343600 Finance Banking and Investment
345200 Public Administration

Szkola Glowna Handlowa – Warszawa

Instytut Funkcjonowania Gospodarki Narodowej
(Institute of National Economy*)Al. Niepodlegtosci 162, 02-554 Warszawa
Tel.: (48-22)495374, Fax: (48-22)495312, Tlx: 816031 sgpis pl
Entity: University, Est.: 1972, Head: Jan Szczepanski, Professor
Staff: 60(45), Profile: Education, research, consulting, Bank account: Powszechny Bank Kredytowy SA w Warszawie, VIII O/Warszawa.

The Institute carries out basic and applied research in the field of economic sciences. The main areas of research include the theory of economics, theoretical problems of transforming a centrally controlled economy into market economy, structural transformations of Polish commerce and industry, adaptability of economic entities to changing economic conditions, changing of the financial structure of enterprises, functioning of the public financial system and marketing strategies. The results of the above research work are published in two newsletters of the institute "Materiaty i Prace" (Materials and works) and "Monografie i Opracowania" (Monographs and papers) and also in the form of reports and expertises supplied to the national economic authorities and other economic entities. The institute's staff includes researchers of the Warsaw Scholl of Economics and other economic universities, institutions and scientific centers.

The institute offers marketing services and implementation of research projects to specific orders as well as studies of economic condition of enterprises and consulting services.

Recommendations: Szkota Glowna Handlowa, Warszawa, Poland.
Contact: Mr. Witold Wlodarczyk, (French, Russian), tel.: (48-22)495374,
Szkola Glowna Handlowa – Warszawa, Centrum, Ksztalcenia Obcokrajowcow
(Training Centre for Foreign Students), Al. Niepodleglosci 162, 02-554 Warszawa
Tel.: (48-22)495144, 485061, 491251 ext. 760-1, Fax: (48-22)495312 Tlx: 816031 sgh pl
Entity: University
Head: Bogdan Radomski, Ph.D., Profile: Education, research
Bank account: Powszechny Bank Kredytowy SA w Warszawie, VIII O/Warszawa

The center offers graduate studies and study programmes for foreign students in the fields of economics, political sciences, history of Poland and East-Central Europe, Polish literature, film and fine arts and social sciences; postgraduate studies on implementation of the market economy system in postcommunist countries, social and political transformations in the post-communist East-Central Europe; specialized postgraduate courses in investment feasibility and technology acquisition and special programmes for foreign scholars on post-communist Poland and its political, social and economic problems. All courses are in English, French and German languages for students from the U.S., Canadian and European Universities.

Contact: Mr. Bogdan Radomski,
Tel.: (48-22)495144, 485061, 491251 ext. 760-1, Szkola Glowna Handlowa – Warszawa

Instytut Gospodarki Krajow Rozwijajacych sie, (Research Institute for Developing Economies)
Rakowiecka 24, 02-521 Warszawa, Tel.: (48-22)495192
Fax: (48-22)495312 Tlx: 816031 sgpis pl, Entity: University
Head: Bohdan Jung, Professor, Est.: 1962, Staff: 14(10)
Profile: Education, research, consulting, information
Bank account: Powszechnv Bank Kredvtowv SA w Warszawie, VIII O/Warszawa
The institute is a research and didacting unit focused on the ways of overcoming

economic and social under development. It is engaged in studies, publishing and specialized expert services in the fields of comparative transitions to market economy, applicability of development policies pursued in the newly industrialized countries, international trade, privatization of the public sector, financing of development, international economic assistance, debt management strategies, transnational corporations and direct foreign investments. Its staff received awards of the Rector of the Warsaw School of Economics and of the Minister of National Education.

Future cooperation can include implementation of research projects to orders.

Contact: Mr. Bohdan Jung (English, French), tel.: (48-22)495192

Szkola Glowna Handlowa – Warszawa, Instytut, Gospodarstwa Spolecznego (Institute of Social Economy)

Al. Niepodlegtosci 162, 02-554 Warszawa, Tel.: (48-22)495112, 491251 ext. 411

Entity: University, Head: Irena Kostrowicka, Professor, Est.: 1922

Profile: Education, research

Bank account: Powszechny Bank Kredvtowy SA w Warszawie, VIII O/Warszawa

The institute specializes in social research. Before the Second World War it was involved in the research among unemployed and poor people – blue collars and peasants. At present it carries out scientific investigation of such problems as living conditions and needs of families, unemployment and poverty, the situation of Polish emigrants, industrial conflicts, adaptation of local societies to the consequences of socio-economic transformations in Poland.

The institute offers the benefits of its 70 year long experience in the field of social research.

Contact : Ms. Irena kostrowicka

Tel.: (48-22)495112,491251 ext. 411, Szkola Glowna Handlowa – Warszawa

Instytut Statystyki I Demografii, (Institute of Statistics and Demography)

Al. Niepodlegtosci 162, 02-554 Warszawa

Tel.: (48-22)495397, Fax: (48-22) 495312 Tlx: 816031 sgpis pl, sgpis, Entity: University

Head: Jerzy Holzer, Professor, Est.: 1948, Staff: 31(25)

Profile: Education, research

Bank account: Powszechny Bank Kredvtowy SA w Warszawie, VIII O/Warszawa

The institute offers graduate studies in applies statistics and demography. It also carries out research in the fields of socioeconomics aspects of demographic processes, populaion forecasts, demographic modelling, studies on poverty and income distribution and social indicators of living conditions. The institute organizes courses and workshops in cooperation with UN agencies such as UNFPA for students from developing countries.

It offers a joint venture partnership and implementation of research projects to orders.

Contact: Ms. Janina Jozwiak (English), tel.: (48-22)495397

Leon kozminski Academy of Entrepreneurship and Management

Programme objective

The undergraduate programme lasts four years and is divided into eight semesters. Its 301200 Economics (Production)objective is to teach students practical skills which enable them to run their own company or perform effectively at a middle-management level.

Organisation of classes

Classes take place during the weekdays, Monday to Friday, in the building complex at 59, Jagiellonska Street. They are conducted in a variety of forms: lectures, classes and seminars. Classes start on 1 October 1998.

Admission requirements

An applicant can choose between two paths of admission for full-time studies.

First path

An applicant sends the required documents and the school gives the information regarding acceptance to the programme within 1 month after receiving the documents but not later than 20 September 1998

Your are required to submit:

1. Application form together with the following documents:
High school certificate – original
Résumé (CV), Health certificate, 4 photographs
zerox copy of identity card (pages 2 and 3 – Polish citizens)
military ID (Polish citizens-men)
receipt for entry fee
2 Photocopy of GMAT or GRE score
3. Photocopy of proficiency in English certificate
4. Essay expressing your interest in the programme and your goals.

Second path

Admission for full-time studies is based on the result of:

1. See point 1 above
2. Interview concerning candidate's interests
3. General knowledge Test (GMAT type taken at the school) including a written essay.

Required documents should be submitted at least 10 days before the interview.

Tuition fee

The fee for the first semeser of studies is PLN 2,950.
In the course of the four year programme the fee per one semester will not exceed the PLN equivalent of USD, 1,500.

Terms of payment

50 % of the fee should be paid within 7 days after enrollement.
the second 50% by 15 Decemeber 1998.
An 8% discound is given if an advance payment is made.

Where to get information

Full information about the Academy, the curriculum.
temrs of admission can be obtained at:

Wyzsza Szola Przedsiebiorezosci i Zarzadzania
im. Leona Kozminskiego
ul. Jagiellonska 59, 03-301 Warszawa
tel: (22) 811 30 67
or reception 811 30 61 ext. 12
internet : http://www.wspiz. edu.pl
email: english@wspiz.edu.pl

Information Meetings

All those interested in studying in our school are kindly invited to attend information meetings held on.
3 and 29 April, 7 and 28 May, 9 June, 1998/
Meetings will start at 17:00 at the school premises.

Band Accound Number.
PKO S.A. II O/Warszawa
12401024-21033797-2700-40112-001

School of Polish Language and Culture of the University of Silesia in Katowice invites you to take part in its summer school.

The School of Polish Language and Culture was founded in 1991. The School, open throughout the years, has welcomed hundreds of students from all over the world.

The summer school takes place in August on the campus of the Local Branch of the University of Silesia in Cieszyn – a picturesque old town situated near the border with the Czech Republic at the foot of the Beskidy Mountains.

The summer school lasts for four weeks (28 days).

The syllabus of the course includes:

- Intensive course of Polish language,
- Lectures and seminars 'Knowledge about Poland",
- rich cultural programme,
- trips to picturesque parts of the country, historic sites and architectural monuments.
- Recreatsion.

Classes are held in small goups (5-10 students). The lecturers and teachers live in the same hall of residence and can be consulted by members of the school all day. The summer school offers a friendly and relaxed atmosphere.

Address:

Szkola Jezyka i Kultury Polskiej. Uniwersytet Slaski w Katowicach. Pl. Sejmu Slaskiego 1, 40-032 KATOWICE.

Tel./fax: +48-32/512991, tel.: +48-32/2551260, wew.424.

E-mail: szkola@homer.fil.us.edu.pl.

Program

The summer school program includes:

- Polish language course, • Polish Studies course, • Cultural program, • Excursions,
- Recreation.

Participants receive a Certificate of Attendance stating the level of Polish attained.

School fee

In 1998 the fee is 595 USD, which covres language classes, extra classes, lectures, cultural events, excursions, on-campus recreation, meals and hostel accommodation (double room).

A person attending the school for a second time as well as students in full-time education are given a 10% discount. A person who received a special diploma in the previous year is granted a 50 per cent discount.

Participation

The course is open to anyone over 18 years who has completed secondary education.

To take part in the summer school complete the application form and send it to the School.

Deadline for applications: 30 May 1998.

Following notice of admission from the School, the summer school fee should be paid into the School's bank account and acknowledgement of the payment sent to the School not later than 30, June 1998.

After receiving the acknowledgement the School will send an invitation and further details of the program.

The number of places is limited so the date of application is important. If you wish to apply for all or part of the fee to be waived, please state this on your application form.

We regret that the School is unable to offer any scholarships.

If an application is withdrawn before 10 July, the School will return the School fee deducting 10 per cent. Applicants withdrawing after that date will not be refunded.

Further details can be had from:

Embassy of the Republic of Poland, 50-M Shantipath,
Chanakyapuri, New Delhi – 110021, Tel: (0-09111) 6889211, 4679158,
Fax: 6871914

Spain

Procedures for Applying for Spanish Grants

- First of all, the application forms for these grants are available generally at the Embassy, at the beginning of each year and these applications must be sent to Spain from this Embassy, generally by April. (Dates can be conveyed when collecting the application forms).
- Secondly, there are various grants as follows:

(I) *Pre-graduate grants and professional training*

(II) *Post-graduate grants* for longer periods, 1 year. These include:

(a) Ph.D Thesis (b) Masters (c) Specialization Courses

(d) Investigation (e) Medical Specializations (f) Temporal Stays

The concerned candidate must apply for the reservation of a seat in the periods established by each University and Centre of studies in which they wish to enter, for which they shall contact directly with the institution or organization concerned before hand.

(III) *Art Disciplines*

It will be a requisite to hold a professional activity in accordance to the subject of studies or practical training in the subject that the candidates desire to take and/or to have the appropriate degree in each case.

The concerned must have been accepted by a centre of studies, a cultural centre or an enterprise related to cultural industries to develop a project in Spain.

For applying for scholarships of postgraduates and art disciplines, along with the application form

For the scholarship duely filled, the candidates must send a photocopy of the admission in their respective courses from the Centre of Studies of their choice.

(IV) *Specific Courses* (May change, Information in regard of the Specific Courses will be available only at the beginning of the year). For 1998-99.

General Requisites for the Candidates are as follows:

(*i*) To be a non Spanish resident

(*ii*) Candidates must take care of the necessary validations of their studies in order to take the course of their choice in Spain.

(*iii*) Sufficient knowledge of Spainsh for the courses they intend to take.

(*iv*) To be in good health and free of any contagious disease or tropical illness.

(*v*) For studies which will take longer than 6 months, the candidates must not exceed 40 years of age in the current year.

General Documents that should be enclosed along with the application form are as follows:

(*i*) Application form duly filled in duplicate.

(*ii*) Letter of admission of the Centre of Studies or in its place, letter of the candidate to the centre of studies applying for the admission and making a reservation in the same centre.

(*iii*) Certificate of birth or attested photocopy of the document of identification or whatever other may be in its place.

(*iv*) Biodata

(*v*) Certificate of Studies with specification of the length of the same, the subjects taken and the degrees obtained in the same.

(*vi*) Copy of the University degree or diplomas.

(*vii*) Certificate of the Spanish validation of the studies undertaken abroad or evidence in support of having requested the same.

(*viii*) Supporting certificate of knowledge of Spanish with specification of the degree achieved.

(*ix*) Project of Studies and reasons for applying for the scholarship.

(*x*) Medical certificate to be in good health to take the desired courses and to be free of any contagious and tropical diseases, issued no more than a month prior to the application of scholarship.

(*xi*) Two photographs, names and surnames must be written on the back.

All the papers must be translated into Spanish and must be attested by the Embassy of Spain.

The application forms must be filled in Spanish and the documents accompanying the application form should not be originals (since these documents will not be returned).

LIST OF UNIVERSITIES OF SPAIN

Universidad De Alcala De Henares
Plaza de San Diego s/n, Edificio San Ildefonso, Alcalá de Henares (Madrid)
Tel. (91) 8882220, Telex. 23896

Universidad De Alicanté
Crta. de San Vicente del Raspeig, San Vicente del Raspeig (Alicante)
Tel. (96) 5903474, Telex. 66616, Fax. (96) 5668867

Universidad Autonoma De Barcelona Campus de Bellaterra, Bellaterra (Barcelona)
Tel. (93) 5811101, Telex. 52040, Fax. (93) 5812000

Universidad Autonoma De Madrid
Crta. Colmenar Viejo, Km. 15, 28049 Madrid Tel. (91) 3975000, Telex. 27810, Fax. (91) 3975058

Universidad De Barcelona
Gran Via de les Corts Catalanes, 585, Barcelona Tel. (93) 3182496, 3184266, Telex. 54549, Fax. (93) 3025947, 3170689

Universidad De Cadiz
Ancha, 16, Cádiz, Tel. (956) 223808, 225706, Telex. 76197, Fax. (956) 226809

Universidad De Cantabria
Avda. de los Castros s/n, Santander, Tel. (942) 201222, Telez. 35861 Fax. (942) 201103

Universidad Carlos III De Madrid
C/ Madrid, 126-128, 28903 Getafe (Madrid), Tel. (91) 6249500 Fax. (91) 6249757

Universidad De Castilla-La Mancha
Paloma, 9, 13071 Ciudad Real, Tel. (926) 251754, Telex. 48127 Fax. (926) 221553

Universidad Complutense De Madrid
Ciudad Universitaria s/n, Madrid, Tel. (91) 5490244, Telex. 22459 Fax. (91) 5438643

Universidad De Cordoba
C/ Alfonso XIII, 17, Córdoba, Tel. (957) 218000, Telex. 76561, Fax. (957) 218030

Universidad De La Coruña
C/ Juana de Vaga, 2-6, 15003 La Coruña, Tel. (981) 213344, Fax. (981) 213829

Universidad De Extramadura
Avda. de Elvas s/n, Badajoz

Universidad De Extremadura
Plaza de los Caldereros s/n, Caáceres, Tel. (924) 274800, Fax. (924) 272983

Universidad De Girona
Plaza de Sant Domench s/n, Edifici "Les Aligues", 17004 Girona, Tel. (972) 418011
Fax. (972) 418031

Universidad De Granada
Cuesta del Hospicio s/n, Granada, Tel. (958) 243000, Telex. 78435 Fax. (956) 243066

Universidad De Las Islas Baleares

Son Lledó. Campus Universitari, Crta. de Valldemossa, Km. 7,5, 071071 Palama
Tel. (971) 173000, 173001, Telex. 69121, Fax. (971) 172852

Universidad De Jaume I De Castellon
Campus de Penyeta Roja, 12071 Castellón, Tel. (964) 345680, Fax. 964) 345840

Universidad De La Laguna
C/ Molinos de Agua s/n, La Laguna, Tel. (922) 603000, Telex. 92137 Fax. (922) 259628

Universidad De Leon
Avda. de la Facultad, 25, Tel. (987) 291600, Telex. 89892, Fax. (987) 291514

Universidad De Lleida
Rambla d' Aragó 37, 25003 Lleida, Tel. (973) 702000, Fax. (973) 702062

Universidad De Malaga
Plaza de Ejido, s/n, Málaga, Tel. (952) 131000, Telex. 77173, Fax. (952) 263858

Universidad De Murcia
Avda. Teniente Flomesta, Edificio Convalecencia, Murcia, Tel. (968) 363000 Telex. 67058
Fax. (968) 221569

Universidad De Oviedo
C/ San Francisco 3, Oviedo, Tel. (98) 5103000, Telex. 84322, Fax. (98) 5227126

Universidad Del Pais Vasco
Campus de Leioa, Tel. (94) 4647700, 4648800, 4649600, Telex. 33259 DUCI Fax. (94) 4649550

Universidad De Las Palmas De Gran Canaria
C/ Alfonso XIII, 2, Las Palmas de Gran Canaria, Tel. (928) 451000 Telex. 95238, Fax. (928) 451022

Universidad Politecnica De Cataluña
Avda. Dr. Gregorio Marañón s/n, 08028 Barcelona, Tel. (93) 4016200, Telex. 52821
Fax. (93) 4016201, 4016110

Universidad Politecnica De Madrid
C/ Ramiro de Maeztu, Madrid, Tel. (91) 3366000, Telex. 23780, Fax. (91) 3366173

Universidad Politecnica De Valencia
Camino de Vera s/n, Valencia, Tel. (96) 3877000, 3878000, Telex. 62800 Fax. (96) 3874208

Universidad Pompeu Fabra
Plaza de la Mercé, 12, 08002 Barcelona, Tel. (93) 5422000, Fax. (93) 5422002

Universidad Publica De Navarra
Campus Arrosadia s/n, 31006 Pamplona, Tel. (948) 169000, 169001

Universidad Rovira I Virgili
Plaza Imperial Tarrcao 1, 43005 Tarragona, Fax. (977) 243319, 244256

Universidad De Salamanca
Patio de las Escuelas Menores, 1, Salamanca Tel. (923) 294400, Telex. 26828 Fax. (923) 294502

Universidad De Santiago De Compostela
Plaza de Obradoiro, Santiago de Compostela, La Coruña, Tel. (981) 583800, 588522

Universidad De Sevilla
San Fernando 4, Sevilla, Tel. (95) 4551000, Telex. 72161, Fax. (95) 4212803

Universidad De Valencia
C/ Nave 2, Valencia, Tel. (96) 3864100, Telex. 64298, Fax. (96) 3864117

Universidad De Valladolid
Plaza de Santa Cruz, 8, Palacio de Santa Cruz, 47002 Valladolid, Tel. (983) 423000
Telex. 26357, Fax. (983) 423234

Universidad De Vigo
C/ Oporto, 1, 36201 Vigo (Pontevedra), Tel. (986) 813636, Fax. (986) 813554, 432075

Universidad De Zaragoza

Plaza de San Francisco s/n, 50009 Zaragoza, Tel. (976) 354100 Telex. 58064, Fax. (976) 350558

Universidad Nacional De educacion a Distancia (UNED)

Ciudad Universitaria, Madrid, Tel. (91) 3986090, 3986095, Telex. 45256, 47844

Universidad Internacional Menendez Pelayo

Isaac Peral, 23, 28040 Madrid, Tel. (91) 5495000, Fax. (91) 5430897

Universidad De Navarra

Campus Universitario, 31080 Pamplona, Tel. (948) 252700
Telex. 37017, Fax. (948) 173650

Universidad Pontificia De Comillas

Alberto Aguilera 23, 28015 Madrid

Universidad Pontificia De Comillas

Cantoblanco, 28049 Madrid, Tel. (91) 7343950, 5422800
Telex. 49006, Fax. (91) 5596569, 7344570

Universidad Pontificia De Salamanca

Comapñia 5, Salamanca Tel. (923) 212260 Telex TGMA, Fax. (923) 262456

Universidad Ramonlllull

Comte de Salvatierra 8, entl 1, 08006 Barcelona, Tel. (93) 4154881
Fax. (93) 4158726

Universidad San Pablo (CEU)

Isaac Peral, 58, 28040 Madrid, Tel. (91) 5351998, Fax. (91) 5548496

For admission requirements and other details contact them directly. Other information can be had from Spanish embassy.

Embassy of Spain

12 Prithviraj Road, New Delhi-110011, Tel: 3792085, Fax: 3793375

United Kingdom

Introducing British Education

The British education system is complex, like those of all modern, industrialized countries. It has developed over many hundreds of years to achieve its worldwide reputation for quality. For the international student, the centre of the British system is the qualification structure from the age of sixteen involving A-levels and then degrees.

There are, however, many other educational opportunities in the United Kingdom (UK) which you will read about in this Guide. These opportunities can be divided into a number of different areas:

- English as a Foreign Language or for special purposes;
- British qualifications for training either to do a job or to gain a professional award;
- GCSEs (General Certificate of Secondary Education) and A-levels (Advanced Levels);
- Access courses to assist in getting a place on a degree programme;
- Degrees, both academic and vocational;
- Postgraduate qualifications, including master's degrees and doctorates

All these areas will be explained as you read through the guide, but to give you an introduction to how the system works, let us look at the British degree system.

British Degrees

A degree from a British higher education institution is accepted everywhere, whether it comes from a historic university founded more than five hundred years ago, or a new technology university planning for the twenty-first century.

There are two types of higher education institutions in the UK:

(1) Universities, which have the power to award their own degrees at all levels (first degree and postgraduate, including research and postdoctoral awards)

(2) Colleges or institutes of higher education (also known as university sector colleges), some of which award their own degrees but the majority of which do so through a university.

A degree improves your curriculum vitae (c.v) because it tells potential employers a lot about you.

It tells them you know your subject. In the United Kingdom, standards are carefully monitored. The establishment of a university or university sector college and the award of degree qualifications are carefully restricted by law.

(1) It tells them you have the get-up-and-go to come to the UK for your degree.

(2) It tells them you speak good English—good enough to study at a high level in the language.

Many British degrees are designed to equip you for a profession. Courses which cover media studies, engineering, and business are for students who want to be, or who already are practitioners in the field.

Students from outside the European Union (EU) often make very good use of the chance to study in a EU member country and to see first-hand how that great trading bloc operates. Many British universities and university sector colleges run exchange programmes with European universities, allowing students on some courses to spend up to a year in Europe.

British degrees are respected throughout the world because:

(1) Britain provides information on the quality of its education (international students can obtain summaries from their nearest British Council offices);

(2) British universities and university sector colleges have both a vision of academic excellence and a tradition that goes back over five hundred years.

In recent years Britain has created new universities and expanded existing ones so that more students can be taught. Nearly a third of the British population under twenty-one now goes to a university or university sector college compared with about one in eight a decade ago. The quality of the British degree has been carefully maintained throughout this expansion.

Pathways

During your further education, you can follow three different pathways: academic, vocational and a 'middle' route.

Academic Pathway

Students who choose this pathway want to go to a university or university sector college to do a degree. International students can choose further between a two-year or a one-year programme, depending on academic qualifications from their home country and their level of English.

Vocational Pathway

Students who choose this path are those who wish to develop skills and knowledge in a specific work area and wish to become qualified in that area so that they can go to a job when they finish.

Middle Pathway

Many colleges now offer the international student the opportunity to take a course that is a mix of both knowledge and skills. Students will have an opportunity to have some unpaid work experience as part of the course. This type of course will normally be for two years and will enable the student either to enter a university or university sector college for a degree programme or to enter work.

The defining feature of distance learning is that you do not need to attend the awarding university/institution in person. This style of study is not new. The University of London established its External Programme in 1858 to make its degrees accessible to students who, for one reason or another, could not come to London to study, and since the turn of the century, many professional organizations have offered qualifications by correspondence. In 1966 the Open University was formed and now a growing number of other UK institutions are offering you the chance to study without leaving your home.

Distance learning suits people for many different reasons but is ideal, for instance, if you have family commitments or if your job requires regular travel or irregular working hours. In most cases you have the choice of when to study and how quickly you progress through the programme. Some programmes have minimum and maximum study times (one university allows its undergraduates up to eight years in which to complete their degree). Many business people have obtained professional qualifications while still keeping up a hectic schedule of travel and work.

The support you are given as a distance learning student varies from programme to programme and from institution to institution. The focus is on self-study. In its simplest form, you may receive basic academic guidance through specially written study guides and past examination papers and reports. However, many programmes provide an extensive range of materials including videos, computer disks, audio tapes and annotated texts. Some institutions have introduced programmes of study which can be delivered to your home by internet.

Direct tutor support may not always be available, but, if it is, it may be provided through seminars given by visiting academics and e-mail/fax responses to assignments returned to the home institution, residential summer schools, and/or revision weekends. Some universities and colleges have local partners who provide on-the-spot advice and support. Assessment is also varied, ranging from end-of-year examination to a mixture of examination and assessed course work.

The choice of qualifications is wide, from A-levels to undergraduate diploma and degrees, master's programmes and Ph.D by research. You will find information on all levels of distance learning at UK-wide institutions in a guide called *Distance and Supported Open Learning* UK published by Hobsons Publishing in conjunction with the Open University.

Although studying at a distance is usually cheaper than attending university, it is not an easy option: it demands hard work and dedication. However, those who use this style of learning agree that the results can be well worth the effort. Entry is normally at age eighteen or older. There is no maximum age. Sometimes exceptional students under eighteen are admitted to degree courses. Your qualifications are the key factor. They may enable you to enter a degree course in the second or, occasionally, in the third year.

To start a postgraduate course, you must normally have an acceptable first degree. There are some exceptions in certain subjects for mature students with relevant employment experience.

Degrees from some other countries may not be regarded as equivalent to one from a British university or university sector college. You should check with the institution of your choice or with the British Council in your country.

INDIA/UK: ENTRY POINT EQUIVALENCE

Position in Indian Education System	*UK Entrance Point*
• Holders of the secondary school or matriculation certificate (awarded at Standard X) with 75% and above marks under the Delhi board or 50-60% marks under certain state boards	Begin A-levels
• Higher secondary school certificate holder (awarded after completion of Standard XII) with 75% and above marks under the Delhi board and 50-60% marks under certain state boards (*applicants with lower marks would be expected to do either A-levels or a foundation course before entry into the first year of a degree programme at a British institution)	Entry into first year of bachelor's degree
• Holders of polytechnic diploma	First year of bachelor's degree
• Graduate with bachelor's degree from a central university, institute of national importance or centre of advanced study	Master's degree programmes
• Master's degree	Second master's or MPhil
• Master's degree from a central university, institute of national importance or centre of advanced study	MPhil or Ph.D

STUDYING IN THE UK: HOW DOES THE COST COMPARE? FUTHER EDUCATION

(i.e. non-degree courses of the duration of an academic year or longer offered by further education colleges or equivalent institutions outside of the UK).

The further education figures are average figures for guidance. (The UK figures include GCSEs, A-levels, Scottish Highers, certificate, diploma, GNVQ, GSVQ and other vocational courses.) There are variations in fees between different universities in the same country, and variations in living costs between different cities and regions in the same country. The estimates of average living costs include accommodation, food, books, local travel, clothing, medical insurance (if required) and incidental costs for a single student.

Further education cost per year of study	*Average tuition fees per academic year*	*Average living costs per academic year*	*Average total further edu. costs per academic year*
United Kingdom	3,529	4,350	7,879
USA (private)	6,138	5,793	11,931
USA (public)	2,813	5,793	8,606
Australia	4,149	5,928	10,077
Canada	3,022	4,379	7,401
New Zealand	5,550	4,433	9,983

HIGHER EDUCATION

The undergraduate and postgraduate figures are average for guidance. There are variations in fees between different universities in the same country, and variations in living costs between different cities and regions in the same country. The estimates of average living costs include accommodation, food, books, local travel, clothing, medical insurance (if required) and incidental costs for a single student. An academic year may be eight, nine or ten months

Undergraduate: total cost of first	*Average total tuition fees per undergraduate Course*		*Average total living costs per undergraduate Course*	*Average total costs per undergraduate course*	
	Science	Other[1]		Science	Other[1]
United Kingdom[2] England, Northern Ireland and Wales					
Honours (3 years)	22,266	18,222	13,050	35,316	31,272
Scotland[3]					
Ordinary (3 years)	22,266	18,222	13,050	35,316	31,272
Honours (4 years)	29,688	13,050	17,400	47,088	41,696
USA					
Public (4 years)	22,820	17,400	45,992	45,992	45,992
Private (4 years)	48,412	23,172	71,584	71,584	71,584
Australia					
Ordinary (3 years)	21,042	23,172	38,826	38,826	33,081
Honours (4 years)	28,056	17,784	51,768	51,768	44,108
Canada					
Ordinary (3 years)	10,572,	23,712	23,709	23,709	22,914
Honours (4 years)	14,096	13,137	31,612	31,612	30,552
New Zealand					
Ordinary (3 years)	20,196	17,516	33,495	33,495	27,966
Honours (4 years)	26,928	13,299	44,660	44,660	37,288

[1]*Medicine is not included.*

[2]*In the UK foundation courses of one academic year are offered by universities,further education colleges and independent colleges for undergraduate admission. The average tuition fee for these courses, also known as university access or bridging courses, is £5,206.*

[3]*International students with appropriate qualifications may be eligible for advanced entry, in some subjects, to honours degree courses in Scotland and are advised to check their position with the university of their choice or the British Council.*

POSTGRADUATE: COST PER YEAR OF STUDY

Figures for the total cost of postgraduate degrees are not given because the length of time required to obtain master's and doctorate degrees varies. In the USA, for example, master's degrees normally take two years to complete compared to one or two years in the other countries. Most UK taught master's courses are of only one year's duration.

Postgraduate Cost Per Year of Study	*Average Postgraduate Tution Fees Per Academic Year*			*Average Living Costs Per Year*	*Average Total Postgraduate Costs Per Year of Study*		
	Sci.	Med.	Other		Sci.	Med.	Other
UK	7,622	14,350	6,267	5,800	13,422	20,150	12,067
USA (private)	11,045	15,723	11,045	7,724	18,769	23,447	18,769
USA (public)	5,928	6,338	5,928	7,724	13,652	14,062	13,652
Australia	7,710	9,353	5,930	7,114	14,824	16,467	13,044
Canada	3,389	3,418	3,389	6,568	9,957	9,986	9,957
New Zealand	9,776	8,955	6,251	6,985	16,761	15,940	13,236

The Education Counselling Service, 1996: conversion rates used £1 = $1.5535 US/$1.9467 Australian/$2.1262 Canadian/$2.2557 New Zealand

Applications overview

Application procedures for admission to a course of study in Britain depend on:

- the type of institution
- the level of the course
- the subject of study.

One of the services offered by the Education Counselling Service (ECS) is the provision of a standard application form for study at ECS member institution — these are used for applications to schools and for study at further education and postgraduate level. UCAS forms, used by undergraduates, are also available to ECS offices. ECS staff will advise and help in the processing of applications to all subscriber institutions.

Application can also be made direct to the following institutions on their own application forms:

- independent schools
- English language schools
- private colleges
- further education colleges for vocational or further education courses
- higher education institutions for non-degree English language courses, access courses and most postgraduate courses.

British Council offices will be able to help you to obtain these application forms.

Schools and colleges are always happy to accept applications from international students and you will find that there is much flexibility in the applications procedure.

If you are applying for a first degree course at a British university, or at a college of higher education or college of further education, there is a centralized applications procedure. This is run by the Universities and Colleges Admissions Service (UCAS). You need to complete just one application form on which you make six choices.

Applications for undergraduate courses in social work may go through UCAS or through their own central admission system, Social Work Admissions Service (SWAS).

Applications for pre-registration courses in nursing in England go through the Nursing and Midwifery Admissions Service and in Scotland through the Centralised Applications to Nurse Training Clearing House. Applications for degree courses are made through UCAS. In Wales, applications are made directly to the individual school of nursing.

ADDRESSES

GENERALINFORMATION

The British Council

International Student Services Unit, Bridgewater House, 58 Whit worth Street
Manchester M1 6BB, Tel: + 44161 9577000, Fax: + 44161 9577111

Prime source of information on coming to live and study in Britain. The Council provides an education counselling service from its local offices and organizes local exhibitions and education fairs.

UKCOSA

The Council for International Education
9-17 St Albans Place, London N1 0NX, Tel: + 44171 2263762, Fax: + 44171 2263373

An important source of information on coming to live and study in Britain. produces a series of pamphlets, which are available either directly from UKCOSA or from your local British Council office. You can find further information on UKCOSA under the heading Publications and information sources—general.

GOVERNMENT EDUCATION DEPARTMENTS

Department for Education and Employment

Sanctuary Buildings, Great Smith Street, London SW1P 3BT Tel: + 44171 9255000
Fax: + 44171 256000

Responsible for the education system in England. Gives advice about student matters including course fees and grants.

Department for Education (Northern Ireland)

Rathgeal House, Balloo Road, Bangor, County Down BT19 7PR Tel: + 441247 279279
Fax: + 441247 279100

Responsible for the education system in Northern Ireland. Gives advice about student matters including course fees and grants.

Department of Health

Corporate Affairs, Eileen House, 80-94 Newington Causeway
London SE1 6EF, Tel: + 44171 9722765

Gives information on eligibility for NHS treatment.

The Scottish Office Education and Industry Department

Victoria Quay, Edinburgh EH6 6QQ, Tel: + 44131 5568400, Fax: + 44131 2448240

Responsible for the education system in Scotland. Gives advice on student matters including course fees and grants.

The Welsh Office Education Department

Cathays Park, Cardiff CF1 3NQ, Tel: + 441222 823207, Fax: + 441222 826016

Responsible for the education system in Wales. Gives advice on student matters including course fees and grants.

Home Office

Immigration and Nationality Department, Lunar House, 40 Wellesley Road
Croydon CR9 2BY, Tel: + 44181 6860688

Deals with all immigration and visa matters.

INDEPENDENT SCHOOLS

Boarding Schools Association

Ysgol Nant, Valley Road, Llanfairfechan, Gwynedd LL33 0ES Tel/fax: + 441248 680542

Provides information on the 450 boarding schools that are members of the Association.

Gabbitas Educational Consultants

Carrington House, 126-130 Regents Street, London W1R 6EE, Tel: + 44171 7340161
Fax: + 44171 4371764

Provides individual advice on entry to all stages of the British education system in both the state and the independent sector.

Independent Schools Examinations Board

Jordan House, Christchurch Road, New Milton, Hampshire BH25 6QJ

Tel: +441425 621111, Fax: +441425 620044

Sets the Common Entrance Examination, past papers of which are also available.

Independent Schools Information Service (ISIS) International

56 Buckingham Gate, London SW1E 6AG, Tel: +44171 6308790 Fax: +44171 8288483

The prime source of information on independent schools in the United Kingdom.

Independent Schools Joint Council

Grosvenor Gardens House, 35-37 Grosvenor Gardens, London SW1W 0BS

Tel: +44171 6300144, Fax: +44171 9310036

Umbrella organization for many independent schools. It seeks to maintain and improve academic, pastoral, financial and administrative standards.

Further Education

Association of Colleges, 7-8 Rathbone Place, London W1P 1DE Tel: +44171 6373919, Fax: +44171 6373864

An important source of information on further education in the UK.

British Accreditation Council for Independent Further and Higher Education (BAC)

27 Marylebone Road, London NW1 5JS, Tel: +44171 4874643 Fax: +44181 4864253

Accredits independent colleges of further and higher education.

Conference for Independent Further Education (CIFE)

Buckhall Farm, Bull Lane, Betherden, Nr Ashford, Kent TN26 3HB Tel: +441233 820797

Association of independent further education colleges, which are accredited by BAC.

The Further Education Funding Council for England

Cheylesmore House, Quinton Road, Coventry CV1 2WT, Tel: +441203 863000

Fax: +441203 863100

Funds and assesses the quality of provision of the state further education colleges in England.

HIGHER EDUCATION

Centralised Applications to Nurse Training Clearing House (CATCH)

National Board for Scotland, PO Box 21, Edinburgh EH2 1NT

The centralized admissions service for all pre-registration diploma-level nursing courses in Scotland. Students must apply in writing for an application pack.

Graduate Teacher Training Registry (GTTR)

Fulton House, Jessop Avenue, Cheltenham, Gloucestershire 50 3SH

Tel: +441242 225868, Fax: +441242 263555

Centralized application system for the postgraduate certificate in education.

Higher Education Funding Council for England (HEFCE)

Northavon House, Coldharbour Lane, Bristol BS16 1QD Tel: +441179317317, Fax: +441179317203

Funds universities and institutions of higher education in England and assesses the quality of their research.

Higher Education Funding Council for Wales (HEFCW)

Lambourne House, Cardiff Business Park, Llanishen, Cardiff CF4 5GL

Tel: +441222 761861, Fax: +441222 763163

Funds universities and institutions of higher education in Wales and assesses the quality of their research.

Higher Education Quality Council/QAA

344-354 Gray's Inn Road, London WC1X 8BP, Tel: +44171 8372223 Fax: +44171 2781676

Carries out external audits of the quality of programmes and awards in higher edcuation institutions.

National Union of Students (NUS)
Nelson Mandela House, 461 Holloway Road, London N7 6LJ, Tel: + 44171 2728900
Fax: + 44171 2635713
Gives advice to students in further and higher education. Holders of an NUS card get student discounts on travel services.

Nursing and Midwifery Admissions Service
Fulton House, Jessop Avenue, Cheltenham, Gloucestershire GL50 3SH Tel: + 441242 544949, Fax: + 441242 263555
The centralized admissions service for all pre-registration diploma-level nursing courses in England.

Scottish Higher Education Funding Council (SHEFC)
Donaldson House, 97 Haymarket Terrace, Edinburgh EH12 5HD,
Tel: + 44131 3136500, Fax: + 44131 3136501
Funds universities and institutions of higher education in Scotland and assesses the quality of their research.

Social Work Admissions Service (SWAS)
Fulton House, Jessop Avenue, Cheltenham, Gloucestershire GL50 3SH
Tel: + 441242 225977, Fax: + 441242 263555

Student Affairs Branch
Department for Education and Employment, Sanctuary Buildings, Great Smith Street
London SW1P 3BT, Tel: + 44171 9255000, Fax: + 44171 9256000
Gives advice about student matters including course fees and grants.

Universities and Colleges Admissions Service (UCAS)
Fulton House, Jessop Avenue, Cheltenham, Gloucestershire GL50 3SH
Tel: + 441242 227788 (applications number), Fax: + 441242 221502
UCAS is the body that receives and processes applications for undergraduate admission to all British universities and colleges of higher education.

Welsh National Board for Nursing, Midwifery and Health Visiting
2nd Floor, Golate House, 101 St Mary's Street, Cardiff CF1 1DX
Tel: + 441222 261440, Fax: + 441222 261449
Provides information on all pre-registration diploma-level nursing courses in Wales. Applications are made directly to the individual colleges.

QUALIFICATIONS

Business and Technology Education Council Edexcel Foundation (formerly BTEC)
Central House, Upper Woburn Place, London WC1H 0HH
Tel: + 44171 4138400, Fax: + 44171 3876068
Approves vocational courses in a wide range of business subjects.

National Council for Vocational Qualifications (NCVQ)
222 Euston Road, London NW1 2BZ, Tel: + 44171 3879898, Fax: + 44171 3870978
Sets the framework for NVQs and GNVQs including accreditation and monitoring procedures.

Scottish Qualification Authority
Hanover House, 24 Douglas Street, Glasgow G2 7NG, Tel: + 44141 2487900
Fax: + 44141 2422244
Body responsible for accrediting, awarding and developing vacational qualifications in Scotland.

The UK NARIC
ECCTIS 2000 Ltd, Oriel House, Oriel Road, Cheltenham, Gloucester GL50 1XT
Tel: + 441242 260010, Fax: + 441242 258600
The UK NARIC advises on overseas qualifications accepted by UK educational institutions. All queries should be sent to UK NARIC in writing.

GRANTS AND SCHOLARSHIPS

Charities Aid Foundation
Kings Hill, West Malling, Kent ME19 4TA, Tel: + 441732 520000
Commonwealth Scholarship Commission in the UK
Association of Commonwealth Universities
36 Gordon Square, London WC1H 0PF, Tel: + 44171 3878572 Fax: + 44171 3872655
Offers scholarships and fellowships for study and research throughout the Commonwealth to candidates proposed by Commonwealth governments and universities.
Education Grants Advisory Service/Family Welfare Association
501-503 Kingsland Road, London E8 4AU, Tel: + 44171 2496636, Fax: + 44171 2495443
English Speaking Union of the Commonwealth (ESU)
Dartmouth House, 37 Charles Street, London W1X 8AB, Tel: + 44171 4933328
Administers educational awards for students and teachers. The ESU has offices overseas.
Overseas Research Student Awards Scheme
Committee of Vice-Chancellors and Principals
29 Tavistock Square, London WC1H 9EZ, Tel: + 44171 3879231 Fax: + 44171 3834573
The Committee of Vice-Chancellors and Principals administers this scheme on behalf of the Department for Education and Employment.

ENGLISH LANGUAGE TEACHING

Association of Recognised English Language Services (ARELS)
2 Pontypool Place, Valentine Place, London SE1 8QF, Tel: + 44171 2423136 Fax: + 44171 9289378
Professional body for independent English language teaching institutions, which are recognized by the British Council.
British Association of State English Language Teaching (BASELT)
Francis Close Hall, 1 Swindon Road, Cheltenham GL50 4AZ, Tel: + 441242 227099
Fax: + 441242 227055
Association of state edcuational institutions that teach English language, the courses of which are validated by the British Council.
The British Council Accreditation Unit
Bridgewater House, 58 Whitworth Street, Manchester M1 6BB,
Tel: + 44161 9577097, Fax: + 44161 9577074
The Unit administers the English in Britain Accreditation Scheme. This validates courses run in state colleges and accredits independent English language teaching institutions
FIRST
c/o David Vann, 27 Leeson Road, Bournemouth, Dorset BH7 7AZ Tel/Fax: + 441202 392799
An association of independent English language teaching institutions running a mutual audit scheme in addition to being accredited by the British Council.
The following boards all run English Language Proficiency Examination Courses:
The Associated Examining Board
Stag Hill House, Guildford, Surrey GU2 5XJ, Tel: + 441483 506506
Fax: + 441483 300152:
CITO, PO Box 1203, 6801BE, Arnhem, Netherlands Tel: + 31 263521 480
Administers TOEFL Test of English as a Foreign Language.
Edexcel Foundation London Examinations
Stewart House, 32 Russell Square, London WC1 5DN, Tel: + 44171 3934444 Fax: + 44171 3314022
English Speaking Board (International) Ltd
26A Princes Street, Southport PR8 1EQ, Tel: + 441704 501730 Fax: + 441704 539637

London Chamber of Commerce and Industry Examinations Board
112 Station Road, Sidcup, Kent DA15 7BJ, Tel: + 44181 3020261 Fax: + 44181 3024169
Northern Examinations and Assessment Board
Devas Street, Manchester M15 6EX, Tel: + 44161 9531180, Fax: + 44161 2737572
Oxford—ARELS Examinations
University of Oxford Delegacy of Local Examinations
Ewert House, Ewert Place, Summertown, Oxford OX2 7BZ
Tel: + 441865 554291, Fax: + 441865 510085
Pitman Qualifications
1 Giltspur Street, London EC1A 9DD, Tel: + 44171 2942400, Fax: + 44171 2942403
Trinity College London External Examinations Department
16 Park Crescent, London W1N 4AP, Tel: + 44171 3232328, Fax: + 44171 3235201
The University of Cambridge Local Examinations Syndicate (UCLES)
1 Hills Road, Cambridge CB1 2EU, Tel: + 441223 553311, Fax: + 441223 460278

DISTANCE LEARNING

Association of British Correspondence Colleges
6 Francis Grove, London SW19 4DT, Tel: + 44181 5449559, Fax: + 44181 5407657
Centre of information and advice on correspondence courses.
Open and Distance Learning Quality Council
27 Marylebone Road, London NW1 5JS, Tel: + 44171 9355391Fax: + 44171 9352540
Accreditation body of colleges offering courses in open and distance learning.

INFORMATION ABOUT THE UNITED KINGDOM

The following tourist boards will provide details of the history, geography, accommodation and amenities in their locality:

English Tourist Board
Thames Tower, Blacks Road, London W6 9EL, Tel: + 44181 8469000 Fax: + 44181 5630302
London Tourist Board
26 Grosvenor Gardens, London SW1W 0DU, Tel: + 44171 7303450 Fax: + 44171 8248506
Northern Ireland Tourist Board
St Annés Court, 59 North Street, Belfast BTI 1NB, Tel: + 441232 231221Fax: + 441232 310933
Scottish Tourist Board
23 Ravelston Terrace, Edinburgh EH4 3EU, Tel: + 44131 3322433 Fax: + 44131 3431513
Welsh Tourist Board
Brunel House, 2 Fitzalan Road, Cardiff CF2 1UY, Tel: + 441222 475291Fax: + 441222 475322

BRITISH INSTITUTIONS OF HIGHER STUDIES

* Abacus College Oxford
* Accrington and Rossendale College
* Anglia Polytechnic University
* Aston University
* Bath Spa University College
* Bellerbys College
* Bilston Community College
* Birmingham, The University of
* Blackpool and The Fylde College
* Bosworth Tutorial College
* Bolton Institute
* Bournemouth and Poole College of Further Education
* Brunel University
* Bradford, University of
* Bradford and Ilkley College
* Brighton College of Technology
* Brighton, University of
* Bristol, University of
* Brooklands College
* Buckinghamshire University College
* Canterbury Christ Church College
* Central England, University of

* City College Manchester
* City University, London
* Coventry University
* Davies's College
* Derby, University of
* Durham, University of
* East London, University of
* Essex, University of
* Glamorgan, University of
* Glasgow University of London
* Grantham College
* Heriot-Watt University, Edinburgh
* Huddersfield College
* Hull, The University of
* Kent at Canterbury, University of
* King Alfred's College, Winchester
* Leeds Metropolitan University
* Leeds, Trinity and All Saints University College
* Leicester, University of
* Liverpool Hope University College
* London Business School
* The London Institute
* Luton, University of
* Manchester, The University of
* Middlesex University
* Newcastle College
* North London, University of
* Nottingham, The University of
* Oxford Brookes University
* Peterborough Regional College
* Queen Margaret, Edinburgh
* The Queen's University of Belfast
* The Regency School of English
* The Robert Gordon University, Aberdeen
* Royal Holloway, University of London
* St Mark & St John, The University College of
* Sherborne School International Study Centre
* Solihull College, England
* Southampton, University of
* Staffordshire University
* Sunderland, University of
* The Surrey Institute of Art & Design
* Sussex, University of
* Thames Valley University
* Thanet College
* University of London External
* City of Bath College
* Concord College
* David Game College
* De Montfort University
* Dundee, The University of
* East Anglia, University of
* Edinburgh, The University of
* Falmouth College of Arts
* Glasgow Caledonian University
* Goldsmiths, University of London
* Greenwich, The University of
* Holborn College
* Huddersfield, University of
* Keele University
* Kent Institute of Art & Design (KIAD)
* Lancaster University
* Leeds, The University of
* Lincolnshire and Humberside University of
* Liverpool John Moores University
* London Guildhall University
* London School of Economics
* Manchester Metropolitan University
* Melton Mowbray College
* Nene College of Higher Education, Northampton
* Northumbria at Newcastle, University of
* The Nottingham Trent University
* Paisley, University of
* Portsmouth, University of
* Queen Mary, University of London
* Reading, The University of
* Regents Business School
* Roehampton Institute London
* The Royal Wolverhampton School
* Salford, The University of
* Sheffield, The University of
* SOAS—University of London (School of Oriental and African Studies)
* Southampton Institute
* South Bank University, London
* Stockport College of Further and Higher Education
* Surrey, University of
* Taunton International Study Centre (TISC)
* University College Writtle
* University of Wales College, Newport

Programme
* University of Wales, Aberystwyth
* University of Wales, Swansea
* Westminster, University of
* York, The University of
* University of Wales Institute, Cardiff
* University of Wales, Bangor
* West Herts College
* Wolverhampton, University of

BRITISH IMMIGRATION AND VISA REQUIREMENTS

Information for Students

The British Government welcomes people from overseas who wish to study and train in the United Kingdom.

This leaflet explains:

- The UK Immigration Rules for overseas students
- When an entry clearance is needed
- What is an entry clearance
- Which nationals must have an entry clearance
- How to apply for an entry clearance

This leaflet is only a brief guide. It does not cover all the rules for immigration entry. The law is mostly set out in the Immigration Act 1971 and the Statements of Changes in the UK Immigration Rules. The Rules for entering the UK differ if you are a national of a Member State of the European Union, Iceland, Norway and Liechtenstein or if you can claim British Citizenship or other connection with the UK, for example, by ancestry. Details are available from the nearest British Mission which offers an entry clearance service.

What is an Entry Clearance?

A United Kingdom entry clearance is a visa or an entry certificate which you apply for before you travel to the United Kingdom. Even when you hold an entry clearance you will still need to pass through immigration control at the United Kingdom port of entry, e.g. Heathrow or Gatwick. But if you are holding an entry clearance you will not be refused permission to enter the United Kingdom unless there has been some change in your circumstances or you gave false information or did not disclose important facts when you obtained the entry clearance. Holders of entry clearances may also be refused on medical grounds, if they have a criminal record, if they are subject to a deportation order or if there are other exceptional reasons why they should not be admitted.

When you arrive in the United Kingdom, you may be questioned by an Immigration Officer so take all relevant documents in your hand luggage.

Do I Need An Entry Clearance ?

If you are a national of one of the countries listed for exemption or if you are stateless or hold a non-national travel document or a passport issued by an authority not recognised by the UK you must have a valid UK visa on each occasion you enter the UK. It is not possible to switch from visitor to student status once in the UK. You must therefore have the correct visa before you travel.

Other nationals do not have to have prior entry clearance to study in the UK. However, you will have to satisfy the immigration officer on arrival in the UK that you qualify for entry. If you are in any doubt about your eligibility you are advised to apply for an entry clearance before you travel.

The Rules

You must be able to support and accommodate yourself and any dependants and pay for your studies without working in the UK and without recourse to public funds. It is acceptable for support and accommodation and the cost of your studies to be provided by relatives or friends in the UK.

It is not necessary to have finalized your arrangements but you must intend to study at a university, a college of further education, independent school or other genuine private educational institution.

You must also be able to follow your intended course.

Your course of study should occupy the whole or a substantial part of your time (as a general rule at least 15 hours a week organised day-time study of a single subject or of directly related subjects leading to a particular qualification).

You must intend to leave the UK when your studies are completed.

How to Apply for a Student Entry Clearance

If you wish to apply for an entry clearance you should fill in form IM2A (and related forms if applicable) which you can get free of charge from the nearest British Mission offering an entry clearance service. You should check with the Mission whether or not they are able to process student applications, if they cannot they will advise you where to apply.

Your application form may be submitted by hand or by post together with:

(*i*) Your Passport*

(*ii*) Two recent passport-sized Photographs

(*iii*) The entry clearance fee which is non-refundable

(*iv*) Any relevant diplomas or educational certificates which you hold

(*v*) A letter from the University, College or School confirming your acceptance for the course of study in the UK and a statement of charges for the course

(*vi*) Evidence of Government sponsorship (if appropriate)

In certain countries it may be inadvisable to send your passport through the post.

Fees must be paid in local currency, (i.e., the currency of the country in which the British Mission is located). You should not send cash through the post, but bank drafts, postal or money orders payable to the Mission may be enclosed.

The entry clearance officer may then be able to decide your application without further enquiries. However, you might have to attend an interview. In addition to the documents listed above you may be asked for :

(*i*) Evidence of funds to pay, for your stay and your course of studies in the UK or

(*ii*) A letter from your host or sponsor in the UK to say that s/he will support and accommodate you during your courses of studies, together with evidence that s/he can do so.

You should not buy a tickety or pay all or part of the cost of a course of studies if delay or refusal of your application will result in financial loss. The entry clearance officer may ask you for other documents: production of those listed above does not guarantee that entry clearance will be issued. If in doubt, you can obtain advice from the nearest British Mission.

Customs and Excise

Advice on importing personal effects and goods into the UK may be obtained from:

HM Customs and Excise, Dorset House, Stamford Street, London Sei 9 PY

Immigration Advisory Service (IAS)

The IAS is an independent charity which gives free and confidential advice, assistance and representation to persons who are applying for an entry clearance for the UK. Their address is:

County House, 190 Great Dover Street, London Sei 4YB, Telephone : 44 171 357 6917

Duty Office : 24 hrs: 44 181 814 1559, Fax : 44 171 378 0665

Health Insurance

Before you travel, please check that you have adequate health insurance cover. Medical treatment in the UK can be expensive and visitors are not covered by the United Kingdom's national health insurance scheme (unless they are covered by a reciprocal health care agreement).

United Kingdom Visa Fees

1. From 09.12.1997, entry visa applications in the following categories attract the following charges:

Single Entry Clearance for Tourism or Business

	Rs. 2300
Single Entry Clearance for Studies	Rs. 2300
Multiple Entry Clearance for Six Months	Rs. 3150
Multiple Entry Clearance for upto Two Years Validity	
	Rs. 4550
Multiple Entry Clearance for upto Five Years Validity at the Discretion of the Visa Officer	Rs. 5600
Applications for Settlement or Marriage	Rs. 16800
Other Long-Term Entry Clearance	Rs. 3500
Direct Airside Transit	Rs. 1750

2. All fees are payable in advance and will be non-refundable (unless the application is withdrawn in writing before interview)
3. The above charges will apply to each applicant seeking a visa for the United Kingdom.
4. If an application is made during *personal attendance at this office* cash will be accepted. Otherwise, fees should be paid by bank draft *only.* Please do not send cash by postand should be forwarded with the visa application form.
5. MICR Bank drafts should be made payable to "The Office of the British Deputy/High Commissioner, Bombay" and be in the form of a demand draft negotiable at a Bombay branch of the bank concerned.
6. Notes in denominations of Rs. 500, Rs. 100 and balance in Rs. 50 only will be accepted, and the cashier has instructions to accept only new bank notes. If your fees come to over Rs. 10,000, then payment should be made by bank draft. In exceptional circumstances cash will be accepted as long as the bulk of the payment is made in Rs. 500 notes.
7. We regret that for operational reasons change cannot be given.

United Kingdom Visas

The office of the British Deputy High Commission, Mumbai, would like to advise travellers to the United Kingdom of Great Britain of the following policy changes:

* All visa applications, including children must be in possession of a separate valid national passport;
* The British Deputy High Commission will no longer affix visas to additional pages of Indian passports;
* These rules will apply with immediate effect;
* All visa applicants must ensure that their passports have at least one blank page in which to place a visa before making an application.

THE BRITISH COUNCIL EDUCATION COUNSELLING SERVICE

Introduction

With an increasing number of Indians choosing to study in Britain, it is important that prospective students have access to comprehensive information about courses, institutions, and the associated facilities and costs.

The Education Counselling Service (ECS) run by the British Council, was established to meet this need and has helped several students who have gone to Britain for higher studies.

Prospectuses

At the ECS students find an extensive range of information materials from British educational institutions; these highlight the subjects and level of courses at the respective institutions as well as providing information on welfare and accommodation facilities. There is also a collection of institutional videos, which offer a visual perspective of student life on the various campuses.

Multi Media

There are a number of multi media CD RoMs like PUSH CD, Which University, Which school, etc: giving the students a lot of information on the institutions.

Reference Materials

In order to help students find their way around the various institutions, there are also reference books which describe the recognised educational institutions in Britain and the courses they offer, providing summaries of entry criteria and duration of course. Other books provide subject guides to enable students to understand more about the nature of the various subject disciplines.

Information Sheets

In addition, the British Council has produced a large amount of supplementary material in the form of subject Information Sheets. There are also handouts on the various aspects of study in Britain.

Counselling

While students are free to come in and browse through the materials at leisure, counsellors are available to guide them through the process.

Assistance with Applications

The ECS offers to self-funding students an application package consisting of the standard British Council application form, help in processing it, visa screening and pre-departure briefing.

Presentations and Exhibitions

A group briefing for students is held every Saturday from 10.30 am to 11.30 am. This includes a video, a talk and a question-answer session. The ECS also administers visits by British University representatives who give lectures and counselling.

The ECS organises education fairs and exhibitions. University representatives are available during these fairs and students can get information on the various courses directly from them.

For Further details please contact

New Delhi

British Council Division, British High Commission, 17, Kasturba Gandhi Marg, New Delhi - 110001, Tel. : 011 3711401, 3710555 (Ext. 115), Fax : 91-11-3710717

Hyderabad

The British Library, Sarovar Centre, 5-9-22, Secretariat Road, Hyderabad - 500004
Tel. : 040 210267 Fax : 040 598273

Bangalore, The British Library, 39, St. Mark's Road, Bangalore - 560001, Tel. : 080 2240763
Fax : 2240767

Chennai

British Council Division, British Deputy High Commission, 737, Anna Salai
Chennai - 600002, Tel.: 044 8525002, 8525432, Fax : 91-44-8523234

United States of America

The story of American education reflects a unique attempt to explore human individuality as a means to the goals of freedom and democracy. This emphasis on human individuality has led to the creation of diverse institutions of postsecondary education that accommodate the many different needs and values of the American population.

There are over 3200 accredited colleges and universities in the United States. Of these, 1100 offer master's degree programs and 430 offer doctorate programs. Some of them are private and others are state universities. Both private and public universities receive varying amounts of funds from government sources. In spite of this, both types of institutions are completely autonomous. Thus, while the government may contribute financially to a university it has no control over its substance and practice. There is no ministry of education in the United States. Bureaucratic interference in intellectual matters or freedom are resisted and fought fiercely. The faculty of the college or university decide who shall be taught and how and who shall have the right to teach. Their primary concern is improving quality and enhancing their eligibility to complete successfully with other institutions for the best students, the best faculty and research funds.

The American educational philosophy believes in non discrimination and in comprehensive curricula. The curricula range is far beyond the classical subjects to technical fields. The practical is as important as the theoretical in the Sciences, where laboratory requirements are extensive. People are admitted to institutions of higher learning irrespective of their age, sex, race, religion, or national background. As a result of diverse features in institutions there is no one "best" university. Each university has its own strengths and must be rated according to the academic needs of individual students.

The United States does not publish any official list of best universities. Several privately compiled "best" lists have been created based on such factors as research funds or the opinions of professionals in a given field. Copies of some privately compiled lists are available at the USEFI reference library. Privately compiled lists vary considerably in their conclusions, which is not surprising given that over 3,200 institutionally accredited US universities and colleges currently operate, each with its own goals and strength. We, therefore do not recommend selection of universities based only on ranking lists published by private agencies. It is, however, important to ensure that universities are institutionally accredited.

The Application Process

The Application process takes about 12-15 months. Selection of universities will occur at various points in the application process.

Pre-Application Stage

The first stage occurs at the beginning of the process when you are selecting universities for the purpose of sending pre-applications. Remember that you do not have to wait for your test scores to initiate contact with the universities. Generally, students select 25 to 40 universities by looking at:

1. Program offerings (MA, MS, MPhil, MFA, PhD, DA, etc.);
2. Specializations/faculty research interests/thrust of the program;
3. Program length (1 or more years);

4. Cost (tuition, fees, living expenses);
5. Availability of financial assistance and policies on assistance to international students;
6. Entrance requirements (bachelor's degree in same field, standardized tests, previous work/research experience);
7. Tests required and average scores (e.g. minimum TOEFL score, minimum GRE/GMAT score);
8. Accreditation status (professional accreditation for some programs);
9. Entrance difficulty - ratio of number of applicants and per cent accepted;
10. Student profile - Number of full-time students, number of international students, percentage of students with work background, etc.

By this point of time, you should have a relatively long list of schools (may be 50) that seem to meet your criteria. At this juncture, go back and prioritize your criteria. Your priorities could be for example :

1. Specific topic of research;
2. Financial assistance;
3. Low cost if financial assistance is not available;
4. Do not want to give subject GRE; not well prepared;
5. University should be preferably in and around a certain state.

Make a similar list of your preferences or priorities and use a worksheet to identify the 30 schools that meet your priorities/preferences the best. Once each applicant has his/her own preferences, shortlisting of schools becomes a much simpler process. During the pre-application stage, we find that the most frequently asked questions are on the subjects of academic eligibility, grade point average, tests, and financial assistance. We are, therefore, giving you some information on each of these areas of discussion.

Suggested Guidelines/Schedule for the Application Process

The time frame given below is a general guideline to students in order that they may plan, work on and despatch applications in good time. Please keep in mind that university deadlines differ and therefore, this schedule may vary for individual cases. Please apply for your passport 18 months prior to the date you plan to enroll.

Step	*Process*	*Fall 96 (Aug-Sep)*	*Spring 97 (Jan)*
I	**Background Requirements** Attend the VTR presentation "If you want to study in the US" and "Harvard, Here I come" group counselling session.	Mar-Sep 95	Feb-April 96
II	**Preliminary Selection of University** Some useful books are *Peterson's Guides, Directory of Graduate Programs* and individual college catalogs.	Apr-Jul y95	Feb-Apl 96
III	**Despatch of Preliminary Application Forms** Do not restrict your choice to well known universities only as there are other universities that offer excellent courses and financial assistance.	May-Sep 95	Mar-May 96
IV	**Registration and Preparations for Tests**	No later than Dec. 95	No later than Jun. 96

V Review of Application Forms Received From the Universities and further- Selection of Universities (a) Attend USEFI Programs on specialized fields of study (b) Attend USEFI group counselling session on preparing good application packages (c) Request ETS to send your scores to selected universities if you have not done so at the time of taking the tests.	Aug-Nov 95	April-Jun 96
VI Mailing of Applications and other Documents It is advisable to file the papers well in advance of deadlines	Nov. 95-Jan. 96	May-July 96
VII Response from Universities and Acceptance of Admission Offer (a) If two or more colleges have offered admission accept the offer from only one and notify the others of your decision. (b) Attend Group Counselling Sessions on Visa application procedures organized by the USEFI. (c) Apply for campus housing, if required.	Mar-July 96	Sep-Nov. 96
VIII Predeparture Formalities (a) Wait for 1-20/IAP-66 (Certificate of Eligibility Form) from the University; (b) Apply for student visa/confirm ticket and collect permissible travel allowance; (c) Attend the pre-departure orientation program organized by the USEFI offices (d) Depart for University prior to their orientation programs.	April-Aug. 96	Oct.96-Jan. 97

Academic Eligibility

Each university in the United States has its own requirements for admission. It is important to note that graduate schools in the United States are looking for students with qualifications comparable to a US Bachelor's degree (four year degree program). Universities and departments within these universities do not adhere to standard policies with reference to what they consider to be an equivalent of a US Bachelor's degree. Hence, there is considerable flexibility in the acceptance policies of U.S. Schools. The best thing to do is to write directly to graduate schools and departments of your interest.

If you have completed a 3 year degree program in India, the advisable plan of action to maximize eligibility for US graduate schools is to apply for a postgraduate degree here in India. A one year university affiliated full time program will make up for the fourth year of a US undergraduate degree. Professional programs like the CA, ICWA, part time diplomas from a university such as those in management, communication, and independent certificate courses offered by private institutions like NIIT, Apple Industries, etc. may get accepted based on each individual university/department's evaluation. No standardized policy exists regarding the acceptance of such programs. Confirmation can only be obtained by either writing directly or formally applying to the schools concerned.

The standardized tests to be completed are:-

TOEFL (Test of English as a Foreign Language)

This test is compulsory for any one proceeding abroad and is required by all US College and Universities.

GRE (Graduate Record Exam) to be completed by all those who are seeking admission for Biology, Chemistry, Computer Science, Engineering, Languages, Mathematics and the like avenues.

SAT (Scholastic Aptitude Test) for English Writing, Mathematics, and like fields, depending on the subject they wish to specialize.

GMAT (Graduate Management Admission Test) is for students seeking admission to the management programs.

Details of the above tests can be had from:

The Director,

Institute of Psychological and Educational Measurement, (IPEM), 119/25-A, Mahatma Gandhi Marg, Allahabad - 211 001 U.P. State.

Financial Assistance

Many Indian students are concerned about the high cost of education in the United States and seek information on opportunities for financial assistance. The cost of education in the United States could range from $11,000 to cover $40,000 per year. In addition to tuition and fees, books and food, you have to plan for the expenses towards housing, health insurance and transportation. State schools and schools in the South and Mid-West are often cheaper than private schools and those located in California or the North-East region.

In reviewing opportunities for financial assistance, it is important to understand that graduate schools in the United States offer financial assistance to international students based primarily on merit and rarely on need. The amount and type of assistance offered varies based on the university, department and level of study. Availability of assistance is more likely in fields like engineering, physical sciences and biological sciences than humanities, social sciences, business and management, law, arts, and communication. There is a greater possibility of assistance at the doctorate level than at the master's level. Resources available to individual departments at a university, in a particular year, depend on the funding they receive from federal and state agencies and private institutions.

Types of Assistance

Merit based assistance is awarded in the form of tuition and fee waivers, scholarships (also called fellowships, competitions, prize, awards research assistantship, teaching assistantships, national training and research grants, prizes, awards), research, assistantships, restricted fellowships, and travel and research grants.

(a) *Tuition waiver*—This means that the student does not have to pay the tuition fees at the university. However, general fees (for the use of university facilities like the library, computers, and sports and health services) usually have to be borne by the student. A tuition waiver is frequently awarded in conjunction with a scholarship or teaching/research assistantship.

(b) *Scholarship/Fellowship*—This is usually an outright grant based on the student's academic ability and performance. Hence, only a truly outstanding student may be considered for this type of award, before enrolling at the university. A full scholarship would pay for a student's entire living expenses at that university, whereas a partial scholarship would require additional funds from the student.

(c) *Assistantship*—Most graduate students who receive assistance do so in the form of an assistantship, i.e. usually a cash stipend, sufficient for their living expenses, and/or tuition waiver, in return for which they have to work for a maximum of 20 hours a week. The duties normally consist of teaching or research. You should keep in mind that teaching assistantships may be more readily available in those subjects and at those universities in which considerable research is being carried on. Information brochures of universities would give this information. Often, teaching or research abilities must be proved before assistantships are granted. Hence, many universities only award them to foreign students after the first semester or the first year. To be considered for a teaching assistantship, you may be asked to give the Test of Spoken English (TSE). Universities have other kinds of special awards, about which you may read in their catalogs.

Who Should Apply

Students will have a greater chance of obtaining financial assistance if they:

1. Show evidence of a high level of academic achievement;
2. Achieve high standardized examination scores (GRE/GMAT, and TOEFL);
3. Demonstrate financial need but have private funding to cover some of the cost. Financial need is not crucial for some awards;
4. Enroll in a field or have teaching experience in a subject offered at the undergraduate level (to increase opportunities for a teaching assistantship);
5. Specialize in a field or have a research interest which parallels that of the department and faculty or a private funding source (which increases opportunities for research assistantships and grants);
6. Have outstanding letters of recommendation and an impressive statement of purpose;
7. Send a sample of professional writing, published or otherwise.

There are some Indian agencies such as Rotary, and the Inlaks Foundation that offer financial assistance. These scholarships are generally advertised in leading newspapers.

USEFI does not offer financial assistance to students. Limited pre-doctoral and post-doctoral study grants are offered as part of the USEFI administered Fulbright Program. These grants are usually announced in leading English newspapers in April of each year and they are restricted to full-time employed persons eligible for leave of absence. You may refer to the financial aid file available at the USEFI reference library for further information.

You are strongly advised not to write to the Institute of International Education, Rockefeller Foundation, Ford Foundation or USAID as they do not offer any financial aid to Indian students.

Once you have made your selection and you have a ready list of about 30 schools, you are ready to send your request to universities for application material. This request should contain a brief description of your educational background, academic objectives, sources of financial support, English proficiency and standardized test scores. The request can be made on preliminary application forms (PAFs), available for sale at USEFI offices. They must be sent to the Director of Graduate Admissions at each university of your choice. It is advisable to begin this process 18 months prior to your intended date of admission in a university in the United States. In response to the PAF, you should receive application forms along with other assorted information, such as, policies and procedures, special instructions for international students, financial aid information and application, program or department brochures.

You could also send a letter to the department attaching a bio-data giving your educational background, your goals, the degree you would like to pursue, and the type of research you are interested in. This might save you time and money as often departments will respond by sending you detailed brochures (sometimes catalogs) of their requirements, or encourging you to apply by writing to you that they are looking for people similar to your interests and background.

Use international mail for PAFs and request that universities reply by airmail. Do not send copies of any certificates at this time.

The Application Stage

Once you start receiving application forms and material, you may be overwhelmed by the volume of information you receive and the differences in the requirements of various universities and departments. For instance, some may have deadlines in January and others in February; some departments require three recommendation letters and others four; application fees range from $30 to $120; some may require a minimum TOEFL score of 550 and others 600.

To get a grasp on the similarities and differences, it would be a good idea to first read the information a couple of times (in case you have missed out something in your first reading) and then make a list of the universities that match your requirements.

You could group the universities under three categories:

(A) Those that seem to match your requirements;

(B) Those that are not suited to your needs;

(C) Those that do not completely fit into the above two categories.

Once you have eliminated the ones that do not meet your requirements, you can begin by developing a preferential ranking based on the departments that have most of what you are looking for (categories A and C). You could also rank the colleges on the basis of their selectivity. So you can begin to get a realistic idea of your chances of admission.

Your list of departments could be ranked according to a three-tiered approach:

First tier : departments you would most like to attend and are the most competitive.

Second tier : May not be as competitive as first tier, but are strong choices for you and represent something close to the challenge offered by your top choice. They meet most of your important criteria, but may lack a few less crucial characteristics.

Third tier : Schools not as selective as the first two tiers, but still possess basic characteristics important to you. Be sure to spend as much time selecting these schools as the first two tiers.

Insist on selecting colleges from each of the three tiers. For this, you could prepare another worksheet giving a more detailed profile of the universities (mainly categories A & B) based on information they have sent. The criteria for this stage of shortlisting would be more specific than the first stage.

You would now look at:

1. Objectives of the program—what are they preparing students for? research careers, industrial careers etc.? do they stress on a particular kind of approach, methodology, super specialization?
2. Admissability/entrance requirements—academic preparation and performance of students, average test scores, work/research experience, entrance difficulty, size of department/class;
3. Availability of assistantships and funding, amount and type of scholarships, application procedures and requirements for funding eligibility;
4. Thrust of the program;
5. Faculty research interests and the number of faculty in area of student interest;
6. Specific facilities/equipment, etc., for research;
7. Special programs like internships;
8. Overall reputation of the program and faculty;
9. Discouragement/encouragement of any special category (women, international students);
10. Profile of students enrolled;
11. Location.

From the three tier ratings, you should be ready to choose between 7 to 12 universities to which you intend to apply for admission. For instance, you could select a total of 8 schools and distribute it as follows: 3 from tier 1; 3 from tier 2; and 2/3from tier 3. This is done to enable you to achieve a measure of success.

Once you have identified the 7-12 schools to whom you intend to apply, it is very important to keep records on your application correspondence with them.

The Admission Stage

Universities usually inform students of their admission decisions well in advance of the beginning term. If you have received admission in more than one university, you will have to decide which one you want to attend. At this stage, you will compare a few objective, but mostly more subjective criteria. You may look at:

Objective Criteria

1. Best program offer—curriculum, length of program, choice of courses etc.;
2. Best funding offer or best program *vis-a-vis* cost;
3. Cost of living;
4. Strength of related departments/program;

Subjective Criteria

5. Overall reputation of university/department/faculty;
6. Location—region, urban/rural, safety of neighbourhood, etc.;
7. Housing-cost, availability, safety;
8. Climate;
9. Services—campus facilities, resources, placement services etc.;
10. Social life.

In comparing offers from among the best programs, for instance, you may decide to go to the University of Southern California and not Tufts University because of the climate. Or you may go to Florida State University because you have a relative living in the area.

In short, at this stage, the university you decide to attend will be based on a combination of the following:

1. Best Program;
2. Best funding offer;
3. Best for your personal goals and needs.

Remember that no decision is fully right or wrong, so weigh the pros and cons carefully and go ahead and make the decision that you feel is the best for you! In explaining the steps to the process of shortlisting schools, we have encouraged you to do a careful college search and develop a sound application strategy. The key to do this involves:

1. The use of multiple criteria and indicators to evaluate institutional quality and appropriateness, and
2. The use of information drawn from multiple sources.

It is essential to do research on the universities and their offerings. Colleges and universities offer varied educational packages. You will have to find out which of these are likely to meet your goals by spending time in the reference library. The more time and effort you put in and the better you utilize your researching skills, the greater are your chances of achieving your goals.

The United States Educational Foundation in India

The United States Educational Foundation in India (USEFI) was established on February 2, 1950 under a bilateral agreement to promote mutual understanding between the peoples of the United States and India through academic and educational exchange programs. Under this program, known as the Fulbright program, every year, a number of Fulbright and other fellowships are awarded to Indian scholars and professionals. This prestigious Fulbright Program is operational in more than 130 countries.

As part of its mission to promote Indo-US understanding through academic exchanges, USEFI, also offers information and advice to non-sponsored students from India seeking higher education in the United States. The Educational Advisory Service (EAS) does not act as a placement agency for students intending to enter American colleges/universities, neither does it offer grants or financial assistance for students pursuing degree programs in the United States. USEFI has four offices at New Delhi, Bombay, Calcutta and Madras. The Educational Advisory Service offers the following services:

(a) Group counselling and advising : various large and small group counselling sessions are organized throughout the year. These sessions include basic orientations, sessions on shortlisting universities, guidelines for preparing an application packet, student visas, predeparture orientations and specialized information programs;

(b) Individual counselling by appointment is available to students after attendance at the basic orientation program and preliminary work at the library;

(c) The USEFI reference library has a useful collection of guidebooks, subject specialized directories, subject files, and catalogs of American institutions. These contain important information on fields of study, universities offering degree programs in different fields, tuition and living expenses, financial aid opportunities, admission requirements, etc. at individual American colleges/universities. Admission to the reference library is restricted to members only;

(d) Request for application material, commonly known as preliminary application forms, are available for sale;

(e) Provision of information to outstation students by mail; on campus orientations at various universities, colleges; satellite center services are being developed through other non-profit organizations and university bureaus to enable outstation students to access basic literature on education in the United States;

(f) Videos on higher education in the United States and college campuses;

(g) Other services specific to each region.

Please consult the USEFI office in your region to get specific information on library reference hours, membership fees, cost of pre-application forms and other educational advisory services.

Addresses

United States Educational Foundation in India

"Fulbright House", 12 Hailey Road, New Delhi 110 001.

Phones : 332 8944, 332 8945 Student Advising: 2 p.m.-4 p.m.

Library Hours : 10 a.m-12:45 p.m., 2 p.m.-4:30 p.m.

(For: *Jammu & Kashmir, Himachal Pradesh, Punjab, Haryana, Uttar Pradesh, Rajasthan, and all Union Territories in North India*).

United States Educational Foundation in India

"Sundeep", 4 New Marine Lines, Mumbai 400 020., Phones : 262 4590, 262 4603

Student Advising : 1 p.m.-4:30 p.m., Library Hours: 1 p.m.- 4:30 p.m.

Telephone Calls : 11 a.m. 4:00 p.m.

(For : *Gujarat, Maharashtra, Madhya Pradeh, Goa and all Union Territories in West India*)

United States Educational Foundation in India

American Center, 38-A Jawaharlal Nehru Road, Calcutta 700 071. Phones : 245 1636, 245 1211 Student Advising : 9:30 a.m.- 12:30 p.m., 1 p.m.- 4 p.m. Library Hours : 9:30 a.m.- 5 p.m.

(For : *Bihar, West Bengal, Nagaland, Arunachal Pradesh, Mizoram, Tripura, Manipur, Assam, Meghalaya, and Sikkim*)

United States Educational Foundation in India

Fulbright Regional Office, American Consulate Building, Anna Salai
Chennai 600 006, Phones : 827 3040, 825 7196
Student Advising : 1:30 p.m.- 4 p.m., Library Hours: 1 p.m.- 4 p.m.

(For: *Andhra Pradesh, Karnataka, Tamil Nadu, Kerala and all Union Territories in South India*)

U.S. Universities and Colleges

Alabama

Alabama A & M University, Normal, AL 35762-1357
Alabama State University, Montgomery, AL 36101-0271
Auburn University, Auburn University, AL 36849-0001
Auburn University at Montgomery, Montgomery, AL 36117-3596
Birmingham Southern College, Birmingham, AL 35254
Jacksonville State University, Jacksonville, AL 36265-9982
Livingston University, Livingston, AL 35470
Samford University, Birmingham, AL 35229-0002
Spring Hill College, Mobile, AL 36608-1791
Troy State University, Troy, AL 36082
Troy State University at Dothan, Dothan, AL 36304-0368
Troy State University in Montgomery, Montgomery, AL 36103-4419
Tuskegee University, Tuskegee, AL 36088
University of Alabama, Tuscaloosa, AL 35487-0132
University of Alabama at Birmingham, Birmingham, AL 35294
Univesity of Alabama in Huntsville, Huntsville, AL 35899
University of Mobile, Mobile, AL 36663
University of Montevallo, Montevallo, AL 35115
University of North Alabama, Florence, AL 35632
University of South Alabama, Mobile, AL 36688

Alaska

Alaska Pacific University, Anchorage, AK 99508
University of Alaska Anchorage; Anchorage, AK 99508-4672
University of Alaska Fairbanks, Fairbanks, AK 99775-7480
University of Alaska Southeast, Juneau, AK 99801-8625

Arizona

American Graduate School of International Management, Glendale, AZ 85306-3236
Arizona State University, Tempe, AZ 85287
Grand Canyon University, Phoenix, AZ 85017-3030
Northern Arizona University, Flagstaff, AZ 86011
Prescott College, Adult Degree Program, Prescott, Az 86301-2990

University of Arizona, Tucson, AZ 85721
University of Phoenix, Phoenix, AZ 85072-9382
Western International University, Phoenix, AZ 85021-2718

Arkansas

Arkansas State University, State University, AR 72467-1630
Arkansas Tech University, Runssellville, AR 72801-2222
Harding University, Searcy, AR 72149-0001
Henderson State University, Arkadelphia, AR 71999-0001
Southern Arkansas University, Magnolia, AR 71753
University of Arkansas, Fayetteville, AR 72701
University of Arkansas at Little Rock, Little Rock, AR 72204-7199
University of Arkansas at Pine Bluff, Pine Bluff, AR 71601-2799
University of Central Arkansas, Conway, AR 72035-0001
University of the Ozarks, Clarksville, AR 72830

California

Academy of Art College, San Francisco, CA 94105-3410
Antioch Southern California/Los Angeles, Marina Del Rey, CA 90292-7090
Antioch Southern California/Santa Barbara, Santa Barbara, CA 93101-1580
Armstrong University, Berkeley, CA 94704- 1489
Azusa Pacific University, Azusa, CA 91702-2701
California Institute of Integral Studies, San Francisco, CA 94117-4013
California Lutheran University, Thousand Oaks, CA 91360-2700
California Polytechnic State University, San Luis Obispo, CA 93407
California State Polytechnic University, Pomona, Pomona, CA 91768-1022
California State University, Bakersfield, CA 93311
California State University, Chico, Chico, CA 95929-0150
California State University, Dominguez Hills, Carson, CA 90747-0001
California State University, Fresno, Fresno, CA 93740
California State University, Fullerton, Fullerton, CA 92634-9480
California State University, Hayward, Hayward, CA 9542-3000
California State University, Long Beach, Long Beach, CA 90840-0119
California State University, Los Angeles, Los Angeles, CA 90032-4221
California State University, Northridge, Northridge, CA 91330-0001
California State University, Sacramento, Sacramento, CA 95819-6048
California State University, San Marcos, San Marcos, CA 92096
California State University, San Bernardino, San Bernardino, CA 92407-2318
California State University, Stanislaus, Turlock, CA 95382
California Western School of Law, San Diego, CA 92101-3046
Chapman University, Orange, CA 92666-1011
Claremont Graduate School, Claremont, CA 91711-6163
Coleman College, La Mesa, CA 91942-1532
College of Notre Dame, Belmont, CA 94002
Concordia University, Irvine, CA 92715
Dominican College of San Rafael, San Rafael, CA 94901-8008
Fielding Institute, Santa Barbara, CA 93105-3538
Fresno Pacific College, Fresno, CA 93702-4709
Golden Gate University, San Francisco, CA 94105-2968
Holy Names College, Oakland, CA 94619-1699

Humboldt State University, Arcata, CA 95521-8299
John F. Kennedy University, Orinda, CA 94563-2689
La Sierra University, Riverside, CA 92515
Loma Linda University, Loma Linda, CA 92350
Loyola Marymount University, Los Angeles, CA 90045-2699
Mills College, Oakland, CA 94613-1000
Monterey Institute of International Studies, Monterey, CA 98940-2691
Mount St.Mary's College, Los Angeles, CA 90049-1597
National University, San Diego, CA 92108-4107
Occidental College, Los Angeles, CA 90041-3392
Pacific Oaks College, Pasadena, CA 91103
Pacific Union College, Angwin, CA 94508
Pepperdine University, Culver City, CA 90230-7615
Point Loma Nazarene College, San Diego, CA 92106-2899
Saint Mary's College of California, Moraga, CA 94575
San Diego State University, San Diego, CA 92182
San Francisco State University, San Francisco, CA 94132-1722
San Joaquin College of Law, Fresno, CA 93726-6968
San Jose State University, San Jose, CA 95192-0001
Santa Clara University, Santa Clara, CA 95053
Simpson College, Redding, CA 96003-8606
Sonoma State University Rohnrcrt Park CA 94928-3609
Southwestern University School of Law, Los Angeles, CA 90005-3905
Stanford University, Stanford, CA 94305-9991
United States International University, San Diego, CA 92131-1799
University of California at Berkeley, Berkeley, CA 94720
University of California, Davis, Davis CA 95616
University of California, Hastings College of the Law, San Francisco, CA 94102-4707
University of California, Irvine, Irvine, CA 92717-1425
University of California, Los Angeles, Los Angeles, CA 90024-1301
University of California, Riverside, Riverside, CA 92521-0102
University of California, San Diego, La Jolla, CA 92093-5003
University of California, Santa Barbara, Santa Barbara, CA 93106
University of California, Santa Cruz, Santa Cruz, CA 95064
University of La Verne, La Verne, CA 91750-4443
University of Redlands, Redlands, CA 92373-0999
University of San Diego, San Diego, CA 92110-2492
University of San Francisco, San Francisco, CA 94117-1080
University of Southern California, Los Angeles, CA 90089
University of the Pacific, Stockton, CA 95211-0197
West Coast University, Los Angeles, CA 90020-1765
Western State University College of Law of Orange County, Fullerton, CA 92631-3000
Whittier College, Whittier, CA 90608-0634
Woodbury University, Burbank, CA 91510

Colorado

Adams State College, Alamosa, CO 81102
The Colorado College, Colorado Springs, CO 80903-3294
Colorado State University, Fort Collins, CO 80523

Regis University, Denver, CO 80221-1099
University of Colorado At Boulder, Boulder, CO 80309
University of Colorado at Colorado Springs, Colorado Springs, CO 80933-7150
University of Colorado At Denver, Denver, CO 80217-3364
University of Denver, Denver, CO 80208
University of Northern Colorado, Greeley, CO 80639
University of Southern Colorado, Pueblo, CO 81001-4990

Connecticut

Central Connecticut State University, New Britain, CT 06050-4010
Connecticut College, New London, CT 06320-4196
Eastern Connecticut State University, Willimantic, CT 06226-2295
Fairfield University, Fairfield, CT 06430
Hartford Graduate Center, Hartford, CT 06120-2991
Quinnipiac College, Hamden, CT 06518-1904
Sacred Heart University, Fairfield, CT 06432-1000
Saint Joseph College, West Hartford, CT 06117-2700
Southern Connecticut State University, New Haven, CT 06515-1355
University of Bridgeport, Bridgeport, CT 06601
University of Connecticut, Storrs, CT 06269
University of Hartford, West Hartford, CT 06117-1500
University of New Haven, West Haven, CT 06516-1916
Western Connecticut State University, Danbury, CT 06810-6885
Yale University, New Haven, CT 06520

Delaware

Delaware State University, Dover, DE 19901-2277
University of Delaware, Newark, DE 19716
Wilmington College, Newcastle, DE 19720-6421

District of Columbia

American University, Washington, DC 20016-8001
Catholic University of America, Washington, DC 20064
Gallaudet University, Washington, DC 20002-3625
Georgetown University, Washington, DC 20057
The George Washington University, Washington, DC 20052
Howard University, Washington, DC 20059-0002
Southeastern University, Washington, DC 20024-2788
Strayer College, Washington, DC 20005-2603
Trinity College, Washington, DC 20017-1094
University of the District Columbia, Washington, DC 20008

Florida

Barry University, Miami Shores, FL 33161-6695
Embry-Riddle Aeronautical University, Daytona Beach, FL 32114-3900
Florida Agricultural and Mechanical University, Tallahassee, FL 32307
Florida Atlantic University, Boca Raton, FL 33431-0991
Florida Institute of Technology, Melbourne, FL 32901-6988
Florida International University, Miami, FL 33199
Florida Southern College, Lakeland, FL 33801-5698
Florida State University, Tallahassee, FL 32306
Jacksonville University, Jacksonville, FL 32211-3394

Lynn University, Boca Raton, FL 33431-5598
Nova Southeastern University, Fort Lauderdale, FL 33314-7721
Orlando College, Orlando, FL 32810-5674
Rollins College, Winter Park, FL 32789-4499
St. Thomas University, Miami, FL 33054-6459
Stetson University, Deland, FL 32720-3781
Tampa College, Tampa, FL 33614-5899
University of Central Florida, Orlando, FL 32816
University of Florida, Gainesville, FL 32611-8140
University of Miami, Coral Gables, FL 33124
University of North Florida, Jacksonville, FL 32224-2645
University of South Florida, Tampa, FL 33620-9951
The University of Tampa, Tampa, FL 33606-1490
University of West Florida, Pensacola, FL 32514-5750

Georgia

Albany State College, Albany, GA 31705-2717
Augusta College, Augusta, GA 30904-2200
Berry College, Mount Berry, GA 30149-0159
Brenau University, Gainesville, GA 30501-3697
Clark Atlanta University, Atlanta, GA 30314
Columbus College, Columbus, GA 31907-5645
Covenant College, Lookout Mountain, GA 30750
Emory University, Atlanta, GA 30322-1100
Fort Valley State College, Fort Valley, GA 31030
Georgia College, Milledgeville, GA 31061-3262
Georgia Institute of Technology, Atlanta, GA 30332-0001
Georgia Souther University, Statesboro, GA 30460-8100
Georgia Southwestern College, Americus, GA 31709-4693
Georgia State University, Atlanta, GA 30303-3083
Kennesaw State College, Marietta, GA 30061-0444
Lagrange College, Lagrange, GA 30240-2999
Mercer University, Macon, GA 31207-0003
North Georgia College, Dahlonega, GA 30597-1001
Oglethorpe University, Atlanta, GA 30319-2797
University of Georgia, Athens, GA 30602
Valdosta State University, Valdosta, GA 31698
West Georgia College, Carrollton, GA 30118

Hawaii

Chaminade University of Honolulu, Honolulu, HI 96816-1578
Hawaii Pacific University, Honolulu, HI 96813-2785
University of Hawaii At Manoa, Honolulu, HI 96822

Idaho

Albertson College, Caldwell, ID 83605-4494
Boise State University, Boise, ID 83725-0399
Idaho State University, Pocatello, ID 83209
Northwest Nazarene College, Nampa, ID 83686-5897
University of Idaho, Moscow, ID 83843-4140

Illinois

Aurora University, Aurora, IL 60506-4892
Bradley University, Peoria, IL 61625-0002
Chicago State University, Chicago, IL 60628
College of St. Francis, Joliet, IL 60435-6188
Columbia College, Chicago, IL 60605-1997
Concordia University, River Forest, IL 60305-1499
Depaul University, Chicago, IL 60604-2287
Eastern Illinois University, Charleston, IL 61920-3099
Governors State University, Univesity Park, IL 60466
Illinois Benedictine College, Lisle, IL 60532-0900
Illinois Institute of Technology, Chicago, IL 60616
Illinois State University, Normal, IL 61761
John Marshall Law School, Chicago, IL 60604-3968
Keller Graduate School of Management, Chicago, IL 60606-3708
Lake Forest Graduate School of Management, Lake Forest, IL 60045-2497
Lewis University, Romeoville, IL 60441
Loyola University, Chicago, Chicago, IL 60611-2196
National-Louis University, Evanston, IL 60201-1730
North Central College, Naperville, IL 60566
Northeastern Illinois University, Chicago, IL 60625-2864
Northern Illinois University, Dekalb, IL 60115
Northeastern University, Evanston, IL 60208
Olivet Nazarene University, Kankakee, IL 60901-0592
Quincy University, Quincy, IL 62301-2699
Rockford College, Rockford, IL 61108-2393
Roosevelt University, Chicago, IL 60605-1394
Rosary College, River Forest, IL 60305-1099
Rush University, Chicago, IL 60612-3832
Saint Xavier University, Chicago, IL 60655-3105
Sangamon State University, Springfield, IL 62794-9243
Southern Illinois University At Carbondale, Carbondale, IL 62901-6806
Southern Illinois University At Edwardsville, Edwardsville, IL 62026-0001
Trinity Evangelical Divinity School, Deerfield, IL 60015-1241
University of Chicago, Chicago, IL 60637-1513
University of Illinois at Chicago, Chicago, IL 60680-5220
University of Illinois at Urbana-Champaign, Urbana, IL 61820-5711
Western Illinois University, Macomb, IL 61455-1396

Indiana

Ball State University, Muncie, IN 47306-1099
Butler University, Indianapolis, IN 46208-3485
Indiana State University, Terre Haute, IN 47809-1401
Indiana University at Kokomo, Kokomo, IN 46904-9003
Indiana University Bloomington, Bloomington, IN 47405
Indiana University Northwest, Gary, IN 46408
Indiana University Southeast, New Albany, IN 47150
Indiana University-Purdue University at Fort Wayne, Fort Wayne, IN 46805-1491
Indiana University-Purdue University at Indianapolis, Indianapolis, IN 46202-2896
Indiana University at South Bend, South Bend, IN 46634-7111

Indiana Wesleyan University, Marion, IN 46953-4999
Manchester College, North Manchester, IN 46962-1225
Purdue University, West Lafayette, IN 47907-1968
Purdue University Calumet, Hammond, IN 46323-2094
Purdue University of North Central Campus, Westville, IN 46391-9543
Saint Francis College, Fort Wayne, IN 46808-3994
University of Evansville, Evansville, IN 47722-0002
University of Indianapolis, Indianapolis IN 46227-3697
University of Notre Dame, Notre Dame, IN 46556
University of Southern Indiana, Evansville, IN 47712-3590
Valparaiso University, Valparaiso, IN 46383-6493

Iowa

Clarke College, Dubuque IA 52001-3198
Drake University, Des Moines, IA 50311-4516
Iowa State University of Science and Technology, Ames, IA 50011-2010
Loras College, Dubuque, IA 52004-0178
Maharishi International University, Fairfield, IA 52557-0001
Morningside College, Sioux City, IA 51106-1751
Northwestern College, Orange City, IA 51041-1996
St. Ambrose University, Davenport, IA 52803-2898
Teikyo Marycrest University, Davenport, IA 52804-4096
University of Dubuque, DubuqueIA 52001-5099
University of Iowa, Iowa City, IA 52242
University of Northern Iowa, Cedar Falls, IA 50614
University of Osteopathic Medicine and Health Sciences, Des Moines, IA 50312

Kansas

Baker University, Baldwin City, KS 66006-0065
Emporia State University, Emporia KS 66801-5087
Fort Hays State University, Hays, KS 67601-4009
Friends University, Wichita, KS 67213
Kansas State University, Manhattan, KS 66506
Pittsburg State University, Pittsburg, KS 66762-5880
United States Army Command and General Staff College, Fort Leavenworth, KS 66027
University of Kansas, Lawrence, KS 66045
Washburn University of Topeka, Topeka, KS 66621
Wichita State University, Wichita, KS 67260

Kentucky

Bellarmine College, Louisville, KY 40205-0671
Cumberland College, Williamsburg, KY 40769-1372
Eastern Kentucky University, Richmond, KY 40475-3102
Morehead State University, Morehead, KY 40351
Murray State University, Murray, KY 42071-0009
Northern Kentucky University, Highland Heights, KY 41099
Spalding University, Louisville, KY 40203-2188
University of Kentucky, Lexington, KY 40506-0052
Univesity of Louisville, Louisville, KY 40292-0001
Western Kentucky University, Bowling Green, KY 42101-3576

Louisiana

Centenary College of Louisiana, Shreveport, LA 71134-1188
Grambling State University, Grambling, LA 71245
Louisiana State University and Agricultural and Mechanical College, Baton Rouge, LA 70803-3103
Louisiana State University in Shreveport, Shreveport, LA 71115
Lousians Tech University, Ruston, LA 71272
Loyola University, New Orleans, LA 70118-6195
Mcneese State University, Lake Charles, LA 70609-2495
Nicholls State University, Thibodaux, LA 70310
Northeast Louisiana University, Monroe, LA 71209-0001
Northwestern State University of Louisiana, Natchitoches, LA 71497
Our Lady of Holy Cross College, New Orleans, LA 70131-7399
Southeastern Louisiana University, Hammond, LA 70402
Southern University And A & M College, Baton Rouge, LA 70813
Tulane University, New Orleans, LA 70118-5669
University of New Orleans, New Orleans, LA 70148
University of Southwestern Louisiana, Lafayette, LA 70504-1770
Xavier University of Louisiana, New Orleans, LA 70125-1098

Maine

Maine Maritime Academy, Castine, ME 04420
Saint Joseph's College, Windham, ME 04062-1198
Thomas College, Waterville, ME 04901-5097
University of Maine, Orono, ME 04469
University of Southern Maine, Portland, ME 04103

Maryland

Bowie State University, Bowie, MD 20715
College of Notre Dame of Maryland, Baltimore, MD 21210-2473
Coppin State College, Baltimore, MD 21216-3698
Frostburg State University, Frostburg, MD 21532-2302
Goucher College, Towson, MD 21204
Hood College, Frederick, MD 21701-8575
John Hopkins University, Baltimore, MD 21218-2699
Loyola College, Baltimore, MD 21210-2699
Morgan State University, Baltimore, MD 21239
Mount Saint Mary's College, Emmitsburg, MD 21727-7799
Salisbury State University, Salisbury, MD 21801-6837
Towson State University, Towson, MD 21204-7097
University of Baltimore, Baltimore, MD 21201-5779
University of Maryland College Park, College Park, MD 20742
University of Maryland Graduate School, Baltimore, MD 21228-5329
University of Maryland University College, College Park, MD 20742
University of Maryland-Eastern Shore, Princess Anne, MD 21853
Western Maryland College, Westminster, MD 21157-4390

Massachusetts

American International College, Springfield, MA 01109-3189
Anna Maria College, Paxton, MA 01612
Arthur D. Little Management Education Institute, Cambridge, MA 02140-2301
Assumption College, Worcester, MA 01615-0005

Babson College, Babson Park, MA 02157-0315
Bentley College, Waltham, MA 02154-4705
Boston College, Chestnut Hill, MA 02167-9991
Boston University, Boston, MA 02215
Brandeis University, Waltham, MA 02254-9110
Bridgewater State College, Bridgewater, MA 02325-0001
Cambridge College, Cambridge, MA 02138-4907
Clark University, Worcester, MA 01610-1477
Curry College, Milton, MA, 02186
Eastern Nazarene College, Wollaston, MA 02170-2999
Elms College, Chicopee, MA 01013-2839
Emmanuel College, Boston, MA 02115
Fitchburg State College, Fitchburg, MA 01420-2697
Framingham State College, Framingham, MA 01701-9101
Harvard University, Cambridge, MA 02138-2395
Hebrew College, Brookline, MA 02146-5495
Lesley College, Cambridge, MA 02138-2790
Massachusetts Institute of Technology, Cambridge, MA 02139-4307
Mount Holyoke College, South Hadley, MA 01075-1414
North Adams State College, North Adams, MA 02147-4100
Northeastern University, Boston MA 02115-5096
Salem State College, Salem, MA 01970-5353
Simmons College, Boston, MA 02115
Smith College, Northampton, MA 01063
Springfield College, Springfield, MA 01109-3797
Suffolk University, Boston, MA 02108-2770
Tufts University, Medford, MA 02155
University of Massachusetts At Amherst, Amherst, MA 01003-0001
University of Massachusetts At Boston, Boston, MA 02125-3393
University of Massachusetts Dartmouth, North Dartmouth, MA 02747-2512
University of Massachusetts Lowell, Lowell, MA 01854-2881
Western New England College, Springfield, MA 01119-2654
Westfield State College, Westfield, MA 01086
Wheelock College, Boston, MA 02215
Worcester Polytechnic Institute, Worcester, MA 01609-2247
Worcester State College, Worcester, MA 01602-2597

Michigan

Andrews University, Berrien Springs, MI 49104
Aquinas College, Grand Rapids, MI 49506-1799
Calvin College, Grand Rapids, MI 49546
Central Michigan University, Mount Pleasant, MI 48859
Detroit College of Law, Detroit, MI 48201-3454
Eastern Michigan University, Ypsilanti, MI 48197
Ferris State University, Big Rapids, MI 49307
Grand Valley State University, Allendale, MI 49401-9403
Lake Superior State University, Sault Sainte Marie, MI 49783
Lawrence Technological University, Southfield, MI 48075-1058
Madonna University, Livonia, MI 48150-1773

Marygrove College, Detroit, MI 48221-2599
Michigan State University, East Lansing, MI 48824-1020
Michigan Technological University, Houghton, MI 49931-1295
Northern Michigan University, Marquette, MI 49855-5301
Oakland University, Rochester, MI 48309-4401
Saginaw Valley State University, University Center, MI 48710
Siena Heights College, Adrian, MI 49221-1796
University of Detroit Mercy, Detroit, MI 48221-0900
University of Michigan-Ann Arbor, Ann Arbor, MI 48109
University of Michigan-Dearborn, Dearborn, MI 48128-1491
University of Michigan-Dearborn, Dearborn, MI 48128-1491
University of Michigan-Flint, MI 48502-2186
Walsh College of Accountancy and Business Administration, Troy, MI 48007-7006
Wayne State University, Detroit, MI 48202
Western Michigan University, Kalamazoo, MI 49008

Minnesota

Augsburg College, Minneapolis, MN 55454-1351
Bemidji State University, Bemidji, MN 56601-2699
College of St.Catherine St. Paul, MN 55105-1789
College of St. Scholastica, Duluth, MN 55811-4199
Concordia College- St. Paul, St. Paul, MN 55104-5494
Hamline University, St. Paul, MN 55105-1284
Mankato State University, Mankato, MN 56002-8400
Moorhead State University, Moorhead, MN 56560
Saint Mary's College of Minnesota, Winona, MN 55987
St. Cloud State University, St. Cloud, MN 56301-4498
University of Minnesota-Duluth, Duluth, MN 55812-2496
University of Minnesota-Twin Cities Campus, Minneapolis, MN 55455-0213
University of St Thomas, St. Paul, MN 55105-1089
Walden University, Minneapolis, MN 55401
William Mitchell College of Law, St. Paul, MN 55105-3076
Winona State University, Winona, MN 55987-5838

Mississippi

Alcorn State University, Lorman, MS 39096
Delta State University, Cleveland, MS 38733-0001
Jackson State University, Jackson, MS 39217
Millsaps College, Jackson, MS 39210-0001
Mississippi College, Clinton, MS 39058
Mississippi State University, Mississippi State, MS 39762
Mississippi University for Women, Columbus, MS 39701-9998
University of Mississippi, University, MS 38677
University of Southern Mississippi, Hattiesburg, MS 39406-5001
William Carey College, Hattiesburg, MS 39401-5499

Missouri

Avila College Kansas City, MO 64145-1698
Central Missouri State University, Warrensburg, MO 64093
Drury College, Springfield, MO 65802-3791
Lincoln University, Jefferson City, MO 65102

Lindenwood College, St. Charles, MO 63301-1695
Maryville University of St. Louis, St. Louis, MO 63141-7299
Northeast Missouri State University, Kirksville, MO 63501
Northwest Missouri State University, Maryville, MO 64468-5001
Rockhurst College, Kansas City, MO 64110-2561
Saint Louis University, Saint Louis, MO 63103-2097
Southeast Missouri State University, Cape Girardeau, MO 63701
Southwest Baptist University, Bolivar, MO 65613
Southwest Missouri State University, Springfield, MO 65804-0094
St. Louis College of Pharmacy, St. Louis, MO 63110-1088
University of Missouri-Columbia, Columbia, MO 65211
University of Missouri-Kansas City, Kansas City, MO 64110-2499
University of Missouri-St. Louis, Saint Louis, MO 63121-4499
Washington University, Saint Louis, MO 63130-4899
Webster University, St. Louis, MO 63119-3194

Montana

Montana State University, Bozeman, MT 59717
Northern Montana College, Havre, MT 59501
University of Montana, Missoula, MT 59812-0002

Nebraska

Chadron State College, Chadron, NE 69337
Clarkson College, Omaha, NE 68131-2739
Creighton University, Omaha, NE 68178-0001
Hastings College, Hastings, NE 68902
University of Nebraska at Kearney, Kearney, NE 68849
University of Nebraska at Omaha, Omaha, NE 68182
University of Nebraska-Lincoln, Lincoln, NE 68588
Wayne State College, Wayne, NE 68787

Nevada

University of Nevada, Las Vegas, Las Vegar, NV 89154-9900
University of Nevada, Reno, Reno, NV 89557

New Hampshire

Antioch New England Graduate School, Keene, NH 03431-3516
Dartmouth College, Hanover, NH 03755
Franklin Pierce Law Center, Concord, NH 03301-4197
Keene State College, Keene, NH 03431-4183
New England College, Henniker, NH 03242-3293
New Hampshire College, Manchester, NH 03106-1045
Notre Dame College, Manchester, NH 03104-2299
Plymouth State College of the University System of New Hampshire, Plymouth, NH 03264-1600
Rivier College, Nashua, NH 03060-5086
University of New Hampshire, Durham, NH 03824

New Jersey

Fairleigh Dickinson University, Florham-Madison Campus, Madison, NJ 07940-1099
Fairleigh Dickinson University, Teaneck-Hackensack Campus, Teaneck, NJ 07666-1996
Georgian Court College, Lakewood, NJ 08701-2697
Jersey City State College, Jersey City, NJ 07305

Kean College of New Jersey, Union, NJ 07083
Monmouth College, West Long Branch, NJ 07764-1898
Montclair State College, Upper Montclair, NJ 07043-1624
Rider College, Lawrenceville, NJ 08648-3001
Rowan College of New Jersey, Glassboro, NJ 08028-1702
Rutgers, The State University of New Jersey-Cadmen, Cadmen, NJ 08102-1401
Rutgers, The State University of New Jersey, Newark, Newark, NJ 07102-3192
Rutgers, The State University of New Jersey, New Brunswick, New Brunswick, NJ 08903
Saint Peter's, College, Jersey City, NJ 07306
Seton Hall University, South Orange, NJ 07079-2697
Stevens Institute of Technology, Hoboken, NJ 07030
Trenton State College, Trenton, NJ 08650-4700
Upsala College, East Orange, NJ 07019-1186
William Paterson College of New Jersey, Wayne, NJ 07470-8420

New Mexico

College of Santa Fe, Santa Fe, NM 87505
Eastern New Mexico University Portales, NM 88130
New Mexico Highlands University, Las Vegas, NM 87701
New Mexico State University, Las cruces, NM 88003-8001
University of New Mexico, Albuquerque, NM 87131-2039
Western New Mexico University, Silver city, NM 88061-0680
New Mexico State University, Las Cruces, NM 88003-8001

New York

Adelphi University, Garden City, NY 11530
Albany Law School of Union University, Albany, NY 12208-3494
Alfred University, Alfred, NY 14802-1232
Bank Street College of Education, New York, NY 10025-1898
Baruch College of City University of New York, New York, NY 10010-5585
Brooklyn College of the City University of New York, Brooklyn, NY 11210-2889
Brooklyn Law School, Brooklyn, NY 11201-3798
Canisius College, Buffalo, NY 14208
City College of the City University of New York, New York, NY 10031
City University of New York School of Law at Queens College, Flushing, NY 11367-1358
Clarkson University, Potsdam, NY 13699-5557
Colgate University, Hamilton, NY 13346-1386
College of Insurance, New York, NY 10007-2165
College of New Rochelle, New Rochelle, NY 10805-2308
College of Saint Rose, Albany, NY 12203-1419
College of Staten Island of the City University of New York, Staten Island, NY 10314-6600
Columbia University, New York, NY 10027
Cornell University, Ithaca, NY 14853-0001
Dowling College, Long Island, NY 11769-1999
D'Youville College, Buffalo, NY 14201-1084
Elmira College, Elmira, NY 14901
Fordham University, New York, NY 10458
Graduate School and University Center of the Cuny, New York, NY 10036-8099
Hofstra University, Hempstead, NY 11550-1090
Hunter College of the City University of New York, New York, NY 10021-5085

Iona College, New Rochelle, NY 10801-1890
Lehman College of the City University of New York, Bronx, NY 10468-1589
Long Island University, Brooklyn Campus, Brooklyn, NY 11201
Long Island University, C.W. Post Campus, Greenvale, NY 11548
Long Island University, Southampton Campus, Southampton, NY 11968
Manhattan College, Bronx, NY 10471-4698
Manhattanville College, Purchase, NY 10577-2132
Marist College, Poughkeepsie, NY 12601-1387
Mercy College, Dobbs Ferry, NY 10522-9988
Mount Saint Mary College, NewBurgh, NY 12550-3494
Nazareth College of Rochester, Rochester, NY 14618-3790
New School for Social Research, New York, NY 10011-8603
New York Institute of Technology, Old Westbury, NY 11568-8000
New York Law School, New York, NY 10013-2959
New York Medical College, Valhalla, NY 10595
New York University, New York, NY 10012-1019
Niagara University, New York, NY 14109
Pace University, New York, NY 10038
Polytechnic University, Brooklyn Campus, Brooklyn, NY 11201-2990
Polytechnic University, Farmingdale Campus, Farmingdale, NY 11735-3995
Queens College of the City University of New York, Flushing, NY 11367-1597
Rensselaer Polytechnic Institute, Troy, NY 12180-3590
Rochester Institute of Technology, Rochester, NY 14623-5604
Russell Sage College, Troy, NY 12180-4115
St. Bonaventure University, St. Bonaventure, NY 14778-2284
St. John Fisher College, Rochester, NY 14618-3597
St. John's University, Jamaica, NY 11439
St. Lawrence University, Canton, NY 13617-1455
St. Thomas Aquinas College, Sparkill, NY 10976
State University of New York at Binghamton, Binghamton, NY 13902-6000
State University of New York at Buffalo, Buffalo, NY 14260
State University of New York College at Brockport, Brockport, NY 14420-2997
State University of New York College At Buffalo, Buffalo, NY 14222-1095
State University of New York College At Fredonia, Fredonia, NY 14063
State University of New York College At Geneseo, Geneseo, NY 14454-1401
State University of New York College At New Paltz, New Paltz, NY 12561-2449
State University of New York College At Oneonta, Oneonta, NY 13820
State University of New York College At Oswego, Oswego, NY 13126
State University of New York College At Plattsburgh, Plattsburgh, NY 12901
State University of New York College At Potsdam, Potsdam, NY 13676
Syracuse University, Syracuse, NY 13244-0003
Teachers College, Columbia University, New York, NY 10027-6696
Union College, Schenectady, NY 12308-2311
University of Albany, State University of New York, Albany, NY 12222
University of Rochester, Rochester, NY 14627-0001
Wagner College, Staten Island, NY 10301
Yeshiva University, New York, NY 10033-3201

North Carolina

Appalachian State University, Boone, NC 28608
Campbell University, Buies Creek, NC 27506-0546
Catawba College, Salisbury, NC 28144-2488
Duke University, Durham, NC 27708-0586
East Carolina University, Greenville, NC 27858-4353
Elon College, Elon College, NC 27244
Fayetteville State University, Fayetteville, NC 28301
Gardner-Webb College, Boiling Springs, NC 28017
Lenoir-Rhyne College, Hickory, NC 28603
Meredith College, Raleigh, NC 27607-5298
North Carolina Agr and Téch State University, Greensboro, NC 27411
North Carolina Central University, Durham, NC 27707-3129
North Carolina State University, Raleigh, NC 27695
Pembroke State University, Pembroke, NC 28372-1510
Pfeiffer College, Misenheimer, NC 28109-0960
Queens College, Charlotte, NC 28274-0002
Salem College, Winston-Salem, NC 27108-0548
University of North Carolina At Chapel Hill, Chapel Hill, NC 27599
University of North Carolina At Charlotte Charlotte, NC 28223
University of North Carolina at Greensboro, Greensboro, NC 27412-0001
University of North Carolina at Wilmington, Wilmington, NC 28403-3201
Wake Forest University, Winston-Salem, NC 27109
Western Carolina University, Cullowhee, NC 28723
Wingate College, Wingate, NC 28174

North Dakota

Minot State University, Minot, ND 58707-0002
North Dakota State University, Fargo, ND 58105
University of Mary Bismarck ND 58504-9652
University of North Dakota, Grand Forks, ND 58202

Ohio

Ashland University, Ashland, OH 44805-3702
Baldwin - Wallace College, Berea, OH 44017-2088
Bowling Green State University, Bowling Green, OH 43403-2394
Capital University, Columbus, OH 43209-2394
Case Western Reserve University, Cleveland, OH 44106
Cleveland State University, Cleveland, OH 44115
College of Mount St. Joseph, Cincinnati, OH 45233-1670
Franciscan University of Steubenville, Steubenville, OH 43952-6701
Heidelberg College, Tiffin, OH 44883-2462
John Carroll University, University Heights, OH 44118-4581
Kent State University, Kent, OH 44242-0001
Lake Erie College, Painesville, OH 44077-3389
Malone College, Canton, OH 44709-3897
Marietta College, Marietta, OH 45750-4000
Miami University, Oxford, OH 45056
Muskingum College, New Concord, OH 43762
Notre Dame College of Ohio, South Euclid, OH 44121-4293
Ohio State University, Columbus, OH 43210

Ohio University, Athens, OH 45701
Otterbein College, Westerville, OH 43081
The University of Findlay, Findlay, OH 45840
Tiffin University, Tiffin, OH 44883
University of Akron, Akron, OH 44325-0001
University of Cincinnati, Cincinnati, OH 45221
University of Dayton, Dayton, OH 45469-1611
University of Rio Grande, Rio Grande, OH 45674
Univesity of Toledo, Toledo, OH 43606-3398
Walsh University, North Canton, OH 44720-3396
Wright State University, Dayton, OH 45435
Xavier University, Cincinnati, OH 45207-5311
Youngstown State University, Youngstown, OH 44555-0002

Oklahoma

Cameron University, Lawton, OK 73505-6377
East Central University, ADA, OK 74820-6899
Northeastern State University, Tahlequah, OK 74464-2399
Northwestern Oklahoma State University, Alva, OK 73717-2799
Oklahoma City University, Oklahoma City, Ok 73106-1402
Oklahoma State University, Stillwater, Ok 74078
Oral Roberts University, Tulsa, OK 74171-0001
Philips University, Enid, OK 73701-2335
Southeastern Oklahoma State University, Durant, OK 74701
Southern Nazarene University, Bethany, OK 73008-2694
Southwestern Oklahoma State University, Weatherford, OK 73096-3098
University of Central Oklahoma, Edmond, OK 73034-0172
University of Oklahoma, Norman, OK 73019
University of Oklahoma Health Sciences Center, Oklahoma City, OK 73190
University of Tulsa, Tulsa, OK 74104-3126

Oregon

Eastern Oregon State College, La Grande, OR 97850-2899
Lewis and Clark College, Portland, OR 97219-7879
Linfield College, Mcminnville, OR 97128-6894
Marylhurst College, Marylhurst, OR 97036-0261
Oregon State University, Corvallis, OR 97331
Pacific University, Forest Grove, OR 97116-1797
Portland State University, Portland, OR 97207-0751
Southern Oregon State College, Ashland, OR 97520
University of Oregon, Eugene, OR 97403
University of Portland, Portland, OR 97203-5798
Western Oregon State College, Monmouth, OR 97361
Williamette University, Salem, OR 97301-3931

Pennsylvania

Allentown College of St. Francis De Sales, Center Valley, PA 18034-9568
American College, Bryn Mawr, PA 19010-2105
Beaver College, Glenside, PA 19038-3295
Bloomsburg University of Pennsylvania, Bloomsburg, PA 17815-1905
Bucknell University, Lewisburg, PA 17837

Cabrini College, Radnor, PA 19087-3699
California University of Pennsylvania, California, PA 15419-1394
Carlow College, Pittsburgh, PA 15213-3165
Carnegie Mellon University, Pittsburg, PA 15213-3891
Chestnut Hill College, Philadelphia, PA 19118-2695
Cheyney University of Pennsylvania, Cheyney, PA 19319
Clarion University of Pennsylvania, Clarion, PA 16214
College Misericordia, Dallas, PA 18612-1098
Drexel University, Philadelphia, PA 19104-2875
Duquesne University, Pittsbugh, PA 15282-0001
East Stroudsburg University of Pennsylavania, East Stroudsburg, PA 18301-2999
Eastern College, Saint Davids, PA 19087-3696
Edinboro University of Pennsylavania, Edinboro, PA 16444
Gannon University, Erie, PA 16541
Gwynedd-Mercy College, Gwynedd Valley, PA 19437
Holy Family College, Philadelphia, PA 19114-2094
Immaculata College, Immaculata, PA 19345-0900
Indiana University of Pennsylvania, Indiana, PA 15705
King's College, Wilkes-Barre, PA 18711-0801
Kutztown University of Pennsylvania, Kutztown, PA 19530
La Roche College, Pittsburgh, PA 15237-5898
La Salle University, Philadelphia, PA 19141-1199
Lehigh University, Bethlehem, PA 18015-3094
Mansfield University of Pennsylvania, Mansfield, PA 16933
Marywood College, Scranton, PA 18509-1598
Millersville University of Pennsylvania, Millersville, PA 17551-0302
Moravian College, Bethlehem, PA 18018-6650
Pennsylvania College of Optometry, Philadelphia, PA 19141-3323
Pennsylvania State University At Erie, The Behrend College, Erie, PA 16563
Pennsylvania State University Great Valley Graduate Center, Malvern, PA 19355-1488
Pennsylvania State University University Park Campus, University Park, PA 16802-1503
Pennsylvania State University at Harrisburg-The Capital College, Middletown, PA 17057-4898
Philadelphia College of Textiles and Science, Philadephia, PA 19144-5497
Point Park College, PittsBurgh, PA 15222-1984
Robert Morris College, Coraopolis, PA 15108-1189
Saint Joseph's University, Philadelphia, PA 19131-1376
Shippensburg University of Pennsylvania, Shippensburg, PA 17257
Slippery Rock University of Pennsylvania, Slippery Rock, PA 16057
Temple University, Philadelphia, PA 19122
University of Pennsylvania, Philadelphia, PA 19104
University of Pittsburgh, Pittsburgh, PA 15260-0001
University of Scranton, Scranton, PA 18510-4622
Villanova University, Villanova, PA 19085-1699
Waynesburg College, Waynesburg, PA 15370-1222
West Chester University of Pennsylvania, West Chester, PA 19383
Westminster College, New Wilmington, PA 16172-0001
Widener University, Chester, PA 19013-5792

Wilkes University, Wilkes-Barre, PA 18766-0002
York College of Pennsylvania, York, PA 17405-7199

Rhode Island

Brown University, Providence, RI 02912
Bryant College, Smithfield, RI 02917-1287
Johnson and Wales University, Providence, RI 02903-2807
Providence College, Providence, RI 02918
Rhode Island College, Providence, RI 02908-1924
Salve Regina University, Newport, RI 02840-4192
University of Rhode Island, Kingston, RI 02881

South Carolina

Charleston Southern University, Charleston, SC 29423-8087
Clemson University, Clemson, SC 29634
Converse College, Spartanburg, SC 29302-0006
Francis Marion University, Florence, SC 29501-0547
Furman University, Greenville, SC 29613
Lander University, Greenwood, SC 29649-2099
Medical University of South Carolina, Charleston, SC 29425-0002
South Carolina State University, Orangeburg, SC 29117-0001
The Citadel, The Military College of South Carolina, Charleston, SC 29409
University of South Carolina, Columbia, SC 29208
Winthrop University, Rock Hill, SC 29733

South Dakota

Augustana College, Sioux Falls, SD 57197
Black Hills State University, Spearfish, SD 57783-9501
Dakota Wesleyan University, Mitchell, SD 57301-4398
Northern State University, Aberdeen, SD 57401-7198
Sinte Gleska University, Rosebud, SD 57570-0490
Sioux Falls College, Sioux Falls, SD 57105-1699
South Dakota State University, Brookings, SD 57007
University of South Dakota, Vermillion, SD 57069-2390

Tennessee

Austin Peay State University, Clarksville, TN 37044-0001
Belmont University, Nashville, TN 37212-3757
Bethel College, Mckenzie, TN 38201
Carson-Newman College, Jefferson City, TN 37760
Christian Brothers University, Memphis, TN 38104-5581
Cumberland University, Lebanon, TN 37087-3554
East Tennessee State University, Johnson City, TN 37614-0734
Freed-Hardeman University, Henderson, TN 38340-2399
Lincoln Memorial University, Harrogate, TN 37752
Meharry Medical College, Nashville, TN 37208-9989
Middle Tennessee State University, Murfreesboro, TN 37132
Milligan College, Milligan College, TN 37682
Tennessee State University, Nashville TN 37209-1561
Tennessee Technological University, Cookeville, TN 38505
Tennessee Temple University, Chattanooga, TN 37404
Trevecca Nazarene College, Nashville, TN 37210

Tusculum College, Greeneville, TN 37743
University of Memphis, Memphis, TN 38152
University of Tennessee at Chattanooga, Chattanooga, TN 37403-2504
University of Tennessee at Martin, Martin, TN 38238-1000
University of Tennessee, Knoxville, TN 37996
Vanderbilt University, Nashville, TN 37240-1001

Texas

Abilene Christian University, Abilene, TX 79699
Amber University, Garland, TX 75041-5595
Angelo State University, San Angelo, TX 76909
Austin College, Sherman, TX 75091-4440
Baylor University, Waco, TX 76798
Dallas Baptist University, Dallas, TX 75211-9299
East Texas State University, Commerce, TX 75429-3011
East Texas State University at Texarkana, Texarkana, TX 75501-0518
Hardin-Simmons University, Abilene, TX 79698-0001
Houston Baptist University, Houston, TX 77074-3298
Incarnate Word College, San Antonio, TX 78209-6397
Lamar University-Beaumont, Beaumont, TX 77710
Midwestern State University, Wichita Falls, TX 76308-2096
Our Lady of the Lake University of San Antonio, San Antonio, TX 78207-4689
Prairie View A & M University, Prairie View, TX 77446-2610
Rice University, Houston, TX 77251-1892
Sam Houston State University, Huntsville, TX 77341-2448
South Texas College of Law, Houston, TX 77002-7000
Southern Methodist University, Dallas, TX 75275
Southwest Texas State University, San Marcos, TX 78666
St. Edwards University, Austin, TX 78704-6489
St. Mary's University of San Antonio, San Antonio, TX 78228-8507
Stephen F. Austin State University, Nacogdoches, TX 75962
Sul Ross State University, Alpine, TX 79832
Tarleton State University, Stephenville, TX 76402
Texas A & M International University, Laredo, TX 78040
Texas A & M University, College Station, TX 77843-1244
Texas A & M University-Corpus Christi, Corpus Christi, TX 78412
Texas A & M University-Kingsville, Kingsville, TX 78363
Texas Christian University, Fort Worth, TX 76129-0002
Texas Southern University, Houston, TX 77004-4584
Texas Tech University, Lubbock, TX 79409
Texas Wesleyan University, Fort Worth, TX 76105-1536
Texas Woman's University, Denton, TX 76204
Trinity University, San Antonio, TX 78212-7200
University of Dallas, Irving, TX 75062-4799
University of Houston, Houston, TX 77204
University of Houston-Clear Lake, Houston, TX 77058-1098
University of Houston-Victoria, Victoria, TX 77901-4450
University of Mary Hardin-Baylor, Belton, TX 76513
University of North Texas, Denton, TX 76203-6737

University of Texas at Arlington, Arlington, TX 76019
University of Texas at Austin, Austin, TX 78712
University of Texas at Dallas, Richardson, TX 75083-0688
University of Texas at El Paso, El Paso, TX 79968-0001
University of Texas at San Antonio, San Antonio, TX 78249-1130
University of Texas at Tyler, Tyler, TX 75799-0001
University of Texas of the Permian Basin, Odessa, TX 79762-0001
University of Texas-Pan American, Edinburg, TX 78539-2999
Wayland Baptist University, Plainview, TX 79072-6998
West Texas A & M University, Canyon, TX 79016-0001

Utah

Brigham Young University, Provo, UT 84602-1001
Southern Utah University, Cedar City, UT 84720-2498
University of Utah, Salt Lake City, UT 84112
Utah State University, Logan, UT 84322
Weber State University, Ogden, UT 84408-0002
Westminster College of Salt Lake City, Salt Lake City, UT 84105-3697

Vermont

Castleton State College, Castleton, VT 05735
College of St. Joseph, Rutland, VT 05701-3899
Goddard College, Plainfield, VT 05667
Johnson State College, Johnson, VT 05656-9405
Lyndon State College, Lyndonville, VT 05851
Saint Michael's College, Colchester, VT 05439
School for International Training, Brattleboro, VT 05302-0676
University of Vermont, Burlington, VT 05405-0160
Vermont Law School, South Royalton, VT 05068-0096

Virginia

Averett College, Danville, VA 24541
College of William & Mary, Williamsburg, VA 23187-8795
George Mason University, Fairfax, VA 22030
Hampton University, Hampton, VA 23668
James Madison University, Harrisonburg, VA 22807
Judge Advocate General's School, U.S. Army, Charlottesville, VA 22903-1781
Liberty University, Lynchburg, VA 24506-8001
Longwood College, Farmville, VA 23909-1800
Lynchburg College, Lynchburg, VA 24501-3199
Mary Baldwin College, Staunton, VA 24401
Marymount University, Arlington, VA 22207-4299
Norfolk State University, Norfolk, VA 23504-3907
Old Dominion University, Norfolk, VA 23529
Radford University, Radford, VA 24142
Regent University, Virginia Beach, VA 23464
Shenandoah University, Winchester, VA 22601-5195
University of Richmond, Richmond, VA 23173
University of Virginia, Charlottesville, VA 22906
Virginia Commonwealth University, Richmond, VA 23284-9005
Virginia Polytechnic Institute and State University, Blacksburg, VA 24061-0202

Virginia State University, Petersburg, VA 23806

Washington

Anitoch University Seattle, Seattle, WA 98121-1211
Central Washington University, Ellensburg, WA 98926
City University, Bellevue, WA 98004-6442
Eastern Washington University, Cheney, WA 99004-2431
Gonzaga University, Spokane, WA 99258
Heritage College, Toppenish, WA 98948-9599
Pacific Lutheran University, Tacoma, WA 98447
Saint Martin's College, St. Louis, MO 63108
Seattle Pacific University, Seattle, WA 98119-1997
Seattle University, Seattle, WA 98122
University of Puget Sound, Tacoma, WA 98416-0005
University of Washington, Seattle, WA 98195
Walla Walla College, College Place, WA 99324-3000
Washington State University, Pullman, WA 99164
Western Washington University, Bellingham, WA 98225-5996
Whitworth College, Spokane, WA 99251-0001

West Virginia

Marshall University, Huntington, WV 25755-0001
Salem-Teikyo University, Salem, WV 26426-1227
University of Charleston, Charleston, WV 25304-1099
West Virginia Graduate College, Institute, WV 25112-1003
West Virginia University, Morgantown, WV 26506
West Virginia Wesleyan College, Buckhannon, WV 26201
Wheeling Jesuit College, Wheeling, WV 26003-6295

Wisconsin

Beloit College, Beloit, WI 53511-5596
Cardinal Stritch College, Milwaukee, WI 53217-3985
Carroll College, Waukesha, WI 53186-5593
Concordia University Wisconsin, Mequon, WI 53097-2402
Edgewood College, Madison, WI 53711-1998
Marian College of Fond Du Lac, Fond Du Lac, WI 54935-4699
Marquette University, Milwaukee, WI 53233-2278
Mount Mary College, Milwaukee, WI 53222-4597
Silver Lake College, Manitowoc, WI 54220-9319
University of Wisconsin-Eau Claire, Eau Claire, WI 54702-4004
University of Wisconsin-Green Bay, Green Bay, WI 54311-7001
University of Wisconsin-La Crosse, La Crosse, WI 54601-3742
University of Wisconsin-Madison, Madison, WI 53706-1380
University of Wisconsin-Milwaukee, Milwaukee, WI 53201-0413
University of Wisconsin-Oshkosh, Osshosh, WI 54901-3551
University of Wisconsin-Parkside, Kenosha, WI 53141
University of Wisconsin-Platteville, Platteville, WI 53818-3099
University of Wisconsin-River Falls, River Falls, WI 54022-5013
University of Wisconsin-Stevens Point, Stevens Point, WI 54481-3897
University of Wisconsin-Stout, Menomonie, WI 54751
University of Wisconsin-Superior, Superior, WI 54880-2873

University of Wisconsin-Whitewater, Whitewater, WI 53190-1790
Viterbo College, La Crosse, WI 54601-4797
University of Wyoming, Laramie, WY 82071

Expenditure likely to be Incurred in the Application Process

The estimate given below is the cost likely to be incurred by a student in applying for graduate studies in the United States. The assumption is that the student requests information from 20 Universities and eventually applies to 7 Universities. Calculations are based on the rate of $ 1 = Rs. 32.00

		Rs. P.
1.	USEFI Annual library membership	250.00
2.	Two sets of Pre-application forms	40.00
3.	Tests	
	TOEFL $ 50	1600.00
	GRE $ 81	2592.00
	GRE Subject $ 56	1792.00
	GMAT $ 80	2560.00
4.	Additional score report	
	TOEFL $ 11 per score report	1208.00
	GRE $ 13 per score report	1664.00
	GRE Subject Test $ 13 per score report	1664.00
	GMAT $ 10 per score report	1280.00
5.	Application fees for 7 universities at the rate of $ 50 per University. Could go upto $ 120 at some universities	11200.00
6.	Attestations, telephone, fax, xerox	3000.00
7.	Visa:	
	(a) Processing fee	640.00
	(b) Stamp paper	10.00
	(c) CA's Fees	1000.00
	(d) Fees $ 100	3200.00
8.	Postage (for mailing Pre-application form and Application Packets)	3000.00
9.	Preparation before, travel (luggage, Winterwear, clothes, etc.)	10000.00

Student Visas - Documents and Guidelines

The following must be presented to the consular section by you at the time you apply for a student visa:

1. **Form I-20 or IAP - 66** (obtained directly from the University you intend to attend)
2. **Visa Application** form and **USEFI survey form** (Available at the Mount Road gate of the American Consulate General, Chennai, Monday through Friday (from 9.00 a.m. to 5.00 p.m.)
3. One passport size photograph
4. As Valid passport
5. Application processing fee, a demand draft in Indian rupees for Rs. 1935/- **(equivalent of $45) drawn in favour of American Consulate General, Chennai**
6. Visa fee, 4 demand drafts in Indian rupees for **Rs. 1075/- each, (the total being equivalent to $100) drawn in favour of American Consulate General, Chennai**

7. Test Score reports (Original)
8. Latest degree/mark sheets
9. Evidence of financial support as described below:
   (a) If financial assistance has been awarded by the University, please enclose letter from the University to that effect;
   (b) If your sponsor is in India, you will need the following documents:
      (i) Affidavit of support on stamped paper (Rs. 10, 15 or 25) from your sponsor promising to bear the costs of study your program for the entire duration of your stay in the United States. This document has to be notarized as well.
      (ii) Verification of your sponsor's financial resources by a certified Chartered Accountant. This statement should indicate that your sponsor has the means to support you during the entire duration of your study and stay in the United States. All original documents for the sources mentioned in the Charterd Statement, including bank pass books should be brought along, to be produced before the Consular Officer, if necessary.
   (c) If your sponsor is in the United States, the following documents must be provided:
      (i) I-134 (available at Immigration and Naturalization Service (INS) offices in the United States) promising to bear the costs of your program for the entire duration of your study and stay in the United States.
      (ii) Bank account statement of your sponsor
      (iii) Salary statement of your sponsor
   (d) If your sponsor is from a country other than India or the United States, the documents must be provided:
      (i) a notarized letter or statement from your sponsor promising to bear the costs of your program for the entire duration of your study and stay in the United States. The affidavit of support from your sponsor can also be submitted by form I-134 available at the American Consulate or Embassy in the country where your sponsor is a resident.
      (ii) Bank account statement of your sponsor
      (iii) Salary statement of your sponsor

You may apply for a student visa not earlier than 90 days prior to the reporting date mentioned on the I-20. For example, if the reporting date shown on the I-20 is September 05, you may apply for a student visa between June 5 and September 5.

The Consular Office opens at 7.30 a.m. (Monday through Friday) to receive applications. Since the office can process only a limited number of applications per day, it would be in your interest to come as early as you can to file your application. No prior appointment is necessary to apply for a visa. If you need additional information, please call the Consular Section at 8273040 between 2.00 p.m. and 4.00. p.m., Monday through Friday.

Dos and Dont's During a Student Visa Interview

1. Do remember that the issuance of a visa is a privilege and not a right.
2. Do have clear and realistic educational and career goals. Be prepared to state them at the interview if queried.
3. Do not give vague and general answers to questions that are asked. Use the brief interview time that you have to provide specific information that would strengthen your applications and prove family, economic and professional ties to India.
4. Do not misrepresent your educational and career objectives, your ties to India or the state of your financial resources.
5. Do not try to memorize a set of answers to questions you think may be asked.